AN ECONOMIC GEOGRAPHY OF THE SCANDINAVIAN STATES AND FINLAND

AN ECONOMIC GEOGRAPHY OF THE SCANDINAVIAN STATES AND FINLAND

W. R. MEAD M.SC.(ECON.) PH.D.

Professor of Geography at University College, London

UNIVERSITY OF LONDON PRESS LTD

SBN 340 08706 4

Fourth impression 1968
University of London Press Ltd
St Paul's House, Warwick Lane, London EC4

Printed and bound in Great Britain by
Hazell Watson & Viney Ltd, Aylesbury, Bucks

FOREWORD

I AM told that geographers claim regions as the focal points of their study. This is one among a very limited number of books which deal with my home region in Europe, and I am happy that it has been written.

In London, as Ambassador of Finland, I came to know Dr. Mead as a regular visitor to and energetic student of the Northern Countries. More particularly, as a former Honorary President of the Anglo-Finnish Society, I knew him as its Honorary Secretary. In this book, Dr. Mead writes about some aspects of the economic geography of an area which he knows well. He has also been much interested in the historical links which have bound Britain to the Northern Countries. While I have known him as a specialist in the area, he nevertheless prefers—too modestly, I think—to be called simply an enthusiast.

Indeed, only an enthusiast would write a book such as this. If there are any shortcomings in this book I am sure nevertheless that even the most critical will find much to admire in it. Moreover, although this book is intended for university geographers, there are a good many pages which will have a wider appeal—not least for those whose duties or business carry them across the North Sea. All too many people who have dealings with the Northern Countries are unaware of the geographical realities to which the daily life of the North must be adjusted.

Dr. Mead has done much to introduce students to these Northern lands. In putting his work forward, he must be mindful of the singer Väinämöinen, in the last canto of *Kalevala*, who sang that "the young who now are growing" might follow his beaten pathway and transform it with their fuller powers of appreciation. It is a pleasure for me to add my token to a book which I wish well.

SAKARI TUOMIOJA
Executive Secretary
Economic Commission for Europe
United Nations

Geneva
October, 1957

Note on the Third Impression, 1965

Since the second impression of this book, my friend Sakari Tuomioja has died. He wrote the foreword at the beginning of this book. Sakari Tuomioja was United Nations mediator in Cyprus at the time of his death. During the course of his most active life he had been Prime Minister of Finland, Ambassador to the Court of St. James and Governor of the Bank of Finland. He was a source of much inspiration.

UNIVERSITY COLLEGE, LONDON   W. R. M.
   May, 1965

Note on the Second Impression, 1964

This reprint, which has been undertaken at short notice, contains a number of amendments, but it cannot attempt the revisions that would be possible in a new edition. A considerable geographical literature has been published since 1957. Much was in response to the meeting of the Nineteenth Congress of the International Geographical Union in Stockholm in 1960. There is good reason to believe that the interest of the outside world in the geography and geographers of the five northern countries has increased correspondingly.

UNIVERSITY COLLEGE, LONDON   W. R. M.
   January, 1964

PREFACE

"I COULD be bounded in a nutshell and count myself a king of infinite space." Such was the ability of Hamlet. Where format is as finite and facts are as infinite as in a regional study of Scandinavia and Finland pitched for advanced university students, an author must envy the capacity of the Prince of Denmark. This book, which represents the gleanings of nearly twenty years, aspires to be something more than a mere compilation. It must give a measure of background information, but it cannot be encyclopædic. It is its difficult task to select and reject from the observations of widespread travels in the north, from the results of personal investigations in the field, from the gossip of people in their homes or at their work, from the harvest of archives and from the industry of the professional geographers of the Scandinavian countries and Finland. The very nature of its source material means that this book can never be finished. It is only possible to call a halt by arbitrarily casting a frame around the manuscript. Equally, it is of its nature that it must show a measure of unevenness—about different aspects of the economic geography of the north and in emphasis between the constituent countries. I have felt it worthwhile to let my enthusiasm assert itself where it has been kindled by particular topics or places, believing that what a writer enjoys writing some readers at least will enjoy reading. The surest way of revealing one's shortcomings (but the most certain way of soliciting help for their correction) is to commit them to paper.

The tolerance and sympathy of many friends and colleagues in Scandinavia and Finland have much eased my task. I am grateful to them for introductions to their countryside and its literature. It is a literature all too little known outside the compass of their own lands; though its accessibility has been increased in recent years by the employment of the major world languages at least for its summaries if not for the main body of its printed texts. This literature takes two principal forms—the published dissertations from the university departments (or their equivalent high schools of commerce) and the substantial output from the old-established geographical societies of the Northern Countries. Between the geographical departments of the Scandinavian and Finnish universities there is considerable regional integration. The Scandinavian geographers read and understand one another's languages (Finnish and, to a large extent, Icelandic apart). They share a common pool of knowledge, and have technical facilities for the pursuit of their subject second to none in the world. They may not concern themselves greatly with investigations beyond their national borders, but within their home countries they have produced an almost unrivalled array of publications. Upon these, I have leaned heavily and I have acknowledged them in footnotes with a view to providing suggestions for further reading. It is also natural that in such a book as this information should be drawn from sources beyond those commonly accepted as geographical.

In the preparation of any book which deals with other countries and necessitates extended periods of residence and travel in them, there must always be a multitude of people whose hospitality and generosity have made this possible. As every page which follows reminds me of some of the hundreds of homes which have been opened to me on my annual journeys, so each page may help to explain to many of my hosts the mission of the curious visitor who was introduced into their midst. I am grateful to the University of London for a research grant which enabled me to prepare Chapters VIII and XI in 1953. To Mr. John Bryant of University College I am much indebted for his patient and painstaking work in the preparation of the maps and diagrams. My colleagues, Dr. W. Glyn Jones, Mr. S. H. Bergmann and Mr. T. Stöverud of the Department of Scandinavian Studies at University College, and Miss M. Ormala of the Finnish Embassy have provided much kind assistance. Finally, I am grateful to Mr. David Thomas of the Department of Geography at University College, who has prepared the index.

UNIVERSITY COLLEGE, LONDON   W. R. M.
  June 6, 1957

CONTENTS

PART 4

SOME PRIMARY ECONOMIC ACTIVITIES

VII. *The Contribution of Farming*

VIII. *The Northern Fisheries*

IX. *Sources of Energy*

X. *The Network of Communications*

XI. *The Softwood Industries*

XII. *Mining and Metallurgy in the Pattern of Industrial Activity*

PART 5

THE LAPP WORLD

PART 6

UNITY AND DISUNITY IN SCANDINAVIA AND FINLAND

LIST OF MAPS AND DIAGRAMS

LIST OF PLATES

ACKNOWLEDGMENTS

ACKNOWLEDGMENT is gratefully extended to the following in respect of maps, diagrams and plates:

Dr. E. Hulten (Fig. 6); The Swedish Geographical Society (10, 91); Prof. B. Gutenberg and the Geological Society of America (11); The Finnish Geographical Society (15); The Swedish Meteorological Society (17); Prof. A. Säntti (18); Falk Verlag, Hamburg (19); Prof. I. Hustich (20); Prof. T. Hägerstrand (30, 31); Prof. W. William-Olsen (32, 38, 40, 89); Dr. L. Heikinheimo (41); The Editor of *Economic Geography*, Worcester, Mass. (50); E. Schweizerbart'sche Verlagsbuchhandlung, Stuttgart (56); Voima ja Valo (61, 62); Svensk Vattenkraft Föreningen (63); Cappelen Forlag, Oslo (65); Dr. A. Kiiskinen (76); Dr. A. Winberg (79); Dr. B. Ternstedt (80); Messrs. Martin Secker & Warburg Ltd. (81); The Swedish Banks' Association (82); The Geological Society of Sweden (92, 93, 95); Uddeholm AB. (96); Dr. K. Nickul (98).

Landmaelingar rikisins, Iceland (Plates 1, 2); Widerøe's Flyveselskap og Polarfly A/S (3, 4, 16, 17(b)); The Finnish Air Force (5, 6); Geodetic Institute, Denmark (7); Esbjerg Ehrvervskontor (8); Dr. Erkki Palosuo, Helsinki (9); The Swedish Air Force (10 (a), 10(b); The Swedish Embassy (13, 15, 17(a), 19); Statistisk Centralburå, Stockholm (12); Bermondsey Public Library (14); The Danish Embassy (18(a), 20); Uddeholm AB. (21); Norsk Jernverk A/S (22); The Finnish Embassy (15); The Norwegian Embassy (18(b)).

PART I

THE POINT OF VIEW

"I know nothing that hath greater share in my thoughts and desires than the promotion
of the septentrional learning."

William Nicolson (1683–1727) in a letter to Humphrey Wanley

IT is easier to write a book than to define its terms of reference. In the title of this work, two terminological problems are posed at the outset. First, what is economic geography? Secondly, what is understood by the regional concept "Scandinavia"? Economic geography has been the subject of debate by professional geographers since the time when the phrase was first given general currency by the German W. Götz in 1882.[1] Scandinavia has been the cynosure of statesmen for generations. No definition of either concept has satisfied nor, indeed, will satisfy everyone.

ECONOMIC GEOGRAPHY

Economic geography may be said to concern itself with those distributional patterns on the face of the land which affect man or are affected by him as he makes his living. In making a living, he is confronted with the disposal of certain scarce means. The patterns of use and movement which he traces against the physical background of the land are an expression of his choice in the disposal of these means. Choice is limited by physical availability and generated by demand. Demand commonly expresses itself in price. The object of the great economic activities is to create goods to meet the demand at a price. In some respects, then, man as the object of economico-geographical study reacts to two fields of forces—physical forces and economic forces. Theoretically, it is in his interest to employ the minimum of effort in the physical field and the minimum of available means in the economic field for the achievement of a desired end. When motivated in this way, his behaviour follows what is popularly called the line of least resistance in the physical field and the line of least cost in the economic field.

A study in economic geography may adopt one of two primary approaches—the unitary or the systematic. The systematic approach considers the great economic activities generically: it deals with their description and classification. Such an approach, however, treats them in isolation. The unitary approach looks at the economy in the aggregate and in process of evolution. It attempts to explain as well as to describe the complex of distributional features. A study which employs the systematic approach and avoids explanation is less likely to trespass into other fields of knowledge than one which adopts the unitary approach. All studies in economic geography are in danger of crossing frontiers into other fields of knowledge; those which deal with the economy in the round are especially susceptible. In defence, it must be admitted that it is not always easy to distinguish the internal structure and operation of an organisation (which is a technical purview) from the external forms (which are its geographical expression). It may, in fact, be pleaded that reference to material beyond the scope of geography—where due acknowledgement is made to the discipline—can often illumine the subject of study.

Given a primary definition and an approach, several simple propositions must be introduced to provide the framework within which this study is set. The first proposition is that, at any given time, two variables are operating to give character to a particular economy or to a particular area. These variables are its natural resources and the human element. Natural resources embrace all of the facilities of the physical environment. They constitute "land" in the widest classical sense of the term, and capital as derived from it through

[1] *Zeitschrift der Gesellschaft für Erdkunde*, Berlin, 1882, 354–87.

saving. The introduction of the human element raises a problem in classification, because man is, in a sense, a natural resource as well. His labour (including the managerial function) is essentially a component of the productive system. Man, however, is both a resource directed and a directing agent. He is the agent of appreciation and propulsion in the exploitation of natural resources. He is variable as a natural resource; he is also variable as a consuming force. In the choice which he makes as a consumer is rooted the particular as distinct from the general character of an economy.

The second proposition is an obvious extension of this dichotomy. It states that natural resources and human behaviour are largely independent variables. Natural resources vary between areas. Moreover, within and between areas resources will not only differ qualitatively but also quantitatively. Qualitative variations are seen most clearly in the nature of the land itself. Quantitatively speaking, a resource must be viewed from two angles. It has first a particular significance in relation to the quantity of other resources in a locality. It is significant in the second place according to the amount of the resource available in alternate localities. In short, it is the relative availability of a resource which is the final measure of its importance.

This leads to the third proposition—that the resource is variable in time as well as in place. It is extremely important to remember that the natural resource is not necessarily a static concept in itself. In the long run, all the natural resources, being physical facts, are changing. Depending on their character, of course, they change at different rates. Two types of change may be distinguished—long-period changes which represent relatively permanent modifications in a resource, and short-period changes of a temporary character. Instances of the former are found in isostatic adjustment, changes in plant associations and modifications in soil quality. In Chapter III below, short-period variations are illustrated by the cycle of seasonal change. The temporary transformation of Northern Europe by the winter freeze changes the value of many resources and the responsive pattern of economic activity. In few areas are seasonal variations of greater importance than in the North European world.

To the variable natural resource as illustrated in the changing natural environment must be added the human variable. Man's varying interpretation of his resources is represented by his effective demand as a consumer. Expressed collectively, effective demand creates a market (or a series of markets). In response to this demand (or in forecast of it), the producer organises combinations of productive factors. The organisation takes place over a particular area. As a result of organisation and to a greater or lesser degree of changing natural circumstances, the producer modifies distributional patterns of natural resources. Because demand is continuously shifting areally and changing in effectiveness, the combination will show continuous modification. Simultaneously, this modification will tend towards increasing refinement as a society expresses its wants more precisely. Any distributional pattern in the field of economic geography is, therefore, a relatively unstable concept and, in general, falls short of its optimum expression as a result of the residue of the past. All these facts call for caution in the interpretation of an area from the standpoint of economic geography.

THE METHOD OF APPROACH

The plan of this book springs out of the introductory statement on economic geography. It begins with a brief descriptive appreciation of Scandinavia and Finland, and then proceeds to examine in more detail instances of long-term and short-term physical variations which affect their setting and resource. The human resources of the northern lands are next considered as variables in their own right. Appraisal of the physical resources of Scandinavia and Finland has both economic and social origin. Economic revaluation and social revaluation of setting and resource are distinguishable from each other, though the materials for their study overlap.

Given this background, a systematic appreciation of the great economic activities provides opportunities for enlarging upon the interplay of the twin variables in specific fields.

In dealing with these great activities, however, two other objectives are also attempted: first, an investigation of the interplay of the two variables at various points in the economic fabric; secondly, an overall attempt to illustrate the resulting patterns of interaction at different orders of magnitude.

The different orders of magnitude are constituents in what might be called a hierarchy of functional units. These units, distinguishable elements within themselves, can be arranged in a significant order. Units such as the farm (cf. Chapter VII), the factory (cf. Chapter XI and Chapter VI), the mine or the tramp steamer could frequently—if not always—be defined as units of the first order. They might be regarded as the economic equivalents of those primary elements in the landscape pattern classified by Unstead as "stows", by K. Pfaffen as "ecotypes" or by J. Schmithüsen as "Fliese". They are the smallest operational units embracing use of the land and its resources which contribute to the needs and wants of man.[1] In this particular work, these micro-studies provide a corrective to a survey which perhaps too frequently looks at its field through the wrong end of the telescope. Units of the second order might be illustrated by the farm complex which is comprised in a fiord microcosm, by the small factory and residential complex giving rise to the loosely knit Swedish *tätort*[2], the port which is base for the tramp or fishing steamer or the export harbour (cf. Chapter VI) for the farm and forest hinterland. The operational units are collectively grouped together to form recognisable, if less precisely definable, wholes which are the units of the third order of magnitude. They may be distinguished by their predominant enterprise as agricultural regions, industrial regions, mining regions (cf. Chapter XII), fishing regions (cf. Chapter VIII) and so forth. In general, precision in definition and the degree of significant detail included are reduced progressively away from the first order of magnitude. Yet all orders are legitimate fields for geographical enquiry and are, in the phrase of Richard Hartshorne, "sections of reality" showing an interaction of people and place. Finally, the economies of Scandinavia and Finland are not without a corporate unity in themselves. Perhaps a fourth constituent order can, therefore, be distinguished in "Fenno-Scandinavia" as a whole.

Consciousness of unity and the effects of integrating forces within the frame of Scandinavia and Finland are the subjects of comment in Part 6. This chapter begins by casting an eye back to the first rounded geographical picture of "the Scandinavia cosmos", presented in map and text by Olaus Magnus in the sixteenth century. To this retrospect are then added observations upon the prospect of unity in the northern community. The penultimate chapter provides the ideal foil for such considerations, for it views the interaction of physical and human variables at a different cultural level. In its Lapp community and economy, the Scandinavian region has something unique for Europe.

The methods adopted for investigating the sample units selected within the hierarchy naturally vary widely. At the lowest levels, they embrace field work and discussion with factory operators. From this point of view, site facts will be of considerable consequence, and there remains a gap in the means of quantitatively analysing such features. Indices for the description of such data have yet to be satisfactorily devised. In intermediary scales, cartographic means of investigation are of greater value. For larger areas and longer periods, statistical analyses make a significant contribution—uncovering trends and revealing features not clearly visible to the eye. Each method suffers inaccuracies, and the degree of time-lag resulting from absence of up-to-date information is one of those facts most disturbing the economic geographer.

Another problem arises in the selection of the material. In this study no attempt is made to be comprehensive. Much that is essential is necessarily reduced to a subordinate level as a result of the approach which is adopted.

[1] A classification of the type used here is hinted at by K. H. Pfaffen, *Œkologische Landesgliederung*, Erdkunde, 1948, 167–73. Cf. also H. Carol, "Die Wirtschaftslandschaft und ihre kartographische Darstellung," *Geographica Helvetica*, 1946, 246–79, and J. F. Unstead, "A Systematic Method of Determining Geographical Regions," *Geographical Journal*, 48, 1916, 230 ff.
[2] Cf. for Norway, J. C. Hansen, "Industriell utvikling og tettstedsvekst," *Norsk Geografisk Tidsskrift*, 20, 1965–6, 182–265.

At any period of time, however, no one person can master all of the facts about an area to give a wholly faithful and balanced account. The material to be mastered and the means of mastery differ appreciably at different times. Four hundred years ago, the principal means of building up a picture were observation in the field and (what is known today as) the "interview technique". Olaus Magnus had travelled widely on pastoral missions in the territory which he described; in Danzig, over a period of years, he had also ready access to shippers and traders familiar with the northern world. His problem was to master the unknown. Today, the geographer who would interpret the same territory is faced with the problem of assimilating the known. For the "Fenno-Scandinavian" countries of the twentieth century have assembled a mass of geographical information about their lands, and have frequently collected it with a degree of thoroughness rare beyond their frontiers. This book, selective rather than comprehensive, is then also interpretative.

In the final place, economic geography is a branch of human geography. Its material derives from man and the land, and it is the pleasurable duty of the economic geographer, no less than of his physical colleague, to have personal contact with his ultimate sources. The labour of men in the field—the reason for it and the result of it—is fundamental to the problems which he studies. It is fitting that the responses of the economic geographer should be at their most sensitive when he is in the company of his prime mover, 'economic man' or 'marginal' man at the seat of his activity. The hills do not answer back when the physical geographer poses his questions; but man working in the field may ease or discomfit his questioning economic colleague. In the category of his accomplishments, perhaps none is better cultivated than the capacity to strike simply a happy and sympathetic contact with those whose work is his interest but who may not necessarily be interested in his work. In brief, no matter how assiduously the physical landscape may be eyed, however intently its economic content may be viewed, he should seek to be, above all, a very human geographer.

SCANDINAVIA

The area to which this approach is to be made consists of five countries—Denmark, Finland, Iceland, Norway and Sweden, with their dependencies. A bond of common interests unites them as an accepted group in international affairs. They are loosely and not very precisely known as "The Scandinavian Countries". The term Scandinavia—variously called Scatinavia, Scadin-auja, Skandia, Codanovia—is of at least Dark Age origin.[1] It has been applied to various regions about the Baltic "estuary", and has been most consistently associated with the major peninsula of Norway-Sweden. Yet, for British mapmakers, Moll defined it as "one of the thirteen parts into which Europe is generally divided", and he included in its frame Norway, Sweden, Denmark and Finland. Atlas editors found the area a convenient unit and Fig. 1 shows how its outline evolved in the mapmaker's eye. "Scandinavia" became an especially convenient name for the "Siamese twins" of Norway and Sweden during their uneasy union under a dual monarchy from 1814 to 1905. The association of Denmark with the epithet may be dated from the period of the Prusso-Danish Wars (1848–50, 1864), when pan-Scandinavianism reached a romantic climax. In popular language, Finland was spoken of as "The Fourth Scandinavian State" after its graduation to nationhood in 1917. Iceland, becoming an independent republic in 1944, is the fifth constituent. Within the area defined there is some opposition to the inclusive term "Scandinavia". Some elements in Finland are intermittently sensitive about its inclusion in the Scandinavian fraternity, in spite of the historical mould in which it was cast.

An alternative concept—Fennoscandia—is employed: but it is essentially a geological frame of reference.[2] As such, moreover, it includes the Karelian A.S.S.R., but excludes Denmark. A more inclusive and elaborate

---

[1] The range of names and their application is given in F. Nansen, *In Northern Mists*, London, 1911, I, 103–4.
[2] A. G. Högbom, *Fennoscandia, Handbuch der regionalen Geologie*, Heidelberg, 1913. The term is attributed to the Finnish geologist Wilhelm Ramsay in 1898.

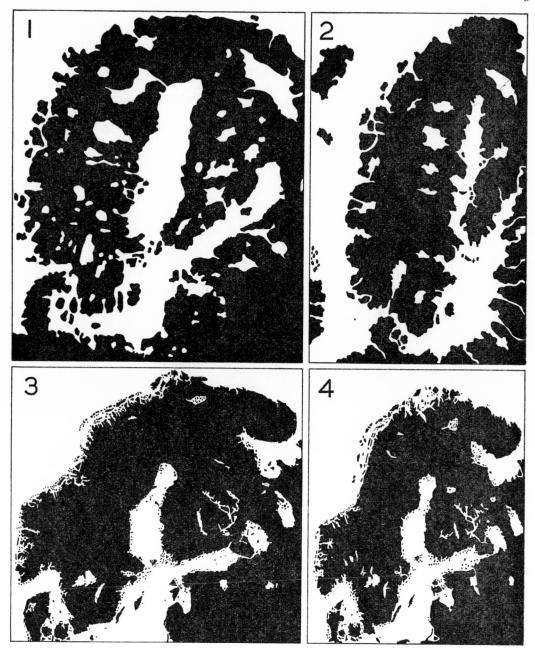

FIG. 1. Four silhouettes to show the emergence of the Scandinavian world in the cartographer's eye. (1) Mid-sixteenth century. (2) Late sixteenth century. (3) Mid-seventeenth century. (4) Mid-eighteenth century.

arrangement was proposed in the 1920s by Sten de Geer, in which he defined Fennoscandia as the geological core of the North European world and Baltoscandia as the complementary concept in the field of human geography.[1] But this merely introduced the problem of

[1] "Das geologische Fennoscandia und das geographische Baltoscandia", *Geografiska annaler*, 1928.

putting a boundary around Baltoscandia. "Fenno-Scandinavia" is another possible name for the group; but then one of the youngest and least focal constituents of the group assumes the dominant position in the nomenclature.[1] Because of its convenience, however, the phrase is used from time to time in this work. Within the borders of the five countries, the collective name *Norden* (the north) is used freely. *A Geography of Norden* is the title of the volume their geographers prepared for the International Geographical Congress in 1960.[2] The alternative "Northern Countries" is as unsatisfactory as is the ambiguous "United Kingdom". Economists of the northern world have played with corporate phrases of a Benelux character; but the least euphonistically offensive—Uniscan—has yet to gain more than commercial circulation. The British Foreign Office

deals with the five countries from its "Northern Department". The Royal Institution of International Affairs, in its last publication dealing with the area, remained uncompromised by entitling it *The Scandinavian States and Finland* (London, 1951). Andrew O'Dell called the first British geographical study which dealt exclusively with the area, *The Scandinavian World* (London, 1957). Roy Millward employs the title *The Scandinavian Lands* (1964).

The mission-field of the ninth-century Archbishop Ansgar of Bremen—Denmark, Iceland, Finland, Sweden and Norway with the Faeroes—wanted a name. Over a thousand years later, the issue is unresolved, and the geographer who would place a frame around the same historical community of people has to face at the outset the problem of definition.

[1] Georges Chabot gives Finland pride of place cf. *Finlande et les pays Scandinaves*, Paris, 1958.
[2] Axel Sømme (ed.), Bergen, 1960.

PART 2

THE RESOURCE VARIABLE

Chapter I[1]

THE SETTING

"... the first part which describeth the northern countries in Europe, tis a fayre impression."
Sir Thomas Browne in a letter to his son, *Works* (ed. Wilkin), I, 293

FORM AND STRUCTURE

THE Scandinavian countries and Finland belong to the high-latitude lands of Europe. The southern boundary of Jutland touches 55° N.; the northernmost peninsulas of Troms and Finnmark, lying far north of Iceland, touch latitude 71° N. The longitude of the Scandinavian states and Finland is commonly overlooked. Western Scandinavia belongs to Atlantic Europe; but Stockholm, centre-point of eastern Sweden, is of the longitude of Berlin and Vienna. Finland has a longitudinal location comparable with that of Rumania or Bulgaria. In general, however, latitude prevails over longitude in the Fenno-Scandinavian scene, and the feature which Zachris Topelius called "the hegemony of the north" has a habit of making its presence felt. Yet there is something more than mere "northerliness" which identifies the Scandinavian world. The German geographer, Alexander Supan, viewed Scandinavia and Finland as a distinct European province; while to Gustav Braun, for whom *Mitteleuropa* is a regional reality, Scandinavia and Finland (save possibly for the politically complicating Eastern Karelia and Kola) form a complementary *Nordeuropa*.[2]

The outline of this northern province is for the most part of recent origin; although in structure its primary components are among the oldest and most stable in the world. Three principal subdivisions may be recognised:

(1) Scandinavia proper—the peninsula springing out of what W. Ramsay christened the Fenno-Scandinavian isthmus and physically the most impressive unit;

(2) Jutland and the Danish archipelago, and

(3) The isthmus of Fennokarelia, only the Baltic half of which is embraced within the frame of the territory considered here.

To this area adhere politically or are related historically the Atlantic islands of Scandinavia —Iceland, the Færoes and more remotely Svalbard and Greenland.

The structural background to the greater part of the mainland area is a peneplaned shield of granites. The relative extensiveness of this can be appreciated from Fig. 2; while the detailed geology of it is best given in *Geologisk översiktskarta över Norden* (1:1 m., Stockholm, 1933). On its south-eastern edge the shield yields to the Cambrian and Silurian formations of the Russian plain. In Central Sweden, it is fractured along the "midland" axis, to the south of which it reasserts itself in the Småland plateau. This outlier of the shield, which gives to southern Sweden a Deccan-like shape, commands from the south-west a prospect of the Mesozoic and Tertiary formations of Skåne with its neighbouring territories and of Sjælland. On the Atlantic border, the shield encounters the Caledonian fold mountains, which form a crumpled and differentially eroded series several thousands of feet in altitude. Into these—and into the

[1] In the preparation of this chapter, the following primary works have been employed: *The Atlas of Sweden*, Stockholm, 1953 (in progress); *Atlas of Denmark* (and text), Copenhagen, 1949 (in progress); N. E. Nørlund, *Danmarks kortlægning*, Copenhagen, 1943; *Atlas of Finland*, Helsinki, 1925–8 (a fourth edition of which appeared in 1960); *Handbook of Finnish Geography*, Helsinki, 1952; O. Holtedahl, *Norges geologi*, Oslo, 1953; N. E. Nørlund, *Islands kortlægning*, Copenhagen, 1944.
[2] *Nordeuropa*, Berlin, 1926.

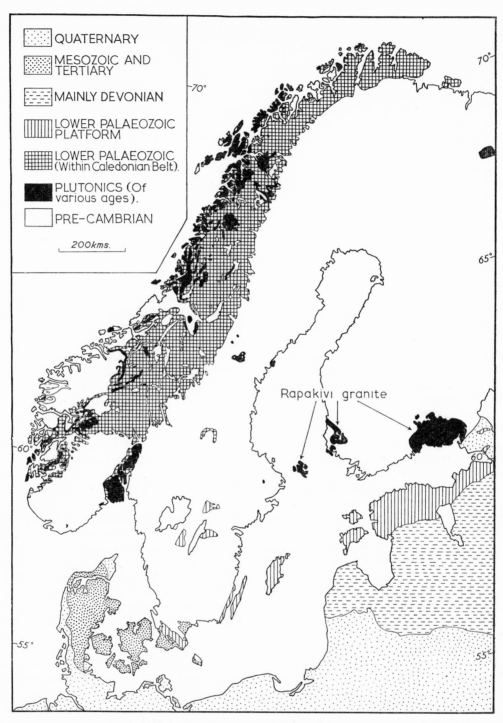

QUATERNARY

MESOZOIC AND TERTIARY

MAINLY DEVONIAN

LOWER PALAEOZOIC PLATFORM

LOWER PALAEOZOIC (Within Caledonian Belt).

PLUTONICS (Of various ages).

PRE-CAMBRIAN

200 kms.

Rapakivi granite

FIG. 2. A simplified geological map of Scandinavia and its neighbouring territories. (Sources: J. J. Sederholm, *Fennoscandia*; O. Holtedahl and J. A. Dons, *Geological Map of Norway*, Oslo, 1953.)

older shield—have been injected Plutonic rocks of various ages. The Caledonian backbone—"the huge, bare ribs of the globe", as Capell Brooke called it—is a full thousand miles long from the broad plateaux of western Norway to its physical (if not geological) extension in the Koli Heights of east central Finland. For the most part, it has remained above sea-level since Devonian times, experiencing prolonged aerial erosion, extensive peneplanation, Tertiary epeirogenic uplift[1] and rejuvenation, and sedimentary accumulation in its depressions. The mountains lack a collective name; though he Lund geographer Eric Ljungner sought without success to popularise the term Scandes (Scanderna to the Scandinavians) to parallel Andes.

The uplands form a half-ellipse which is at the same time the main watershed of Northern Europe. This ellipse is complemented by the extended depression of a natural watergate central to the region (cf. Fig. 3). The arc of this depression from den norske rennen (popularly translated as Norway Deep and dropping to 400 fathoms) to the White Sea throat is a second striking feature of the area. The zone of weakness continues from the Skaggerak, through the Swedish Midlands, the Gulf of Finland, Lakes Ladoga and Onega to Onega Bay. Closely related to it are the four great lakes of the Swedish Midlands.

Upon this background, the Quaternary Ice Age has exerted a powerful influence. Fennoscandia, indeed, was the seat of a continental ice-sheet. Ice radiated from and retreated to the fells of the keel ridge. Of the successive outpourings which are conjectured, the earlier were probably thicker and more prolonged. There is evidence to suggest that later advances left nunataks above the ice surface. On three scores glaciation has been a fundamental force shaping Scandinavia and Finland for human settlement and use.

First, as a result of glaciation the area emerged as a territory of erosion. To complement this, a great crescent of the North European Plain became a territory of glacial accumulation. Of the Scandinavian area, only

Denmark and southernmost Sweden are included within the accepted territory of deposition. The last ice-lobes retreated from Denmark about 12,000 years ago (cf. Atlas of Denmark, p. 31). The retreat of the ice, the succeeding seas and the emergence of the Scandinavian world to its present familiar shape are illustrated in Fig. 10. But within the territory dominated by erosion, there is a distinctive pattern of depositional features related to the final stages of retreat. Deposition, in esker and drumlin features, has stirred the human imagination at least since the Dark Ages, when Närke folk-legend identified the former as "petrified serpents" and Upland lorists described the latter as giants' burial-mounds. The handwriting of the past is still identified in this depositional pattern, but in a different manner by such investigators as Gerard de Geer. De Geer's experiments in dating the past from the layered clay deposits which he defined as "varves" has been widely applied.

"Geochronology was born in the Stockholm region," he wrote when recording the results of his investigations, "and it was during the intense evolution of that town within the past five decades and with the accompanying innumerable different kinds of digging that it became possible to bring together in the Geochronological Institute in Stockholm such a great number of detailed observations on the late Quaternary date that Stockholm will have a good chance to compete for the title 'a capital of Quaternary Geology'."[2]

Deposition, obstructing drainage, has given rise to an extent of fresh water within the territorial confines of the area rivalled only by that in Ontario and Quebec. The term "lakescape" has, in fact, been suggested as more fitting than landscape for such a countryside. The feature reaches its extreme expression in the province of Savo in central Finland: though the most impressive water body is Lake Vänern in central Sweden (5,546 sq. km.). In some parishes the water area may be as great as the land area. Dwindling lakes leave behind a legacy of bogland. It is a "desert of lakes and morasses", wrote Emanuel Bowen in his map of 1752 across a part of the shield area. Much still is.

---

[1] Perhaps in two stages—Miocene and Pliocene; cf. K. M. Ström, "Geomorphology of Norway", Geographical Journal, CXII, 1949.
[2] Geochronologia suecica—principles, Vetenskapsakademiens handlingar, 3, 18, Stockholm, 1939, p. 96.

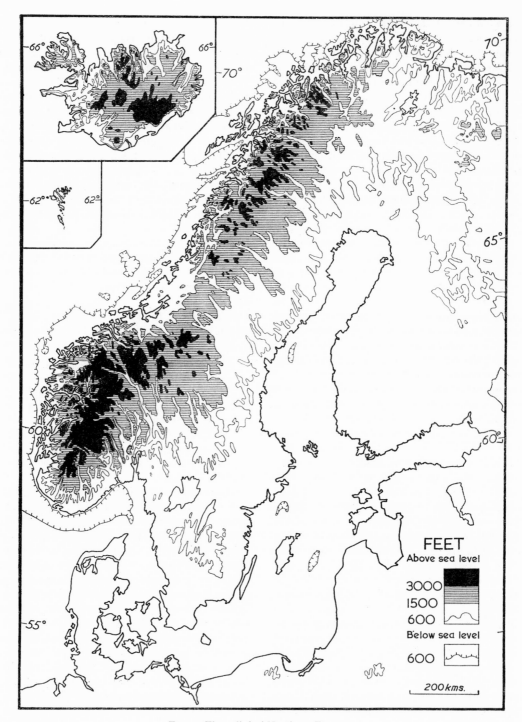

FEET
Above sea level

3000
1500
600

Below sea level

600

200 kms.

Fig. 3. The relief of Northern Europe.

The complementary erosive force of glaciation in creating land and water intricacies is nowhere more strikingly illustrated than in the skerries of the Stockholm archipelago or the fiorded coast of south-west Norway. The general rejuvenation of drainage brought about by the Ice Age has given an immature character to most of the water-courses linking or draining the lake systems. Partly as a result of glaciation, land meets sea in a highly articulated shore-line. In each case estimates of its length are subject to substantial variation. Thus, measured on the 1:2 million map, that of Sweden is about 2,500 km., while other official estimates raise it to 7,500 km.

Glaciation has shaped Fennoscandia in a third and less direct manner through isostatic uplift. As a result, a primary distinction may be made between those areas which have experienced post-glacial marine submergence and those which have remained above the limit of marine intrusion. The upper marine limit may have the appearance of a contour line on the map, but owing to differential uplift, it does not follow the same altitude in all areas. In Sweden, the limit is therefore found as high as 250 m. in West Bothnia, drops to 200 m. in Dalarna and Värmland, to 130 m. in Östergötland and Vestergötland, to 60 m. in Halmstad and to 20 m. in Hälsingborg before it finally disappears in Malmö. The limit has corresponding expression in Finland. It is also elaborately evident around the coast of Norway, where deposits on offshore banks have been elevated in terraces of reassorted material. Glacial upwarping is still significant around the shore of the Bothnian Sea (cf. Chapter II). In the Bothnian lands, it has also had its effect upon the profiles of the outstanding series of rivers which drain into the central gulf.

Bearing in mind the importance of glaciation for Scandinavia and Finland, it is not surprising that the region should have bred a lively school of glaciologists—from anonymous Icelanders whose long use of the word *skridjökull* (or moving ice) indicated their appreciation of its mobile character through the naturalist J. Esmark[1] who, five generations ago, insisted on the formerly widespread extension of an ice-sheet in Norway to such classical field-workers as Gerard de Geer and the contemporary Hans Wilson Ahlmann.

To the picture of the land must be added a picture of the surrounding seas. All these glacial forces—erosive, cumulative and isostatic—have combined to produce the form and coast-lines of the Baltic Sea. The Gulfs of Finland and Bothnia, its northern antechambers, are 250 and 350 miles long respectively. They meet in the Åland Sea, and are richly islanded with archipelagos. Their island clusters have a distinct personality of their own, which has already attracted the attention of the human geographers, prompted the publication of *skärgård* books[2] and encouraged the preparation of a *skärgård* atlas.[3] August Strindberg once captured the mood of Stockholm archipelago in *Hemsöborna* (1887)[4] and *Skärkarlsliv* (1888). They are books rich in a distinctive skerry vocabulary, the words of which are frequently unique to the Stockholm *skärgård*, and which belong to a world which still retains relics of many earlier ways of life. The southern basin of the Baltic Sea is a flooded continuation of the North European plain, and has been described by Albrecht Penck as a "transgression sea". Two main coastal types are found along the continental shore. The eastern half, a coast of wave-built spits and lagoons which is historically known to the Scandinavians as *"den stora östen"*, recalls for mariners the coast of west Jutland. Westwards, this is transitional to the so-called *föhrden* coast of the Belt Sea and eastern Jutland. The Baltic outlet has an estuarine character, with the congested Danish archipelago looking at first sight like some giant deltaic formation. This inner sea, standing at a higher level than the outer ocean, is virtually tideless; though wind forces may affect the sea-level. As a result of receiving an immense volume of water from its tributary rivers, it has fresh-water characteristics in some areas.

The second water body in the North European scene is sometimes called "The Scandi-

[1] "Bidrag til vor Jordklodes historie," *Magazin for naturvidenskab*, **2**, 1, Christiania, 1824.
[2] E.g. *Skärgårdsboken*, Nordenskiöld Samfundet, Helsingfors, 1954; B. Hedenstierna, *Stockholms skärgård*, Stockholm, 1949; and a study of the problems of archipelagic people, I. Hustich, *Finlands skärgård*, Helsingfors, 1964.
[3] S. Jaatinen (ed.) *Atlas över Skärgårds-Finland*, Helsingfors, 1960.   [4] *The People of Hemsö*, London, 1959.

navian Sea". It consists of the Kattegat and Skaggerak. The north–south axis of the Kattegat is extended in the longitudinal zone of structural weakness evidenced in the Vik region of south Norway, and bifurcates northwards in Gudbrandsdal and Østerdal (with their Lågen and Glomma rivers respectively). The Scandinavian Sea is transitional between inner sea and outer ocean, and shares characteristics of each. It is of direct interest to four of the five Scandinavian countries, and control of it invests the tributary lands with an authority international in importance.

The "outer" ocean is the third maritime element in the life and economy of Scandinavia. It strikes the coast in three different components—the shallow North Sea, the North Atlantic Ocean (locally called the Norwegian Sea) and the Arctic Ocean. The continental shelf narrows rapidly northwards, and is intruded upon in the Skaggerak by the trough of the Norway Deep. Denmark exposes to the North Sea a dune coast faced with broad beaches and a treacherously shallow foreshore. Save for local artificial modifications, it is harbourless from Blaavands Huk to the Skaw. South of the Huk, the dunes are breached so that south Jutland shares in the coastal forms common to the north-west German coast— dune islands, *watten*, *geest* and outwash plain. The coast of Norway offers a complete contrast. It abuts on the Atlantic in deeply dissected fells from southernmost Lindesnes to northernmost Nordkyn (not the tourist focus of North Cape!). Paralleling the coast and of varying width and intensity is the low-lying strandflat, in the lee of which feature runs the historical "Inner Lead". About the latitude of the Arctic Circle the Lofoten Islands thrust southwestwards a spectacular dragon's back of islands some eighty miles into the Norwegian Sea. The Arctic coast of Norway is virtually skerry free, curving back on itself to give an eastern aspect to Varanger fiord. The continental shelf follows roughly the contours of the Norwegian coast, save in three main areas where it advances a hundred miles seaward. Here it expresses itself in the Lofoten, Halten and Sunnmøre "banks" upon which are supported the great coastal fisheries (cf. Chapter VIII). The detail of submarine contour—

much the object of contemporary survey— may well make a contribution towards the understanding of earlier Norwegian glacial behaviour. The "outer" ocean is tidal—so vigorously in some parts that cartographers continued to locate the *malstrøm* in the Lofotens (off Moskenes) until the eighteenth century. It is of high salinity (3·5% or more) and ice free; though in harder winters the interior fiord areas may ice over. The Atlantic drift, giving water 9% warmer than the average for its latitudes, transmits an influence directly to Atlantic Scandinavia. Perhaps it is not surprising, in view of this intimate association with the sea, that few countries have shown a livelier or more diverse interest in oceanography and marine biology than Norway and Sweden.

The continental foreland of Baltic Scandinavia is balanced by the maritime foreland of Atlantic Scandinavia. The interest which Baltic Scandinavia has displayed in the land beyond the inner sea is complemented by that which Atlantic Scandinavia has shown in the land beyond the outer ocean. The Atlantic island arc—represented by Great Britain, the Orkneys, Shetlands, Færoes, Iceland, Jan Mayen and Svalbard—was historically or remains contemporarily, a natural extension of Atlantic Scandinavia.

These are the essential features of the anatomy of Scandinavia and Finland. The annual round of the climate which plays upon it, the character of the soils which are a skin upon its bones, and the nature of the vegetation which mantles it must precede a summary of its human division.

THE ROUND OF THE CLIMATE

The climatic régime prevailing in Scandinavia and Finland derives from a high-latitude location, a somewhat obscured continental situation and a vital maritime relationship. The interplay of continental and oceanic forces in the northern environment give the general character to the weather picture. Local variations are explained in the context of the anatomy of Scandinavia.

Nearly a third of the peninsular world (albeit the least important part from the point of view of settlement) lies within the Arctic

Circle. This third loses sight of the sun completely for a period during winter. When the Icelandic novelist Gunnar Gunnarsson described Scandinavia's "nightless summers and dayless winters", he placed his finger upon a cardinal climatic fact. Artificial day must be created at the Norrland mineral workings and flood-lights illumine the vessels which haul in Finnmark cod. Within a second third at midwinter, as the Finnish poet, Alexis Kivi, has written in *The Bear Hunt*:

> "... the rayless
> Round of the sun
> Travels on the rim of the sky and earth."

Many sizeable towns fall within this zone. Nor are the capitals of four out of the five countries far removed from it. For a compensating period at midsummer there is no darkness.

The annual curve of daylight (Fig. 4) has imprinted itself upon the mental and physical development of the Scandinavians through its effect upon their daily pursuits. Small wonder that early farmers were sun-worshippers, that Bronze Age sun discs of their votary rights are still yielded by Danish bogs, and that Middle Age field patterns paid deference to sun and shadowland. In saga and medieval times, the passage of time was counted in nights rather than days; the reckoning of years in winters rather than summers. The pagan midwinter Mother Night celebration of the shortest day complements that of St. John on the shortest night, Midsummer Eve. Celebrations may mark the reappearance of the sun over the shoulder of the Norwegian fells. The guns of Vardø fortress greet the return of the sun to Varanger fiord with a kind of royal salute; most northern fiords, in fact, have their "sun coffee day". Winter gloom has left an especially deep imprint upon Norse and Finnish mythology. The Kalevalan legend of Pohjola, the queen of darkness, springs to mind. The poets have sensed the long night—none more than Eino Leino, a Finnish poet who is a virtual prince of darkness. The reaction of the Norwegian poet Bjørnstjerne Bjørnson to the country's waterfalls on the eve of the hydro-electric power era

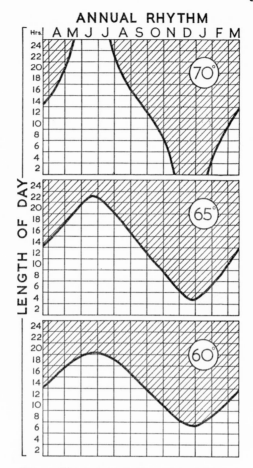

FIG. 4. The annual rhythm of daylight and darkness at different latitudes in Scandinavia.

was to "turn to light the raging torrent". Medieval cartographers responded by calling the Scandinavian countries *"Die mitternachtiger Länder"*. In this dark period (*mørketiden*), the Norwegians are liable to a complaint which they call *"mørkesyke"* or dark sickness.[1] Physically, the people have experienced an incidence of disease relative to the maldistribution of sunshine. It is not wise to account for the former ravages of tuberculosis by climate alone; but it is worthy of note that mortality rates from it in the provinces north of Trøndelag have been double those for south Norway. The most afflicted provinces of Sweden have been Jämtland, Västerbotten

---

[1] Of direct interest in this connection is N. and H. Kleitman, "The Sleep-wakefulness Pattern in the Arctic", *Scientific Monthly*, LXVII, 3, 1953. Cf. also William Sansom, *The Icicle and the Sun*, London, 1958

and Norbotten.   A happier climatic reflection was observed by Emily Lowe (*Unprotected Females in Norway*, 1857), who noted that Norwegians only married in spring and autumn, summer being "too short and important for such a waste of time".   Mid-twentieth-century statistics still reveal October, November and December to be the principal marriage months!   Economically, the contrast between summer and winter is expressed in the varying number of activities.   The late-winter peak of unemployment reflects the dearth of jobs; while summer pursuits are multiplied contrastingly to crowd the nightless months. The energies of farming people are then spent to the point of exhaustion—as is well illustrated in F. E. Sillanpää's classic of Finnish country life, *The Maid Silja*.

The seasonal rhythm of light and darkness is balanced by a rhythm of heat and cold. Winter controls annual isotherms over the greater part of the area.   Three winters, indeed, may be defined—autumn winter, spring winter and high winter; while in Lapland it is said that there are nine months of "white winter" and three months of "green winter". This seasonal refrigeration is the theme of Chapter III.   The thaw comes relatively slowly.   On the white-cap student festival of May 1st, it is rare for leaves to have broken green on the trees in Helsinki.   Small wonder that an eighteenth-century Earl of Buckingham in these areas should write of the "very concise summers".   Yet the contrasting cumulative effect of continuous summer sun raises temperatures to remarkable levels in late June and July, producing what the Earl called "a magic celerity of growth".   Perhaps the July isotherm of 60° F. is of rather more significance than January isotherms for assessing agricultural potentialities in the area.

The dominance of latitude in the annual climatic round is modified by oceanic or continental influences generally and regionally. Baltic Scandinavia is naturally more susceptible to the extended influence of the continental high pressure; the Atlantic slope of Scandinavia to the cyclonic westerlies.   Of the five countries, Iceland and Norway (with the exception of the south-eastern area) have the most maritime climate; Finland the least maritime.   The Scandinavian keel, receiving the full impact of the westerly air-stream, reduces the Atlantic influence in the northern two-thirds of Sweden and Finland.   Only in its south, by way of the "Midland Gate" of Sweden, do cyclonic eddies commonly penetrate, and there is a discernible "storm track" along this axis.[1] South-western and south Finland experience the weakening influence of the intrusive cyclonic system.   The oceanic influence restricts the number of frost days, and they may be as few in the outer Lofoten archipelago as along the south coast of Norway.[2]   It also contributes a high positive thermal anomaly during the winter.   The winter thermal anomaly of 10° is a forceful expression of surplus warmth derived from western sources.   It also reflects topographical modification for, if inscribed on the map, it traces a boundary between an inner and outer peninsular area.   Such a boundary line is a highly generalised but useful symbol for marking a zone of variable width and character which nevertheless separates two appreciably different areas.[3]

A second "inner" peninsula can be traced, the outline of which derives from the pattern of isohyets.   There are differences between the precipitation régime of the Atlantic and Baltic slopes of the area: the former (save for local differentiation) receives generous precipitation at all seasons; the latter experiences the summer maximum of the Central European régime.   Norway, the western fells of which vie with the western highlands of Britain as the wettest area in Europe, is an "umbrella" country in more senses than one.   Recorded averages for the wetter stations exceed 120 inches; but there are clearly many unrecorded areas with fully 200 inches.   Norway established a reputation for raininess in early times. Edrisi, the medieval Arab geographer, knew that Norwegians reaped their corn green, because the sun so seldom shone in that land of "frequent rain and continuous wet".   Norway

[1] B. J. Birkeland and N. J. Føyn, *Klimat von Nordwesteuropa*, Berlin, 1932.
[2] H. W. Ahlmann, *Norge*, Stockholm, 1943, Fig. 18.
[3] Some idea of the sequence of weather from Western Norway to Karelia is given in R. R. Platt, *Finland and its Geography*. New York, 1955. Fig. 57.

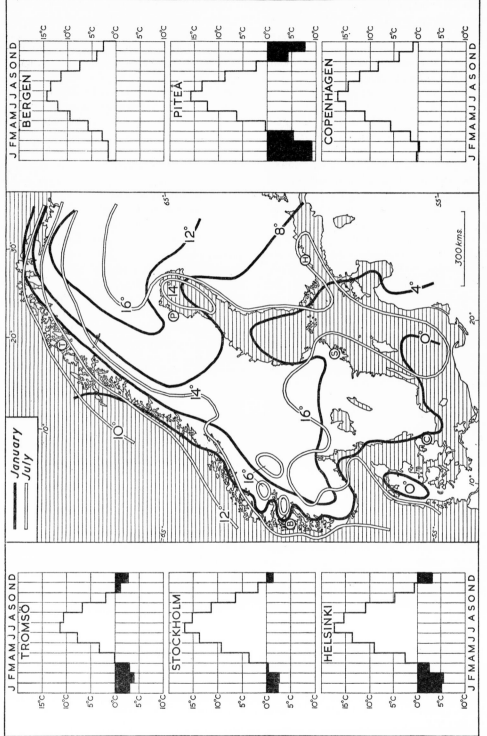

Fig. 5. A pattern of isotherms for Scandinavia and Finland coupled with sample annual temperature charts.

emerges on the small-scale map as a land of uniformly high precipitation; but the local topography must not be overlooked.[1] Thus, irrigation can have a place in dry spring weather in such valleys as Gudbrandsdal, Ottadal, Østerdal and Årdal. Extreme conditions prevail at such places as Lom in Dovre where precipitation falls to little more than 10 inches—and this at an altitude of over 1,000 ft.[2] A complete contrast is provided by Finland, the driest of the five countries.

Much precipitation comes as snow, a maximum depth of which is usually reached in late spring—as late as April, for example, in such places as Myrdal in western Norway. A visual feature of some interest is the limit of permanent snow which ranges from about 4,000 ft. in the Trondheim area to 2,500 ft. in Finnmark. The role of snow in the northern scene is considered more fully in Chapter III.

Precipitation effectiveness, tied both to relative humidity and to evaporation, is of greater significance than absolute precipitation. Humidity is both highest and most persistent on the Atlantic slope, and directly related is the high percentage of cloud. Insolation is accordingly modified differentially over the area. In high latitudes, evaporation tends to diminish—a fact of recurring importance in the appreciation of the Fenno-Scandinavian precipitation pattern.

A fourth climatic characteristic related to the cyclonic system is the variable distribution of air currents over the area. Again, the Atlantic slope is characterised by exposure, while the Baltic area is relatively sheltered. The upstanding keel ridge of Norway receives the most pronounced impact, and the highest recorded wind strengths are associated with Lofoten latitudes. Not without cause was English imaginative literature of the sixteenth and seventeenth centuries rich in descriptions of the way in which Lapps and Finns (i.e. Finnmarkers) bought and sold wind.[3] It is doubtful if the lands of the "Roaring Forties" could rival in incredible stories the experiences

of Norwegian meteorologists in Nordland. Equally significant, though less spectacular, are the winds of Jutland. The detail of the rural economy is rich in response to them. Thus, Iron Age fields were enclosed in protective balks, which are believed to have been erected as a shelter against the strong western wind. Within the range of contemporary experience, crops have had to be resown after a high wind has carried away surface soil and seed grain. An apocryphal story may be recalled of the West Jutish farmer who declared to the East Jutlander: "I have seventy tunland of land when it is all at home." And the winds which blow the soil out blow sand in. The most outstanding feature of Jutland is the spit of the Skaw, which owes its origin primarily to wind action, and old Skagen church, inundated by sand, is a measure of the mobility of sand in the area.[4]

These features of the westerly cyclonic system are challenged increasingly towards the east, and the interplay between them and continental "controls" is nowhere more marked than in the "Midland Gate" of Sweden. The extension of the continental high-pressure system contributes a distinctly different character to the summers and winters of Baltic Sweden and Finland. The prolonged summer daylight and slight cloud cover favour unexpectedly high July temperatures. Thunderstorms and convectional rain showers increase in frequency from the Atlantic coast inland, giving a summer rainfall maximum. After November, which can also be a time of fogs,[5] general absence of a cloud blanket favours the intensification of cold through radiation. This effect is exaggerated with the freezing of the inner reaches of the Baltic. Depending on the intensity of the continental high-pressure system, its control extends intermittently to western Scandinavia.

These are the principal forces which outline the broader climatic characteristics of the area and form a synthesis of which climatic regions may be built up. Within their frame, how-

[1] *Økonomisk-geografisk Atlas over Norge*, Oslo, 1923, amplifies the climatic data given here.
[2] O. H. Johansson, "The Distribution of Precipitation in Norway", *Geografiska Annaler*, XIX, Stockholm, 1937.
[3] E. Seaton, *Literary Relations of England and Scandinavia in the Seventeenth Century*, Oxford, 1935, 582 et seq.
[4] Cf. the diagrams in *Atlas of Denmark*, I, p. 108, and A. Fuglsang, "Bidrag till sandflugtens historie", *Jydsk Samling*, 5, VIII B, 1947–9, Copenhagen.
[5] E. Lindskog, "On the Geographical Distribution of Fog in Sweden", *Geografiska Annaler*, 1931.

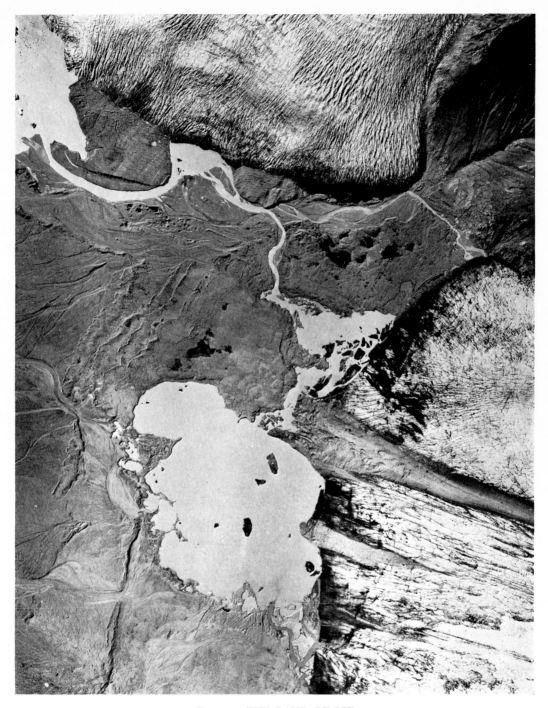

PLATE 1. THE LAND OF ICE

The retreating lobes of Breiðamerkurjökull and Hvitarjökull (16° 22′ W, 64° 02′ N) and their related
melt-water features.

PLATE 2. THE LAND OF FIRE

Old lava formations and dissected volcanic ash at Kollafjorður and Mosfellssveit. This is one of the more favoured and accessible tracts of developed farmland in south-west Iceland.

ever, local climates proliferate. In the first place, they are a reaction to the intermarriage of water and land. For example, the penetration of warm Atlantic waters has a marked effect upon the character of Norwegian coastal climates; the great lakes of Sweden and Finland also behave as temperature regulators. Again, the behaviour of the extensive mosslands affects local climates, though their influence may be less easily assessed. Local climatic variations are also attributable to marked relief changes. Fiord Norway displays a dual contrast. There is the contrast between fiord-edge climate and fell-top climate, with temperatures diminishing at the rate of 1·2° for every 300 ft. and the exposure of the uplands juxtaposed with the protection of the fiord shore. There is contrast also between fiord mouth and fiord "bottom". The fiord interiors will enjoy higher summer temperatures than the fiord mouths; but in winter they may suffer biting local winds, like the *Elvegust* or *Sno*, which are produced by cold air slipping down from the fells. Indeed, a continental winter exists above a maritime winter along the coasts of Norway, and an Ice Age exists locally beside the hot "interglacials" of the summer months. In explaining local climates, there is a third feature to be remembered—the pattern of vegetation. A heavy woodland mantle, for example, can have a considerable positive effect.

In the catalogue of climatic characteristics, at least one further feature must be mentioned—the summer frost. Where the frost-free period is, in any case, restricted in compass, the unpredictable hazard of summer frosts presents a formidable challenge to farm husbandry. Most of the northern two-thirds of Fenno-Scandinavia are liable to this affliction. The origins and causes remain the subject of scientific debate. There may be seemingly simple explanations—when, for example, the outpouring of a cold northerly airstream is coupled with radiation. Alternatively, only a complex combination of facts—local and regional—can begin to explain the phenomenon. It is clear that certain areas are more susceptible than others, though this distribution defies simple geographical explanation. It is evident that certain types of

territory are relatively safe, e.g. the lower lake terraces. In some areas, temperature inversion is undoubtedly the cause. Low August temperatures with clear night skies favouring radiation may give rise to them. There is evidence of association with bogland, though this connection must not be pressed too hard. Summer frosts, indeed, present a phenomenon so neglected and so challenging that the head of the Finnish Meteorological Bureau has undertaken their investigation as the most worthy of possible retirement projects.

THE TOP SIX INCHES

Generalisations on the continental scale which is commonly employed in atlases usually define the dominant soil type of Northern Europe as podsolic. To the south-west of the area, some discrimination is made in favour of the so-called brown forest soils which are associated with deciduous woodlands. This broad generalisation is unsatisfactory, for podsolisation is a process which affects soils of many differing primary characteristics, and it is a process which can be artificially checked—and naturally arrested or speeded—according to a number of circumstances. The means for correcting the erroneous atlas impression are, however, being made available but slowly, so that although correct regional impressions of the soils of Scandinavia and Finland become increasingly available, the total picture is still unobtainable. Soil survey is a time-consuming activity, and over large areas in these high latitudes is restricted to a limited period of the year. Moreover, soil classification calls for increasing refinement so that conditions may be expressed in international terms. Assuming that a soil map of Fenno-Scandinavia were prepared, it would therefore display numerous lacunæ and not inconsiderable differences in the fundamental terms of reference.

Physical history and climatic setting are primary indicators of the nature of soils. In spite of the widespread reassortment of surface deposits in Scandinavia and Finland, it is still possible to say that a broad relationship exists between bedrock and fertility. Distinct regional contributions are imparted to soils by the bedrock from which general weathering takes place. Thus, the richest soils spring from the limited tracts of marls and shales born of the Palæozoic and younger formations. There has, of course, been a measure of re-distribution of weathered bedrock—through glacial action, for example. Soils relatively rich in limestone constituents have therefore been spread beyond the zone of occurrence of limestone rocks. An extensive limestone out-crop is assumed to exist beneath the Bothnian Sea, largely on the diffusionist evidence (cf. *Atlas of Sweden*, 15–16, 4). Contrasting areas of infertility are associated with the quartzites and quartzitic sandstones; while exposed rock outcrop has a relatively extensive occurrence. In the latter circumstance, the surface mantle of soil is missing. Sometimes the areas of rock outcrop support a shatter of weathered debris; sometimes they are smoothly eroded areas of coastal emergence. Bohuslän pro-vince, for example, has extensive areas of bald rock without soil.

Marked fertility is also found in association with marine deposition, so that an essential difference occurs in both the mechanical and chemical structure of soils in those areas which have experienced submergence and in those which have remained above the level of former seas.

There are other ways of classifying soils than by origin of parent materials. For practical purposes of land use and of farm economy, they may be usefully divided into those of mineral and those of vegetable character. In comparison with most European countries, Scandinavia and Finland have a relatively high percentage of vegetable or humus soils. In general, however, the occupation of these "softlands" has been delayed in comparison with that of the "firmlands", so that primary colonisation in Northern Europe has been against the background of the mineral soils. As a result of long and careful cultivation, considerable changes have taken place in many quite poor soils.

Mineral soils may be subdivided into a clay and a sand group. They are essentially de-positional, for new residual formations have not had time to develop to any great extent

since the retreat of the Quaternary ice-sheet. In certain areas easily weathered rocks occur, e.g. the Cambro-Silurian shales of the Lake Mjøsa area; but they are of restricted extent. By contrast, widespread stretches of clay are to be found. The coastal plains of Finland, the lake plains of central Sweden, the coast-lands of Oslofiord[1] and Trondheim fiord pro-vide examples. Sands are associated largely with glacial deposition or fluvial redistribu-tion. They are extensive in the outwash plains of Jutland, they are basic to the anastomosing eskers which streak the physical maps of Fennoscandia. Virtual "deserts" of sand are to be found locally in interior areas of Sweden and Finland, while broad dunes occur at the head of the Gulf of Bothnia as well as along the Danish coasts. The extreme mineral form—pebble and boulder wastes—are also associated with glacial deposition. They are so pronounced at Bergö in the Replot Archipelago of Finland, that the parish priest once called his home tract "Stony Arabia"; while imaginative travellers east of Lovisa have described the boulder litter as a battle-field of giants.

Humus soils are widely scattered and also vary greatly in character.[2] In the coniferous-dominant tracts, the humus contribution from leaf shedding is slight and only over a limited area in the extreme south-west do rich humus soils with a mineral base occur. The Fenno-Scandinavian soils of vegetable origin are for the most part those in which *Sphagnum* is a dominant constituent. In their unimproved state, they are commonly known as boglands. The collective word embraces such contrasting types as bog blankets of the Norwegian fells, the 5-m. deep quaking bogs of interior Finland and Sweden, the shallow peat-encrusted lands of West Bothnia and East Bothnia, and the widespread peatlands of Jutland. The impact of the boglands is evidenced in the multiplicity of words which have evolved in the Swedish and Finnish languages for the various bogland types—words which are not readily translat-able.[3] The study of boglands has a long his-tory in Northern Europe, and each country

[1] Cf. *Norwegian Geological Survey*, Oslo; 1:250,000, 1949.
[2] *Atlas of Finland*, Map 18, 8–9; *Atlas of Sweden*, Map 41–42.
[3] L. Mali, *Peatland Terminology*, Helsinki, 1956.

has established a peatland research organisation during the last sixty years. Probably no single soil type has claimed so much attention in more recent years among North European pedologists as the peatland. There are a number of reasons for this. First, the limited extent of good mineral soils for reclamation has directed attention to the humus soils—in Denmark especially after 1864, in Finland especially after 1944. Secondly, much peatland is under timber or is potential timber land, and bogland drainage can make its contribution to increased timber supply as well as to increased farm production. Thirdly, the humus soils are in any case inherently rich once their water surplus is brought under control and their acidity modified by scientific improvement. Moreover, bogland improvement can ameliorate local climate. Revaluation of the bogland is reflected in the fundamental change in the approach of the Northern Countries to their reclamation. Formerly, small-scale and private reclamation dominated; though there were certain large-scale centrally promoted schemes a full century ago, e.g. Pelso in the north Finnish valley of the Oulu river. Today, peatland potentialities are being tested by extensive and intensive experiments, and peatland utilisation changes responsively. The most important feature about peatland is that it is not a static element. It is in continuous process of accumulation and expansion or of reduction and contraction. The nature and speed of its development in Scandinavia and Finland are indicative of long-period climatic changes independently of the humanly induced changes which affect its margins.

THE MANTLE OF VEGETATION

The greater part of Norway, Sweden, Denmark and Finland were originally wooded; their Atlantic outlands, locally timbered at one time, are today virtually unforested. Timber cover everywhere represents a postglacial reoccupation by the forest; though lesser flora probably persisted along the periglacial margins of the west and in other places of refuge at least during the last advance of the ice. Reoccupation of the land has been by a succession of trees in time. Thus, the spruce re-entered the Norwegian scene later than the pine; while deciduous trees such as the beech are still expanding. Few appreciated this vegetational advance more clearly than Bjørnstjerne Bjørnson in his novelette *Arne*, in the opening chapter of which moss, heather, birch and conifer slowly assault a mountain flank. The reoccupation of Fennoscandia by plants has shown a differential advance and retreat. Here, indeed, is one of the most sensitive indicators of climatic change. Here, at the same time, is an indicator which has left a trail from the past. For, through contemporary pollen analysis, the reconstruction of past floras has become a local and regional possibility.

As a broad generalisation it may be said that the mantle of vegetation in the Scandinavian area is most varied in the west and south-west; least varied in the east and north-east. Distributional patterns traced in floral atlases bring out this point.[1] Within the boundaries of the easternmost unit, Finland, the diminution in species from south-west to north-east illustrates the tendency in more detail.[2] In the search for the boundaries of Fenno-Scandinavia the ecologist has also made his contribution—seeking for those changes in flora and fauna which announce a differing environment.[3]

Woodlands dominate. The type of woodland is a primary reflection of the anatomy of Scandinavia and Finland, and of their climatic background; though the distribution and composition of timber stands have been substantially altered by human action. The distribution of woodlands in Norway is modified by altitude: in Sweden and Finland, mostly by latitude; in Denmark and the Scandinavian outlands, mostly by man. Woodland covers 67% of Finland, 56% of Sweden, 25% of Norway and 8% of Denmark. There are two main forest types—coniferous and deciduous, the former taking generous precedence over the latter. The westernmost tongue of the great Eurasian coniferous mantle is known in Sweden as *barrskog*. Within the *barrskog*, the

---

[1] E.g. E. Hulten, *Atlas över växternas utbredning i Norden*, Stockholm, 1950; H. Sjörs, *Nordisk växtgeografi*, Stockholm 1956, and the collection of botanical maps in Riksmuseets botanical department, Stockholm.
[2] *Atlas of Finland*, Map 17, 1–6.
[3] H. Luther, "Fennoskandiens gräns i Vita Havet", *Mem. Societatis pro Fauna et Flora Fennica*, **29**, Helsingfors, 1954.

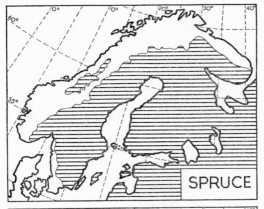

FIG. 6. Two essential distributions of trees in Northern Europe. (After E. Hulten, *Atlas över växternas utbredning i Norden*, Stockholm, 1950.)

Scotch pine (*Pinus sylvestris*) is dominant on dry soils and the Norway spruce (*Picea excelsa*) on moist soils. There are local admixtures of birch (*Betula odorata* and *Betula verocosa*), aspen (*Populus tremula*) and black alder (*Alnus glutinosa*). From the spread of the principal coniferous species, as seen in Fig. 6, it will be seen that the distribution of spruce and pine is not identical. The divergence becomes most pronounced in Norway, where there is a popular distinction between the spruce area (*granskog*) of the east and the pine areas (*furuskog*) of the west. The northernmost coniferous outliers occur in the Porsanger area of Finnmark.[1]

Hardwood and softwood meet and mingle along the previously defined arc of structural weakness of central Scandinavia. Quite extensive oak and beech stands are found in Sørlandet, south Norway. The northernmost deciduous groves occur around Trondheim fiord. The zone of transition between the two forest types is most extensive in Sweden, where a distinction of historical standing is made between *Nordanskog* (the northern woodland) and *Sunnanskog* (the southern woodland).[2] "Dalälven marks the boundary between [two regions]," observed Elias Fries,[3] ". . . north of [it] vegetation takes on a wholly different character". *Sunnanskog*, the southern woodland type, expresses itself most fully in Skåne. Oak and beech are dominant there, as they are naturally dominant throughout Denmark. As in England, the conifer, which has been introduced into plantations during the last two hundred years, has naturalised itself and provides a contrasting constituent in the Danish arboreal scene.

The apparent uniformity of the coniferous woodland is deceptive. This is evident from the classification of forests which has been undertaken with increasing precision during the last generation.[4] Variety is expressed in a number of ways. Regional differences in height and density of stand as well as composition are one expression. "High forest", for example, is a regionally different concept. Thus, pines in the south of the area, maturing at an optimum seventy or eighty years, commonly attain 100 ft. in height; while on the northern margins of growth, maturity may be delayed for well over a century and maximum height may be no more than 40 ft. The shape and colouring also changes from north to south. Variety in stand may also be illustrated from a micro-environment—for instance, the wood-lot out of which displaced farmers carved their holdings in post-war Finland. These lots, surveyed by local foresters, adopted the simplified classification of the *Foresters' Calendar*. Each of the varied ecological subdivisions found on these holdings has meaning for the farmer. Variety in

---

[1] The meagreness of timber in north Norway is shown cartographically in *Det norske Skogselskap, 1898–1948*, Oslo, 1949, II, 232.
[2] E. Fries, "Limes norrlandicus-studier", *Svensk botanisk tidskrift*, **42**, 1, 1948, 51–69.
[3] E. Fries, "Den skandinaviska jordens växtlighet", *Botaniska utflykter*, Stockholm, **3**, 21.
[4] Y. Ilvessalo, *Publications of the Forest Research Institute*, 30, Helsinki, 1943; cf. also Chapter XI.

natural vegetation may also be expressed in terms of potential variety. The arboretum has for long been the subject of attention in Scandinavia and Finland. There are possibly superior foreign species which might be introduced to replace native species—or at least to add to their variety. The range of exotics found growing around Bergen—Himalayan, Mediterranean, Pacific—are not merely expressions of a trading people but are a telling reminder of new vegetational possibilities.

For most people living in Norway, Sweden and Finland, the forest has been and remains an integral part of the daily life and thought. Throughout the greater part of the area, the forest-farm is dominant over the timberless holding; the conifer marches up to the doorsteps of the three capital cities. At all levels a rational forestry is encouraged. Inter-Nordic forestry congresses are held at four-yearly intervals; the six-year course of the university degree of forestry is held in a virtual palace of silviculture; a dozen foresters' journals spur popular interest. In Finland, once a year, there is a grand national forest assault (*metsä marsi*), when every owner of a timber-lot from the president downwards devotes a week's labour to its specific improvement. Led by Denmark, the Northern Countries have created a great agricultural *légende*; it is the aspiration of Norway, Sweden and Finland through popular education to create a parallel forest *légende*. Woodlands frequently represent a climax vegetational form, but in the contemporary economy it is only through concerted action and common appreciation that free play can be given for the natural optimum to occur.[1]

Woodland not merely frames the panorama, but closes it. There are four contrasting types of open landscape. First, there are the boglands, which the spruce fringes and colonises if the water-level is reduced. Secondly, there are the heathlands, of which the pine is the natural colonist. The role of the heath in the economy of the Northern Countries varies greatly. It has been of greater consequence in Denmark, where the agricultural reclamation of the *Calluna* heaths has been a saga in itself. Thirdly, there are the water-meadows —the open grasslands of the flood plains. "Natural" grasslands are most widespread on the Atlantic slope, so that while the skerries and outer islands may be robbed of forests, they are partly compensated by the extent and variety of their grasslands. Finally, there are the open fells, where the woodland blanket yields through birch and willow scrub to the tundra. In Norway and Sweden the tundra covers an area equal to the surface area of Denmark; its extent in Finland has been reduced as a result of loss of territory to the U.S.S.R. The distribution of this virtually useless terrain—save in so far as it provides a refuge for the diminishing number of trans-humant Lapps—is shown in Fig. 38. Iceland, contemporarily void of more than scrub woodlands (e.g. around Akureyri in the north) has not only extensive areas of tundra, but also widespread cinder deserts and lava flows. As with north Norway and much of western Norway, high winds and exposure reduce the possibilities of plant cover.

The marine margins might be classified as a fifth type of open landscape. They have a contrasting character along the tidal shores of Atlantic Scandinavia and the virtually non-tidal reaches of the inner sea. Both support their own distinctive vegetational cover. The rocky foreshores of Norway and Sweden sustain a range of seaweeds. Great quantities of *Laminariæ* are gathered for fertilising cropland, while *Alarici esculenta* is among the seaweeds used for fodder. The marine forelands of Denmark, probably equal to 10% of the surface area of the country, offer regional examples of the seaward advance of vegetation.[2] In few parts of the world do the marine margins offer such a sensitive and unique zone for the empirical appreciation of plant colonisation as around the inner coasts of the Baltic Sea.[3] For here, the slow upheaval of the land provides a continuous succession of virgin lands for plant colonisation.[4]

[1] S. S. Paterson, *The Forest Area of the World and its Potential Productivity*, Göteborg, 1956.
[2] A. Schou, *Det marine Forland*, Copenhagen, 1945.
[3] An example is provided by S. Jaatinen, *Bidrag till kännedom om de Ålandska sjöarnas strandvegetation*, Helsingfors, 1950.
[4] E. Valovirta, *Untersuchungen über die säkulare Landhebung als pflanzengeographischen Faktor*, Helsinki, 1937.

THE LANDS WITHIN THEIR POLITICAL BOUNDARIES

Geology, relief, climate, soils and vegetation provide five particular patterns of distribution. Collectively, they produce a varied and varying background to the life of the people who have created their economies against them. But there is an additional human framework superimposed upon the physical features. A system of political boundaries has been evolved which distinguishes five distinct units. The boundaries, although showing a marked alignment with physical features, are of variable natural character and of varying age. Their overriding importance is that in defining the shape and size of the constituent northern states, they divide up their resources. Fig. 7 gives a rough impression of the results of the division. There may be tendencies towards functional unity between the five countries, but the separate economies as outlined by existing political boundaries are the real func-tional units. It is therefore helpful to outline briefly the type of land which is embraced by the several political elements of the "Scandinavian world".

Denmark

The Scandinavian world is not all Pyramus's "raging rocks and shivering shocks". Denmark (42,931 sq. km.) is a low-lying and dissected territory of Quaternary moraine superimposed upon a largely concealed Tertiary platform. On the east, in the islands of Sjælland and Møn, the platform shows itself in the upstanding cliffs of so-called Danian limestone and Senonian chalk. The retreating cliff face exposes flint bands in Stevns Klint and weathers to rounded pinnacles along the more impressive Møns Klint. To the north-west on the Jutish coast, Danian limestone and Senonian chalk outcrop in Bulbjerg and Svinkløv respectively, while their proximity to the surface around Aalborg is reflected in lime burning and cement manufacturing (cf. Plate 20). For the most part, however, the mantle of glacial deposits—as sparse as several metres in the morainic flats of Fyn and Sjælland, as thick as 200 metres in east Jutland—restricts the significance of the Tertiary mosaic in landscape control. Save in the isthmus of south Jutland, 68 km. broad, where the political boundary was stabilised after the First World War, the boundaries of the kingdom are maritime. The Sound has been the eastern boundary since the seventeenth century. Land meets sea in more than 7,000 km. of coastline.

The Jutish peninsula, which accounts for more than half of the surface area of Denmark, is a prolongation of the North German Plain and tapers to the hook of Skagen. Its western half is composed chiefly of old moraines which have been much modified by solifluction during later periods of ice advance and winnowed by the western wind since the retreat of the eastern ice. The scattered "hill islands" (*Bakkeøer*), smooth in contour compared wi h the irregular shapes of the young moraines, are the most pronounced relic features of this landscape. They are lapped about by level outwash plains which are traversed by shallow but mature valleys. Soils of this area are

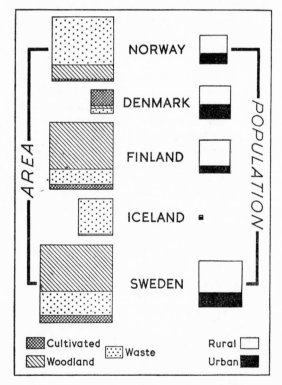

FIG. 7. A comparison of essential population and area data for the five countries (1951).

commonly defined as podsolised and a hard pan is widely encountered, 12–20 *"thumbs"* (as the Danes put it) below the surface. Brown coal is also found, e.g. on the sandy wilderness of Troldhede, beyond Kilbæk.

On the North Sea side, the plains are invaded by a complex dune system up to 10 km. in width. This sandy cordillera has a shifting character over extended areas which is only partly reduced by the resilient and artificially encouraged *Psamma* grass. Behind such distinctive components as Holmsland bar is the great lagoon of Ringkjøbing, while the groined tongues of duneland broken by Tyborøn channel protect Nissum broads in westernmost Limfiord. Seaward, broad and hard sand beaches yield to a shallow coast on which the North Sea surf breaks. South of Skallingen, the rampart of dunes is breached, but it continues to form the backbones of Fanø, Mandø and Rømø. Sand, indeed, is one of the most memorable features of Jutland, and the theme is picked up by Hans Andersen in *The Sandhills of Jutland* as well as in the traditional folk legends of the goblin with his leaking sandbag.

In the lee of the north Slesvig islands is found *Vadehavet*, the Wadden Sea. Its tidal flats (*vader*), the submerged extent of which depends upon changing tidal depths, are colonised by pioneer plants like *Salicornia* and are chequered by the ooze yards of reclamation schemes. Within the protection of old-established dikes, marsh grazings extend inland to the margins of the outwash terrain upon which may be faintly discerned the relics of former marine features. The juxtaposition of salt-marsh with the arable along the degraded shoreline, the gravel tongues of earlier spits and the ditched water-meadows of shallowly entrenched streams, the peat mosses (with their rectangular pattern of diggings) and the sandy "blow outs" of the half-planted heaths, offer a diversity of forms all within a few kilometres of each other to be carefully integrated into the local economy. Such an intimacy of adjustment to minor features of the land must delight a human geographer.

The area around Ribe affords an excellent example.

Elsewhere in Jutland, this intimacy of adjustment can be even more satisfying. A traverse through Vendsyssel down to the raised marine flats above Limfiord will reveal correspondence of archæological remains from the Danish Stone Age onwards with a succession of marine levels. There is also the persistent association of settlement with the same dry sites through successive cultural epochs, with the noticeably delayed assault on the "high bogs" which have often developed on the raised sea floor. Viggo Hansen has demonstrated the fine points of human adjustment in his patient large-scale recording of earlier settlement sites, while something of the mystique of the novelist Johannes V. Jensen is rooted in the continuity of human association with place.

The choppy hill country of East Jutland provides a distinct contrast to the western lowlands, some stretches of which have been fittingly described in the *Atlas of Denmark* as "two dimensional".[1] The young moraine country is characterised by sharp contrasts of relief. Closed depressions, which may be filled with relatively extensive lakes, e.g. Silkeborg area, sit beside rounded hills which may rise to 170 m. Powerful water erosion has given rise to deep "dry valley" features. Most unique are the strikingly eroded tunnel valleys, possibly cut by meltwater beneath ice. These "sub-glacial gutters", as the *Atlas of Denmark* describes them, provide east–west routes from the margins of the outwash plains to the eastern fiords. The succession of fiords, continued south into Germany, are fiords in name only, for by origin they are sea-invaded tunnel valleys. The tunnel valleys carry the North Sea/Kattegat watershed through the eastern hills to the central lowlands. Chains of small lakes may occur in the valley bottoms —those along the course of the Vejle river, between Vejle fiord and the Nörup area, provide instances. The most extensive area of "enclosed" water is Limfiord in north Jutland. The most diminutive features are the

---

[1] The *Atlas of Denmark*, which is rich in block diagrams to illustrate most of the land forms of the country, and *Geodætisk instituts generalstabskort*, 1 : 100,000, Copenhagen, 1933, 3 volumes, are useful reference works. Cf. also V. Madsen, "Summary of the geology of Denmark", *Dansk geologisk utredning*, V, 4,1928, and Guidebook Denmark, I.G.U. Congress, 1960, *Geografisk Tidsskrift*, **59**, 1960.

scattered ponds—virtual back-garden lakes—which owe their origin to the waning of dead ice. The suburban tracts north of Copenhagen offer examples.

In the lee of Jutland lies an archipelago of several hundred islands which, with their jig-saw coastlines and offshore shoals, congest the Baltic approaches. Fyn, the second largest island, is separated from the peninsula by the Little Belt (cf. Plate 7) and from Sjælland, the largest island, by the Great Belt. The islands are composed of younger moraines, with the semi-circle of hills in Fyn contributing the most upstanding features. As with Jutland, they display a diversity of landscapes in close juxtaposition. The dunes and marshes of the coasts are not modelled so forcibly by wind and wave; the peat bogs and outwash flats may not be so extensive as in Jutland. Esker "trains" add their contribution to Fyn and Sjælland—the Mogenstrup esker in south Sjælland being thrown into relief by its timber cover, in an almost classical manner. Islands multiply to the south of Fyn and Sjælland in the Belt Sea, which is more popularly known as the South Sea. Lolland, Falster and Langeland are the largest of these "South Sea Islands". The Sound (Øresund) is the deepest of the three channels between the Baltic and the Kattegat.

Distinct from Jutland and the archipelago are Bornholm (400 sq. km.) and the Færoes (1,400 sq. km.)—the former an island legacy of the inner sea: the latter, of the outer ocean. In Bornholm a varied granitic sub-structure takes control of the landscape features where the glacial overburden is thin, where it has been coastally eroded or where the occasional gorge-like joint valleys occur.[1] Bornholm, with its principal centre of Rønne, is a virtual outlier of the geological province of Fennoscandia.

The Færoes provide a remarkable contrast in physical geography to the rest of Denmark.[2] Their mountainous archipelago of eighteen principal islands rises from the Wyville-Thomson ridge to reach its highest point on Esturoy (Østerø, to the Danes) in Slattara-tinden (882 m.). The Færoe islands belong to the basalt area of the North Atlantic. They have been subjected to much more severe erosion—marine as well as glacial—than Jutland and the Danish islands, and were probably an area of separate glaciation. Erosional forms take precedence over depositional forms in the landscape. As with Iceland, the highlands often assume "table mountain" shapes, while the western face of Viderø can claim some of the sheerest cliffs which ever offered challenge to the fowler. *Fuglebjærge*, inscribed along the cliffs on atlas maps, is enough to indicate the nature of Færoese cliff profiles. Yet, as Captain Flore wrote on his map for mariners (Leith, 1781), "The whole shore is bold and nothing to be feared but what is visible". There are also good harbours. The limited cultivable areas, intruded upon by screes on their landward side and marine erosion from the sea, suffer inherent problems of drainage. *Færøernes Kortlægning*, with its excellent series of maps (scale 1:20,000), illustrates the modest human impact made on the natural landscape. The detachment of the Færoes has prompted the islanders to seek—unsuccessfully—political independence from Denmark. Thórshavn, on Strømø, is the administrative centre of the archipelago.

Finland

Nearly three hundred years ago, Moses Pitt in his *New English Atlas* described the eastern principality of Sweden as "called by the natives Somi or Soma, but by the Swedes first and after them by all strangers—Finland". Finland (337,000 sq. km.) is still Suomi to its countrymen. It occupies the greater part of the pre-Cambrian peneplane to the north-east of the Baltic basin and assumes a peninsular shape in the south-west. Earlier geographies, indeed, distinguished between Suomenniemi (or peninsular Finland) and Suomensaari (or the island of Finland, embracing the Finnish-speaking lands between the Baltic and the White Sea). Väinö Auer, adopting an even more vivid metaphor, speaks of Finland as a *saaristo* or archipelago.

---

[1] *Atlas of Denmark*, I, 69–75.
[2] K. Williamson, *The Atlantic Islands*, London, 1949, provides a very readable and informative account of the day-to-day life of the Faroese. Reference should also be made to A. C. O'Dell, *op. cit.*, Chapter 12. N. E. Nørlund, *Færøernes Kortlægning*, Copenhagen, 1944, is the principal atlas.

The coast of Finland is surrounded by an almost continuous zone of islands.[1] They assume their greatest concentration in the south-west, where the Turku (Sw. Åbo) archipelago extends into the central Baltic and the channel of Skiftet distinguishes it from the administratively distinct Åland archipelago. The Åland islands, a neutral and demilitarised group, were given autonomy within the Finnish realm, by League of Nations authority, following a challenge by Sweden, in 1921. A lesser concentration of islands occurs at Kvarken, where the outermost skerries of the Vaasa archipelago are within sight of Umeå archipelago on the Swedish side of the gulf.

The archipelago *motif* may be appropriately applied to more than coastal Finland. Postglacial emergence implies that as Finland is around much of its coast, so formerly was much of its interior. At first sight, it is difficult to distinguish between the extensive archipelagoes of Lake Saimaa and those of the southwest coast. Even the tall stands of *Phragmites* are tolerant of the brackish waters of the Baltic foreshore. Standing upon the fells of Kuusamo and looking across the waters of his wide parish, Elias Lagus wrote in 1772 that the landscape resembled that of an archipelago. The *motif* can also be applied in another way to northern Finland, where firm land traces a pattern of islands in the midst of the predominant boglands.

Finland is an essentially low-lying country. Its basement complex of richly varied granites rises in a shallow amphitheatre from the Baltic Cape to the Arctic watershed.[2] It is linked to the Scandinavian peninsula through the "isthmus of Lapland", which, as M. Zimmerman has laconically remarked, counts for more cartographically than historically. In the south, the highest stretches of the land occur in the terminal moraines of what the surveyor C. W. Gylden christened the Salpausselkä. The higher parts of this complex ridge reach altitudes of 200 m., e.g. south of Lahti, where the morainic rampart commands some of the most widespread

views in south Finland. The extreme prolongation of its sandy spurs is found in the Hanko (Sw. Hangö) peninsula. In this southwestern corner of Finland is found what J. Playfair called "an agreeably diversified" country. Principal among its modest valleys in the role of human relations has been that of the river Aura. The first capital of Finland— Turku was established at its estuary. The multiplicity of churches with their fragmented parish boundaries, the number of estates (it is popularly called *herrgårds hörnet*) and its reputation as "the garden of Finland" reflect the historical role played by the *Regio Aboensis*.

Finland's highest altitudes (1000 m.) occur in the Kilpisjärvi area of the Scandinavian Keel Ridge. High fells (or *tunturi*) also characterise the Russian frontier lands in the parishes of Salla and Kuusamo. A series of gorges, carved by rivers such as Kitkäjoki and Oulankajoki, carry Finnish waters eastwards to the White Sea. Finland, at large, has an average elevation of 152 m. A false illusion of height is given by such bald rock summits as those of the Koli Heights in North Karelia, the *vaara* uplands to their south and the lookout towers which are lifted above the tree tops of such eminences as Puijo in central Savo.

A tenth of Finland is covered by lakes: in Mikkeli province, the figure rises to a quarter. Their precise nomenclature, already the concern of the editors of *Åbo Tidning* in 1795, still perplexes atlasmakers. Watersheds, almost everywhere diffuse, are another problem. The principal drainage channels of the country consist of five major rivers to which the greater number of lakes are tributary. The three southern river systems are the Vuoksi, Kymi (Sw. Kymmene) and Kokemäki (Sw. Kumo). The Vuoksi river, with its Imatra rapids— which John Pinkerton already claimed to be celebrated a hundred and fifty years ago— drains Saimaa, the largest of the Finnish lake complexes. It flows into Lake Ladoga. The Kymi river, with Lake Päijänne tributary, enters the Gulf of Finland. The Kokemäki is the principal river of western Finland and

[1] Their regional integration with the mainland parishes emerges from a number of studies, e.g. O. Granö, "Natur und Wirtschaft an der Schärenküste vor Porvoo in Südfinnland", *Fennia*, **78**, 5, 1955; W. R. Mead (ed). "Saltvik, Studies from an Åland Parish", *Geographical Field Group*, Nottingham, 1964; Guidebook Finland, I.G.U. Congress, 1960, *Fennia*, **84**, 1960.
[2] A valuable bibliography of the geology of Finland is given by A. Laitakari, *Geologische Bibliographie Finnlands, 1555–1933*, Helsinki 1935.

drains to the Bothnian Sea. Its broad plains (cf. Plate 6) are among the oldest continuously occupied farmlands of Finland. The plains of Ostrobothnia (F. Pohjanmaa) support a series of parallel rivers which pick up the SE/NW orientation of the rivers of Swedish Norrland: they are, however, of moderate size. Finland's two principal northern rivers are the Oulu and Kemi, the latter having the most extended course, but lacking the characteristically large lake reservoirs. The Torni river (Sw. Torneå) forms the boundary with Sweden along its lower reaches. North of the Arctic watershed is Lake Inari, which empties into Varanger fiord by the Pasvik (F. Patsjoki), the boundary river between Norway and the U.S.S.R.

Although it is subdivided in regional studies of Finland which reached their fullest expression in the work of J. R. Granö,[1] the lake plateau is the most extensive, homogeneous as well as ethnographical distinctive area. Its southern margins are marked by the Salpausselkä: its north-western boundary is in the low and infertile watershed of Suomenselkä—"the spine of Finland", as it used to be called. Eastwards, it continues through into Russian Karelia, where the White Sea slope is a kind of mirror image. The lake plateau is at the same time a well-known country of eskers, containing some of the longest and loftiest in northern Europe. The small-scale depositional map of Finland suggests that they have a SE/NW orientation, but a geomorphologist of the stature of V. Tanner has likened an explanation of them as equivalent to the unravelling of Penelope's web.[2]

The political shape which encompasses this land is of recent origin and has been less stable than those of the other "Northern Countries". The boundaries of the Russian Grand Duchy were assumed by independent Finland in 1917, though a northern corridor to Fisherman's Peninsula on the Arctic coast was later acquired by agreement with Russia. The Petsamo corridor, amputated in September

1944, had been of limited economic value down to that time, though contemporary Finland feels increasingly its loss of contact with the Arctic Ocean. The north-western arm of Finland, extended into the Keel Ridge, gives common frontiers with Norway (729 km.) and Sweden (536 km.). Here, the most important boundary river on the northern slope is the Tenojoki (N. Tana). On the southern slope, the Muonio extends the boundary function of the Torni river. The present eastern boundary, bent westward to bisect the sub-Arctic parishes of Salla and Kuusamo in 1944, marches for 1,246 km. beside the U.S.S.R. to Virolahti parish on the Gulf of Finland. The principal territorial loss in 1944 was immediately beyond this boundary in Ladogan Karelia and the Karelian isthmus.[3] The territory through which most of the eastern frontier runs has been defined as "topographically demilitarised".[4] It is an absolute boundary from the human point of view and there is no contact across it except at the frontier stations on the south-east. The border parishes suffer extreme isolation—the more so where they drain to Lake Ladoga. Community of interests in this border society is expressed in an association of frontier parishes called *Rajaseutuyhdistys*. These associated parishes are more than the borderlands of Finland; they are the borderlands of western Europe. At once the most northern and most continental of the "Nordic Countries", Finland has been appropriately described by Zachris Topelius as "a land set by nature on the defensive".[5]

Iceland

The republic of Iceland, 103,000 sq. km. in area, is the largest of the Scandinavian islands. It is located between 63° N and 67° N, so that it does not share such extensive areas within the Arctic Circle as Finland, Norway and Sweden. Iceland is of recent geological origin: its oldest rocks are of the Eocene period. It has been literally born of fire.[6] While the

[1] *Die landschaftskundliche Gebietseinteilung*, Helsingfors, 1930.
[2] "The Salpausselkä ridge in Finland," *Fennia*, **58**, 3, 1933.
[3] W. R. Mead, "The Finnish Outlook, East and West", *Geographical Journal*, CXIII, 1949.
[4] J. H. Marshall-Cornwall, *Geographic Disarmament*, London, 1935.
[5] *Föreläsningar*, Pt. 6, manuscript, University Library, Helsinki.
[6] The best summary of many of these features is S. Thorarinsson, *The thousand years' struggle against ice and fire*, Reykjavik, 1956 and Guidebook Iceland, I.G.U. Congress, *Geografiska Annaler*, 31, 1949.

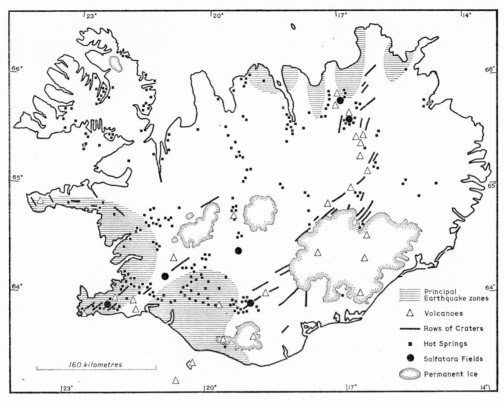

FIG. 8. Features of ice and fire in Iceland.

same is true of the Færoes and parts of Spitsbergen, Iceland is unique in Scandinavia in that vulcanicity continues to be a force of importance in shaping its land forms. The island consists primarily of a complex of basalt rocks which represent outpourings in a long succession of volcanic episodes. In some areas, the basalt series exceed a thousand metres in thickness. Bands of sand and clay, beds of lignite, injections of igneous rocks are incorporated in the series. The major land forms reflect these facts. Mount Esja, with its table mountain rising above Kollafjorður, announces a very representative form for those who arrive at Reykjavik. The panorama of Iceland from the coast is that of a land of high latitudes. Its surface averages 400 m. above sea level.

For the geologists who speculate on Iceland's remoter volcanic outpourings, recent evidence and practical demonstration (albeit on a reduced scale) are available to illustrate the processes. During the thousand years of its recorded history, Iceland has known fully a hundred eruptions. These have been associated with about a score of volcanoes. There have been submarine eruptions, too. In 1963, they gave birth to the island of Surtsey, 40 km. south of the Vestman Islands and rising 300 m. above sea level. Of Iceland's volcanoes, Mount Hekla remains the most active. It was given a place of prominence on early north European maps. Among literary references, few are more graphic than the *Lagmans annal* of Einar Haflidson (1307–93), recording the thirteenth-century eruption of Hekla which affected nearly two-thirds of the island. Extensive lava flows and cinder deserts of varying ages are the geological testimony of eruptions. Odáðáhraun, the biggest of the lava deserts, covers more than 3,500 sq. km. (an area larger than Sweden's island of Gotland). The lava deserts are invariably sterile and their rough, dissected surfaces obstruct movement across them. The *Atlas of Iceland* identifies block lava (*Apalhraun*) and stratified lava (*Helluhraun*) with special symbols. Plate 2 shows a small area of lava flow on the south side of Faxaflói in the hinterland of the capital.[1] Closely associated with the volcanic zone are the hot springs (*laugar*) and the boiling springs (*hverir*). The springs have become a resource of growing consequence in recent years. Stóri Geysir, a spouting hot spring, is the type feature which has given its name to geysers.

But Iceland, as its name implies, is not only a *tierra del fuego*—it is also a land of ice. Ice has done much to shape the outlines of the island, perhaps most of all in fiording its west, north and east coasts. Plate 1 illustrates a stage in the growth of an outwash plain in front of retreating ice lobes. Ice remains not merely a sculpturing force but also a major landscape feature. Indeed, 13,000 sq. km. of the surface of the country are covered by glaciers (*jökull*), of which the largest—Vatnajökull, in the south—accounts for nearly two-thirds of the ice-covered area and is one of the largest glaciers in Europe. The other principal glaciers are Hofsjökull in central Iceland, Langjökull in the west centre, Drangajökull in the north-west and Myrdalsjökull in the south. The most elevated ice-sheet is found in Oræfajökull, which rises to 2,119 m. Fig. 8 includes the general distribution of the major ice-sheets, none of which reaches the coast. It is not surprising that Iceland has a special journal—*Jökull*—which is concerned with this feature.

In addition to the direct effect of ice, the indirect effect of ice-edge weathering has been and remains a powerful force in modelling the detail of the land forms. Permafrost conditions prevail over wide areas, frost heaving afflicts soils during the spring thaw, the telltale pattern of polygons is written in the stony wastes. All have a restrictive effect upon the variety and intensity of natural vegetation. A heavy burden of loose superficial debris has been carried down to the coast by the vigorous rivers to build up broad deltaic flats which form the most agreeable areas for Icelandic settlement. Sometimes, the forces of ice and fire conflict—in the eruption of ice-capped volcanoes. *Jökullhlaup* or glacial "bursts" may then occur, giving rise to large-scale flooding. Several have been experienced in recent decades, Hekla providing an example in its eruption of 1947–8.

Iceland is a country of proverbially strong winds and of frequently heavy rainfall. Wind and rain, as well as ice, are therefore active agents in weathering the exposed rocks and in redistributing surface deposits. Parts of Iceland have been described as "the most pronouncedly Arctic wind erosion regions in the northern hemisphere". This is especially true of altitudes over 500 m. Elsewhere, the wind has graded the disintegrated tuffs and volcanic ashes, leaving the heavier deposits as gravel barrens and redistributing the lighter materials as a kind of loess. Around the south coast, there are broad stretches of blown sand. Wind and melt-water impart an especially dynamic character to the *sanðr*[2] or broad outwash plains between the south-eastern margins of Vatnajökull and the sea.[3]

The drainage system etches a radial pattern against the background of the interior plateaus. Both heavy precipitation and summer snow-melt give rise to large rivers and abundant tributaries. The pattern of waterways, however, shows an uneven distribution which reflects the presence or absence of cinder, sand or lava spreads. Much surface water percolates through their porous deposits to give rise to spring lines when it meets impervious underlying materials. Thingvallavatn, in the neighbourhood of the historical meeting ground, and Myvatn in the north-east are among the principal lakes.

The focus of Iceland from the human point of view is the bight of Faxaflói in the south-west. It is the broadest of the great bays (the others are Breiðifjörður and Húnaflói) on the west side of the island. Between its bounding peninsulas, fiord forms are developed, but they are not so impressive as those on the

---

[1] It can be identified on sheets 27, 37 of the *Atlas of Iceland*, scale 1:100,000.
[2] The Hoffellssandur, a sample area, has been described in detail by P. Hjulström, *Geografiska Annaler*, 37, 1955. Cf. also C. A. M. King, "The coast of south-east Iceland near Ingólfshöföi", *Geographical Journal*, CXXII, 1956.
[3] *Atlas of Iceland*, sheets 78, 88.

north-west coast. The 6,000 km. of coastline are neither so fully nor so frequently fiorded as those of Norway. Coastal sandbars and wide lagoons typify much of the south coast, which offers scanty harbourage and is treacherous for navigation. The coast of Iceland is largely free of islands and skerries. Breiðifjörður has island clusters, and the most interesting off-shore group are the Vestmanna islands in the south. Among the most isolated islands is Grimsey, off the north coast and 60 km. from the mainland. It is an outpost, the nature and life of which have been recently described by Robert Jack.[1]

In spite of its detachment, Iceland has not been topographically neglected and there is a rich literature of travellers' tales in most West European tongues. A renaissance in the fullest sense of the word is upon Iceland. Revaluation of setting and resource has simultaneously sponsored a new scientific interest in its geography.

Norway

The Scandinavian peninsula is marked by a strong asymmetry of slope, and the political boundary of Norway and Sweden is such that to Norway (323,000 sq. km.) is ascribed the abrupt descent to the Atlantic coast. Fig. 9 illustrates the contrasting character of the Norwegian and Swedish slopes and indicates the narrowness of parts of Nordland. Indeed, the Swedish frontier approaches to within 7 km. of Norwegian waters at Hellemofiord. The land boundary of Norway exceeds 2,500 km. and the Swedish portion of it is defined along the heights of the Keel Ridge. This highland thrust area takes on a much more rugged appearance on the Norwegian side of the border. It is complemented by the great south-western massif, which forms the background to most of Norway south of the Trondheim depression. This depression is an effective boundary zone between the northern and southern halves of the country. In general, the characteristic physical features of Norway are written on a grander scale to the south.[2]

Norway is an upland country with an average elevation exceeding 500 m. Its upland surface is expressed in a series of plateaux which take on their most characteristic appearance in the high fells. The fell area is commonly divided into six parts: Jostedalsbreen, the Jotunheim and the western *vidder*; Dovrefjell, Trollheimen and the eastern *vidder*. The "fell" area is not arbitrarily outlined by a contour: it is decided by a variety of botanical and agricultural criteria.[3] Fully 3,000 sq. km. of the fells are under icefields, the most extensive of which is that of Jostedalsbre (1,500 sq. km.). Svartisen in Nordland is the only Norwegian ice-sheet the tongues of which approach sea-level.

The ice surfaces range from 1,000 to 2,000 m. in altitude; the ice thickness is believed to approach 300 m. in Jostedalsbre. The highest summits of the plateau surface stand out as monadnocks, sometimes 7,000 ft. or more in altitude; occasionally they project through the ice surface as true nunataks.[3] Mountains clutter the topographical map of Norway, and an array of suffixes indicates mountain features: *egg* (crest), *hammer* (precipice), *hord* (a broad summit), *kamp* (a broad top), *knatt* (a crag), *koll* (a rounded top). The *vidder* lift watersheds to high altitudes and passes between the inhabited areas often show corresponding elevation. Those between Gudbrandsdal and Romsdal, and Valdres and Sogn are 612 m. and 980 m. respectively.

Into the plateau surface are incised deep troughs. They take the form of narrow gorges in the interior and, in the vicinity of the icefields, they extend back to where the ice fall drops into their chasms. Seawards, the gorges, with their transverse ancillary valleys, broaden into fiords. The fiord heads are commonly characterised by deltaic flats; their central stretches are of great depth, their mouths are relatively shallow. The fiord zone reaches its greatest breadth in Sogn and Hardanger. Arctic fiords, like Tana, Lakse and Varanger, are broader and shorter. The fiords are complemented by deeply entrenched and what W. M. Davis called "blunt-headed" valleys on the landward side. Glaciated val-

[1] *Arctic Living*, London, 1957.
[2] O. Holtedahl, "Norges geologi", *Norges geologisk undersøkelser*, **164**, 1953; T. Sund and A. Sømme, *Norway in Maps*, Oslo, 1947; Guidebook Norway, I.G.U. Congress, 1960, *Norsk geografisk tidsskrift*, **17**, 1959–60.
[3] Some are outlined in *Effektiviteten av ulike driftsformer i fjellbygdene*, Oslo, 1953.

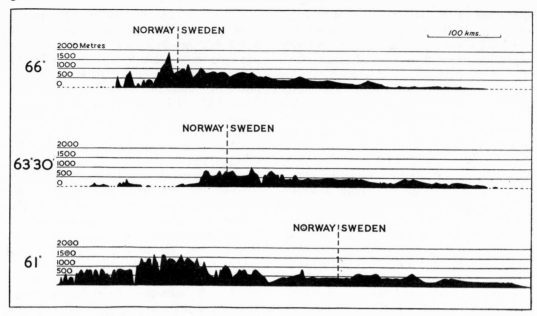

FIG. 9. Three transverse sections through the Scandinavian peninsula.

leys like Setesdal, Numdal, Hallingdal and Valdres, with their extended ribbon lakes, frequently give the illusion of "inland fiords". Lake beds like those of Fyresvatn or Tinnsjø, dropping to 460 m., attain almost fiord depths. The repetitive pattern of submerged glaciated valley and intervening plateau [1] suggests that from the human point of view, Norway might be called "a collection of fiords". The "spiry crags and horrible precipices" which were presented to early geographers, seen by the light of Baedekker stars, have assumed a new meaning.

Deep scouring of the landscape has two results—marked altitudinal variations in the short distance and a landscape dominated by sharp gradients. Much of the slope between fell and fiord is pitched (to use a local expression) "at the angle of inclination of a ski jump". Verticality, indeed, is a feature of much of the Norwegian landscape. It imparts a dynamic quality to the processes of denudation, so that the mobile mantle of the earth behaves in a dramatic manner. Thus, water moves in cataracts, torrents and rapids

in its descent to the sea; water-courses erode savagely in their upper reaches and flood violently towards their mouths. Again, rock-fall after rain or frost may scar the weathered faces of the precipice—one of the earliest written references to Sognefiord, from 1180 in *Scriptores rerum danicarum*, recalls that a mountain fell into a fiord. Screes mask extensive areas of formerly occupied land and prohibit much other to human use. The avalanche of winter, precipitated by instability of climate, reflects a fundamental instability of slope. So, too, does the calving of the glacial ice-fall in summer. At a lowlier level, clay-slides constantly modify terrace features and may invade established farmland.[2] Soli-fluction processes give rise to considerable movement of surface deposits in high latitudes and high altitudes. In the same way that the physical geographers of Cambridge have concentrated attention upon the mechanics of ice movement in Westlandet,[3] those of Oslo have directed investigations towards problems of soil movement.[4] In many respects, then, Norway is a country characterised by physical

[1] Cf. "Unity of the Physiographical History of Norway", *Bulletin of Geological Society of America*, XLV, 1934, 637–54.
[2] Cf. P. Holmsen, "Landslips in Norwegian quick clays", *Geotechnique*, 1953.
[3] Cf. the work of W. V. Lewis as illustrated in "Pressure release and glacial erosion", *Journal of Glaciology*, 1954.
[4] Cf. the work of P. J. Williams as illustrated by "Some investigations into solifluction features in Norway", *Geographical Journal*, CXXIII, 1957.

catastrophe. A catalogue of catastrophes was already compiled for Nord Bergenhus by A. Helland in the early years of the century: local studies of Westland were later initiated by A. Bugge.[1] But the only map to be prepared is limited to the avalanches of Möre and Romsdal.[2]

Catastrophe is accompanied by noise and it is interesting to find the element *hurr* (from the word *hurra*—to roar or rumble) incorporated in local place names. Yet more important than loud noises are those which accompany the gentler wearing away of the surface features. In western Norway, it is rare that the sounds of erosion cannot be heard. They are an essential expression of the environment. And, in a countryside which is never wholly quiet, it is not surprising that the Norwegian belief in the supernatural dies hard.

Except in the south-west and the far north, the coast to which the plateaus fall has a girdle of islands. The island zone reaches its broadest width (over 60 km.) in Fröhavet at the southern approaches to Trondheim fiord. The outer islands, protruding from relatively shallow waters, rarely exceed 30 m. in height: the inner islands may rise to 300 m. The strandflat, a series of rock terraces given expression in the island zone, is a feature much disputed as to origin.[3] Earlier theories turned to marine abrasion as an explanation. Fritjof Nansen made a classical contribution to the discussion by proposing three strandflat levels which he believed to originate in the three inter-glacial periods.[4] Beyond the strandflat is a broad continental shelf upon which are located the shallower banks (cf. Fig. 52).

The strandflat is missing in the extreme south-west, where the peninsula of Jæren provides an exceptional feature. Deep morainic deposits mask the bedrock over an area of about 500 sq. km.

Jæren has been described as a bit of Denmark clinging to Norway, as Skåne is a bit of Denmark clinging to Sweden. Viewing the coast in its entirety, there is an interesting contrast between the longer fiords of the south and the shorter fiords of the north; the larger islands of the north and the smaller islands of the south.

Complementary to the islands are Norway's multitude of lakes, but they do not have the same distinctive pattern as those over much of Sweden and they have a greater diversity of form than those of Finland. Altitudinal variation implies that Norway's lakes are at many different levels. The high fells, with their generously distributed rock hollows, support shallower lakes than the moraine-dammed dales. In south-east Norway, Lake Mjøsa is the largest: in north Norway, high level Lake Røsvann.

Between the south-western massif and the south-eastern fells of the Swedish borderlands is a rich valley complex focusing upon Gudbrandsdal and Østerdal. These two great dales, cutting back into the saddles of the higher Dovre and lower Røros *vidda* respectively, open up routes to the Trondheim lowland. Gudbrandsdal assumes a distinctive identity above Lake Mjøsa: Østerdal, inland from Elverum. The two dales, with their frequent flights of broad and fertile terraces, drain into Oslo fiord. The fiord, of broader and more open aspect than those of the west coast, cuts deeply into the weaker rocks of the Cambro-Silurian countryside and divides what is popularly called Østfold from Vestfold. Around the fiord and in its valley hinterlands, depositional features assume a more extensive distribution than in any other part of Norway. The variety of Quaternary materials is summarised in a special publication of the Norwegian Geological Survey for Oslo fiord (scale 1:250,000, Oslo, 1949). These water-borne deposits also give rise to the most continuous stretches of level lowland in Norway. Østland, as this region is usually called, is the most Swedish part of Norway in its landscapes. Common physical features extend into Värmland and to Bohuslän.

The only other Norwegian area which bears comparison with Østland is Trøndelag, where against a Cambro-Silurian background, the lowlands around Trondheim fiord have experienced parallel development in Quaternary times. Here, too, links across the border are

[1] See K. O. Bjørlykke, "Skredet: Værdalen", *Norsk geografisk tidsskrift*, IV, 1893.
[2] G. Ramsli, *Norsk geografisk tidsskrift*, XIV, 1952.   [3] Cf. E. Dahl, *Norsk geografisk tidsskrift*, XI, 1946.
[4] *The Strandflat and Isostasy*, Kristiania, 1922.

eased by the Trondheim depression which gives access to the complementary Silurian tract around Storsjön. Sørlandet is the regional name given to the southern fringes of the great western buckler, and it extends from Stavanger fiord to Skien on the margins of Østland. It is characterised by a radial pattern of drainage central to which is Byklefjell at the head of Setesdal.

In the regional geography of the country, north Norway is usually defined as the fifth major unit. Apart from the wide inland *vidder* of Finnmark and Troms, it is as dissected as any other part of Norway. Some of the largest islands in Scandinavia—Hinnøy, Senja, Kvaløy, Sorøy—are found in this region. The two most extensive and detached island groups are those of Lofoten (cf. Fig. 57) and Vesterålen. Latitude and exposure mean that much of the land is bare of vegetation—"a geologist's happy hunting-ground", as it has been put.

Norway also has an island empire in the Arctic Ocean to the north of this fifth mainland region. The Spitsbergen archipelago (62,900 sq. km. in size and therefore much bigger than Denmark) was given Norwegian sovereignty in 1920 and the name Svalbard was adopted. Compared with much of the mainland, it has a complex geology with a much greater range of rocks. It shares some of the basalt features common to Iceland and the Færoes. Icefields cover extended areas and surface deposits are subject to permafrost conditions. Coal occurs in several geological horizons. Svalbard, which has been the object of considerable scientific investigation, is the site of the most northerly settlements in Europe. Bear Island (Bjørnøya, 178 sq. km.) is usually included in the Svalbard group. Sovereignty over Jan Mayen island (372 sq. km.) was recognised in 1930.

Apart from Denmark, with its legacy of Greenland and the Færoe islands, Norway is the only other "Nordic" country with overseas possessions. Its interest in whaling caused claims to be extended to parts of Antarctica which were internationally recognised for Bouvet island in 1930 and Peter I island in 1931. Certain mainland stretches of Antarctica are also recognised as Norwegian.

Sweden

Sweden (449,000 sq. km.),[1] with an almost rhomboidal shape, is the largest and most centrally situated of the Northern Countries. As with Norway, its length is impressive—1,574 km. from latitudes 55° to 69° N. Indeed, the Swedes speak of *vårt avlånga land*—our long-drawn-out land. Sweden, however, is a land of lower altitudes and less dissected relief than Norway. The Archæan backgrounds of Finland are shared, but Sweden adds to them more varied relief and landscape. In Skåne, over limited areas, it has identity with eastern Denmark.

Four morphological units can be recognised, though they are of unequal size. The largest is Norrland, which commonly refers to the broad Baltic slope from the lower reaches of the Dal river northwards. Through Värmland and Dalarna, its characteristic features merge with those of the faulted lands of central Sweden. The crystalline outlier of southern Sweden commonly associated with Småland is the third unit. The fourth consists of the restricted area of more recent sedimentaries most fully apparent in the province of Skåne.

Norrland falls readily into three subdivisions. The western highlands follow the Norwegian frontier and are lifted to peaks of more than 2,000 m. Kebnekaise is the highest of these. The massive overthrusts of the Caledonian orogeny have brought the relatively younger rock series to the eastern side of the Keel Ridge. Prolonged erosion has, however, reduced much of the surface to a plateau form and most of this upland third is classified as the fell zone. As in Norway, the word "fell" has a number of meanings, and depending upon its precise interpretation 4–12% of Sweden falls into this category. Associated with the depressions of this upland zone are a series of major lakes, most of which lie somewhat more than 300 m. above the level of the Baltic. Torneträsk (317 sq. km.), Luleträsk with Langas (220 sq. km.) and the intercon-

---

[1] The *Atlas of Sweden*, with its summarised English text, provides the first full-scale geography of the country. In originality of presentation and in depth of understanding it establishes a new standard in national atlases. See also the Guidebooks Sweden, I.G.U. Congress, 1960 and *Sverige, Land och Folk*, Stockholm, 1966, 3 volumes.

PLATE 3. A MORAINIC LANDSCAPE FROM EASTERN NORWAY (NANNESTAD)

Problems of slope in the use of the land are not confined to the mountainous areas of Norway. Snow cover here brings out the local detail in relief.

32]

PLATE 4. REINE IN THE LOFOTEN ARCHIPELAGO

The contrast between the upstanding Gabbro peaks and the *strandflat* assumes its most marked form in Lofoten (cf. Chapter VIII).

[33

nected trio of Hornavan, Uddjaure and Storavan (660 sq. km.) are the largest, but their surface areas are being much extended for reservoir purposes. Norway lacks a series of lakes equally extensive in area, while Finland's expanded water bodies are at low altitudes. The fell zone is true tundra country and its approximate extent is shown on Figure 38. A number of small icefields immediately beyond 66° N. are scattered over the fell country, which is intruded upon by the coniferous forest at about 400 m.

Southernmost of the fell lakes is Kallsjö, to the west of which a lowering of the Keel gives access to the Trondheim fiord and to the east of which opens out the lowlands to which Storsjön is central. Storsjön is the focus of the province of Jämtland, and its setting is repeated in that of Lake Siljan farther to the south in Dalarna province. Östersund, the principal town of Storsjön, lies in the second topographical subdivision of Norrland, though its limestone and sandstone background gives to its tributary area an exceptional character. This second zone, predominantly Archæan in origin, remained above the limit of marine transgression. Its river valleys have experienced considerable rejuvenation through uplift and their courses are marked by falls and rapids. Their pattern is repeated at regular intervals from the southern part of the region to the Finnish border, while the broad monotonous interfluves have spreads of peatland and some of the most extensive forests in Sweden. Seawards, the valleys are continued into the bed of the Gulf of Bothnia. The area has considerable mineral wealth, frequently concealed beneath heavy glacial drifts. The names of rivers like the Kalix, Lule, Pite, Skellefte, Vindel, Ume and Ångerman, with their powerful fell zone tributaries, have a new meaning in contemporary Sweden.

The piedmont zone where these rivers express themselves most fully yields to the third subdivision of Norrland—the Bothnian coastal plain. And the plain merges almost imperceptibly into the sea—wholly imperceptibly during the winter months. Littoral and estuaries are frequently crowded with islands. The emergent plains generally have a low gradient, but they are not as extensive as those of Finnish Pohjanmaa. The Bothnian coast may be divided into three sections —lower, middle and upper. The middle section extends from Örnsköldvik to Skellefteå.

Central Sweden is a "shatter" zone of lakes and plains—the former often areally and scenically dominant over the latter. The two main fault lines—trending north-south and east-west—are detectable in the lineaments of the four principal lakes. These are Vänern, Vättern, Hjälmaren and Mälaren. Lake Vänern has its outlet to the west by way of the Göta river, and it claims Sweden's largest catchment area. Trollhättan falls, on the Göta river, are indicative of the change in level between the lake and the Skagerak coastlands. Lake Mälaren lies only about half a metre above the average level of the Baltic Sea. Post-glacial marine transgression has resulted in the widespread distribution of sedimentary deposits throughout the "Great Lakes" area. These sediments are the background to extensive plains like those of Uppland (centred on Uppsala), Västmanland, Närke, East and West Gothland. Archæological evidence, not least the rich harvest of rune stones, emphasises that this central lake-and-plain tract was the core of early Sweden. As with the Finnish lake district, eskers stretch their sinuous forms across the face of the country, extending into the dale lands north of lakes Vänern and Mälaren. Central Sweden does not lend itself readily to simple regional subdivision, though, as will be evident from Chapter XII, the presence or absence of mineral-bearing rocks can make for important regional contrasts.

While Lake Vättern is partly set in plainlands, it is partly embedded in the south Swedish uplands. This plateau area, which bears a heavy mantle of glacial deposition, lay above the level of post-glacial marine transgression. Its highest altitudes reach 380 m. and its radial drainage pattern has been much modified by rejuvenation.

To its south are encountered the diverse strata and faulted landscapes of Skåne. Horst ridges, aligned in north-west/south-east direction, break up the lowland, so that while Skåne shares the "Danish" landforms of the

Cretaceous period, it also has areas of much more pronounced relief. Denmark lacks features which are equal to the *åser* or ridges of Skåne. Hallandsås, Söderås, Romeleås sometimes exceed 200 m. in height. Because of its structure and its geological history, no part of Sweden has such a variety of local regions compacted together in such a limited space. The long-standing diversity of rural responses to this character is recorded not merely in early maps, but in Linnæus's *Skånian Journey*. Skåne differs from most of Sweden in that its coast is free of islands.

Like the other Northern Countries, Sweden is a richly islanded country. The archipelago of Stockholm shows the most intense concentration of islands, the outermost of which are separated from their Finnish counterparts by the Åland Sea. Of contrasting character is the west coast archipelago of Bohuslän, where a skerry zone continues that bordering Norway's Østfold. In this "zone of conflict between land and sea" (as the author Geijer expressed it) ice, wave and wind have left the skerries bald in appearance. Intervening alluvium-filled valleys in the fractures of the coastlands provide contrasting oases of fertility. The Göta river cuts through the rocky back country to the central plainlands. Sweden's two largest islands are the Silurian outliers of Gotland (3,000 sq. km.) in the Central Baltic and Öland (1,340 sq. km.) off the Kalmar coast. Both are elongated, but Gotland is the more elevated. Gotland's karstic surface has a plateau appearance and its coasts are skirted for the most part with limestone cliffs. Ancylus and Litorina deposits have left their mark upon it, while the coast has some of the finest raised beaches to be seen in the Baltic area. Its central position in the East Sea made it a point of convergence of trading routes in the Middle Ages. Visby is its main city. To the north of Gotland is Gotska Sandön, a low-lying, timber-clad nature reserve.

PARALLELS OF PLACE

The political boundaries which outline the Northern Countries give to each a significantly different resource base and character from the rest. At the same time, the Scandinavian states and Finland are regarded—and, indeed, regard themselves—as having a distinct regional identity within the European framework. There is a common feeling of separateness from the continent, which is essential to any human appreciation or economic assessment of the Northern Countries. Like the British, indeed, Scandinavians "go to the continent"!

It is natural that those who have looked at the geography of Scandinavia and Finland should seek to bring out the essential character by comparative methods. *Nordeuropa*, it has been argued, has a Canadian atmosphere. Compress the distances, eliminate the prairies and the West, and there are elements to sustain the illusion. The topographical works of Per Kalm underlined certain Canadian parallels; *Schlözers Briefwechsel* in 1779 presented Finland to Europe as an Old World Canada. Yet, as national conscience stirred in Finland, H. G. Porthan reversed this opinion, writing in *Åbo Tidningar* (Vol. II, 1797) that it "is not particularly agreeable when we are set side by side with such a wild and uncultivated land". Increasing appreciation of the North American scene has narrowed the search for parallels to the north-west—to Alaska, the Yukon and North-West Territories. For here are the true homoclimes of Fenno-Scandinavia, with related parallels in vegetation and soil as well as familiar land-forms.

Even more interesting is the fact that north-western North America now casts a look into the Scandinavian mirror when contemplating its prospects. "Why is it that Scandinavia and Finland have sixteen million inhabitants while our northern territory of Alaska has only 72,500?" wrote Vilhjalmur Stefansson.[1] Scandinavia (including Iceland) and Finland are roughly identical in area to Alaska. A. S. Carlson, impressing parallels of latitude, has superimposed the map of Alaska upon the Fenno-Scandinavian countries.[2] To push the comparison too far is unwise. The north-western corner of North America cannot aspire to compete with the economic experiences of

---

[1] In *Yearbook of Agriculture*, Washington, 1941, 205–16.
[2] G. E. Pearcy and R. H. Fifield *World Political Geography*, London, 1948, Chapter 16.

Scandinavia and Finland for both external and internal reasons. Externally, it is not supported by the same web of market relations, and it is likely to remain detached from the consuming centres of the continent. Scandinavia, by contrast, has a market on its threshold. Domestically, Alaska is even devoid of a home market. Furthermore, it is impossible to discount the political motive when reviewing the economic emergence of Scandinavia and Finland. They have had not merely to contend with physical hardships comparable to those of the north-western parts of the New World, but they have had to create and maintain sovereign identity. The creation of a national entity is not something which can be explained in wholly rational terms. But there is something in its nature which marks it apart from a tributary territory and encourages it towards objectives less readily attainable by dependent units. For,

in the final place, Alaska, the Yukon and the North-West Territories are dependent lands— their relationship to parent territories being more readily comparable with those of the northern thirds of Norway, Sweden and Finland. The complex of political boundaries superimposed upon *Nordeuropa* is an expression of the human variable which serves to underline the problem of stopping short at a physical parallel. Political boundaries have clearly played a positive role in the stage of development so far attained by the Northern Countries. The degree of their persistence for future evolution is nowhere more thoroughly debated. They are clearly among those human divisions on the face of the earth which must be taken regularly into account in assessment and in comparison. The search for common elements in physical setting must lead to the conclusion that there are no ultimate parallels in place.

Chapter II

SETTING, RESOURCE AND LONG-TERM PHYSICAL VARIATIONS

"Far from the present shores, ships' anchors and the remains of ships have been found.
. . . Where old folk remember having rowed in the days of their youth, children now walk
barefooted in the sand. Where fishermen used to mend their nets, the peasant now makes
his hay."

Zachris Topelius, *En bok om vårt land*

THERE are two groups of physical phenomena which have a long-term effect upon the northern economy. The first are long period changes in climate; the second, changes in coastal form resulting from land upheaval and/or from changes in water-level. The effects of the first are more widespread than those of the second, which may be essentially local in impact. Awareness of the two phenomena is more acute as a result of a steady accumulation of observations. Changes in climate are likely to have an exaggerated significance for high-altitude lands, where any amelioration of even a minor character may be translated into a substantial extension of an area under a given plant association or crop. Similarly, the contribution made by the sea to the land area is a reality for those who farm and fish along the shore. Nor must land upheaval and climatic amelioration be seen solely in their present context. An appreciation of them can help to interpret past behaviour. The imagination of physical geographers in Scandinavia and Finland has been much stimulated by these phenomena and the problem of dating and relating them.

THE CHANGING LEVEL OF LAND IN RELATION TO SEA

(a) *An Enquiry into the Causes*

Land upheaval has been the object of scientific enquiry in Northern Europe for well over 300 years. The phenomenon is of consequence not only because of results from the past but also because of its continuing and direct influence on the economic life of people and places. The greater part of Sweden and Finland has been born of water; land is still being ceded to them regionally by water. In the Baltic area, reference is commonly made to the subaquatic and superaquatic areas—to those areas which stood below and above the highest shore-lines of post-glacial seas. Though land-forms have been subject to considerable sub-aerial modification since that time, there remains an essential contrast between the supramarine and the formerly submerged areas. Moreover, land upheaval and human reaction to it are aspects of an adjustment which is common both to Baltic and Atlantic Scandinavia.

The changing relation of land and water, however, shows little uniformity either on the Atlantic or Baltic littoral. It has varied in tempo regionally in the past and continues to vary in tempo regionally at the present. It is evident that, at some time in the past, emergence has been a much more striking feature of the Norwegian coast than at the present, and, indeed, most settlement in fiord Norway has seized upon land-forms which have their origins in the post-Pleistocene oscillations. Marine transgression in Norway has been most clearly evidenced around Oslofiord and the Trondheim depression. Contemporarily, land emergence is most strongly evidenced in the northern half of the Baltic basin. The speed of uplift is not uniform. It is least at the meeting-ground of the Finnish and Bothnian gulfs and most at the Quarken. There also exists evidence to support the changing altitudinal relationships of the land surface as distinct from those at the zone where land and sea meet. Thus, the changing direction of river currents, modifications in their beds and resulting changes in the outline of watersheds are a reflection of altitudinal adjustments. Eino Jutikkala refers to an early seventeenth-century event, when Lake Pälkänevesi suddenly forced a new channel of exit into Lake Mallasvesi, as historical evidence of this character.[1] Differential emergence of land will also affect the shore-lines of lakes, the form of lacustrine deposits and the nature and distribution of flooding. Other contemporary and precise evidence is found in the levelling of railway tracks. Finns estimate, for example, that at Seinäjoki the level of the land is rising at 82 cm. per century; at Kajaani, 84 cm.; at Tampere, 61 cm.

The story of the investigation of land upheaval is almost as intriguing as the phenomenon itself. Several distinct stages in the advance of knowledge can be detected. It was the scholar priests who first directed attention to land upheaval, and in the mid-eighteenth century they reasoned vigorously about the cause. Historically, first mention is ascribed to Erik Sorolainen, Bishop of Turku, who preached a sermon in 1621 and defined the signs as evidence of an approaching day of judgment. Land upheaval was the object of Swedish tracts by Olaus Rudbech in 1679 and Urban Hjärne in 1702. Hjärne attributed the emergence of land to the erosion of broader outflow channels in the Danish straits. Emanuel Swedenborg (a believer in the Deluge) conceived a more elaborate hypothesis.[2] He argued that the sea-level would naturally continue to fall after the Deluge, and that the more marked changes in high latitude would result from the rotation of the earth, the centrifugal force of which would force the water equatorwards. Swedenborg estimated the emergence to be about 4 or 5 ells a century (1 ell = 60 cm.). A closer approximation was reached by Anders Celsius with 4 ft. per century, though his explanation of water diminution differed profoundly. Natural percolation through the sea-bed coupled with evaporation would cause the Baltic Sea to dry up in 3–4,000 years, he contended.[3] Linnæus supported his water-diminution theory in the same year in a pamphlet succinctly called De terræ habitabilis incremento (Uppsala, 1743). The water-diminution theory raised difficult ecclesiastical issues. Olaf Dalin, a contemporary historian, in his Svea Rikes Historia (Stockholm, 1747) concluded from the theory that Sweden was originally an archipelago and that the age of the earth must be at least 20,000 years according to prevailing estimates of land upheaval. If this archipelago idea was injurious to the dignity of the Swedish realm, the figure of 20,000 years was offensive to churchmen, who commonly adhered to a 6,000-year estimate since the Creation. The Diet officially pronounced the ideas to be inaccurate.

Meanwhile, water-diminution theories were being questioned academically by Johannes Browallius, Professor of Physics and sometime Bishop of Turku.[4] His first cautionary statement averred that if water diminution was the explanation of land emergence, diminution must be differential. His evidence lay in certain thirteenth-century Swedish churches which were still only 2 ells above sea-level. Shifting coast-lines might, therefore, be explained by land upheaval. The relative constancy of sea-level and the changing relation of the land to it were first scientifically proposed by the surveyor E. O. Runeberg. A growing volume of academic support for his hypothesis was forthcoming at the beginning of the last century. Parallel with this, an increasing number of precise records were collected from coastal areas. It is worth noting that English eyes were first opened to Bothnian land upheaval by Charles Lyell,[5] who on visiting Sweden in 1834 cut his own mark on St. Olof's stone in Edskö sound. By the middle of the nineteenth century, more precise comment was being made on the differential emergence of the land.

[1] In 1859, Lake Höytiäinen broke the locks on Pyhäselkä Canal and the innocent canal engineers were blamed, though clearly the rising level of the land played a part which lay outside their calculations.
[2] Om vatnetshöjd och förra werldens starcka ebb och flod, Stockholm, 1719.
[3] Anmärkning om vattnets förmingskande så i Östersjön som i Vesterhafvet, K. Sv. Akad, Handlingar, Stockholm, 1743.
[4] Betänkande om vattenminskningen, Åbo, 1755.
[5] "On the Proofs of a Gradual Rising of the Land in Certain Parts of Sweden", Proceedings of Geological Association, 1835, and Principles of Geology, London, 1875, Vol. II, Chapter 31.

No North European geographer was more fascinated by this feature than Zachris Topelius. Several lectures in his course on the *Geography of Finland*, delivered at the University of Helsinki between 1854 and 1856, were devoted to this topic.[1] His evidence is assembled with the assurance of an investigator who knows the field intimately. Topelius, indeed, had been born and brought up along one of the most active zones of land upheaval in the world. From personal experience he could give scores of examples of coastal emergence: he could cite the rock markings or "water-levels"[2] of surveyors from former decades in Rönnskär and Bergö; he could direct attention to the tide-marks and anchorages on rocks now hundreds of yards from the water's edge; he could comment on the shallows which afflicted British men-of-war as they harried Ekenäs. He romanticised the concept in his popular historical fiction.

There is a third stage in the appreciation of land-sea relations. At the time when Topelius gave his first series of lectures on Finland's geography, theories of glaciation had not entered his reading. Diluvial floods were called in to account for the great boulder-strewn wastes of central Sweden and Finland. By the time that the second series of lectures was given in the mid-1870s, glacial theories were quoted to account in part for the surface deposits of the northern world; but land upheaval as the consequence of isostatic adjustment was still a hypothesis unknown to Topelius.

Both Linnæus, with his discovery of marine molluscs at Uddevalla, and Topelius, with his observations on seashells far from the Bothnian beaches, anticipated those students of organic remains in the soil who were to add depth to the picture of Quaternary oscillations in the Baltic area. The remains of these molluscs, stratigraphically differentiated in surface deposits, have been the means of revealing new facts about past land and water distributions. The molluscs are (i) the *Yoldia arctica*, a salt-water species, (ii) *Ancylus*, a fresh-water snail and (iii) *Littorina*, a salt-water snail. The three creatures have given their names to three phases of development of the Baltic Sea—which, at the same time, imply three distinct changes in shape. Following the retreat of the ice, a proto-Baltic emerged (Fig. 10), now commonly called the Yoldia Sea. This was transformed into the Ancylus Lake, when the water-body lay in detachment from the outer ocean. The third stage in the evolution of the Baltic is commonly known as the Littorina phase—when the western watergate (or possibly gates, since there is some evidence supporting an initial watergate through central Sweden) was reopened. The shore-line of the expanding and contracting water-bodies has been the subject of classical studies by the Swede Gerard de Geer; while the Finn M. Sauramo has applied new precision to his thesis.[3] A silhouette of the conjectured sequence of development is seen in Fig. 10, which, at the same time, brings out the basic north European concept of submarine and supramarine regions. The perspectives opened by this picture implied that the differential emergence already acknowledged by the time of Topelius had now to be set in the frame of long-period expansion and contraction of the water area.[4] It was a topic to stir many minds—even that of Fritjof Nansen; but it was natural that among speculators few should be as vigorous as one who lived under the shadow of an ice-cap—Sigurdur Thorarinsson of Iceland.[5]

The contemporary mathematical approach divorces the study of land upheaval increasingly from geography. So many variables have to be taken into consideration to satisfy contemporary enquiry that the physical aspects of the problem have been shifted to another plane. The problem hinges upon increasing precision in the means of measuring water-level. An initial large-scale attempt to

---

[1] The manuscripts of the lectures are in the University Library, Helsinki.
[2] These are described by F. Bergsten, "Land Uplift in Sweden from the Evidence of Old Water Marks", *Geografiska Annaler*, 1954.
[3] "The Mode of Land Upheaval in Fennoscandia in Late Quaternary Time", *Fennia*, **66**, 2, 1938.
[4] Cf. W. Ramsay, "On the Relations between Crustal Movements and Variations in Sea-level during the Late Quaternary Time", *Bulletin de la Commission géologique de Finlande*, Helsinki, 1924. Ramsay was a pioneer in North European studies concerning the interplay of isostatic uplift and eustatic changes in sea-level.
[5] Cf. "Present Glacial Shrinkage and Eustatic Changes of Sea-level", *Geografiska Annaler*, 1940; F. Nansen, "The Strandflat and Isostasy", *Videnskabselskabets skrifter*, **1**, 11, 1921.

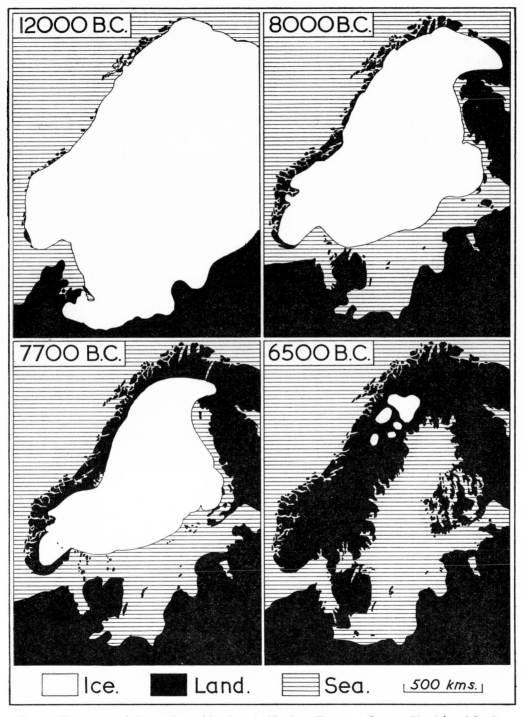

FIG. 10. The retreat of the continental ice-sheet in Northern Europe. (Source: *The Atlas of Sweden*, Stockholm, 1956.)

assess this was made by Rolf Witting during the period of the First World War.[1] At the sixty tide-gauge observation stations attempts were made to correct all disturbing meteorological phenomena. Wind direction and strength can have an important effect in changing the volume of water entering the Danish straits which can elevate the water-level as far north as the twin gulfs by as much as 50–60 cm.[2] Air-pressure differences will affect water-level independently of the whole range of hydrographical influences: rainfall, evaporation, volume of water entering from tributary rivers. These facts may differ substantially from year to year, and are variables which must be eliminated from the picture if the fundamental relation of land to sea is to be discovered.

A synoptic view of the Baltic and Scandinavian picture was assayed by B. Gutenberg in 1943.[3] It is reproduced with some amendments as Fig. 11. The information on his diagram is drawn from a variety of sources which are in themselves of varying degrees of reliability. The map indicates all tidal stations from which information is being drawn, and an attempt is made to show the length of their observations. Gutenberg's map is the conclusion drawn by an outside observer from the succession of isobase maps which began with that of R. Sieger in 1893,[4] and ended with the definitive statement of Sauramo. The map is a simple summary of land upheaval during the last 7,000 years.

(b) An Appreciation of the Consequences

A nineteenth-century author once commented that the sea gave a province every century to Finland.[5] In the past, it has clearly been as generous to both Sweden and Norway. Henrik Renquist estimated the size of this Finnish gift to be 1,000 sq. km. every hundred years. That is a good-sized parish by Scandinavian standards. Within the frame of a single commune or island, land upheaval may be especially significant. In the Vaasa archipelago—where the tempo is probably at its fastest—one island commune (Bergö) has increased in area by a third in less than two centuries; another (Replot), by a fifth. Some mainland parishes (e.g. Malax) are stated to have extended their area on an average by 5 hectares annually. In such areas the feature becomes not merely humanly perceptible, but also humanly significant.

The actual zone in which the effect is apparent and in which adjustments have to be made is narrow and, of course, changing. Within the span of a lifetime it may be limited to a few hundred metres in breadth. The consequences are twofold. In general, they are positive for the farmer, for they increase his land area; they are negative for the fisherman, who must regularly seek new moorings, or for the merchant, who must consider new harbours and ponder new fairways. The detail of adjustment around the fringes of settlement is a real study in human geography.

Few have captured the spirit of place in such an area more completely than Helmer Smeds. His appreciation of his home parish—Malax—naturally embraces some treatment of the emergent shore-line.[6] Here—and in the Vaasan archipelago to the north—the sea slowly surrenders new land for division among the littoral community. Sea-bottom land displays the same features which characterise the coastal plains between the interrupting rock outcrops. Thus, it has its burden of boulders of varying sizes—which must be cleared before it can be satisfactorily cultivated. Sometimes, earlier water-level marks are etched into their sides. Occasionally, iron spikes or staples recall the mooring-places of fishing-boats. Even poles upon which fish-nets used to dry may stand beside the contemporary cornfield. The process of reclamation involves both legal and agricultural

---

[1] R. Witting, *Fennia*, **39**, 5, 1918. There is also a more recent statement in *Fennia*, **68**, 1, 1943.
[2] I. Hela, "A Study of Land Upheaval at the Finnish Coast", *Fennia*, **76**, 5, 1953.
[3] "Changes in Sea-level, Post Glacial Uplift and Mobility of the Earth's Interior", *Bull. of Geol. Soc. of Am.*, New York, 1941, 52.
[4] "Seenschwankungen und Strandverschiebungen in Skandinavien", *Zft. d. Ges. f. Erdkunde*, Berlin, 1893, 28.
[5] In a popular article to *Suomen kuvalehti* (15, 1956) it was pointed out that the land area which had been detached from Finland in the east by political force would be compensated in the west by physical agencies—after 5,000 or 6,000 years!
[6] *Malaxbygden*, Helsingfors, 1935.

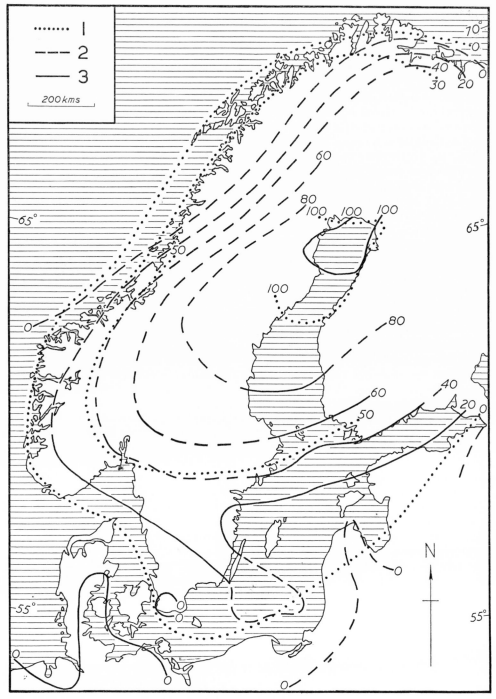

FIG. 11. Land upheaval and its tendencies in Northern Europe. (After B. Gutenberg, *Bulletin of the Geological Society of America*, 52, New York, 1941.) Key: 1. Uplift in metres during past 7,000 years. 2. Conjectured continuation of isobases. 3. Present rate of uplift in cm. per century.

operations. The redistribution of reclaimed land is commonly undertaken upon a commune basis—or upon that of the hamlet in areas of speedy emergence. The reclaimed area is parcelled out among the community after the preparation of a property map. In general, the land is ploughable; but the range of crops may be limited at first because of the salinity of the soil. Grassland is dominant in the initial stages of reclamation. Sometimes the land is subjected to flooding. High winds can pile up the waters and cause their temporary encroachment across the broad zone of mud-flats with their colonising vegetation to the tilled land. Reclaimed land is therefore occasionally diked. At the water's edge one sees the process in operation which has been repeated across the entire breadth of a coastal plain scores of kilometres in width. Extremely gentle slopes cause problems of drainage. Simultaneously, uplift disturbs the profile of the water courses in their lower stretches; it reduces the velocity of flow and results in silting; in their upper reaches, streams become entrenched and their beds are strewn with rapids. On the Swedish side of the Bothnian Sea and Gulf entrenchment is more pronounced. Neither the Finnish nor the Swedish series of parallel flowing rivers is, however, navigable.

An excellent documentary means for the appreciation of changes in the coastal zones of the Bothnian world is provided by the maps compiled by the eighteenth-century land measurers. By a fortuitous accident, some of the most detailed land-measuring operations were made of precisely those areas where emergence has been most pronounced. Needless to say, the degree of accuracy of these early maps is very variable; but with discretion it is possible to reconstruct former coastal outlines. The extent of change differs regionally—being most marked where estuarine deposits are greatest. For some areas it is possible to obtain a succession of three maps over a century and a half.

The eye-witness who sees the process of land emergence and its effect upon a single farmer's land can visualise the evolution of much of the Scandinavian world. Earlier settlers in Nor-

way, Sweden and Finland have not had at their disposal the same area of land that is available for contemporary settlement. The archipelago world provides particularly good examples of former distributions of settlement and activity. Bronze Age, Iron Age and Viking Age finds show an expanding distribution which correlates with the growing land area in the Åland and Stockholm archipelagos.[1] In the Swedish midlands, too, the apparent retreat of waters left new agricultural lands, especially around Lakes Mälaren and Hjälmaren. Some linguists still aver that "Svea", the original component of "Sverige" (Sweden), derives from the old verb "svia"—to dwindle away (of water).

The core of the Swedish realm has developed against an area of marked emergence. Of the facts favouring the location of the present capital—Stockholm—few have been more important than its hinterland of farmland. Stockholm fulfils the requirements pronounced to be of historic interest by Vaughan Cornish for a capital city. To its adjacent storehouse of farm products are added a crossroads setting and a fortress site. Its fortifiable island intercepted the water route from the archipelago to the inner lakes and provided a stepping-stone in the midst of waterways interrupting the north–south routeway. The shift of the centre of control in early Sweden was also related to land upheaval. By the thirteenth century water access to Lake Malären from the outer sea was also obstructed. The arms of the sea into which sea robbers wandered to attack the Mälar retreats of the proto-Swedish realm were converted into the outlet channels of a lake now nearly half a metre above the level of the Baltic. "Slussen", the water-course in the centre of Stockholm, writes in its current the reason for the closure.

The transformation of land and water relations at Stockholm is barely perceptible today; but the differential speed of uplift in the Central Bothnian areas gives an impression of the type of problem with which it had to grapple in a less technical age. Uplift assumes an exaggerated importance because of the extended shallows which surround the

[1] Cf. B. Hedenstierna, *Stockholms skärgård*, Stockholm, 1948, Plates I–III.

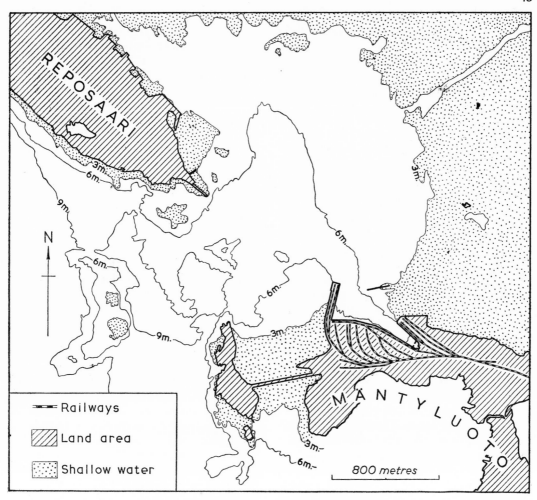

FIG. 12. The present-day harbour at Mäntyluoto.

coasts. One may imagine Olaus Magnus's graphic description and woodcuts of dredging operations as being part of a vain attempt to offset the inevitable. In general, the contemporary effects of uplift are more marked on the Finnish side than on the Swedish side. It is instructive to look at the Baltic harbours illustrated in C. W. Gylden's century-old *Plankartor över Städerna i Finland*, and to consider the present location of the ports in relation to their original sites. Vaasa, where land upheaval is estimated at 87 cm. per century, relocated its harbour at Vaskiluoto as well as reconstructing its city after the great

fire of 1856. Some harbours, e.g. Kemi and Oulu (uplift 107 cm. per century), have partly compromised by employing lighterage as a means of combating their shallowing fairways. Other harbours have advanced seaward into outports—Kokkola, for example, looks to Ykspihlaja (uplift 91 cm. per century). The most involved reaction is found in Pori.[1] Here, upwarping has increased the silting of the River Kokemäki, and the harbour location has migrated seawards six times in as many centuries. The contemporary harbour is Mäntyluoto, and the prospect before it is written in its submarine contours (Fig. 12).

[1] A. A. Säntti, *Die Häfen an der Kokemäenjoki-Mündung*, Turku, 1951.

On the opposite coast, Hudiksvall has changed its location several times in response to "the rising walls of Sweden".

But if national and regional economics direct attention to major centres of export like Mäntyluoto, the fascination of the phenomenon is the greater at a more humble level. Man economising his effort at the physical margin is always a satisfying sight for the economic geographer—who is prone to lose sight of humanity in a sea of statistics. The island of Björkö in the Vaasa archipelago illustrates the adjustment of successive generations of fisher-farmers to land uplift. In its retreat, the ice-sheet left successive ripples of boulder deposits (a feature the origin of which remains debatable). These stand revealed as they are lifted in sequence above the level of the sea. First they appear as low reefs, then as stony corrugations separated by swampy hollows, finally as wooded ridges alternating with cultivated furrows. The harbourage of small fishing craft and the drying or storage sheds for nets or catch are usually located as near the open water as possible. In some places it is possible to detect as many as three sites—one deserted, one in process of decay and one in process of development—on a sequence of three ridges. A handful of fisherfolk are repeating here a response which must be thousands of years old in the coastal economy of the Baltic. At the same time, they are repeating in the simplest possible terms the phenomenon demonstrated more strikingly on the banks of the Kokemäki river. In Sweden, land upwarping has called for a legal redefinition of fishing-grounds. Swedish coastal waters are commonly divided according to private and public fishing-grounds. The private fishing-grounds are bounded by a line drawn 300 m. from the shore-line at the mean height of water. This line is clearly not stationary from a geodetic standpoint and calls for intermittent modification.

CLIMATIC FLUCTUATIONS

(a) *Some Evidence for their Occurrence*

There are various types of climatic change, and those included in this chapter may be more specifically described as climatic fluctuations rather than climatic variations. Climatic fluctuations are of shorter duration; climatic variations are measured more in millennia. Within the span of variations are embraced the glacial and interglacial periods; fluctuations follow a cyclical course within these episodes.

Human history in Northern Europe has recorded a distinct reaction to these fluctuations. A range of features suggests a deterioration during the late Middle Ages—with an advance of the frontier of frost and increased storminess in North-west Europe. New methods of investigating climatic conditions have been widely disseminated in the north. The analysis of palæo-botanical material—especially pollen analysis—has had fruitful results in the widespread bogs of the north.[1] The worsening is illustrated in Iceland by medieval settlement sites which were lost beneath ice and have now been exposed again. It is evidenced on the west coast of Greenland, where a probable lowering of temperature eliminated crop cultivation and fodder collection in this marginal settlement.[2] Perhaps it was an increased storminess which intercepted communications between the Scandinavian mainland and this outermost colony—certainly breaches in the Slesvig coast were extended at this time.

A contrasting amelioration has shown itself during the last century or two. The effects have tended to be cumulative. They have not commonly been perceptible within the human lifetime; but there are many records—natural and mathematical—which provide clues.

The study of these macro-changes is peculiarly fascinating to the geographer, and the method for their appreciation is familiar to him. The method is to assemble and collate an infinite number of pieces of information related in varying degrees to the central theme, and to present them as a unity. The unity in this instance is a grand process of environmental change—or a process of change affecting a broad segment of the earth. The past two hundred years has been a period of collection of statistical information—albeit of variable quality and quantity. Political

---

[1] L. von Post, *The New Phytologist*, **45**, 2, Cambridge, 1946.
[2] Cf. *Meddelelser om Grønland*, **67**, **76**, pp. 88–90, 141, *et al.*

boundaries have not restricted its assembly any more than the phenomena which have prompted investigation. Climatologically speaking, Northern Europe is very much the neighbour of and collaborator with North America and the U.S.S.R. Bearing in mind the sensitivity of northern lands to minor ameliorations in climate, it is not surprising that Scandinavian scientists should be in the vanguard of enquiry. Summarising their arguments are maps which show appreciable positive iso-anomalies centred over the Scandinavian world.[1]

Behind these major conclusions is found a mass of factual information. The longest series of climatic records (from 1760) in Northern Europe is found in Stockholm, and their analysis by A. Ångström suggests that a substantial improvement has taken place in winter temperatures during the last two hundred years.[2] His calculations are based on mean values for periods of thirty years, and a figure approximating to 2·5° is deduced. Simultaneously, spring temperatures have shown a slight tendency to rise, though summer temperatures have remained immobile. In Norway, records date from 1816, and a corresponding amelioration of winter temperatures has been observed. The amelioration is also evident from records extended to Svalbard during the twentieth century.[3] Indeed, the higher the latitude in this northern hemisphere, the more exaggerated the modifications seem to be. This is a conclusion supported in the broader studies of the Danish investigator, Leo Lysgaard. His analyses of Danish temperatures over the period 1798–1947 have more local application but continue the Scandinavian story to its southern limits. The general inference is that mild winters are becoming more frequent, while severe winters, although remaining severe, are less frequent.[4] Pressure analyses also provide evidence of a striking change even within the restricted Danish frame. Thus, between the southern Jutish island of Fanö and the Skagen peninsula, the pressure gradient has sharpened by 39% in half a century. There have been consequent effects upon wind directions and wind strengths. In Finland, climatic fluctuations have claimed the attention of J. E. Keränen, for many years director of the country's meteorological services (and a weather god in the eyes of Finnish country people as powerful as any Ukko from the country's folk-lore). The phenomena have also called forth a special symposium from the Geographical Society of Finland.[5]

Long-period temperature (or precipitation) records are supplemented by historical testimony and visible evidence. In no field of investigation is this more striking than in glaciological studies. In the glacial fringes of the North Atlantic region there seems to have been a common shrinkage. Appreciation of the waxing and waning of glaciers is nothing new. Iceland has been keenly aware of the impact of these macrothermal changes upon its glacial world. Topographers already showed curiosity about the behaviour of ice-masses more than two centuries ago. One of the most explicit comments comes from Eggert Olafsson[6] concerning a northward facing slope of Skardsheidi.

"We noticed high up on the mountains," he wrote, "a fairly large patch which looked like glacier ice. The owner of the nearest farm, Mofellsstadir, in reply to our question whether the ice on Mofell did not melt in summer, not only answered no, but added that when he was a boy he never saw any ice there at all. . . . The place is facing north-west and the ice already shows cracks of a green colour due to the refraction usual on thick glaciers. This indicates that the ice may increase and new glaciers form even on moderately high mountains in this neighbourhood, provided the periodical cold winds persist year after year."

Following in the footsteps of Sveinn Palsson, a glaciological specialist from the eight-

[1] No one has been more energetic in his pursuit of these considerations than Hans Wilson Ahlmann, whose enthusiasm dates back thirty years—*vide* especially the following papers, which are in English: "Glaciological Research on the North Atlantic Coasts", *R.G.S. Research Series*, I, London, 1948; "Researches on Snow and Ice", *Geog. Jour.*, CVII, 1946; "The Present Climatic Fluctuation", *Geog. Jour.*, CXII, 1948.
[2] "Principiella synpunkter på undersökningar över klimatets förändring med tillämpning på det svenska klimatet", *Geogr. Ann.*, 23, Stockholm, 1941.
[3] T. Hesselberg and B. Birkeland, "Säkulare Schwankungen des Klimas von Norwegen", *Geofysiske Publikasjoner*, 14, 4, Oslo, 1940; **14**, 5, 1941; **14**, 6, 1943; **15**, 2, 1944.
[4] E.g. *Conseil permanent pour l'Exploration de la Mer*, CXXV, Copenhagen, 1949, 17–20.
[5] I. Hustich, "The Recent Climatic Fluctuation in Finland and its Consequences", *Fennia*, **75**, 1952.
[6] *Vice-Lavmand Eggert Olafssons og Landphysici Bjarni Povelsons Reise igiennem Island foranstaltet af Videnskabernes Sælskab i Köbenhavn*, Parts I and II, Soröe, 1772.

eenth century, Sigurdur Thorarinsson has married historical evidence and physical observation.[1] Place-name evidence (particularly in so far as it appears in old maps and manuscripts) can be a clue to the presence or absence of ice-masses. On the map which he prepared in 1732 (published 1734), T. H. H. Knopf wrote upon Skerdaràrjökull, "A glacier that slid out 600 years ago. The same glacier moves back and forth". Travellers' accounts of the distances between the ice edge and relatively well-marked topographical points can aid the appreciation of ice fluctuation. Abandoned farms called for comments in Land Registers. Thus of the farm Fjäll by the outlet glacier Hrutar-jökull of the main ice-mass Vatnajökull, the Land Registrar wrote (1708–9): "Fourteen years ago a 'tun' and ruined buildings could be seen, but now all is in the ice." There is regular and widespread reference to the engulfment of grazing grounds or their detachment by the advance of the ice front across access routes. Frontal recession, however, characterises the Icelandic glaciers, and Thorarinsson is of the opinion that they are quantitatively smaller today than at any time since the end of the seventeenth century. Much more difficult is the assessment of ice thinning; though here, too, Thorarinsson emphasises substantial diminution.

Diminution similarly characterises the permanent icefields of Norway. Documentary evidence suggests that many outlet glaciers probably attained their maximum historical advance two hundred years ago. Ice moved down outflow channels from Jostedalsbre to occasion distress among farmers in the inner valleys of the Sogn. Since photography entered to capture visually the rate of retreat of ice, and members of the International Commission on Glaciers (set up at the Geological Congress in 1894) began to keep precise measurements, some Scandinavian ice-lobes have shrunk by more than half a kilometre. In some instances, the retreat has been progressively swifter because the firn-line or snow-line has risen above their highest parts and they no longer receive a significant contribution of snow to feed their ice bodies. W. Werenskiold has indicated that with the rise in level of the snow-line of the Jotunheim area by some 200 m. during the last thirty years, most glaciers in that area lie below it.[2] The retreat of the ice in Norway first manifested itself most strikingly in the north, around Svartisen, and later in the south. One of the most graphic pieces of evidence in Norway was the discovery of wooden-shafted arrows on the surface of a fast-vanishing glacierette in Oppdal—arrows archæologically dated at 1,400–1,500 years old.[3] The "budget" of an ice-mass, in which term its volume is expressed, is very responsive to variation in rainfall or snowfall. Swedish glaciologists and meteorologists have adopted a more humanly comprehensible icefield—Stor glacier, in Swedish Lapland, a 3-km. square area—in order to study the sensitivity of a marginal glacier to climatic changes.

These changes on the land, in general out of the vertical or areal range of the ordinary man's eye, are paralleled by changes occurring in the sea. Again, these changes are not visually detectable, and are only instrumentally recordable over a long period. Norwegian hydrographers have assembled the fullest evidence of surface temperature variations in coastal waters during recent generations. Latterly, mid-North Sea and mid-Atlantic data have been steadily accumulated to complement this coastal material. In all instances, for the greater part of the twentieth century, maritime surface temperatures in the higher latitudes of the northern hemisphere display a positive thermal anomaly. Such anomalies announce themselves visually (and, of course, practically) in the changing distribution of sea ice in high latitudes. Open water prevails for a longer period around Spitzbergen than fifty years ago; the duration of pack-ice off the north coast of Iceland has diminished by roughly two months since regular observations were first recorded sixty years ago. Simultaneously, the extent of the

---

[1] "Oscillations of Icelandic Glaciers in the last 250 Years", *Geogr. Ann.*, **25**, Stockholm, 1943, and *Polar Record*, **5**, Cambridge, 1947.
[2] "Glacial Measurements in the Jotunheim", *Geogr. Ann.*, **31**, Stockholm, 1949.
[3] K. Fægri, "Brevariasjoner i Vest-Norge i det siste 200 år", *Naturen*, 1948, and "Forandringer ved norske breer, 1936–7", *Bergens museums årbok*, 1938.

ice-sheet in the interior Baltic has been ameliorated. Needless to say, in severe winters the ice cover approaches its historical maximum. The Hydrological Bureau at Helsinki[1] estimates, however, that the average extent of Baltic ice today is more than a fifth less than it was a century ago.

Theories concerning the causes of climatic change lie beyond the scope of this book. It seems evident, however, that they are related to increased atmospheric circulation and/or to a greater transfer of heat to higher latitudes from lower latitudes.[2] As a result, a chain reaction is set in motion. If temperatures change, wind modifications will follow: if there is a modification in the wind rose, the thermometer will behave responsively. Further, both of these agents may affect the direction of flow of maritime and ocean currents. Nor does the marine reaction stop here for, as Thorarinsson and Gutenberg have demonstrated, the positive thermal modification—in hastening the retreat of permanent ice-masses—automatically lifts the sea-level (perhaps to the extent of 1 mm. annually). Bearing in mind the relatively limited rise in level, there is appreciable agreement that it is only the margins of the icefields and peripheral glaciers which show marked change. It is further concurred that this retreat is principally due to the extended period of ablation by conduction—or simply to the milder springs and autumns. But at this stage, evidence supporting climatic change is already subject matter more fittingly included with the consequences of climatic amelioration.

(b) Some Consequences of Climatic Amelioration

It is perhaps straining too much after effect to seek for the direct impact of climatic improvement upon man's life in the North European world. The indirect effect is more appreciable, but because of the multiplicity of points at which it asserts itself and the minuteness of the individual impact its analysis is difficult. The "pointilliste" school of painting provides a parallel from the world of art—the entire picture makes sense, but the constituent brush strokes have little meaning. The responses are not simultaneous in all fields. Reaction in the sea is probably more swift than on the land; while changes in insect, animal and bird life occur more quickly than plant-biological changes. There is a chain reaction in the process, and the effects of it tend to be cumulative. They are increasingly discernible over an extended period, and this is the more true because of the relatively limited impact of man on the natural landscape in the northern world. Climatic amelioration also affects his handiwork. Yet the ultimate effect upon his cultivated crops may not be easy to define. Superficially it may appear striking, but it may be deceiving because of the many biological changes simultaneously introduced through plant breeding.

Phenological observations have long been made in the north out of personal interest independently of any scientific aim. The material which they cover is, in general, of a diverse nature. It is possible to conclude, however, that the foliation time for birch and maple trees has advanced by a week or ten days, and that the average "yellowing time" of these trees has been retarded by a similar period in the autumn. The positive variation is more marked in the north than in the south. It is noticeable, too, that blueberries and wild raspberries ripen correspondingly earlier. This slight speeding up in the reproduction process can have important consequences for seed yields. Besides reducing winter mortality, climatic amelioration can also strengthen the status of certain plant species in a community through procreation. By their size and often because of their exotic character, trees naturally claim attention. There are also less noticeable but equally remarkable changes in the ground flora. The changing flora of grazed land, not immediately discernible, can have an indirect effect on animal husbandry. Climatic amelioration also affects evaporation and transpiration—with direct consequences for the extensive swamplands and boglands of Scandinavia. The distribu-

---

[1] R. Jurva, *Fennia*, **75**, 1952, 17–24, and contribution to the *Handbook of Finnish Geography*, Helsinki, 1952.
[2] B. E. Eriksson, "Till kännedomen om den nutida klimatändringen inom områdena kring nordligaste Atlanten", *Geogr. Ann.*, **25**, Stockholm, 1943. There is, of course, considerable literature, and reference should be made to the Bibliography (pp. 42–52), *Conseil permanent international pour l'exploration de la mer*, CXXV, Copenhagen, 1948.

tion of their vegetational associations is too widespread and too little investigated for any broad generalisation to be made. Locally, however, the drying-up of swamplands and boglands has been the object of study in southern Ostrobothnia and Lapland. The colonisation of their margins by softwood timber represents a significant transformation.

The responses of birds and animals have also claimed attention. Bird watching in Northern Europe has not acquired the phenomenal popularity found in Britain; but it has been clear to the rural community for some time that changes in bird habits have been occurring. In Denmark, it is noted that twenty-five new species have made their appearance from more southerly latitudes during the last two or three generations. Fifty years ago the lapwing nested around the southern coastlands of the Bothnian Sea; today, it also nests at the head of the Gulf of Bothnia. Beyond this distributional change, it has been observed that the migrant lapwing is returning to the north earlier than used to be customary. Among animals, the behaviour of the roe deer is noteworthy. In the sixteenth and seventeenth century it was widely distributed in central Scandinavia; subsequently it retreated (and declined in numbers almost to the point of extinction) to the extreme south of the peninsula. The return to its former widespread habitat, though perhaps partly related to changing hunting practices, cannot be disassociated from climatic improvement. In Finland, O. Kalela has shown the advance of the polecat northwards from the south-east. The main diet of the polecat consists of small rodents and frogs, and its movement north assumes their availability.[1] Complementarily, L. Siivonen[2] has demonstrated the northward retreat of the lynx in more recent decades; though here, too, the expansion of the cleared and settled area in the south is an independent deterrent which may have influenced its behaviour. Another Finnish research worker, E. Merikallio, conducting a general study of bird and animal population in the area north of Lake Ladoga in 1919

and 1943, found that the "southern" component in it had increased by over 20% in the interim.[3] Iceland, a country which had known regular visits of polar bears in former times, reports only three occurrences in the twentieth century. This may well be explained by the retreat of northern pack-ice.

The behaviour of marine fauna is not visibly detectable, but distributional changes are occurring in the sea perhaps even more quickly than on the land. Thus, the West Greenland cod fishery has seen a change in its centre of gravity—a northward shift of 300 miles. Observers indicate that Greenlanders who, a generation ago, had never seen a cod now count them as among the commoner fish. In the inner Baltic, changes in salinity, consequent upon temperature and wind modifications, have had their effect upon its maritime fauna. The distribution of three or four different species—of which the cod is the best known—has changed substantially. Established fishing-grounds in the Turku archipelago, the object of close attention for several centuries, have also shown marked changes in yield.

Climatic amelioration becomes the more significant when it affects an economic resource. In the north it is, of course, the coniferous woodland which is the primary resource likely to be affected. The Forestry Research Institutes of all three countries have concerned themselves with tree growth in relation to climatic variation. It has been commonly concluded that the most important factor affecting the development of the tree trunk is the temperature during the growing season. There appears to be a close correlation between summer temperatures and radial growth, so that annual rings are likely to be a reflection of associated summer conditions (always assuming that exceptional aridity has not intruded to modify the control). In Norway it is averred that prime development is related more closely to middle and late summer temperatures, and spruce growth is more responsive to spring and early summer temperatures. Plant morphologists estimate the

---

[1] *Fennia*, **75**, 1952, pp. 38–51.   [2] See also *Fennia*, **75**, pp. 77–88.
[3] *Annals of the Zoological Society*, Vanamo, **12**, 12, 1946.

PLATE 5. THE EASTERN FACE OF FINLAND

An area of "colonial" development from Lapinlahti in east central Savo. The farm of Juho Judin is located on this photograph (cf. Chapter VII).

PLATE 6. THE WESTERN FACE OF FINLAND

A mature human landscape from the valley of the river Kokemäki in south-west Finland.   These clay plains
are a "gift" from the sea and are among the oldest settled parts of the country (cf. Chapter II).

radial development of the pine to last about two and a half months; while vertical growth lasts about one and a half months.[1] Although tree-ring analysis shows the growth of timber in high latitudes to have reached a maximum development in the 1920s, this development has not been sustained in spite of continued climatic amelioration. What is significant, however, is that a less inclement climate speeds the reproductive process and the more frequent occurrence of seeds. Seed years for the pine tree on the Scandinavian polar timber-line have been almost as frequent during the last generation as they have been in the southern part of the country. The process of natural regeneration in Northern Europe is, therefore, favoured increasingly in so far as the climatic amelioration prevails. Although precise growth estimates may therefore be stultified because of the response of timber to even short-term climatic changes, the resources of the northern woodlands are strengthened through improved seeding.

The management of the woodlands of the Northern Countries makes it increasingly difficult to determine the share in timber increment which may be attributed to purely natural causes and to human interference. Economically, the important point is that the increment appears to be increasing. Even more in the agricultural field is it difficult to ascribe increased yields to climatic amelioration. Side by side with the accepted amelioration of the inter-war years, the Northern Countries made rapid strides in plant breeding,[2] in drainage, in rotational practices, in the mechanisation of harvesting and, above all, in natural and artificial manuring. The protagonists of each of these methods of improving crop returns claim a disproportionate share as due to their researches. Undeniably, there is some cumulative effect. It is undeniable, too, that climatic amelioration makes its contribution. Ilmari Hustich has sought to correlate the yields of a number of primary crops in Finland with long-period temperature averages. In his appreciation of cereal cultivation in Finland, he has employed the approach of the American R. Klages (*Crop Ecology*, 1931) and identified a climatic hazard coefficient to express the degree of uncertainty occurring in a crop return. The hazard coefficient will be variable from period to period for different crops. It is clear that any climatic amelioration will spell a reduction of the hazard. The conclusion of Hustich is that for Finland (and for Sweden as well on the basis of this general observation):

"plant improvement, manuring, improved farming methods and seed treatment accentuate the positive aspects of climatic fluctuations and neutralise their negative effects.... We must not... observing the high crops per hectare of the 1930s, imagine that they represent a norm attainable in any conditions."[3]

While Hustich has pinned his faith to one aspect of climate—viz. temperature conditions—others are prepared to admit that the extension of the growing season is more important in the botanical *Drang nach Norden*.

These changes in the reactions of the native plant community are repeated in the behaviour of cultivated species. Absolute boundaries of cultivation change; economic boundaries change. In both Sweden and Finland, economic and absolute boundaries of cultivation of field crops have shifted northwards appreciably in the last two generations. Likewise, fruit cultivation has advanced northwards. This advance may be related especially to the general decline in the severity of winters in spite of the toll taken of established fruit orchards by the succession of severe winters in the 1940s. Apple trees multiply increasingly on the accepted northern margins of cultivation and overwinter with greater certainty; the hazards to pear and plum in the south have certainly diminished.

Even more important than the establishment of these "luxury" or "ornamental" products are the effects of a prolonged growing season or a less severe winter upon the yield and composition of grasslands. The Northern Countries are oriented agriculturally to animal husbandry. The extension of open

---

[1] Cf. *Medd. från Statens Skogsförsöksanstalt*, 22, Stockholm, 1925. The behaviour of the pine in the High North has been most thoroughly investigated by I. Hustich, "The Scotch Pine in Northernmost Finland and its Dependence on the Climate in the Last Decades", *Acta Botanica Fennica*, 42, 1948. Much material in this field has been brought together by D. J. Schove, "Summer Temperatures and Tree-ring Analysis in North Scandinavia, A.D. 1461–1950", *Geogr. Ann.*, 36, 1954.

[2] *Fennia*, 73, part 3, 1950.   [3] *Fennia*, 75, 1952, page 105.

grazing by two weeks can make a significant difference to fodder supplies. Alternatively, the yield of an aftermath crop from the meadows or an additional cut for silage from temporary grasslands are brought within the realm of possibility. The composition of herbage may materially change as a result of including slightly later-ripening species or of ensuring the persistence of more winter-sensitive species. Partly because of its ripening habits and its winter sensitivity, for example, red clover—a sown constituent of temporary grasslands—rapidly disappears. The growing success with the establishment of permanent pasture in higher latitudes cannot be divorced from climatic fluctuation.

It is essentially upon people who are working close to nature that the effects of changing climate are likely to make themselves felt. But even the world of commerce and industry cannot turn a blind eye. Commercially speaking, climatic amelioration is likely to have significant consequences for accessibility. The impact of the winter freeze upon maritime communications (see Chapter III) is a relevant example. For Norway, outside the grip of Baltic icing, access to the coalfields of West Spitzbergen has much improved. Whereas fifty years ago shipping could only use Spitzbergen harbours for three months annually, today they are accessible twice as long. Industrially, Norway may also feel the impact. With the diminution of melt-water flowing from its shrinking ice-masses, the indirect effect is bound to be transmitted to local hydro-electric power resources.[1] But such forecasting assumes the continuation of the present climatic ameliorations.

The synoptic view of the North European climatic scene from this angle of amelioration has an arresting character. Climatic fluctuations must not be ignored as environmental controls, but their effects within the span of a man's lifetime must not be exaggerated. Perhaps the patient assembly of information for posterity may be of more value than the search for significance today.

THE MARGINS OF HABITABLE COUNTRY

All areas are subject to a variety of long-term physical changes. Scandinavia and Finland lie in an area where two distinctive and unusual processes are occurring—frequently in juxtaposition. They are especially aware of any phenomena which modify the shape of their cultivable area and the prospects for obtaining a return from it because of the limitations set by a high latitudinal frame. The appreciation of land upheaval is of long standing; the realisation of climatic fluctuation is of recent origin. A study of both is closely related to new methods of measurement and is pursued by specialists who are increasingly removed from geography. Sometimes investigation takes on the temporary form of an academic exercise, but it is regularly brought back to earth by the experience and observation of husbandmen who operate upon the margins of habitable country. And upon the margins of habitable country have worked such pioneers as Otto Pettersson who, from his hydrographic laboratory above Gulmarfiord, married the deep tidal behaviour of the sea and climatic fluctuations. In a way, he has been the initiator of much contemporary speculation in the north.[2]

[1] O. Rogstad, "Våre breers tilbakegang", *Norsk geografisk tidsskrift*, IX, 129–57.
[2] Cf. "Climatic Variations in Historic and Prehistoric Times", *Svenska hydrologisk-biologiska Kommissionens Skrifter*, **5**, 1912.

Chapter III

SETTING, RESOURCE AND SHORT-TERM PHYSICAL VARIATIONS

Winter cold—
  makes pathless wastes accessible for travellers and hunters, makes all seeds in the ground
  more fertile, makes both dry and live tree trunks split with a great noise, makes taverns,
  fairs and battles repair to the ice, makes Africans who have come as prisoners or otherwise to the North have short lives.

  Olaus Magnus, *De gentibus septentrionalibus*, 1554

A GEOGRAPHY OF WINTER

THE northern world is a completely different geographical concept in winter. With its contours changed by snow and ice, for all practical purposes the land may have a different shape. In its most severe manifestation, winter smothers the entire area in snow and may cover 420,000 sq. km. of the Baltic Sea with ice. The rigours of winter are neither experienced with equal intensity each year nor in the same year over all areas. Ten winters over the last 120 years stick in the mind or stand out in written documents as of remarkable severity: the three nearest at hand in 1940, 1942 and 1947. The certainty that winter months will enforce a new system of adjustments—both in national response and domestic detail—is one of the distinguishing features of the area. The degree of enforcement will naturally vary regionally. Thus, while winter temperatures in Stockholm may only average just below freezing-point, any Briton who spends the year in the northern half of Norway, Sweden or Finland will commonly find the relative severity and, certainly, the length of the winter the most impressive features of the climatic round. It is surprising that this physical transformation has not given birth to a thoroughgoing geography of winter.[1] This chapter, concentrating chiefly upon the effects of snowfall in Norway and ice obstruction in the Baltic, touches upon some of its materials.

THE IMPACT ON LAND

On land, winter makes its most striking visual impression in a snow cover of very variable depth and duration. Extreme contrasts are found in the possibility of July ski competitions on the high glaciers of south-west Norway and open-range grazing of sheep throughout the year in Jæran, where the winter may be snowless. By and large, snow depth correlates closely with annual precipitation, which in turn is related to altitude and location. Thus, there are corresponding adjustments on the Atlantic face of Scandinavia (where a winter maximum is commonly experienced in the precipitation régime) and the Baltic slope (which has a winter minimum). The snow blanket is therefore likely to vary appreciably in depth from west to east—metres in the western highlands being measured against centimetres on the Russian borders. Indeed, a snow deficiency may be one of the fears of the northern farmer and forester. The forester, in particular, recalls winters as "good" or "bad" according to the sufficiency or deficiency of snow. Within the highland area, there is also variation according to westward and eastward-facing slopes and according to latitude. Thus, Finnmark receives less snow than south-west Norway. The persistence of the snow cover is regionally differentiated by both temperature range and short-period change. The south of the area is more likely to be affected by the latter—not merely because of its southern location, but also because of its relative exposure to the Atlantic cyclonic systems. These depressions may bring to the central Baltic lands thaws which can have a positive effect on shipping or a negative result for farming.

[1] Cf. P. Deffontaines, *L'Homme et l'Hiver au Canada*, Paris, 1957, and a most interesting complement to this chapter, J. Bluthgen, "Der Winter in Nordeuropa", *Petermanns Geographische Mitteilungen*, **92**, 1948. This chapter has given rise to a book, W. R. Mead and Helmer Smeds, *Winter in Finland*, London, 1967.

The Scandinavian need to build up a system of snow forecasting upon past experiences against future contingencies has given rise to the publication of snow-accumulation data. Both the *Norwegian Meteorological Institute* and the *Swedish Meteorological and Hydro-graphical Institute* publish snow accumulation maps. In Norway, they are largely confined to the south and appear on January 31st, February 28th, March 31st and April 30th. The "normal period" set up as a standard of comparison is from 1901 to 1930, and there is a division of the approximately sixty recording stations according to their altitude (400, 800 and 1,200 m.). Snow quality as well as snow quantity has also to be considered—the classification according to its various degrees of hardness springing, *inter alia*, from the need to recognise criteria of resistance for clearance purposes.

The effect of winter is nowhere more evident than in the field of transport. It is naturally variable according to the stage of technical development. Winter conditions have eased transport in the past and continue to ease it at the more simple level of movement today. "In the summer", wrote a contributor on the Finns in the *Atlas maritimus et commercialis* (London, 1728):

"the people are, like prisoners, confined at home or near home, there being no travelling for the rivers and lakes, which are innumerable and some very largely impassable for want of bridges and boats, besides the soil is soft and miry, and the roads impassable, the heat not being sufficient at the hottest to dry up the sloughs and low wet grounds, so that the people keep at home . . . but in winter, which begins about October, the frost first hardening the surface moderately and the snows falling for several weeks with little or no intermission, nature puts on a new face. . . . Then [the inhabitants] begin to travel and carry on their needful affairs; and without troubling themselves about night or day, sea or land, rivers or lakes, dry land or wet, the face of the world being smooth and white, they ride in the sledges . . . carrying a compass with them for their way, wrapt in warm furs for the weather and a bottle of *aqua vitæ* for their inside."

The precise contribution made by snow to winter transport in a part of Sweden has been investigated by N. Friberg—who demonstrates the midwinter peak of goods traffic moving to

and from such places as Falköping and Skänninge in the eighteenth century.[1] Everywhere the runner challenges or replaces the wheel in daily movement. On milk wagon or dung cart (which transports manure to the arable land over snow and ice), on push-chair and perambulator, the runner rules. The most ubiquitous form of personal transport, in country districts at any rate, is the "spark" or chair on runners, which is propelled like a scooter.

The ski also has its home in the north—militarily as well as economically. Four centuries ago, Gustav I of Sweden was writing to Claus Fleming about the establishment of the first ski regiment. It is a reflection upon the nature of the winter countryside that a citizen of Oslo, Stockholm or Helsinki might comment in an average February—"There is nothing to stop you from ski-ing from here to Lapland." The ski still has its essential uses for rural movement (especially towards the margins of the modern economy), but it has also occasioned the rise of a new industry in its own right. The growing winter sports industry in Norway, Sweden and Finland is, in some ways, already international in character. It has assumed such a social function that schools have their midwinter ski holiday, and it has acquired a professionalism unrivalled in the Alps. At the same time it makes a direct contribution to the understanding of the winter land. Snow duration becomes a vital consideration for the holiday maker,[2] while all ski-field literature aids the understanding of the fells.

The winter land continues to give birth to its own winter route-ways, which complement or supplement the permanent network. Such winter-ways are commonly shown on topographic maps in Norway, Sweden and Finland. Historically, they are most closely related to frozen water-ways (with their superficial snow burden). Gunnar Hoppe has prepared a map which illustrates the known winter-ways of Norrbotten (cf. his Plate VI), and has even complemented this with a division between the zone of horse and reindeer traction. Winter-

---

[1] *Vägarna i Västernorrlands län*, Stockholm, 1951, p. 276 *et seq.*
[2] Cf. *Norges skiforenings årbok*, 1941, which included a map of south Norway showing with isopleths the areas in which ski-ing conditions prevailed for 10, 10–20 and over 20 weeks. It was based upon thirty years' meteorological observations.

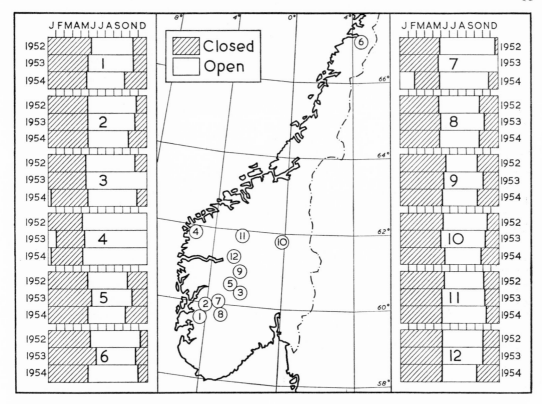

FIG. 13. The open and closed period on twelve major Norwegian highways in three recent years.

ways have gained a different importance with the coming of the automobile; they are a major problem at the time of freeze and break up. In the Swedish province of Norrland, for example, there are over 100 ferries which must be replaced in winter by plank or timber roads across the ice. The minimum ice depth required to ensure a safe car passage is 20 cm.; 35 cm. are required for a three-ton lorry or a tractor.[1] A new form of transport is partly conquering the open snowscapes of the north. *Rutebok for Norge*, the Norwegian *Bradshaw*, listed seven snowmobile routes on Finnmarksvidda operating from January to April 1956, the longest being from Alta to Kautokeino (195 km.).

Snowfall is not, however, "as welcome as ten rains" to all; though, as Yrjö Kokko reminds us, it may be to some. It levies a great

tax upon the modern highway and railway. This tax was already sensed over a century ago as speedier communications were being urged upon the Northern Countries. For instance, the Norwegian Highway Law of 1824 required that "as soon as there are 8 or 9 inches of snow, a snow plough must be used" on main roads. The snow burden, indeed, is heaviest in Norway—a land burden which offers an interesting complement to the sea burden of ice which afflicts Finland.[2] Sweden shares the affliction of the two, though in neither instance is the impact so widespread. The northern two-thirds of Sweden are largely "snow shadow" country; much of southern Sweden escapes the winter freeze in an average winter.

A winter policy is being gradually evolved on the Norwegian highway system. On the score of past meteorological experience and

[1] Cf. *Svenska vägföreningens tidskrift*, 1940, 10. See also G. Hoppe, *Vägarna inom Norrbottens län*, Uppsala, 1945, Fig. 67, p. 325.
[2] Though the official statistics of Finland record that over four million kilometres are covered by snow-ploughs in an average winter.

TABLE I

SNOW OBSTRUCTION AND CLEARANCE COSTS

Tract	Length in km.	Snow in cu. m.	Hours employed	Total cost N.Kr.	kr/ cu. m.	kr/km.
Haukelifjell .	29·3	173,000	300	53,550	0·31	1,830
Strynsfjellet .	3·8	19,000	65	12,733	0·67	3,350
Sognefjell .	13·0	30,000	90	16,430	0·55	1,264
Hemsedalsfjellet .	18·0	13,000	48	7,817	0·60	434

Source: *Meddelser fra vegdirektøren*, 1951, **6**.

prevailing meteorological conditions, decisions must be reached annually upon which roads to keep open and which roads to leave closed, upon when to relinquish the fight against snow closure and when to further the process of snow disappearance. Fig. 13 shows the situation prevailing over main fell routes in three recent winters. Their closure implies a complete cessation of traffic. Aids to clearance will be employed according to the intensity of traffic normally following such highways, as well as according to the particular snow conditions prevailing. Table I balances the cost of mechanical clearance against the volume of snow obstructing certain Norwegian fell roads in a fairly usual spring (1950).

Such clearance operations represent the exceptional local attempts to hasten forward the final spring thaw. They may be retarded until June, as Fig. 13 shows. Side by side with them must be remembered the continuous efforts required to maintain serviceability on the average run of roads not subject to closure (or only subject to closure for a short period). On an average, the winter maintenance of roads amounts to about 15% of the total annual outlay on Norwegian highways. Experience during the last twenty years shows that the figure has been variable between 7% and 25%. Outlay may vary from more than 30% in the most difficult provinces, such as Troms, 1948–9, to 4% in the most favoured, such as Rogaland, 1948–9.[1] To bring such costs down to a tangible figure, it may be added that the average cost of snow clearance per kilometre of maintained highway exceeds

200 Norwegian kroner (£10). It has been estimated that the cost of winter maintenance in Sweden is well in excess of 100 million kronor for an average winter; while a winter with heavy snows may even cost Denmark more than this.[2] Snowdrift estimates were widely investigated at the time when the Bergen railway was finally projected, and alternate routes to the so-called Midtfjellslinjen were considered by way of Hardanger and Sogn. The extra 50–100 km. of track were balanced against the cost of keeping open the high fell route above Voss. It was by a stroke of irony that the first train to follow the track, bearing a load of civic and transport dignitaries, unceremoniously stuck in a snowdrift.[3] The continuing challenge of high fell weather is the theme of Nordahl Grieg's poem *The Night Train*. Denmark, although very marginal to the area of snow disturbance, is not unaffected. Sample maps to show traffic irregularity or stoppage on Danish railways have been prepared by A. Aagesen.[4]

Winter highway management is an increasingly elaborate art, and experiences of it are widely shared between high-latitude lands. Management embraces direct snow removal and indirect checks to snow accumulation. The improved snow-plough has done much to aid resistance to snow closure. A modern snow-plough is able to remove at least half a metre of snow at a rate of 10 km. per hour, while simultaneously compacting the snow-wall. An increasingly elaborate art of snow fencing also checks snow accumulation. Open fences are currently regarded as more

[1] *Meddelelser fra vegdirektøren*, 1951, **7**.
[2] *Ibid.*, 1947, **1, 2.** The feasibility of "atomic" heating of streets in urban areas is seriously discussed.
[3] E. Østved, *De norske jernbaners historie*, Oslo, 1954, II, 254.
[4] *Geografiske studier over jernbanerne i Danmark*, Copenhagen, 1949, Maps 5 and 6.

effective than closed; but a variety of protective features parallels railways and roadways. Hedgerows are planted for snow protection; for example around Aabenraa in south Jutland, where broad spruce shelters have been established. In north Sweden, birch trees may be planted in association with fixed snow fences. Lava-stone walls are found in Iceland performing a snow-shelter function. Snow fencing is a permanent capital investment and is subject to marked regional variations. In Norway, outlay is greatest in Troms, south Trøndelag and Finnmark. Relative costs of outlay in Sweden show a third as much to be spent on snow fences as upon snow clearance. Snow sheds and snow shelters are in many respects more important for the protection of railways than roads. The elaborate arrangement of snow sheds on the Bergen line is a reaction to high fell weather and a means of overcoming the threat to hindrance from snow slide as well as snow fall.

Power-line and telephone present another type of communication subject to winter disturbance. The rime frost, sleet and ice storms to which maritime Norway is peculiarly susceptible are a serious affliction for all overhead cables.[1] The spacing of pylons, improvements in their structure, competition between aluminium alloy and copper wires are all expressions of a search for greater tensility under conditions of winter stress. In recent years, meteorological co-operation has been sought in the selection of routes to be followed by some lines; for example, those of Aura, Røssåga, Vinstra and Hols. Special meteorological observation-posts have even been established; for example, the Holbrudalen post in connection with the proposed transmission line from Lyse to Østlandet. Here, in November 1953, an ice accretion of 50 kg. per hanging metre—or 7·5 tons per 150-m. span—was recorded. Up to 10 kg. per metre of cable is not unusual. If it is recalled that spans of several hundred metres are common (in Vardal a span of 680 m. across the sea occurs), cable and pylon damage can be appreciated. In planning transmission routes, distance must be constantly balanced against the susceptibility to icing of a particular terrain.

Low-temperature conditions prevailing throughout the north also demand widespread domestic adjustments. Conservation of heat has never been so carefully approached as to-day. In an extended letter to the Bishop of Durham in 1778, J. G. King wrote from Karelia: "in the houses of persons of quality the windows are caulked up against winter and commonly have double glass frames". Today, windows are commonly sealed with tape on the inside, and even triple glass may be found. The eighteenth-century traveller who was told that "we can protect ourselves better against the cold than others against the heat" is complemented by the English resident in a Scandinavian industrial town who declared in her draughtless home: "The best way to get pneumonia is to lift the telephone." Heat conservation reaches such remarkable refinement that in town flats which have fireplaces (for ornamental use) chimney tops are only opened on request to the caretaker. J. Keränen has prepared an isothermal map for Finland to show the amount of heat required to offset winter cold. It is a revealing document; for, in the absence of alternative sources of fuel, it represents a tax upon firewood proportionate to the degree of cold in a locality. On the personal level, the incidence of winter is perhaps measured by the number of men who wear fur. John Atkinson's attractive sketch of a Finlander selling his wares, shows that 150 years ago even the street vendor had his sheepskin coat; while on contemporary icebreakers or steamers plying the midwinter Baltic passage, a sailor in a bearskin coat is not an unusual sight. In Norway, Sweden and Finland, a fur hat with ear-muffs is part of the regular army clothing issue.

Animals, too, must be protected. Two hundred years ago, during his visit to Little Gaddesden, in Hertfordshire, Pehr Kalm wrote on the differences between the English farmer and the Swedish farmer. He drew particular attention to the comparative mildness of the English winters, the outdoor pasturing of animals and the general absence of indoor

[1] *Elektroteknisk tidsskrift*, 1954, 26; A. Nyberg, "Om frostbildningar", *Teknisk Tidskrift*, 1942, 178–83; J. Schaefer, "Final Report on Icing Research", *General Electric Research Laboratory*, 1946.

housing during the winter months. Disproportionate investment in large farm buildings has always been an affliction for the northern farmer. Today he economises in labour as well as money by centralising everything in a unitary building. Daily feeding and watering of stock—eased to a limited extent by piped water—remain a major consumer of time.

Once it has established itself, the winter pole of cold over north-eastern Scandinavia and Finland is a noticeably persistent phenomenon. Compilations of frost quantity maps have been of increasing interest to North European engineers[1], for frost penetrates deeply into the ground and may linger for a considerable time. It is more persistent in some soils than others —especially so in bogland soils. The Finnish geographer, Väinö Auer, who began his scientific work as a peatland investigator in Canada, has declared that everywhere in his country where one encounters bogland one encounters a miniature Lapland. The same is true of similar areas of Sweden and much of Norway. Peatland investigators have demonstrated that only during warm summers do boglands entirely thaw out in such stretches as Kainu in north-east Finland. Although the idea of eighteenth-century academic husbandmen—that summer frosts spring from peatland—is now generally discounted, there is undoubted local association. Jacob Bonsdorff, a sentimental traveller in the 1790s, remarked upon the midwinter cold of midsummer mines; the cold of winter is certainly imprisoned in the underground tunnels of Kiruna in midsummer. Glaciologists, investigating ice occurrence in the core of excavated eskers in north-eastern Finland, declare it to have been persistent since the retreat of the ice-sheet. For the engineer, a whole series of problems—each with its direct economic consequences—spring from this frost intensity. *Tele* is a Norwegian word meaning "the crust of frozen ground or earth" which lacks a precise English counterpart. Frost penetration—and its spring reduction—affect all highway and railway tracks. An important aspect of route-way engineering is what is called *telehivingsarbeider*—maintenance work

in connection with soil freeze.[2] A careful selection of road-bed and appropriate drainage is one means of overcoming the problems caused by frost action and frost heaving. This is an issue particularly associated with peatland conditions.

Ice lingers longer than snow lies. Snowmelt transmits a direct springtime effect to the river régime of the northern world. The break-up of ice lifts the discharge of inland waterways to an absolute peak in May or early June according to the locality. Even though the run-off is retarded by the timber cover over the greater part of the country, this phenomenon has widespread flooding as its accompaniment. In lake district and archipelago, where island farms and residences are common, inhabitants are marooned when the ice neither bears nor breaks.

The arrival and departure of winter command increasingly the attention of meteorologists in this corner of the world which has done so much to promote weather studies. They are not satisfactorily measurable by specific rules; for the most part, they are best assessed by phenological records. Phenological observations have been made irregularly and sporadically over all Northern Europe since the stimulus to observation in the natural world prompted by Linnæus. Parish priest, provincial governor or apothecary made their local observations; sometimes publishing them in the incipient series of learned societies. Considerable impulse was given to phenological observations at the meeting of the British Association for the Advancement of Science held in 1841. A body of local information on the seasonal appearance or disappearance of phenomena now complements the scientifically measurable features assembled by weather-recording stations. It enables some boundaries to be set to what is still loosely known as "winter".

THE IMPACT AT SEA [3]

One of the most outstanding features of the northern winter is the freezing of the sea. This made a strong impression upon early topographers like Olaus Magnus, though he was

[1] *Meddelelser fra vegdirektøren*, 1944, **5**.
[2] There are standard chapters on this phenomenon in K. Heje, *Vei og Jernbanebygging*, Oslo, 1941.
[3] I am much indebted to Dr. H. Simojoki of *Merentutkimuslaitos*, Helsinki, for criticism of this section.

more alert to the opportunities for warfare which it offered than the restraints upon trade which it imposed. Woodcuts in his book descend to the minutiæ of ice crystals; at the other end of the scale, his *Carta marina* attempted for the first time to show the distribution of winter ice in the Baltic arena. Historical texts again make much play with such events as the freezing of the Great Belt in 1658, when Charles X and his army crossed the ice from Fyn to Sjælland, and with the ice bridges across the Åland Sea and Quarken in 1808–9, which enabled Russian troops to cross to Umeå and exposed the archipelago of Uppland to their harrying. These outstanding events in the political geography of the north, however, are given disproportionate emphasis to the multitude of smaller incidents in the economic geography which ripple less discernibly the face of history. The sea has become progressively more important for the progress and well-being of the northern peoples. They are today as dependent upon the freedom of the seas in the political sense as in Great Britain; they are at the same time dependent upon the freedom of the seas in a physical sense. To a greater or lesser extent, all five Northern Countries are affected by the icing of their surrounding waters. The impact naturally differs in each country—with Norway and Iceland least implicated and Finland most affected. To the extent that their daily life has become integrated with lands across the seas, their individual economies will be sensitive to beleaguering by winter ice.

The process of icing—of inland waterways as well as seas—is variable according to a number of conditions. The brackish water of the inner Baltic submits more easily to the freeze than the saltier waters around Denmark. Again, the slightness of the tidal range in the inner Baltic minimises turbulence in the water-mass. Relative stillness of the atmosphere with the development of a winter centre of high pressure over the continent reduces water movement and wave formation to a minimum. Snowfall in association with low temperatures results in the formation of surface slush (known as *grødis*—or soupy ice, in

the descriptive Danish terminology), which much hastens the freeze. Wind direction will also affect local freezing and thawing. Frequently, for example, an east wind implies frosts, so that eastward-facing coasts may suffer during its persistence in comparison with westward-facing coasts.

The accumulation of a body of material on the behaviour of sea ice has been increasingly important for the regular operation of sea routes in the Baltic. From the end of the eighteenth century, Swede and Russian were much concerned with the preparation of marine charts; from the end of the nineteenth century, Swede, Russian and Finn have been exercised by the interpretation of ice data. Although a system of posting arrangements was made for regular mail transport across the Åland Sea in the eighteenth century (with a variety of signals to indicate the security of the ice between Signilskär and Grisslehamn), no winter shipping connection was projected until 1839. The tax of winter was summed up for this area in Biorman's road book in 1776—"from October 14 to April 14, double is paid on the Åland ferry" (p. 46). Material dealing with the route is literary rather than scientific, for no Tycho Brahe ever sat in Åland keeping a meteorological diary as in the Danish Sound. Travellers such as Joseph Acerbi (Plate 9a) and Edward Clark have left graphic accounts of the winter post route, traversed in cold "so that there was reason to apprehend the freezing of the blood in the veins". The first regular mail route on the Baltic to defy the winter was the Swedish service started in 1858 between Västervik and Visby. Today, it is known whether the coast is dead or alive to shipping from the presence or absence of flashing beacons. And it was, in the first place, directives to lighthouse keepers which set in motion more detailed ice observations. In 1838, a Russian instruction ordered lighting or extinction of beacons according to whether or not the field commanded by the lighthouse was ice covered. A few years later, Skagen lighthouse signalled to passing vessels the state of the ice in the Danish Sound and Belts.[1]

[1] Historical notes on the evolution of Danish ice records are given in C. I. H. Speerschneider, "Om Isforholdenei danske Farvande, 690–1860, 1861–1906", *Publications of Danish Meteorological Institute*, 2, Copenhagen, 1915; 6, 1927.

Scientific organisation of reporting awaited the latter part of the nineteenth century. In 1871, regular ice observations were established in Swedish lighthouses.[1] Russia followed suit in 1888, and Finland began its observations independently in 1893 at the newly created winter port of Hanko. International co-ordination of observations was encouraged by a consideration of the problem of icing at the Congress of Natural Scientists in Stockholm in 1898. Before long, passenger ships negotiating winter waters were invited to prepare ice-maps along their routes. Initiation of the three primary and persistent lines of research —the pattern of fast-ice, the behaviour of drift-ice and the formation of pressured ice— belongs to the last decade of the nineteenth century. Evidence of a specific geographical interest in these phenomena is found in the series of ice-maps which were prepared for the *Atlas of Finland* (1910). These found their culmination in one of the earliest published ice atlases by Risto Jurva (Helsinki, 1937) and its related text.

As soon as the detail of information became of international interest, issues of terminology presented themselves. First of all, a code of ice conditions was called for—to be finally drawn up at the Fifth Hydrological Congress of the Baltic States in 1936.[2] Two complementary codes—each with some ten specific categories—were formulated. The first referred to ice conditions; the second to the effect of these conditions on navigation. The ten categories of navigability, as defined, proceed from "Navigation possible for steamers, difficult for sailing vessels", through "Navigation difficult to low-powered vessels, closed to sailing vessels", to "Navigation possible for vessels constructed to withstand ice". One outcome of the Baltic Hydrological Commission was a so-called Baltic Ice Week (February 12th to 18th, 1938), at which ice log-books were allocated to all vessels trafficking in Baltic waters.

The terminology of ice conditions is only one of the problems of definition; the language of ice—still unsatisfactorily translated at the international level—demands further refinement. Ice terms have taxed international investigators for a full generation. Recommendations by the Commission for Maritime Meteorology are still not universally acceptable or appropriate. Within their suggestions, five groups of terms are distinguishable.[3] They begin with the terminology of the initial freeze—the first suggestion of ice, for example, is acceptably translated as the "ice film"—a skin but a few millimetres in thickness and quite distinguishable from the "ice rind", which is measured in centimetres. In the Central Baltic the Swedish term *blåis* (Finnish, *sinijää*) is commonly employed to define younger ice of from 5 to 15 cm. But the English expression "blue ice" refers specifically to the oldest and hardest ice found in the glacier! The second group of terms covers the fast-ice, which forms for the most part a broad, smooth girdle around the coast. The principal quality of fast-ice is its immobility, and it can develop in the open sea in the absence of wind. The descriptive Swedish word *fastisbrygga* (firm ice-bridge) belongs to this category, and is the formation which binds together island to mainland or island to island. Thirdly, there are drift-ice terms. Drift-ice usually refers to broken pieces of flat ice commonly more than 10 cm. thick—which may sometimes be "rafted" or laminated in a series of layers. This most commonly encountered marine ice form calls for specific definition of degrees of "openness". Four categories are usually defined—from very open ($\frac{1}{8}$-$\frac{1}{4}$ coverage) to very close ($\frac{7}{8}$ coverage or more)—with corresponding terms "heavy" and "easy" to describe navigation within it. Pressured ice is the fourth main category and results from movement set in motion by wind. Pressured ice is usually ridged around fast-ice—in one or more successive zones of disturbance according to wind conditions at the time of freezing. Such ridges vary in altitude up to a maximum of about 6 m. Finally, there is a range of terms appropriate to the period of the ice-melt. At

[1] The Swedish picture is summarised statistically in C. J. Ostman, "Isförhållandena vid Sveriges kuster, 1870–1935", *Proc. of State Meteorological Institute*, 6, 6, Stockholm, 1937.
[2] They are translated into English in E. Palosuo, "Treatise on Severe Ice Conditions in the Central Baltic" *Publications of Marine Research Institute*, 156, Helsinki, 1953.
[3] *Abridged Final Report of the World Meteorological Organisation*, 10, 2, Geneva, 1952.

sea, as well as on land, there is a veritable language of winter, the vocabulary of which is tied to place and necessarily lacks precise English counterparts.[1]

Today, the changing picture of the Baltic ice scene is composed principally by the marine and meteorological research institutes of Sweden and Finland, centred in Stockholm and Helsinki respectively. Peripheral contributions are added by Germany, Denmark and—for the Skaggerak —by Norway. The behaviour of ice in Russian territorial waters is a closed book. In some respects there has been a retreat from the situation of twenty years ago, when a framework for producing synoptic charts of Baltic conditions was presented to the Hydrological Conference in 1936. The framework and the shore reporting stations are outlined in Fig. 14.

The charts of the inner Baltic conditions are prepared weekly at the present time; daily for certain areas if demand occasions it. They

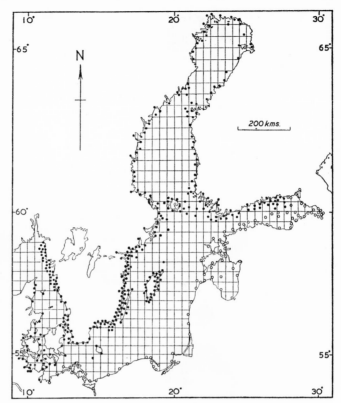

FIG. 14. The framework and shore reporting stations (black circles) for ice-mapping and reporting in the Baltic arena.

are the result of combining a varied range of source material. First of all, harbours in the ice-affected areas submit daily reports to their national central institute. Secondly, all shipping entering these harbours reports on ice experiences encountered; while radio reports are also dispatched from sea-going vessels. Thirdly, when proceeding on their particular missions, ice-breakers supply radio reports. Fourthly, there is an increasingly valuable source of information from air services. Initially, flights were made by aircraft on emergency or extraordinary missions.[2] Thus, the search for icebound steamers or the provisioning of marooned vessels provided a motive for accumulating ice information. In the 1930s the Finnish Air Force initiated reconnaissance flights over the Gulf of Finland

and sketched, for the first time, their observations on maps 1:400,000. Swedish commercial aircraft began regular ice reporting on the Visby route in 1940, and subsequently on their Central European flights; while German military aircraft accumulated much material (destroyed in Hamburg in 1944) during 1940–2. The multiplication of civil air services in the post-war period has provided a source of information which has greatly increased the accuracy of forecasting ice developments and management of winter shipping. The synoptic charts resulting from this pooled material are distributed among North European port authorities and such commercial concerns in the Scandinavian countries, Germany and the United Kingdom as are interested. The material is of practical value not only to

[1] Cf. W. R. Mead, "The Language of Place", *Geographical Studies*, I, London, 1953.
[2] Cf. J. Büdel, "Das Luftbild im Dienste der Eisforschung und Eiserkundung" *Zeitschri t d. Ges. f. Erdk. z. Berlin*, Vols. 7, 8, 9, 10, Berlin, 1943.

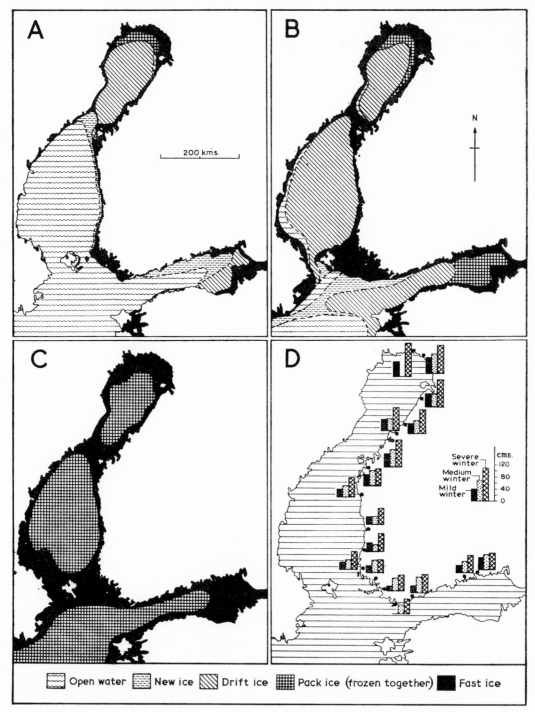

Open water   New ice   Drift ice   Pack ice (frozen together)   Fast ice

FIG. 15. The diagrams show ice conditions in (A) a mild winter (B) an average winter (C) a hard winter. (D) illustrates the ice conditions at the approaches to Finland's chief ports in winters of different severity. (Based on R. Juva, *Ice Atlas*, Helsinki, 1937.)

shipping agencies but also to insurance organisations, the maritime risks of which are assessed according to the "Baltic Warranty" of Lloyds.[1]

Fig. 15 summarises ice conditions in the Baltic. The extent of ice in the middle of a normal winter and the usual period of ice closure for the major ports around the twin gulfs are shown jointly. The extent of different kinds of ice recalls the need for definitive terms; the monthly circles for the ports illustrate the substantially differing period of ice closure between the head of the gulfs and the central Baltic. The major objection to such a concise summary of the ice situation is its wholly static and therefore largely fictitious character. The ice situation is continuously changing and rarely more than momentarily repetitive from year to year. On the basis of accumulated observations, Swedish and Finnish ice reporters have built up formulæ—with accepted stages of development which can be mathematically expressed —to cover the regional extent of icing. In thickness, the ice-sheet will tend to increase from south to north. Three-quarters of a century of Swedish experience shows that the average ice thickness for the central Baltic coast is about 25–30 cm.; for the coast of the Bothnian Sea, about 50 cm.; the Bothnian Gulf, 70–75 cm. Maximum thickness of ice for the coast of Norrland may reach well over 150 cm. The maximum depth of icing will be reached in different areas at different periods —by mid-February on the west, south and south-east coasts; March 10th in the Bothnian Sea and March 15th in the Bothnian Gulf. The old English adage—"as the day lengthens so the cold strengthens"—might with truth be transferred to this area.

The occurrence of ice is a certain fact, but the distribution, depth and duration of ice occurrence are highly variable. The absolute variation between the minimum of 60,000 square kilometres of frozen Baltic and a maximum of seven times this area illustrates the range. Given observations over an extended period, it is possible to conjecture certain sequences of development. Thus, ice forecasting becomes an extension of weather forecasting, though based rather more upon the experience of past situations, especially in more localised areas. From the commercial point of view, it is the extreme conditions rather than the average which command attention. The delayed closure or opening of particular harbours can have marked effects upon local budgets. The coming of the iron-hulled, screw steamer in itself has tended to lengthen the effective open period of ports— especially in association with reliable reports concerning ice distribution. Lack of knowledge in former times greatly affected the movements of trading vessels. A letter from a Hull trader to J. V. Snellman of Oulu ran: "There will always be difficulty in getting English ships to proceed to Uleåborg or other ports high up in the Gulf of Bothnia." Commercial correspondence is littered with experiences like that of a ship chartered by Dresser & Co. of London in November 1851. In order to slip through the enclosing ice-packs, the vessel had to cast overboard 1,500 barrels of tar. Naval records during the Baltic campaigns of 1854–5 show similar nervousness on the part of the fleet, which carefully retreated five or six weeks before any real ice risk was normally manifested. Incidentally, international telegraph systems were first employed at that time to report on Baltic ice conditions. As reopening of the waters approached, consuls in Danzig, Kiel and Copenhagen reported daily on such information as they were able to acquire from local shipping.[2] The steamship, indeed, was the first stage towards the continuity of winter routes. For Finland, it was the preliminary to the creation of a special winter harbour. In the 1870s, a state port was created at the point least susceptible to the winter freeze—Hanko (Hangö) peninsula.

The steamship in association with the ice-breaker has substantially modified the situation in marginal areas and at the sensitive period preceding final closure or complete opening. The periodical publications of the

---

[1] "Isbrytningens ordnande längs Norrlandskusten", *State Publications, Dept. of Commerce*, 31, 1948, Stockholm, lists six groups of vessel according to their ice worthiness. Marine insurance institutions also have a similar classification of vessels.

[2] Cf. W. R. Mead, "Hundra år efteråt", *Finsk Tidskrift*, CLVI, 3, 1954.

TABLE 2
ICE CONDITIONS IN A MODERATE WINTER, 1945–6

	Tornio	Yxpila	Helsinki	Kotka
First ice . . .	Nov. 10	Nov. 10	Dec. 3	Nov. 10
Harbour frozen . .	Nov. 15	Dec. 1	Dec. 17	Dec. 2
Last steamer . . .	Oct. 28	Dec. 24	(Open all	Jan. 14
First steamer . . .	June 6	May 10	winter)	April 16
Last harbour ice . .	May 23	May 7	April 24	May 3
Last ice in adjacent sea .	May 23	May 27	April 24	May 3

(Source: *Marine Research Institute Publications*, **154**, Helsinki, 1952, p. 44.)

Marine Research Institute of Helsinki give some indication of these marginal periods and the situation for sail versus steamships: though today sailing vessels play a minor role in international trade and are only of continuing importance in cabotage.

It will be observed that, in certain instances, harbours are free of ice before their adjacent seas are navigable.[1] This fact recalls the drifting of ice-floes in the open waters consequent upon wind changes. Twenty years of detailed observation of Finnish ports shows that the average maximum period of closure by ice is four-fifths as great as a minimum average. In certain instances, the maximum number of ice days is substantially more than twice as great as the minimum number (for example, Ronnskär, in the Vaasa archipelago, 78:189). The maximum number of ice days is not, however, the sole criterion. The thickness and form of the ice which obstructs a particular port is of considerable consequence. Before the days of steel and steam, a port was closed by ice irrespective of whether the ice cover was six or sixty centimetres. Today, open channels are maintained to ports commonly out of commission for six months of the year a century ago. Turku, with its daily steamer service to Stockholm, is a case in point. Icing statistics for Turku harbour indicate the median of the first freezing to be December 21st, the permanent ice-sheet to last from January 18th until April 11th, and ice to disappear a few days later. The open channel created between the Åland archipelago and Turku harbour is a virtual canal, with solid ice on either side strong enough to bear the weight of a pilot's car or tractor to within a few yards of the

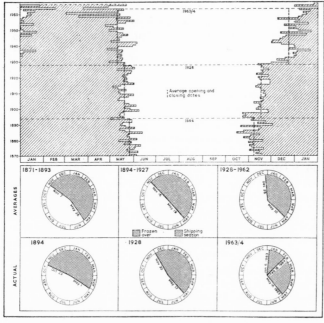

FIG. 16. The Shipping Season at Piteå, 1871–1963/4. (I am grateful to Mr. Ian Layton for permission to reproduce this diagram, which is based on the harbour returns of the port of Piteå.)

[1] Cf. "The Time for Freezing and Ice Break-up on the Finnish Coast for the Winters 1934–53", ed. H. Simojoki, *Marine Research Institute Publications*, **160**, Helsinki, 1953.

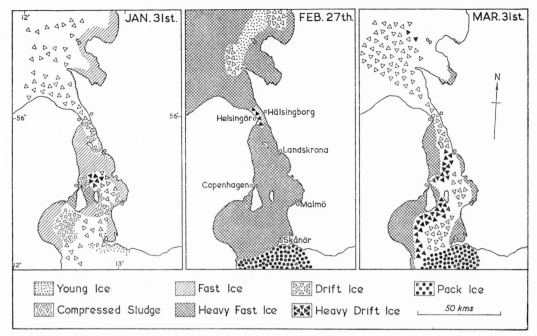

FIG. 17. Ice conditions in the Öresund in an extreme winter, 1946–7. (Source: G. H. Liljequist, *Communications of the Swedish Meteorological Institute*, B.5, Stockholm, 1947.)

passenger vessels. According to the statistical handbook, Hanko harbour is also "closed" from January 23rd until March 27th.

Independently of its depth, the form of coastal icing can substantially affect accessibility. A narrow zone of pack-ice, banded together through wave action, can be an obstruction greater than a broad stretch of sea ice. This fact helps to explain the situation in Fig. 16, where Helsinki is depicted in its winter setting. Accessibility may not be denied by conditions within the harbour, but beyond the harbour. The role of the ice-breaker is especially important for ports such as Helsinki which are marginal to the winter ice. By contrast, it is a physical impossibility to keep open most Bothnian ports throughout the winter: yet, with the aid of an ice-breaker it is possible to keep open all ports longer than would otherwise be the case, and to keep some ports open all the time in some winters (cf. Plate 9(*b*)). The saga of the struggle with ice in the inner Baltic is one not well known outside its encircling shores.[1]

While the freeze in the inner Baltic is a regular phenomenon, the Baltic estuary freezes only occasionally. In severe winters the entrances to the Baltic submit to low temperatures according to their width and depth as well as the nature of their currents. In general, the Sound is the least submissive. However, hard winters—in the language of the North, *isvintrarna* (ice-winters)—do occasionally bring shipping to a standstill in the Sound. Fig. 17 illustrates the response of the Sound to the hard winter of 1946–7.

The effects of the ice cover are transmitted immediately to overseas trade. They will vary from country to country, not only according to the severity of the impact, but also according to the degree of openness of the coast-line. Thus, the absolute effect upon Finland is more serious than that upon Sweden. An approximate estimate would suggest that two-thirds of Finland's foreign trade moves between May and October, one-third between November and April.[2] This figure will be widely variable from port to port.

[1] From the Finnish viewpoint it is told in H. Ramsay, *I Kamp med Österjöns Isar*, Helsingfors, 1947.
[2] W. R. Mead, "Finland and the Winter Freeze", *Geography*, 1939, 221–9.

TABLE 3

MEAN ICEBREAKER COSTS PER SHIPPED TON FOR EACH GROUP OF HARBOURS IN FINLAND
FOR THE 5-YEAR PERIOD 1959–60 to 1963–4.

(The figures are converted into new Finnish marks)

1959–60 1963–4	Kemi– Raahe	Ykspihlaja– Vaasa	Kaskinen– Uusikaupunki	Naantali– Turku	Hanko– Helsinki	Valko– Hamina	Finland
November	0·08	—	—	—	—	—	0·01
December	1·72	0·61	—	—	—	0·06	0·23
Sanuary	5·38	2·51	0·27	0·07	0·13	0·32	0·48
February	3·93	4·04	1·09	0·46	0·63	0·94	0·85
March	18·57	4·02	1·28	1·09	1·04	1·10	1·19
April	14·28	2·36	0·49	0·36	0·30	0·28	0·48
May	0·92	0·22	0·03	—	0·01	0·02	0·11
November– May	1·28	0·99	0·38	0·27	0·28	0·27	0·39

Source, E. Palosuo, "The Share of Ice Breaking Expenses in Winter Navigation", *Terra*, **78**, 4, 1966.

In Sweden, the same picture prevails for the ports north of Stockholm—and a third of Sweden's overseas trade by volume is related to Norrland. Sweden, however, has other outlets rarely disturbed by ice on the west coast; though transport costs will curtail their use for more than a limited number of commodities.

Stock-piling is a common practice in ports closed by ice. When maritime outlets are closed, it is theoretically possible for extensive areas of north Sweden to use Trondheim (over Storlien) as an export harbour. The fuller development of Trondheim to meet such a need has been the subject of a recent Swedo-Norwegian agreement. In the inter-war period, Finland contemplated the development of Liinahamari on the Arctic coast as its ice-free port, and plans were made for a railway-line to link the harbour with Finnish Lapland via the Petsamo corridor. Under war-time conditions the fiord heads of north Norway have provided the supply routes for Finland. Thus, during the First World War, cotton to keep the spindles of Tampere operating was imported by sleigh over Skibotn to the railhead of Rovaniemi. The most outstanding orientation of an export route is referred to in another connection. Fig. 88 indicates that two-thirds of the ore exported from Kiruna-Luossavaara moves over ice-free Narvik; one-third, over ice-affected Luleå.

As a general rule, commodity traffic is re-oriented where its volume is high enough to withstand the new transport costs. Refined commodities rather than raw materials are more likely to move. A specific example of seasonal redirection is given by Auvo Säntti in a study of Finnish rail traffic.[1] Fig. 18 employs statistics of cellulose dispatched from three primary Bothnian producing centres—Kemi, Oulu and Toppila. In Sweden, a corresponding redirection of pulp export to Göteborg takes place. These seasonal changes in the boundaries of port hinterlands provide good examples of a physical impact upon an economic feature.

Into the picture of port management, the ice-breaker enters to reduce or prevent the restraints of winter. Today, ice-breaker employment follows an established routine and one which is complementary to adjustments in commodity transport. The ice-breaker fleet of Sweden begins operations at the head of the Gulf of Bothnia; that of Finland is divided between the headwaters of the two gulfs. As winter strengthens, the divided Finnish fleet moves from north to south in the Gulf of Bothnia and from east to west in the Gulf of Finland. The deployment of ice-breakers in midwinter is variable according to the severity of the freeze. Under relaxed winter conditions, attention is directed to the harbours—

[1] "Railway Traffic in Finland from Centres of Population to Export Ports in 1948", *Publications of Turku Geographical Institute*, 25, Turku, 1952.

PLATE 7. THE DUNE COAST OF WEST JUTLAND

PLATE 8. THE NORTH SEA PORT OF ESBJERG

Esbjerg, a red brick town tributary to the state-sponsored harbour (cf. Chapter VI).

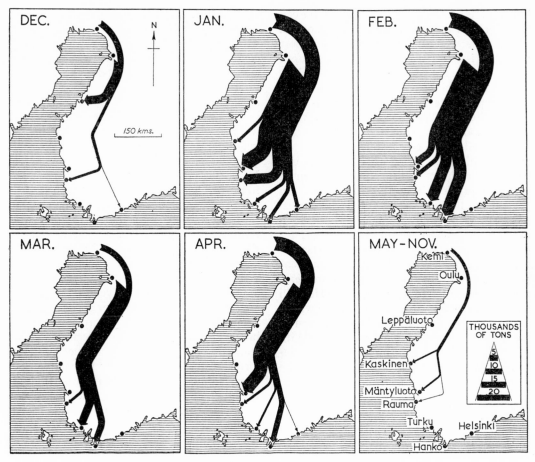

FIG. 18. Seasonal variations in the flow of overland exports from Kemi and Oulu. (Based on A. Säntti, *Publications of Turku Geographical Institute*, 25, 1952.)

such as Hamina, Mäntyluoto and Raumo. Here, approaches will be kept free of ice obstruction or vessels entering will be aided in their passage. Given more strenuous conditions, when "partial" winter harbours are out of commission, ice-breakers will operate in the Archipelago Sea, concentrating their attention upon those harbours it is planned to keep open. Ships using winter harbours and vessels receiving ice-breaker assistance pay appropriate dues.

Employment of ice-breakers will also be dependent upon the character of the ice-breaker fleet. Where there is limited capital, a choice must be made between various types of ice-breaker. Frequently the cost of one major vessel must be balanced against that of

several less highly powered craft which can only play a limited or local role. Policies must be balanced at the national level. In Finland, for example, the urge to tie up ice-breaker capital in Helsinki, Kotka and Hamina must be balanced against dispersed local assistance in ports which cannot hope to escape closure. Investment in deep-draught ice-breakers also automatically prohibits them from operating in the shallow loading-places which so frequently characterise the Baltic coasts. It is noticeable, for example, that thirty-eight of the significant loading-places on the Norrland coast are not accessible by the 4,330-ton ice-breaker *Ymer*.

The ice-breaker fleets are deployed from Helsinki in Finland and Stockholm in Sweden.

E G.—6

The local repercussions of central decisions can be difficult for the operation of port economies. Thus, the status of the entire body of port personnel is affected by the decision to open or close a "partial winter port". Where harbours are definitely closed, port labour can make appropriate arrangements for the duration of closure. Where uncertainty prevails, long periods of unemployment or underemployment may occur. These may be recurrent within the period of winter shipping. The seasonal disposal of surplus port labour is a regular problem in northern harbours. In general, port labour is neither readily transferable nor willingly mobile. There is a measure of transference of dock labour, for example, from closed ports to open ports; but this is only a small-scale solution to a persistent problem. In the light of the human problems raised, the decision to close a port like Helsinki and to concentrate attention upon the winter harbour of Hanko will only be considered in the face of extremely hard weather. With increasingly powerful ice-breakers and an increasingly powerful body of opinion in the capital, Hanko suffers from the growing competition of Helsinki.

For Finland, the sequence of closure of ports in relation to the volume of trade is extremely important. The ports of the inner reaches of the twin gulfs are predominantly export harbours, and this was even more true when Viipuri was the principal export harbour. Today, Kotka has supplanted it in respect of absolute tonnage exported, with Hamina (to its immediate east) following. In succession come Pori, Kemi and Oulu—all Bothnian harbours and the two latter subject to extended closure. As export harbours, the ports of Helsinki and Turku are subordinate to them. Contrastingly, the south-western ports are the leading import harbours and the principal passenger terminals for the lively Baltic traffic. The most accessible winter harbours are, in other words, those farthest removed from the principal sources of export. For a second reason, therefore, imports tend to take precedence over exports during the winter months.

It is natural that aids alternative to the ice-breaker should be the subject of experiment.

In Sweden, attention has been recently focused upon underwater pressure machines, which aim at ice prevention through the encouragement of vertical currents in waterways and port approaches. Installations at 1,500-m. intervals, emitting compressed air bubbles along lengths of perforated pipes, are regarded as adequate to promote the circulation of warmer waters from lower depths and to guarantee open water under normal conditions. Channels have been effectively kept open across Lake Mälaren from Södertälje to Västerås and from the Södertälje canal to the open Baltic.

The ultimate practical contribution of ice-breakers may be measured by at least two results. First, the ice-breaker has extended the average shipping season by six weeks. Secondly, this implies an increase in the volume of trade carried. In Sweden, for example, estimates for an average recent year amount to 18% of the timber goods exported. Translated into total export terms, ice-breaker operations therefore affect a very substantial volume of Swedish commodity movement. Swedish trade is less vulnerable than Finnish, and it may be inferred that the contribution of ice-breakers to the east Baltic shores is no less than that to the western coasts. Setting and resource in Northern Europe, indeed, assume a new character in the light of such short-period variations.

THE HIGH-LATITUDE ANOMALY

The winter transformation of much of Northern Europe, changing the value of many resources and modifying the pattern of many human activities, stands out as one of the physical characteristics of the region. It tends to express itself most markedly in snowfall on the western margins of Fenno-Scandinavia and in icing on its eastern half. These two physical phenomena, with their effects upon the economic life of the Northern Countries, are both shared by Sweden. It is perhaps appropriate to present its bill for winter, measured in what may appropriately be called "cold figures". Table 4 offers an exercise for argument, for debit and credit sides both contain their flaws.[1] But at least it offers a practical conclusion.

[1] After K. M. Savosnick, *Svenska turistföreningens årsskrift*, Stockholm, 1955, p. 139.

TABLE 4

SWEDEN'S BILL FOR WINTER

Item	Millions of Kronor
Outlay on dwellings (a quarter of new building costs, insulation, winter repair) .	435
Seasonal unemployment (600,000 lost labour weeks, 1952–3)	146
Fuel (private consumption) . . .	500
Lighting (private consumption) . . .	67
Warmer clothes	175
More food	25
Chemists' preparations	25
Railway traffic (snow clearance and heating)	12
Road maintenance	90
Automobiles (winter oil, heating, frost damage)	195
Snow clearance in towns (including roofs) .	35
Shipping (including 2,000 unemployed dockers)	10
Agriculture	400
	2,115
Forestry	215
	1,900

This sum represents 5% of the national income and, according to its calculation, winter conditions cost every inhabitant of Sweden 270 kronor. *Per capita* costs for Norway and Finland are not likely to be much less if the same method of compilation be employed.

Yet final correctives must be added. In the first place, perhaps the most remarkable feature of the Fenno-Scandinavian winter is not how much it affects daily life but how slight is its impact compared with that in many other high-latitude lands. In reviewing winter phenomena which are alien to the English eye, this ultimate anomaly of Scandinavia and Finland as a human settlement area must not therefore be overlooked. In the second place, the rhythm is naturally transmitted to the exchange of commodities, but the ultimate effect upon the national exchequer of this seasonal sluggishness tends to diminish. It has been demonstrated, for example, that the seasonal rhythm of trade in Finland is neither repeated in the receipt of orders for export nor in the annual pattern of payments.[1] The modern economy has proved surprisingly flexible in the face of winter. The exceptional winter can, of course, produce a reversal to a medieval situation, and it is not surprising that investigation has concerned itself particularly with a study of extremes. Such extremes have been peculiarly evident in the last fifteen years—oddly enough in the face of an improving climate. Three winters in a decade which correspond to the hard times relished by the inveterate Dutch collector C. Easton, naturally command attention—on practical grounds independently of academic.[2]

In the third place, where and when winter conditions in what William Browne chose to call in *Britannia's Pastorals*, "the congealed North" do reach intense forms, the native does not react to them in the same way as the casual visitor. Alexander Pope might politely remind us:

"What happier natures shrink at with affright
The hard inhabitant contends is right."

[1] V. Holopainen, "The Seasonal Rhythm in the Finnish Exports of Sawn Softwood", *Acta forestalia Fennica*, 61, Helsinki, 1954.
[2] *Les hivers dans l'Europe occidentale*, Leyden, 1928.

PART III

THE HUMAN VARIABLE

Chapter IV

THE HUMAN SETTING

"Wise rulers, therefore, always cherish the increase of their subjects both in numbers
and in fortune." Per Wargentin, *Kunglige vetenskapsakademiens dagbok*, 1754, p. 162

In the Scandinavian states and Finland, a relatively small population inhabits a relatively extensive area, and much of this extensive area has been occupied only a relatively short time. Although the nature and intensity of the impact is widely varied, the effect on the land is out of all proportion to the population numbers. Over the greater part of the area, the process of physical change dominates the attention of layman and professional geographer alike. But there are parts—principally peripheral and/or in the south—where the works of man have been powerful enough to make a significant contribution to the landscape. The origin and distribution of these works, which represent the accumulation of human effort, are tied closely to the origin and distribution of the northern peoples, which is the theme to be expanded in this chapter.

GENESIS

Traces of settlement in Scandinavia date back to the Salpausselkä stage of the Ice Age (*c.* 10,000–8,000 B.C.) when people with a reindeer culture occupied the island clusters at the entrance to the proto-Baltic and inhabited ocean coasts of Norway (e.g. Kristiansund, Stavanger) under the shadow of the ice-cap. The reconstruction of this earlier Scandinavian scene has stirred pre-historian[1] and novelist[2] alike. The evidence of the former increasingly supports the idea that present Scandinavian stock originated in the south-west.[3] Indeed,

H. Melberg goes so far as to declare that "The Danes conquered the Scandinavian peninsula . . . and they founded the nations of Norway and Greater Sweden" in two great bursts of energy associated with the end of the second century A.D. and the third quarter of the sixth century A.D.[4] The origin of the eastern inhabitants of the area under consideration remains much more debatable. More recent archæological evidence would suggest several periods of influx to Finland, the Finns probably arriving about 2,000 years ago. At any rate, a series of loose tribal organisations living in detachment from each other appear to have characterised most of Scandinavia at the time of the coming of Christianity. In Finland, three distinct tribal units had located themselves in south-western Finland, Tavastland and Karelia by the time of the twelfth-century Swedish crusades. For Iceland, the settlement story is almost completely documented in the *Landnámabók* from the thirteenth and fourteenth centuries, which lists about 400 of the principal colonists by origin and location. Iceland was the last of the European countries to be permanently inhabited.

In general, settlement spread from south to north in Scandinavia and Finland, and from the coast to the forested interior.[5] This process of expansion becomes traceable with increasing ease from 1775 in Sweden and Finland, for the parish priest was then requested to list "all new inhabitants, however large or

[1] J. G. D. Clark, *Prehistoric Europe, the Economic Basis*, London, 1952.
[2] Johannes V. Jensen, *The Long Journey*, London, 1923.
[3] G. Schütte, *Our Forefathers the Gothonic Nations*, Cambridge, 1931.
[4] *Origin of the Scandinavian Nations and Languages*. Halden, 1949 and 1951, especially Figs. 12 and 13.
[5] Cf. E. Jutikkala, *Suomen maantieten käsikirja, op. cit.*, diagram, p. 273; E. Byland, *Koloniseringen av Pite Lappmark*, Uppsala, 1956; E. Kivikoski, *Finlands förhistoria*, Helsingfors, 1964; A. Sauvageot, *Les anciens Finnois*, Paris, 1961.

small the property they inhabit".[1] Expansion has been by no means uniform and it has by no means come to an end. Indeed, there has been no period when population mobility has been absolutely greater than in the twentieth century, and when absolute numbers have increased more rapidly. Side by side with a distribution of settlement more widespread than that of any previous generation, there has proceeded an unrivalled concentration of population in urban areas. To each age or stage of domestic evolution there is a related problem of population distribution. A number of stages has passed in quick succession in the Northern Countries, and the fact is detectable in settlement responses. Nor have the stages occurred simultaneously among the group of countries as a whole. Finland, for example, is an especially interesting laboratory for the population geographer on this score. While sharing most of the essential social characteristics of the Scandinavian countries, many of its demographic tendencies are in a stage which has already been passed by others of them. It does not follow that Finland can forecast its population developments by looking to the west, e.g. to Sweden; but it is not infrequent that its western neighbours can detect contemporarily in Finland trends which they have had paralleled in their past experiences. Finland, again, differs from its western neighbours in that the boundaries of Finnish-speaking peoples are not defined by the existing political frontiers. This is not an economic fact, but it is a political issue which has not been without its impact on the Finnish economy. *De finibus patriæ naturalibus multum disputarunt*, wrote the naturalist Wirzen in 1837. Population is a part of the natural world which gives added point to his comment.

NUMBERS

In absolute numbers, the population springing from the historic roots is small. At the time of the last formal census Sweden had 7,480,000 inhabitants; Denmark, 4,448,000, of whom some 32,000 lived in the Færoes; Finland, 4,446,000; Norway, 3,586,000 and Iceland, 176,000. The average density of population is correspondingly small. Relative and regional densities may, however, be considerable, because the spread of settlement is marked by unevenness.

The pattern of population for the Scandinavian countries and Finland suggests a natural predilection for lower latitudes and lower altitudes. It also shows a distinct coastal orientation. All of these characteristics are in keeping with the historical occupation of the land. In addition, it may be generally concluded for the rural areas that a relatively high density of settlement today corresponds with relative antiquity of settlement. Discontinuity of settlement grows more frequent away from the coast, away from the valleyways and towards the north over the greater part of the area.

In the same way that the Scandinavian countries showed an early interest in the counting of heads, so they were pioneers in the representation of population data. From 1908, when he began by experimenting with methods of representation for Gotland, Sten de Geer slowly worked towards the national population map of Sweden which he published with its accompanying text just after the First World War.[2] With this map as an inspiration, it was possible to look backwards and review the possibilities for presenting changes in the distribution of the kingdom's population at different periods of time.[3] It was possible also to look forward to a refinement in method. The method of proportional spheres which de Geer employed on his map is also used in Fig. 19. Except for Denmark, the biggest single problem in the mapping of population data is the variable and frequently extensive size of the administrative units against which the data are collected.[4]

---

[1] The contemporary student is recommended to pay an immediate visit to the population registers at the local vicarage, the office of which is a key to parish demography.
[2] *Befolkningens fördelning i Sverige*, Stockholm, 1919. Cf. also the sequence of maps in *Ymer*, 1908, 1915 and 1916.
[3] *Op. cit.*, pp. 267–70. At the International Geographical Congress in Paris, the Norwegian Geographical Society presented a map of population distribution for 1801 based upon the material of the *Matrikel*.
[4] There is an intermittent urge for the redefinition of units against which census data are collected. Recommendations for the increase in size of recording units in the south of the country and a reduction in their number were proposed in "Riktlinjer för en revision av rikets indelning i borgerliga primärkommuner", *Svenska officiella utredningar*, 1945, 38, 39. Proposals for a rationalisation of rural districts paralleled these recommendations; cf. S. Godlund, "Ny länsindelning", *Plan*, Stockholm, 1953, **1**, 17–18.

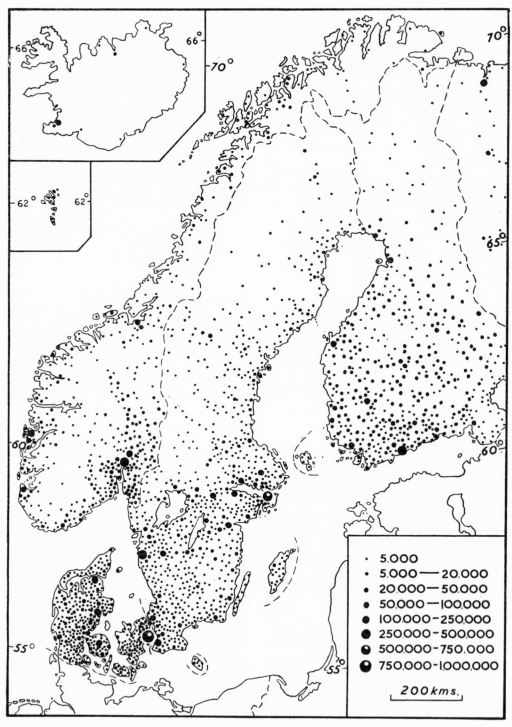

FIG. 19. Population distribution in the Northern Countries.   (Source: F. Burgdoerfer, *Weltbevölkerungs Atlas*, Hamburg, 1954.)

Fig. 19 suggests that the most even spread of settlement is found in the most southerly and low-lying parts of the area—Denmark, with the adjacent parts of southern Sweden. In Sweden, which extends farther south than either Norway or Finland, the geometrical centre of population lies in lower latitudes.[1] The axis of concentration is found along the midland zone between Stockholm and Göteborg, and there is every indication that this concentration is strengthening. Yet, even in southern Sweden extensive areas are meagrely peopled. The midland concentration extends itself eastwards through the Åland archipelago to the coastlands of south-western and southern Finland. Two of Finland's largest population groups are found around Helsinki and Turku.[2] Easternmost of the more densely peopled areas is Kotka, at the Kymi estuary, which has taken over many of the commercial functions of ceded Viipuri. The Vik region of Norway—co-extensive in certain respects with the midland zone of Sweden—has the greatest population concentration of Norway. It extends south-westwards into the southern coastlands—Sør-landet. Away from the south, population distribution is closely related to physical accessibility, with river and waterway showing distinct concentrations and their interfluve areas thinly peopled.

Areas with a relatively high and uniform distribution of population are commonly associated with fertile soils—soils which, it will be recalled, have often been born of uplift from the surrounding seas. But the form of settlement in these areas takes on a variety of charac-

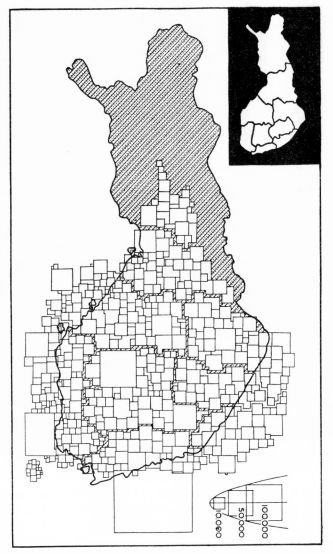

FIG. 20. A framework of reduced parish areas to serve as a model for population distribution maps in Finland. (Source: I. Hustich and S. Lindstrahl, "An area cartogram of Finland", *Terra*, **68**, 2, Helsinki, 1956.)

ters. In the first place, the nucleated village has a limited distribution; the isolated farm is a much more common feature.[3] The nucleated village as it is familiar in south-

---

[1] Relatively recent material showing general population distributions in the Northern Countries is found in H. W. Ahlmann, *Norge, op. cit.*, p. 59. The population map in the *Atlas of Finland*, 1925, provides a contrasting example in method.

[2] H. Smeds, "Var ligger Finlands befolkningstyngdpunkt?", *Terra*, 1942. Cf. also H. Smeds, "The distribution of urban and rural population in south Finland", *Fennia*, **1**, 1957.

[3] A representative example of this distribution for central Finland is given in W. R. Mead, *Farming in Finland*, London, 1953, Fig. 37.

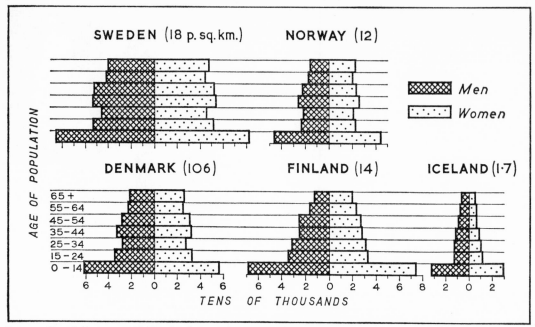

FIG. 21. Population pyramids for the five northern countries, showing the density for each country. (Source: *Yearbook of Nordic Statistics, 1962*, Stockholm, 1963.)

eastern England is repeated in Denmark, where it was less frequently broken up on the re-allocation of open field lands than in other parts of Scandinavia. In part, this was due to the constructional materials from which the village was built. Brick and stone were much less easy to pull down and rebuild than timber. So frequently, too, in the wooded parts of Scandinavia timber for new farm buildings was available in abundance on the spot. On the other hand, the inflammability of timber frequently encouraged dispersal, while lack of durability not infrequently occasioned re-siting. The break up of hamlet and village settlement forms has been widespread over Sweden and Finland, to a lesser extent in Norway. The Geographical Institute at Uppsala has mapped the degree of dispersal of rural population and represented the different types of homestead grouping against the intensity of cultivation.[1] In measuring dispersal, a criterion of isolation has had to be selected. The method merits emulation.

The rural settlement pattern of Norway, Sweden and Finland tends towards agglomerations with several hundreds of inhabitants.[2] The significance of such agglomerated places which lacked administrative expression was already pointed out two decades ago.[3] Their importance in population studies has given rise to a specific term of reference for them— the *tätort*. The *tätort* may, at the lower level, refer to a loose cluster of fifty dwellings presumed to house 200 inhabitants. In the hierarchy of settlements, the smallest named unit is the town, with its minimum of 2,000 inhabitants. A feature of the *tätort*, even at its lowest level, is that its inhabitants do not belong to the farming community proper; and in the smallest clusters to which the name is given is recognisable in embryo the rural service centre. The term of reference has become sufficiently concrete for recognition by the census authorities.[4] Students of population

[1] *Atlas of Sweden*, Plates 61–2.
[2] A useful Icelandic source for settlement appreciation is *Vidskipta skrain*, a gazetteer published at intervals.
[3] M. Overton, *Svensk geografisk årsbok*, 1937, 148–63, and M. William-Olsen, "Utveckling av tätorter och landsbygd i Sverige, 1880–1935", *Ymer*, 1938, **4**, 243–80.
[4] In *Näringslivets lokalisering*, S.O.U., Stockholm, 1951–6, a classification of four commune types is announced—A: having less than 75% of the population tied to agriculture but not settled in agglomerated habitations; B: 50–75% agriculturists but not in agglomerated settlements; C: 50% or less conforming to these two conditions; D: at least two-thirds of the population in agglomerated settlements and not tied to agriculture.

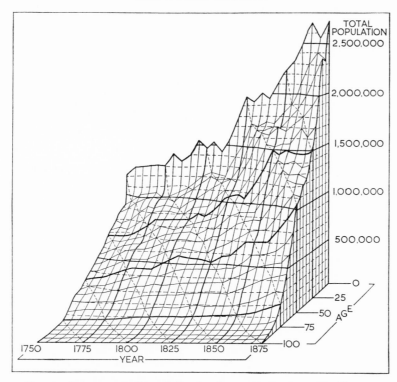

FIG. 22. A stereogram of population development in Sweden. The diagram also gives some idea of the completeness of Swedish population statistics. (Source: M. Perozzo, *Jubilee Volume of the Royal Statistical Society*, London, 1885.)

geography find it a most sensitive unit for investigation.[1]

The *tätort*, not being coincident with any specific administrative frame, has been frequently the subject of erroneous classification. The recognition of its peculiar—and essentially non-rural—character becomes of especial interest in a country like Finland or northern Sweden, where the fabric of rural society is subject to fundamental readjustments. The problem of identifying a meaningful frame within which distributional considerations can be studied calls also for other solutions. Thus, the administrative framework as a setting in which to consider aspects of population has been challenged for Finland by Ilmari Hustich. As a control to be set beside the commune map of a conventional type, a cartogram has been prepared in which the sizes of the communes have been constructed to be directly proportionate to their population figures. Against this basis (cf. Fig. 20), choropleth maps can be more reliably constructed.[2]

Side by side with quantitative distributions, qualitative aspects must be remembered. Fig. 21 gives an approximate impression of the age structure of the five countries concerned. The form of the population pyramids—a concept initially proposed by Wargentin himself (*op. cit.*, p. 162)—at the same time indicates the differences in their absolute numbers. Fig. 22 is an early experiment in the representation of Swedish population statistics. War casualties of 79,000 are one of the unique features of the Finnish pyramid.[3] Regional differences in the age structure of population

[1] In Sweden, a register of *tätorter* has been prepared at Handelshögskolan, Stockholm, by Sven Dahl. J. Wallander, *Flykten från landsbygden*, Stockholm, 1949, deals with these sensitive units in the Klarälv valley, a problem area in central Sweden.
[2] I. Hustich and S. Lindstahl, "An Area Cartogram of Finland", *Terra*, **68**, 2, 33–40.
[3] The differing character of the population pyramid for Swedish- and Finnish-speaking elements is given in R. A. Platt, *op. cit.*, p. 46.

TABLE 5

(*Per* 1,000 *inhabitants*)

Country	Year	Marriage-rate	Live Births	Deaths	Increase
Denmark	1965	8·8	18·0	10·1	8·1
Finland	1965	7·9	16.5	9·6	6·1
Iceland	1965	8·1	24·7	6·7	18·3
Norway	1965	6·8	17·8	9.5	7·8
Sweden	1965	7·8	15·9	10·1	10·0

(Source: The comparative tables from the *Yearbook of Nordic Statistics*, Stockholm, 1967.)

are likely to be considerable—the base of the pyramid still being broadest in rural areas. Table 5 brings together other population data of a qualitative character. There are some unexpected facts revealed by comparison— the remarkably high birth-rate of Iceland; the fact that it also has the lowest death-rate of the five countries; the fact that Sweden had (in 1954 at any rate) the highest death-rate in the group. The marriage-rate has a fair uniformity throughout the area.

These maps, diagrams and tables sum up in simple terms some of the essential characteristics of the human variable in the Scandinavian scene. They answer the questions "Where?" "How many?" and "What kind of people?" There is, however, another aspect which must be mentioned. What do these people do for a living? The detail of the northern economies will emerge at a later stage, but at this juncture the general distributional pattern of employment may profitably be given.

If taken at their face values, the occupation tables[1] show industry and manufacturing to absorb the greatest percentage of the labour force in Sweden. Both Denmark and Norway show a balance between agricultural and the industrial labour forces. In Finland and Iceland, the agrarian force still dominates. Naturally, the classification employed will give rise to certain misunderstandings. One immediate problem is the number of people employed part-time in occupations other than their major pursuit. Scandinavia is a field particularly rich in subsidiary occupations—

binäringar as the Swedish language puts it. Forestry combined with building, agriculture combined with industry, fishing combined with farming, all add to the difficulties of reducing statistics of employment to neat occupation tables. As in Western Europe at large, the number of women tends to exceed slightly the number of men. One characteristic of Scandinavia and Finland is the more widespread and varied employment of female labour than in many parts of the Old World. The pool of labour therefore tends to be larger than might appear at first sight. It must be observed that "housework" is identified as a form of employment for censal purposes.

EXODUS

Population mobility has been a well-defined characteristic of the northern peoples.[2] Historically, this movement has been closely related to a cultivable area with limited resources (bearing in mind the techniques available) and the corresponding need to seek for food. It has also been related to the possibilities of movement offered by the open waterway of summer and unimpeded sledway of winter. Population mobility has throughout recorded history been characterised by regular short-period rhythms as well as intermittent larger-scale migrations. The short-period rhythmic migrations are commonly a response to a particular resource base. Sometimes they disappear with the revaluation of resources; sometimes they decline in importance; sometimes new movements are set in motion.

[1] Censuses of occupations for Sweden (including Finland) are available from the middle of the eighteenth century. For earlier periods they are summarised in *Emigrationsutredningen*, Appendix IX, Stockholm, 1909.
[2] D. S. Thomas, *Social and Economic Aspects of Swedish Population Movements, 1750–1933*, New York, 1941, has much of relevance to this section.

TABLE 6

Country	Total Labour Force	Farming and Related Activity	Mining, Manu- facturing, Electricity	Building	Trade	Communi- cations	Services and Housework	Other Activity
Denmark	100	17·5	29·3	7·2	15·0	7·2	22·1	1·7
Finland .	100	35·5	22·8	8·7	11·6	6·3	14·8	0·3
Iceland .	100	22·6	25·6	10·7	12·8	7·8	15·2	5·3
Norway .	100	19·5	27·0	9·5	13·3	11·9	18·4	0·4
Sweden .	100	13·8	36·0	9·1	13·5	7·5	19·8	0·3

(Source: The comparative tables from the *Yearbook of Nordic Statistics*, Stockholm, 1967.)

Most primitive but most fundamentally responsive are the rhythms tied to reindeer movement (cf. Part 5); there are the weakening rhythms tied to the pastoral system of the *seter* economy (cf. Chapter VII); there is the persistent rhythm of the fisher- man's response along the Norwegian coast (cf. Chapter VIII); there is the winter call to labour in the coniferous forest (cf. Chapter XI)—a relatively new short- period migration called into being by the transformation of softwood values. The de- gree of population mobility—whether large- scale and secular or small-scale and seasonally rhythmic—was never greater than today. But the historical *raison d'être* (the essential search for food) and the control of the his- torical routeway (open waterlane or frozen highway) were never weaker.

There are four movements of population to which reference may be made. Two are of major importance; two of specialist interest. The two principal movements are overseas migration and the domestic migration from rural to urban areas. The two movements of specialist interest are the minor stream of movement to the north and the movement of displaced people from the ceded territories of Finland. Overseas migration is by no means a closed chapter, and Norwegian migration to the high seas should perhaps be considered as part and parcel of it. Domestically, redistri- bution of population was never livelier than today. The movement to the north has be- come essentially a movement of technicians;

the resettlement of Finland's displaced people is a completed fact.

(a) The Way to the West

The Norwegian historian A. W. Brøgger be- lieved emigration to be an integral part of the mentality of the Scandinavian people.[1] Cer- tainly a steady stream of migrants has flowed out of the north since at least the Dark Ages. Part and parcel of the urge to count heads in eighteenth-century Sweden was the attempt to explain population loss through migration.[2] The great age of emigration, which reached its peak two generations ago, was, however, unique in its magnitude and in the relatively limited landfall to which it was directed. By world standards, the absolute number of emi- grants was not large but, remembering the relatively small Scandinavian populations, a considerable percentage of their totals was represented. The final analysis of reasons for this exodus beyond the seas has not yet been written, though for over a century there have been attempts to explain the movement. In the Norwegian Commission on Emigration in the early 1840s, it was admitted at the outset that "in physical respects Norway puts obstacles in the way of the mass of the people in their attempt to win a good livelihood".[3] Next, the threat of famine was suspended regularly above two-thirds of the countryside of Scandinavia and Finland. Sometimes ex- treme lengths of land division having been reached, farmers were forced to leave their dwarf holdings. In Ostrobothnia a peasant is

[1] *Ancient Emigrants*, Oxford, 1928, 68.
[2] P. Wargentin, *Folk Utflyttningen . . . åren 1750–73*, Stockholm, 1780, 244–65.
[3] Analysed by T. Blegen, *Norwegian Migration to America, 1825–60*, Northfield, 1931. Official Norwegian statistics covering this theme were published under the title *Utvandringsstatistik*, Oslo, 1921. See also Ingrid Semmingsen, *Veien mot Vest, Utvandringen fra Norge til Amerika, 1825–65*, Oslo, 1941.

reported to have said, "We don't own enough on which to lie flat"; in south Norway, it was locally regarded as a positive sign that pressure on the land should be reduced by emigration. Religious and social motives stirred others to leave, for nineteenth-century Scandinavia was not without restraints upon freedom. Cyclical and seasonal unemployment were an additional threat to security, though there was no guarantee that these would not be repeated in the new world. In Finland, the issue was complicated by tenantry—"no land, no fatherland" was the reply of some urged to stay behind.

Collectively, these forces have been described by Dorothy Thomas as the "push" behind emigration. There was also a "pull"— the lure of the land beyond the seas. The Scandinavian countries had no overseas dominions of significance at the time when emigration fever struck.[1] The land beyond the seas was America. There were "American letters" no less appealing than those of Crévecœur; "American travellers" and "American books" no less beguiling than Charles Dickens's *American Notes*. The Norwegian was enthusiastically encouraged by such volumes as Ole Rynning's *True Account of America for the information and help of peasant and commoner* (Christiania, 1839)[2]; while the northern world at large was invoked by Fredrika Bremer: "What a glorious new Scandinavia might not Minnesota become. Here would the Swede find his clear romantic lakes, the plains of Scania rich in corn and the valleys of Norrland."[3] Indeed, the work of Helge Nelson[4] and Olof Jonasson would suggest that the territories of emigration intensity and even the times of greatest intensity were not necessarily related closely to economic conditions. Cautionary advice was largely ignored. So was the anti-emigration school of such as the Norwegian poet Henrik Wergeland who averred: "It is the most dangerous disease of our time,

a bleeding of the fatherland." Between 1865 and 1882 official restraints were sought by the Swedish Riksdag, but powers were not forthcoming.

The "disease" affected Norway first. When the 50-ton sloop *Restaurationen* left on its journey to North America in July 1825 with its first group of emigrants, Norway had just about a million inhabitants. Within thirty-five years, 44,000 Norwegians had found their way to America. Swedish and Danish emigration proceeded less rapidly; though during the same period, 18,600 Swedes and 10,000 Danes moved. But the rising tide was to affect them also. By the last quarter of the nineteenth century, the absolute peaks of movement were being experienced by Sweden.[5] In 1888, 45,000 left Sweden; but peaks of 33,000 and 35,000 were reached in 1902 and 1903. Nor did the numbers sag greatly during the First World War, in spite of the hazards of transport. The steady 11,000 Swedish emigrants per annum reached a new peak of 25,000. Within the span of a century, Sweden lost a million and a third of its people. The Danish and Icelandic peak periods accompanied the Swedish, although they did not reach the same absolute figures. 1887 was the peak year for Iceland, when there was an exodus of 2,000. The Finnish[6] migration was more retarded, but the loss is estimated at about 400,000. In the *Atlas of the Historical Geography of the U.S.A.* there are a series of diagrams to show the shifting centre of gravity of origin of European emigrants to America.[7] Not until after the turn of the twentieth century did the east European tide flow full spate—and the Finnish stream was part of it. There had, of course, been Finnish movement before then, but it was more commonly of Swedish-speaking Finns especially from the Ostrobothnian coastlands. Some, too, was concealed in that it flowed through other Scandinavian countries and became

[1] Cf. W. R. Mead, "Problems of Scandinavia and Finland", in W. G. East and A. E. Moodie, *The Changing World*, London, 1956, Chapter V. It is always interesting to observe in the publications list of the Statistical Bureau references to the census of the Danish East and West Indies.
[2] Cf. also R. W. Swanson, "Some Swedish Emigrant Guide-books", *Swedish Historical Society of America Yearbook* 1926.
[3] *Den nye verden*, København, 1855.
[4] H. Nelson, *The Swedes and Swedish Settlements in North America*, Lund, 1943.
[5] G. Sundbärg, *Emigrationsutredningens betänkande, Utvandringsstatistik*, Stockholm, 1913.
[6] Cf. J. I. Kolehmainen, *The Finns in America, a bibliographical guide to their history*, Hancock, 1947.
[7] C. O. Paullin, Washington, 1932.

merged with their population. Thus, in the late 1860s famine-afflicted Finns moved through north Norway to be classified in North American immigrant records as Norwegians or Scandinavians. Only after 1900, following a petition to the commissioners of the census, were Finnish immigrants classified independently of Russians.

Emigration was principally to North America and, although it might be by way of Canada, commonly to the U.S.A. There is a widespread distribution of Scandinavian elements, but there are distinct regional concentrations. These concentrations are related in part to the period when emigration occurred; for the virgin territories of the U.S.A. were staked out by claimants in a well-defined sequence. Norwegian, Swede and Dane have claimed extensive areas of Minnesota and Wisconsin as their own—later arrivals, like Ole Rølvaag's characters, pushing westwards to the Dakotas.[1] Ethnographic concentrations characterise middle Minnesotan counties like Chisago (with 85% "Swedish" population) or Isanti (with 87%). The Finns, arriving later, perforce occupied the marginal areas of settlement—frequently the cutover lands, such as northern Wisconsin, or the poorer unoccupied lands within the settled areas.[2] Icelanders moved principally to Manitoba and Saskatchewan. The censuses of Canada and the U.S.A. show that out of roughly 30,000 persons of Icelandic descent, three-quarters are resident in Canada and one-quarter in the U.S.A. Some emigration took a different form. Colonisation projects claimed attention sporadically. Ole Bull's settlement of Oleana in Pennsylvania provides an example. Some emigration took a different direction. South America exerted a limited appeal; while the beginning of Dano-Norwegian migration to Australia called for translations of literature about the Antipodes and their opportunities.

The Scandinavian countries have been reluctant to admit the loss of these emigrants, and it has been a common practice for their numbers to be included with those of other nationals in the domestic censuses. Indeed, to strike a statistical balance between the territories losing people and those acquiring them is a fundamental problem. American statistics first began to take precise account of immigrants from particular Scandinavian countries in 1860, but the heavy movement of immigrants by way of Quebec was disregarded.

There has been a continuous return stream of emigrants. Some of those who have taken the road to the west have done so with the deliberate intention of accumulating enough wealth to return to their home countries. It is not unusual to encounter the younger sons of farmers who have taken industrial work in the New World with a view to purchasing a farm in the old.[3] Partly out of the savings of New World pioneers also sprang the transatlantic Scandinavian passenger lines (1895–1914). To the return stream must be added that of migrants who have moved between the Scandinavian countries. There has, for example, always been a movement of Ostrobothnians across to Vestrobothnia. Sometimes this movement is permanent, but more frequently it is of a seasonal or long-term character. The Finnish constructional labourer returning from Umeå to Vaasa on the summer boat is a character typifying the attractions of Swedish working conditions. The existence of a common labour market in Scandinavia gives increasing substance to inter-Nordic migration.

Two hundred years ago the Swedish Academy of Sciences, depressed by the disinterestedness of the Swedes in emigration, offered a prize for an essay on the causes promoting overseas movement of people. It is an excellent example of the irony of history that subsequently, and in proportion to their populations, the Scandinavian countries contributed more heavily to the stream of emigration than almost any other part of Europe.[4] This contribution, moreover, was essentially a

[1] O. E. Rølvaag has two unsurpassed Scandinavian emigrant novels set against this background—*Giants in the Earth* (1927) and *Peter Victorious* (1929). They are complementary to I. Moberg's saga of emigration from Småland—*Utvandrarna*.
[2] J. I. Kolehmainen and C. W. Hill, *Haven in the Woods*, Madison, 1951.
[3] In Ostrobothnia, I have met five farm owners in succession who had been to Canada or the U.S.A. in the 1920s to make money in order to buy their holdings.
[4] B. J. Hovde, "Effects of Emigration upon Scandinavia", *Journal of Modern History*, 1934, 253–80.

contribution from rural areas, so that the emigrant was likely to be a land-breaker in his own right. It was a feature which distinguished him from the West European city-dweller, who lacked a tradition of land-making. Only after 1890 did an urban element begin to make itself felt in the emigrant stream from Northern Europe. By and large, the Scandinavian was a welcome immigrant. Not only was he highly literate, he was also readily assimilable. Emigration has fallen to a relatively lowly figure today.

(b) The Way to the Towns

In the pattern of domestic migration, the way to the towns dominates. It has been naturally encouraged by the rise of industry and commerce. The balance from a predominantly rural to a predominantly urban distribution of settlement has been tipped protractedly in Scandinavia and Finland. It might have been turned more swiftly if the stream of emigration had not diverted much rural labour just at the time when technical changes were beginning to affect the workshops of the area. As a result of the early development of population statistics and the delayed urbanisation, there exists remarkably good material for the investigation of the movement. Per Wargentin was already publishing tables of population migration in 1780. Until recent years, however, the study of domestic migration has excited relatively little attention in Scandinavia and Finland.

Urbanisation has proceeded farther in Denmark and has attained a well-marked maturity in Sweden.[1] According to the 1950 census of Sweden, more than half of the population was living in cities and boroughs. If the urban agglomerations were included, the figure rose to approximately two-thirds. In Norway and Finland, the process of urbanisation has been more delayed. In Finland, for example, a strong urban tendency did not become appreciable until the 1930s. In Iceland the urban balance was effectively tipped during the war years, though if the definition "urban" be taken to include all "trading places with a population exceeding 300", Iceland has been dominantly urban for more than a generation.[2]

The way to the towns has not been a simple phenomenon, though it has been the over-riding issue in domestic migration. In the birthplace statistics for the inhabitants of the larger towns is found the primary evidence for their high mobility. Next, it is evident that active growth in urban areas has given rise to significant new differences in the size and importance of existing towns. In this differential growth, with a limited number of exceptions, the biggest towns and cities have tended to grow progressively bigger. The old phenomenon of what Mark Jefferson called "the law of the primate city" operates with increasing strength. It implies that in each of the Northern Countries the capital cities have emerged as major urban concentrations.[3]

The five capitals all have a coastal location, and in each case they have a greater or lesser element of eccentricity in their position. Oslo, founded in the eleventh century, is in the extreme south of Norway. Helsinki, founded 1550 and administrative successor to Turku after the transference of the Grand Duchy to Russia in 1809, is also in the "Deep South". Reykjavik is in the extreme south-west of Iceland. Copenhagen, founded in the twelfth century, lies in the extreme east of Denmark, although it was central to the most fertile circle of Danish territory down to the seventeenth century. Stockholm, late medieval successor to Birka and Sigtuna, is more centrally located in relation to the extended land of Sweden, but it is also on the eastern margins. Again, this eastern location is an historical legacy, and recalls a time when, with tributary territories beyond the central Baltic, Stockholm possessed a fine centrality.

The capitals of the Northern Countries all contain a substantial percentage of the in-

[1] G. Ahlberg, *Befolkningsutvecklingen och urbaniseringen i Sverige, 1911–50*, Stockholm, 1953.
[2] *Population and Vital Statistics*, Reykjavik, 1952, 13.
[3] The following urban studies are of direct interest: L. Aario, "Helsinki suurkaupunkina", *Terra*, 1952, **2**, 43–56; H. W. Ahlmann (ed.), *Stockholms inre differentiering*, Stockholm, 1934; W. William-Olsson, *Huvuddragen av Stockholms geografiska utveckling*, Stockholm, 1937, and *Stockholms framtida utveckling*, Stockholm, 1941; J. Reumert, "The Commercial-Geographic Importance of the Situation of Copenhagen", *Geografisk Tidskrift*, Copenhagen, 1929; T. Sund, *Bergens by-område*, Bergen, 1947; publications of *Regionalplan-komitéen for Oslo-Området*, Oslo; W. William-Olsson, *Stockholm, Structure and Development*, Uppsala, 1960.

habitants of their lands. Curiously enough, the proportion is greatest in Iceland, where Reykjavik is the unrivalled "big city"; northern Akureyri, the second urban settlement, has only 7,000 inhabitants. The proportion is also high in Denmark, where the excessive expansion of the capital has given rise to much domestic concern. Although cities other than

TABLE 7

POPULATION IN CITY AND SUBURB

City	Date of Census or estimate	Population
Copenhagen .	27/9/1965	1,377,605
Helsinki . .	1/1/1965	642,372
Reykjavik .	1/12/1965	89,393
Oslo . .	1/11/1960	579,498
Stockholm .	1/1/1966	1,247,254

(Source: The comparative tables from the *Yearbook of Nordic Statistics*, Stockholm, 1967.)

the capitals of the Northern Countries may have shown a relative growth as great, none can rival the capitals in absolute population increase. Moreover, while the increase in Copenhagen and Stockholm has assumed a relatively modest rate, that in Helsinki and Oslo is being speeded up detectably. Iceland apart, each country has at least one city which lays some regional or historical claim to certain capital functions and to some European stature. In Finland, Turku (124,243), the capital of Swedish times, now vies with Tampere (126,573). Aarhus (119,186) is the regional capital of Jutland. Göteborg (408,292) is the west-coast rival of Stockholm and Malmö (233,352) its southern complement. In Norway, there are also two regional rivals to the authority of Oslo—Bergen (116,241) and Trondheim, which is still the Norwegian archbishopric. The historical stature of the northern cities can frequently be judged according to their inclusion in the volumes of city perspectives issued during the seventeenth century.

The road to these great urban centres is frequently by way of the smaller towns. The process of migration has naturally interested the Scandinavians—not least their geographers. If the conclusions of Jane Moore are to be taken as valid, it is rare for the migrant to the large town to proceed directly from a rural area[1]; more commonly, he arrives "by stages". An extension of this idea is the "chain migration" which has been discerned by T. Hägerstrand. The younger people from the big towns who move to the large cities leave a vacuum which is filled by their counterparts who migrate from smaller towns where, in turn, the process is repeated at another level.

Twentieth-century growth is reflected in the texture of urban areas. In general, their density per unit area of land is relatively low, and they have a population dispersal which contrasts with the densities of many European urban cores. Copenhagen has the highest density per square kilometre—a feature which emphasises its many affinities with the older established cities of Western Europe. Within the communes of the core area its population density of 8,000 per square kilometre gives to it one of the highest for the European capitals after Paris and London. Comparative densities for the central communes of Stockholm (4,250), Oslo (1,038) and Helsinki (2,441) carry with them contrasts in building pattern and urban plan.

While the capital cities attract a disproportionate percentage of population migrating to the towns, there are other types of urban development which claim a share. Industrialisation is less commonly identified with urbanisation than in many countries. There are, in particular, those settlements which have grown up around newly established raw-material processing plants, with several thousand inhabitants responsive to the transformation of timber, minerals or energy. The minority of skilled workers are generally immigrant to such centres; while the general pool of labour is recruited from the district. The effects of these settlements can be very positive in an area of unemployment or underemployment. This type of development is very apparent over a comparatively wide area of northern and eastern Finland.[2] Although these settlements are a means of bringing the

[1] *Cityward Migration*, 1938.
[2] H. Smeds and J. Mattila, "Om utvecklingen av tätorter och landsbygd i Finland, 1880–1930", *Geografiska annaler*, 1941; H. Myklebost, *Norges tettbygde steder 1875–1950*, Oslo, 1960; D. Hannerberg, T. Hägerstrand and B. Ödeving (ed.), "Migration in Sweden", *Lund Geographical Studies*, Series B, **13**, 1957.

town to the country without too greatly up-
setting the rural *status quo*, the migration increment absorbed by them must not be exaggerated in its importance. The parishes
which contain them, however, are at least
among the diminishing number of parishes of
increment. For a marked feature of domestic
migration is that the number of administrative
units which suffer relative population decline
grows, while the number which experience a
population increase tends to diminish.[1]

The way to the towns has implied substantial relative losses to rural areas—25,000
annually, for example, over the last decade in
Sweden. Yet, in its early stage the growth of
urban settlement did not necessarily imply the
decline of rural settlement. In Sweden, again,
rural population did not cease to increase until
the 1920s. Yet it remains a point for considerable argument whether this is more
positive than negative for most of Scandinavia
and Finland. Although by absolute standards the majority of the rural districts of
these countries are not overpopulated, by
relative standards the matter may assume a
different complexion—at least regionally.
Bearing in mind the extent of cultivated land,
the type of farming which conforms best to the
physical background and the frequent fragmentation of properties, the absorption by the
towns of the rural surplus can check pressure
on the land. It is clear, for example, that the
movement of population from the fiords of
western Norway to its growing towns is a
healthy migration. Helmer Smeds has similarly viewed the flight from the land in Finland as a positive corrective to rural overpopulation.[2] In any case, there is a tendency
for the birth-rate to be higher in rural than in
urban areas, and the latter can helpfully re-
cruit immigrants from what is likely to be a
rural surplus. Where rural depopulation
causes industrial problems, such difficulties
can usually be overcome by careful management, e.g. the repopulation of such "deserted
villages" as Brunsberget in Värmland by the
Uddeholm concern.

The relative recency of marked urban
growth and the detail of available statistics
has encouraged Scandinavian geographers to
enquire into this field of recruitment. The
analysis of migration fields for urban areas in
Sweden, for example, is regarded as one facet
of the sphere of urban influence. Its definition during the last century has, for most
places, shown a remarkable constancy, so that
for the central parts of most migration fields,
T. Hägerstrand has been able to conclude that
"the present-day pattern existed in embryo a
hundred years ago". It would seem that
more than almost any other fact a network of
established contacts accounts for the persistent form of a migration field and that remarkably persistent channels of population
movement establish themselves. The links
forged between Värmland and the steadily expanding industrial district of Sundsvall may
be cited. Swedish investigators aver that it is
possible to narrow the source of supply to the
central area of Värmland, even to Fryksdalen.
Remembering the pattern of distribution of
towns in Scandinavia and Finland, it is understandable that long-distance migration should
tend to be more common in their northern than
in their southern halves. It has also been observed that long-distance migration tends to
be more common to coastal centres than to
inland centres.

Given the growth of large cities, problems in
urban organisation naturally follow. In the
first place, the growth of the cities is so frequently a growth of their environs rather than
a development of the areas already built up.[3]
In Sweden, for example, the communes which
show a most rapidly expanding population are
those which immediately surround Stockholm,
Göteborg and Malmö. Indeed, the urban
counties which frame these great cities are
commonly spoken of as *storstadslän*, so distinctive is their development. The planned
development of satellite towns frequently
within their frames naturally exaggerates this
tendency to expansion. Secondly, there has
been the usual functional and social differentia-

---

[1] *Lund University Studies in Geography*, Series B, 13, 1955. G. Ahlberg, *Befolkningsutvecklingen och urbaniseringen i Sverige, 1911–50*, Stockholm, 1953. See also *Migration in Sweden*, Lund, 1957.
[2] "Är Finlands landsbygd överbefolkad?", *Ekonomiska samfundets tidskrift*, 1951. A contrasting attitude from Sweden is expressed in *S.O.U. Näringslivets lokalisering*, Uppsala, 1951, 6.
[3] Cf. O. Tuominen, "Das Enflussgebiete der Stadt Turku", *Fennia*, **71**, 1949.

PLATE 9. THE PASSAGE OF THE WINTER ICE

Above.   The "perilous passage" of Joseph Acerbi, a traveller over the Archipelago Sea
in the winter of 1798.

Below.   The contemporary icebreaker aiding a winter convoy in the Gulf of Finland.

PLATE 10. SWEDEN NORTH AND SOUTH

Above. A river valley in Norrland, with settlements and communications on the terraces and woodland back from the water front.

Below. The plains of Skåne, with open, well-drained, arable lands, dispersed farmsteads, and evidence of marl pits.

tion in the towns.[1] There have, in the third place, been the accompanying problems of daily movement. Commuting has already become a widespread feature of the capital cities of the north and of many others.[2] Fourthly, the summer residence has become an established characteristic of the large North European urban centres. In Denmark, where space is restricted, one expression of this is the 50,000 *kolonigaarder*, the discreetly hedged allotments created during the years of urban expansion in order that the town dweller might not lose contact with the soil. In Norway, Sweden and Finland, the summer cottage is within the financial reach of a large proportion of the urban inhabitants. There is, indeed, a summer Stockholm,[3] a summer Oslo and a summer Helsinki to which the urban resident migrates for up to three months of the year, and which is integrated with the city by a seasonal web of transport.

(c) The Way to the North

Most Scandinavians and Finns live in the southern parts of their countries. Statistical evidence indicates a drain from rural to urban areas, and most urban areas are in the south. It is therefore anomalous to find that side by side with a substantial historical and contemporary migration from the north, there has been a small but definable stream of movement to the north.[4] The way to the north has been followed by particular groups of people for special purposes rather than general motives. It is even more anomalous that today the way to the north is at the same time the way to the towns. With certain limited exceptions, the evacuees of Finland did not follow the way to the north. In all countries, the way to the north has often been along a sponsored road.

There was a limited migration to the north which paralleled the migration overseas. Already in the 1880s—though emigration had not reached its peak—it was being proposed that an America should be created in the homeland;[5] for the existence of great colonial demesnes in their northern halves was already being recognised by Norway, Sweden and Finland. Sweden's *Nationalförening mot emigration* urged the opening of the northern lands. Precise emigration enterprises, for example to Saltdalen, took place in Norway, where there was founded in 1909 a similar organisation *Ny Jord*.

Improved communications and revaluation of resources were, however, much more certain means of peopling the empty spaces. One measure of population increase in Norrland is the steady multiplication of administrative units, and it is expressed particularly well in the zone between the occupied coastlands and their *Lappmark* hinterlands. The sequence of occupation has frequently given rise to three units in the place of one—*nederbygd, överbygd* and *Lappmark*. Thus, along the axis of the Torne river are found Neder Torneå parish, Över Torneå and ultimately Torne Lappmark.[6] The way to the north was partly followed by those affected by the restrictions upon immigration to the U.S.A. in the early 1920s and to Canada in the early 1930s. Indeed, these measures really forced the creation of an America in the homeland. High-latitude farming, however, must remain at a premium, and the way to the north—until the present age of agrarian protection and subsidisation—could not be expected to have more than an extremely limited appeal. There are always some adventurers to whom the challenge will present an attraction; the anchoring of a number of Lapps to permanent holdings is also a form of colonisation in the High North.

However, there have been other forces at work which, in bringing amenities, provide new employment opportunities and incentives adequate to overcome the differentials of the south. Thus mineral and power developments call for minor armies of technicians from outside, and have given rise to urban and agglomerated settlements in high latitudes which were without parallel two generations ago. Older towns, like Kiruna, can already

[1] Cf. E. Jutikkala and S. E. Åström, *The Development of Urban Society in Finland*, pp. 625–51.
[2] T. Sund and F. Isachsen, *Bosteder og arbeidssteder i Oslo*, Oslo, 1942.
[3] Cf. S. G. Ljundahl, "Sommar-Stockholm", *Ymer*, 1938, 218–42.
[4] The spread of settlement in Swedish Norrland is brought out effectively in G. Hoppe, *op. cit.*, Plate III.
[5] E. Beckman, *Amerikanska studier*, Stockholm, 1883, I, 182.
[6] S. de Geer, *Befolkningens fördelning i Sverige*, Stockholm, 1919, pp. 107–9, Fig. 11, etc.

claim a stable population. The way to the north has been followed intermittently by speculators and increasingly by the tourist.

Two hundred years ago the Dano-Norwegian government was sending life-prisoners to Finnmark—and the idea of banishment dies hard. Yet it is undeniable that a northern *légende* is being slowly created. Emigration from south to north on any scale seems unlikely. To stabilise northerners and to reduce or arrest their southward drift is probably a better objective than to encourage a token migration from lower latitudes. In Swedish Norrland, the strengthening of regional centres is encouraged as a means of "fixing" population.[1] The way to the north is a path which has been much smoothed in recent decades; but the ways of the north are a perpetual challenge to the social geographer.

(d) The Way of the Evacuee

There has been one major domestic migration in Northern Europe unrelated to any of the preceding movements. It has contributed its modest quota to all three streams— overseas, urban and high latitude; but its main impact has been upon the rural settlement pattern of Finland. In the autumn of 1944, more than a tenth of the population of Finland chose to evacuate the eastern territories which were ceded to the U.S.S.R.[2] The great bulk of these evacuees originated in Karelia, and their reception called for an elaborate resettlement plan. The remaining nine-tenths of the land area of Finland into which they were absorbed was divided into two halves. One half was, in general, excluded from resettlement responsibilities. There were two reasons for this. First, the northern third of Finland does not lend itself readily to agricultural occupation. Given intimate acquaintance with its vagaries, a reasonable living can be extracted from it; but to introduce a south-east Karelian farmer to the conditions of northern Finland was to invite failure. A second and discontinuous tract of Swedish-speaking areas was also excluded

from the receipt of Finnish-speaking refugees. In brief, then, the displaced population was directed essentially to the southern half of the country. Of the displaced people the great majority were farmers. Some 30,000 new holdings had to be created for them, and within a decade of the peace settlement the task was effectively completed. Resettlement in rural areas was necessarily staggered; it was not physically possible to set in process at one and the same time the division and/or occupation of the land for all displaced farmers. Some were, in fact, only receiving their final awards in 1952—after eight years guaranteed but mentally unsatisfactory employment. A minority of the displaced people went to urban areas. Helsinki received absolutely the largest number (35,000), but certain other cities received proportionately more. Lahti, for example, became virtually overnight one of the big towns of Finland (50,000 inhabitants). Valkeakoski was transformed by the establishment of a whole range of new industrial plants; for manufacturers had to be evacuated as well as farmers. Sometimes the movement resulted in the creation of new towns immediately adjacent to the new boundary, for example Uusi Värtsilä in Karelia; sometimes new manufacturing plants were created in old-established but small industrial towns, for example Pietarsaari.

The way of the evacuee has provided Finland with its biggest single post-war problem. The demands of the human variable in the geographical equation have been more insistent and more urgent here than in any other part of Northern Europe. Correspondingly, the reactions have sometimes taken unexpected turns.

OPTIMUM CONSIDERATIONS

The Scandinavian world has 19 million inhabitants, and in many respects it has become a laboratory in which investigators study problems of distribution and integration. Two outstanding issues confront the contemporary student of population geography in

---

[1] *Norrland kommittens principbetänkande, Norrlands utvecklingslinjer*, Stockholm, 1949, 44 *et seq.* The processes of expansion and retreat on the Scandinavian frontiers of settlement have been the object of detailed investigation by Kirk H. Stone, University of Wisconsin.

[2] Directly relevant to this section are: *Farming in Finland*, Chapter IX; "The Cold Farm in Finland", *Geographical Review*, xli, 4 (1951).

the north. The first is one of long standing and springs from numbers; the second is a contemporary consideration and the object of experiment.

In 1747, with a growing population consciousness, H. J. Wrede in his presidential address to the Royal Swedish Academy declared, "An abundance of inhabitants is the country's greatest wealth". It was the beginning of two centuries of speculation concerning the relative overpopulation or underpopulation of the Northern Countries. Jonas Alströmer was asking the Royal Scientific Society of Sweden in 1760 why a land nine times as big as England should not have 45 million people if England had 5 millions. Zachris Topelius, whose imagination naturally gave vent to speculations of this character, thought that if Finland were properly cultivated it could feed 16 millions. Hitlerian Germany had elaborate plans for roughly doubling the population of Norway within the greater Reich. It is clearly impossible to review the optimum population, however, in detachment from the availability of other resources. J. F. Kryger, in a lecture to the Royal Swedish Academy in 1758 (p. 22 *et seq.*), put his finger upon the fundamental issues of density and distribution: "If the whole of Sweden's and Finland's population lived in as limited an area as Småland and Skåne," he averred, "its density would be sufficient." Its "present scattered distribution hinders trade and contact", he continued (p. 26)—and his theme is repeated today. Such a thin scatter of settlement wasted much time on journeying for all sorts of services. Consciousness of the need for population remains strong in contemporary Scandinavia, and in its northern parts the philosophy of numbers is much upheld. Child allowances, representing a substantial subsidy on the large family, form a significant element in the home economics of the area.

Optimum numbers may be conjectured relative to time and space; they may also be conceived relative to place within the Scandinavian setting. Differing optima will in theory prevail in different places at the same time. Moreover, there will be differing optimal distributions for different areas at the

same time. Norway, Sweden and Finland are much concerned by the tendency for population to drain from their northern halves and for a population vacuum to result. It is conceivable that an even spread of population in these areas is undesirable and that local concentrations performing specific functions should be encouraged as a more desirable alternative. Consider Kuusamo parish in north-east Finland, where a conscious policy of dispersed colonial settlement in state forest lands is being undertaken. It may be desirable to have people on the land from the point of view of forest management, but the subsidisation of settlement and the inevitable inroads on the forest must be set against the positive contribution which they make towards its improvement. Perhaps the provision of amenity in such an area should be viewed in a different light from that in more southerly areas. Might not subsidies more profitably be expended on caravan camps, logging camps and cheap abundant transport for woodland workers side by side with the concentration of family life and services in a limited number of larger settlements? On the other hand, man is notoriously unpredictable, and the provision of even modest urban centres might whet the appetite for larger ones and merely speed the progress of emigration to the urban centres of the south.

The mid-twentieth century has seen new attempts to maximise the opportunities of the Scandinavian settlement area. From the economic point of view the population of the Northern Countries no longer consists of Danes, Finns, Icelanders, Norwegians and Swedes. Basic social legislation having been virtually standardised, they may anticipate a wide freedom of mobility throughout the area which is the frame of reference of this book. A common labour market for Norway, Sweden, Denmark and Finland was constituted with effect from July 1st, 1954. In theory, there is nothing to prevent any citizen from taking up employment anywhere in the constituent countries. Population may now flow freely from regions of unemployment to regions of labour deficiency throughout the area. At the time when the common labour market came into existence, Sweden had the largest immigrant "Scandinavian" labour force. A year later, despite fears in certain directions, the influx had increased but slightly. The experience of Norway on April 1st, 1962,[1] was that there were somewhat fewer Norwegians working in Sweden (10,900) than seven years earlier (in the pre-regulation period). Among Norway's 10,000 Scandinavian employees, Danes predominate. In general, Swedish industrial workers are not likely to move away from Sweden, but industrial workers of the other Northern Countries are likely to move into Sweden. Norway has received a minor influx of Danish farm as well as industrial workers (3,000 on September 30th, 1961) and Finnish labourers (400). At the beginning of 1966, there were considerably more than 100,000 Scandinavians and Finns working in another Nordic country than that of their citizenship.

Personal mobility is one of those attributes of the human variable in our equation which disturbs established patterns in economic geography. It is therefore natural that the human geographers should keep an eye open for the great secular constants which appear to be characteristic of it. For Finland and the Scandinavian states, at least three persistent features may be recognised in the general pattern of population movement. First there is overseas migration. Secondly —and domestically—there is the steadily increasing extension of migration distances. Thirdly and less clearly to be discerned, there appear to be stable migration fields for particular centres. There is a fourth characteristic, though this is less scientifically supported—population distribution tends towards an increasingly uneven spread.[2]

Given the collective Scandinavian approach of a common labour market and the effective elimination of a group of international boundaries, these constant tendencies are raised to a new plane. It is unlikely that their validity will be challenged. The new pattern of migration will probably not be large-scale— and the movement seems to be mostly to Sweden. Yet, in considering the relationship between the human variable and the North European scene, such a development always carries with it the germ of significant distributional change.

[1] *Yearbook of Nordic Statistics*, 1962, Stockholm, 1963.
[2] This is especially evident in the growth of a continuous urban area around the Sound. The concentration of Finnish population in the extreme south-west is discussed in I. Hustich, *Finland föryandlas*, Helsingfors, 1967.

Chapter V

SETTING, RESOURCE AND ECONOMIC REVALUATION

"Rivers stream back to the place of your birth,
From east to west revolve, oh earth!
Your dead, oh time, again set free,
As babes in arms return the years to me."
Juhani Siljo, *Loitsu*

THE Scandinavian countries and Finland are among those the resources of which have experienced fundamental changes of value in relatively recent times. Not merely do their combinations of resources differ strikingly from those of many European countries: their courses of development have also been different. Although there are remarkable examples of regional precocity within their midst, their general evolution shows a time lag. For a number of reasons, this lag occurred essentially in the nineteenth century. It follows that when the contemporary economies of the Northern Countries are considered, it is in some ways easier to investigate the process of change within them. For by the time significant modifications were taking place, statistical machinery was well-established and detailed record-keeping had already been long practised. In addition, the constituent countries displayed a different scale of operations from those countries which were in the vanguard of industrial and agricultural progress, and their economies tended to display a less complex structure. In illustrating these points attention will be concentrated principally upon the period 1750–1914. No attempt is made to be comprehensive but certain traits are selected for consideration which have marked the northern economies during the period and which give depth to present perspectives.

CHANGING STATUS

In 1664, one of the many pamphlet publications which appeared in London was headed *Good news for England: or a relation of more victories obtained by the Swedes against the King of Denmark*. The heading gave some idea of the relative significance of Denmark and Sweden in the European scene and presaged a change in their international stature. During its *Storhetstid* or "Times of Greatness", Sweden supported a Baltic Empire which, exceeding a million square kilometres in area, was bigger than the German Reich in 1914. Sir Thomas Roe, writing from the Stockholm Embassy in the mid-seventeenth century, described Sweden as "Master of all the ports and trade from Narva to Stralsund". It was not therefore surprising that Sir Bulstrode Whitelock sought to join the Protectorate and Sweden together in a treaty of "trade and friendship", the three hundredth anniversary of which was celebrated in April 1954. Balancing "Baltic Scandinavia"—with Finland as a Grand Duchy of Sweden from 1556 to 1809—was "Atlantic Scandinavia", consisting of Denmark-Norway and their Atlantic appendages. This is no place to account for the formidable stature of the Northern Countries in the seventeenth-century scene—when Sweden was literally "the hammer of the North". In part it was accountable by the relative weakness of their neighbours. There was also a relative difference in population, for while Britain had about 5 million inhabitants, Denmark-Norway had approximately 2 millions and Sweden-Finland exceeded $1\frac{1}{2}$ millions. Thirdly, Sweden and Denmark had organised their military power upon a sound domestic basis. Expansion beyond their peninsular confines was accompanied by intensified occupation of the homeland. Sometimes this took the form of woodland colonisation as in Värmland and Dalarna. Sometimes it was the promotion of a remote mining enterprise, as with copper at Röros. Sometimes it was the creation of new trading harbours, such as Gamlakarleby and Brahestad in Ostrobothnia.

The spacious days of the Scandinavian powers were however numbered. Sweden shrank to its present confines following the Russian annexation of the Grand Duchy of Finland in 1809; Denmark was reduced by the loss of Slesvig-Holstein to Prussia in 1864. The "dual monarchy" of Sweden-Norway, arranged by the Treaty of Kiel in 1814 and dissolved in 1905, did little to strengthen the European status of the Northern Countries. Finland was to escape to autonomy in 1917, along a nationalist path which gave it a distinctive stamp from the rest of the Scandinavian world.

Moreover, political decline was accompanied by a measure of economic decline—relative if not absolute. The speed and scale of expansion in the iron and steel industry of Britain, Germany and America in the nineteenth century were of another order from that of Sweden. Two hundred years ago Sweden produced 36% of the world's iron output; today it is less than 1%. Population growth, too, was more modest than in the industrialised countries of the west. In addition, the Scandinavian world experienced emigration out of all proportion to its numbers. Fenno-Scandinavia was largely passed over by the industrial changes of the nineteenth century. It lacked the essential prerequisite upon which it was based—coal. Its domestic scenes did not therefore experience that transformation which so profoundly altered the economies and landscapes of Western Europe. But if they suffered the loss of the advantages which industrialisation imparted, they avoided most of the social evils which were its accompaniment. Industrialisation came in due course, though in Denmark apart, principally through hydro-electric power. The urban scene in contemporary Scandinavia reflects the advantage of having escaped the preliminary—and experimental—phase of the "revolution" in industry.

Yet, if there was a time-lag there was not complete stagnation. For, while the industrial transformation of the coal-bearing lands of Western Europe was taking place, the Northern Countries awoke to a slow appreciation of their resources. It was an awakening inseparable from the climate of thought in Western Europe; but it possessed features which sprang directly from the soil of the north. To select dates which mark the beginning of the movement or criteria by which it may be recognised is not easy. Some support could be found for selecting the mid-eighteenth century and, as at least one criterion—the mass of topographical material emanating from the universities in the last half of that period—indicates the presence of a new spirit of domestic enquiry. For here is the beginning of a serious national stocktaking.

The stock-in-trade, however, could not ultimately be assessed in domestic terms. What is important is that when it was eventually expressed in international terms, the Scandinavians were so experienced in the accounting and management of their stock that they were carefully husbanding their resources in a world which had yet to discover the meaning of rational exploitation.

NATIONAL STOCKTAKING

(a) The Topographical Descriptions

The topographical descriptions of the eighteenth century have a twofold importance. First of all, they represent a preliminary attempt to review the resources, condition and prospects of the Scandinavian countries—albeit initially in a piecemeal manner. Secondly, they mark a stage in the geographical appreciation of the constituent parts of the north; they are the purely descriptive, frequently personal material which preceded the organised collection of statistics.

Few were more responsible for their promotion than Carl von Linné (1707–78). Although by appointment Professor of Medicine and by repute a botanical systematist, he fired an enthusiasm for regional descriptions which spread widely. His inaugural dissertation, delivered in Uppsala on October 17th, 1741, was entitled *The usefulness of exploratory expeditions in one's native land*. It looked forward and backward, for he had begun his topographical wanderings at the age of twenty-five, and was to establish a school of enthusiasts who did much to open windows upon the northland. For the twentieth-century field-worker, it is sometimes interesting to reflect upon his antecedents setting out upon their geographical journeys. Here is Linné as he left Uppsala on May 12th, 1732, bound for Lapland at the request of the Society of Science:

"My clothes consisted of a light coat of linsey-woolsey cloth . . . lined with red shalloon, having small cuffs and a collar of shag; a round wig, a green leather cap, a pair of half-boots. I carried a small leather bag, half an ell in length, furnished on one side with hooks and eyes. . . . This bag contained one shirt, two pairs of false sleeves, two half-shirts, an inkstand, pen-case, microscope and spying glass: a gauze cap to protect me occasionally from the gnats: a comb, my journal and a parcel of paper stitched together for drying plants; my manuscript on ornithology and *Flora uplandica*. I wore a hanger at my side and carried a fowling-piece, as well as an octangular stick graduated for the purpose of measuring."[1]

In 1741, by parliamentary decree, Linné went to Öland and Gotland; in 1746, to investigate Västergötland to see "what might be found there of use to the nation"; in 1749, to Skåne and Småland. His approach in describing these areas blends that of the systematist and the comparative regionalist. This is evident in his introduction to *A Journey in Dalarna*:

"Here, one can see how much there is at home . . . how much each province has its own pre-eminence: how it can be refined: what unbelievable profit Sweden would obtain if all these provinces were thus thoroughly explored: how one province can be helped by another's customs."[2]

In the eastern wing of the Swedish Empire, the approach was repeated by Pehr Kalm (1716–79), a disciple of Linné and later Professor of Natural Husbandry in the University of Åbo.[3]

"I wish that we had", he wrote in the introduction to his journeys, "not only of the whole kingdom and of each province, but also of every county and even parish, an accurate description of the rural economy, as by that means we should have a clear light and guide for improving our agriculture."

Among the 146 dissertations supervised by Kalm during his twenty-five years at the university, many conformed to the parish pattern prescribed by the master. Sometimes there was almost an air of regional rivalry about the assembling of the material. Thus a Borgå cathedral directive of 1749 called for assistance from Carelian and Savolax parishes "to add to their lustre, by casting light on those tracts hitherto in darkness".

To the west the descriptive assessment of resource was publicised in such journals as *Danmark og Norges Œkonomiske Magazine* (1757–64); while Bishop Erik Pontoppidan (1698–1765), beginning with what he described as "an initial investigation into the natural history of Norway" (two volumes, 1752–3), subsequently produced the most authoritative statements on the twin kingdom in his celebrated *Danske Atlas* (eight volumes, 1763–81). A special topographical journal founded in Norway by Fredrik Moltke illustrated the continuing interest in regional economic and physical description; although it had a brief life (1792–1808).

It would have been myopic indeed if those who explored their homeland had not cast an eye beyond the seas. Although Linné himself travelled little outside Sweden, his pupils went to the four corners of the world—to Japan, Java, South America and Africa. The experience of Kalm in his early years was representative of them. Before he eventually left on his celebrated journey to North America it had been debated whether he should go to the Levant, to Iceland, to Greenland or follow in the footsteps of Marco Polo across Siberia to China. The purpose of these overseas journeys was less the exploration of unknown lands than the investigation of their homoclimes for useful seeds, shrubs, plants and trees which would probably be of value in the home economy. Kalm summed up the situation when he set sail for the New World. He left in search of new plants which would be capable of producing additional food for men and fodder for animals on Sweden's "poor meadows, acid swamp-lands and dry hills".

Besides these intercontinental travellers, others journeyed to near-by countries to examine the improved methods of British and

---

[1] There is a fine English edition of the resulting *Journey to Lapland* by J. E. Smith, *Lachesis Lapponia*, I, II, London, 1811.
[2] A readable biography is Knut Hagberg, *Carl Linnæus*, London, 1952.
[3] Cf. W. R. Mead, "A Northern Naturalist" *The Norseman*, XII, 1954, 2, 3, and "Pehr Kalm in the Chilterns", *Acta Geographica*, **17**, 1, 1962.

German farming. Typical of such professional travellers was the Swede Rutger Maclean (1742–1816) and the Dane G. O. B. Begtrup (1769–1841), whose personal experience and acquired knowledge of the "New Farming" were embodied in writings which circulated throughout a Scandinavia which had virtual identity of language.

The study tour, indeed, became a feature of the age, and there is a rich Scandinavian literature which indicates how students viewed and reviewed the changes in other lands.[1] For the most part, such tours were undertaken by men of science whose outlook was not narrowly limited to a specialist pursuit, but whose eyes were alert to anything likely to be useful in improving the condition of their home countries. The breadth of vision of such Swedish iron-masters as Gustav Broling, who undertook a series of journeys to study the British economy between 1797 and 1799, is representative. His published works were to become guide-books in themselves for successors like Johan Jacob von Julin (1789–1853)—a founding father of the modern Finnish economy. Such travellers introduced British and continental techniques which were to transform farm, factory and mine—as well, of course, as the communications which integrated them.

(b) The Economic Societies

It was not long before these domestic surveys and reports on overseas study tours or exploratory journeys gave rise to formal organisations, which often took as their models societies already in existence in other countries. The societies encouraged by royal patronage were usually of a general scientific nature, although they were more specifically bent upon the improvement of economic conditions. Among those in the vanguard were the Economic Society of Sweden—known as Kongliga Patriotiska Sällskapet, the regular transactions of which appear from 1770 onwards. Provincial agricultural societies were also set up all over Sweden in the ensuing century. In Finland, the Aurora Society was established in 1771, preceding by more than

a generation the Finnish Economic Society (Finska hushållningssällskapet, 1797). The sponsors, centred in Åbo Akademi, published a small journal, Åbo Tidning, point three in the programme of which was to promote and publish "all that concerns the country's geographical and physical knowledge". Its editor married the topographical tradition with the societies which grew about his university, declaring in a letter in 1782 that he sought "from all districts . . . detailed descriptions about their character". In Denmark, a patriotic society came into existence in 1744, and the volumes of Det Danske Magazin are testimony to its character: it was succeeded by Det Danske Landhusholdingsselskab in 1769. An independent development occurred in Norway after 1809 with the establishment of the Society for the Improvement of Norway (Selskapet for Norges Vel).

The patriotic societies were forums to debate improvements in agriculture, silviculture, communications, handicrafts and rural industries. They kept their fingers on the pulse of the rural communities through the parish priests—whose church farms were frequently exemplary and experimental holdings in their own right. They transmitted knowledge from outside sources, built up libraries (often of imported books) and mustered a mass of records indispensable for the historians' interpretation and understanding of their economic landscapes. Moreover, the societies counted among their members many senior administrators. Such men who were prepared to receive the ideas of the societies and to transmit ideas to them were likely to be of personal importance in the rural districts where they frequently lived. Later eighteenth-century Swedish (and Finnish) materials born of administrators include the reports of the provincial governors (Landshövidings-berättelser). The societies also adopted incentives common to those in other countries. Thus the prize essay, as initiated by the Royal Agricultural Society in Great Britain, was introduced to encourage land improvement.

From the patriotic verse into which their supporters broke, it may be conceded that the

---

[1] A selection of these is given for England in S. Rydberg, Svenska studieresor till England under Frihetstiden, Uppsala, 1951. A topography of unusual interest is J. Chr. Svabo, Indberetninger fra en Reise i Færøe 1781 og 1782, Copenhagen, 1959.

economic societies of Scandinavia represented a high-latitude flowering of the physiocratic idea. Per Tham conceived a new Eden on Swedish soil: an anonymous ode to Panthea seized the imagination of Norway: on the first day of 1800, F. M. Franzén beheld a vision of a new Finland entitled *Finlands upodling* (*Åbo Tidning*, 1, 1800). Today, the functions of most of the old organisations which prompted such enthusiasm have been taken over by government authorities: but relics of them remain in northern capital or provincial city.

(c) The Censuses

Parallel with and partly sponsored by the topographers and their societies went the censuses. They began with the *Tabellverk* in Sweden (February 1748), by which the clergy became responsible for regular returns of vital statistics.[1] Church records of births, marriages and deaths had been kept since at least the end of the seventeenth century, and *Tabellverket* (cf. Plate 12) had been preceded by other experimental record keeping. On the strength of the enterprise of P. W. Wargentin (1717–83), Sweden lays claim to the oldest continuous census material of any country in the world.[2] In Finland, the same early record of age, civil condition and occupation are available, except for the small area of *Gamela Finland* excluded by the Russian settlement of 1743.[3] A preliminary attempt at a modern census was made in Denmark-Norway in 1769:[4] a second in 1789. In 1797, a Danish-Norwegian *Tabelkontor* was established.

The counting of heads was encouraged for a number of reasons. Clearly, there was a growing consciousness of the failure of the Scandinavian population to keep pace with the growth in neighbour states. Moreover, the philosophy of the age averred that a deficiency of population in relation to other resources was cause for economic dismay. The shadow of Rousseau was to wrinkle northern brows—"Moins un pays produit d'hommes, moins il produit de denrées": "La terre produit à proportion au nombre des bras qui la cultivent." The new census material facilitated the assessment of military strength, aided revenue authorities and enabled estimates for food requirements in the face of famine.

Food, indeed, was a primary problem and famine has been a local reality within living memory. During his Scandinavian journey in 1799, Thomas Malthus observed that all that was required to support nine or ten million people in Sweden-Finland was the means of supplying food. Napoleon's well-worn dictum that an army marches on its stomach acquired new meaning where a campaign of colonisation into the northern woodlands was reviewed. Success or failure in settlement was a reaction to adequacy or inadequacy of bread grain and fodder. The threat of famine was exaggerated by the shadow of war which overhung Northern Europe during the Napoleonic period. Small wonder that practical regard should be paid by the administration to the relationship of population and food supply, and that the urge for the preparation of an agricultural census should assert itself simultaneously. Already for some decades parish storehouses had been operating, with varying efficiency, to husband grain in the good years against the bad. Storehouses were not always established in the most needy areas: and even where they were, settlers were likely to be faced with transport difficulties in parishes the size of English counties.

In the same way as the collection of censuses was delegated to the parish priest (and the census office today remains an essential part of the presbytery), so the priest was charged with the recording of rural resources. In Sweden, for example, from 1802 to 1820 during the incipient stages of the record-keeping, priests were supposed to estimate the domestic grain harvest of their parish and to list the cultivated area and numbers of stock at four-yearly intervals.[5] The collection of such material was sporadic and of variable quality. Finland had barely begun to accord with this

---

[1] There had, of course, been earlier assessments; cf. the work of H. Forsell, *Sverige*, 1571, etc., Stockholm, 1872 and 1883.

[2] Y. Fritzell, *Det svenska tabellverket och dess ståndstabell*, Stockholm, 1949.

[3] *Population of Finland, 1751–1805, by Order and Occupation*, G. Fougstedt and A. Raivio, Helsinki, 1953.

[4] *The Community and Its Statistics, 1769–1950*, Copenhagen, 1952.

[5] E. Heckscher, *Sveriges ekonomiska historia*, Stockholm, 1935–49, p. 151.

demand when it changed political sovereignty. However, the enthusiasm of an early secretary of the Economic Society—Carl Christian Böcker—was sufficient to keep the germ of the rural census alive, and his manuscript material represents the beginning of Finland's farm statistics.[1] In Denmark, censuses of land use and cultivated area are found at irregular intervals back to the Middle Ages. The register or *Matrikul* of land assessments established in Denmark in 1664 (first revised 1681–8) applied equally to Norway.[2] Beside the name of the owner, the *Matrikul* might list the farm's arable and meadowland, timber and fisheries, grain and ling production, as well as the number of animals which it could support. An assessment based on the weighted averages of corn, butter and fish yields was then constructed. In Denmark, corn production as a basis of assessment has left behind the phrase *Hartkornsmatrikul*. Norwegian attempts to revise their *Matrikkel* during the eighteenth century never bore fruit, though a new and independent *Matrikkel* for Finnmark was undertaken in 1775. Questionnaires circulated to local administrators in 1803 brought forth a handful of manuscript reports which have been the subject of recent analysis.[3] Parallel with foodstuff estimates in other countries, grain returns were called for in Norway in 1809, but no fuller agricultural census took place until 1835.

The logical conclusion of these many census undertakings was the establishment of central statistical offices in each of the northern capitals. These were born primarily in the middle years of the last century—in Denmark in 1848; Sweden, 1858; Finland, 1866; Norway, 1876. By the time that the offices had come into existence, the tools for the task had been forged; they now had to be refined.

(d) The Maps

Description of the land and the compilation of a political arithmetic from its men and resources were not enough. The land had to be measured in detail and presented in bird's-eye perspective. A man who undertook both of these tasks and whose work was a response to the twin economic and political impulses which urged map-making forward was Anders Bure (1571–1648). His magnificent baroque map of Scandinavia was a synoptic chart commissioned by His Majesty in order that "the location of all provinces and cities could be presented to the eye", that he might review their needs and initiate measures for their improvement and protection. Simultaneously Anders Bure promoted the detailed and systematic survey of Sweden. The mapping of the more populous areas through the great series of "geometrical land books" (*geometriska jordböcker*) was started from the Central Land Survey Office in Stockholm in 1628. Almost from the beginning there is uniformity in the range of data called for in the instructions to land measurers. In 1655, for example, an instruction was issued demanding the accurate location of all properties, churches, estates, settlements, commonlands, royal meadowlands, lakes, streams, rivers, grain-mills and saw-mills. Such maps were calculated to be of inestimable value as the years advanced.

Besides encouraging imperial maps which expressed national aggrandisement, political forces prompted intermittent surveys of frontier areas. Such large-scale surveys commonly included economic data. Swedish War Office archives from the seventeenth century include detailed maps from borderland counties between Sweden and Denmark; complementarily, there are Danish maps covering the strategic Danish territories of Skåne, Bleckinge and Halland—the eighty maps of Johannes Meyer's *General Map of Denmark*, 1658–60, provide a good example. Large-scale surveys of the Kymi river valley of Finland, from the mid-eighteenth century, give a good impression of land use and settlement in this Russian frontier zone. The maps of the boundary survey between Norway and Sweden provide details of the "Keel" lands in the 1750s. A neglected map of south-eastern Norway (also tied into the defence of a vulner-

---

[1] W. R. Mead, "Land Use in Early Nineteenth-century Finland", *Publications of the Geographical Institute of Turku*, 26, 1953.
[2] V. E. Pedersen, *Matrikelvæsen*, Copenhagen, 1951.
[3] Cf. H. Bjørkvik and A. Holmsen, "Gårdsskipnad i Sogn og Fjordane", *Historielaget for Sogn tidsskrift*, 16, 1953.

able frontier zone) is the *Economic Map of Norway* (1805–6, scale 1:10,000).[1]

Measurement of the land in detail was encouraged by two economic motives. The first was fiscal. The land measurers who went increasingly into the field as the eighteenth century advanced, and who acquired a repute as hated as that of Biblical taxgatherers, were concerned with the delineation of property boundaries and land use in order that new assessments could be made. None was more energetic in carrying this work forward from Sweden to Finland than Jacob Faggot (1699–1778). Resulting maps were largely on a scale of 1:5,000 or 1:10,000. At the same time, they initiated a system of land taxation graduated according to both land use and land fertility.

The second economic motive sprang from the redistribution of land holding. The process of map-making was speeded everywhere by re-allotment. The reorganisation of farm holdings in Scandinavia followed a number of distinct legal patterns. The reforms paralleled in time, and were the equivalents in many respects of the intensified enclosure movement of late eighteenth-century England. Since the re-allotment of land was directed not by private landowners but from a central office which charged its cartographers to draw up the appropriate documents, the materials for an appreciation of land reform in Scandinavia are at once more complete and more uniform than their British counterparts.

In Sweden-Finland, the first Great Reform (*Storskifte*) took place at Löfsta in Funbo parish in 1748, two years after Jacob Faggot had published his treatise on the boundaries and aids to Swedish farming. Examples of the open-field picture are given in *Svenska Lantmäteriet* (Vol. III, Stockholm, 1938).

In Denmark, the reorganisation stemming from a Royal Commission of 1785 was paralleled by ownership reforms of a profound nature. These invested property ownership in the hands of the small-holders in contrast to the virtual ejection which many of their English counterparts experienced at the time of enclosure. The Act for the Abolition of the Common Field System (1781) provided that the land "be fully surveyed and mapped and all holders shall share the cost thereof".[2] Historical material for Danish rural areas also exists in the *Matrikelskort* which accompanied the Land Register, scale 1:4,000, from the end of the eighteenth century onwards.[3]

In Norway, land reform was of more limited consequence, because the absolute extent of cultivated land upon which complex property relationships had developed was more restricted and because the system of land holding tended to be much more individual. Reform of ownership has taken place in Norway in a less dramatic manner with the dissolution of the old *tun* or family-type farm. From 1857 a map had to accompany every legal rearrangement of such properties, and the continuing though naturally diminished need for such documents provides an interesting aspect of map-making.[4] The recording of relic family holdings before their reallocation is a cartographical task fondly undertaken by the ethnographers.[5] Simultaneously with the preparation of farm maps, the delimitation of private and publicly owned land was proceeding in northern Norway.

The widespread production of large-scale local maps facilitated and encouraged the construction of small-scale regional maps in Northern Europe. In Denmark-Norway, *Den Danske Atlas* of Erik Pontoppidan represented the initial product of the eighteenth century,

[1] This section is based partly upon the official histories of the Swedish Land Survey (Stockholm, 1928); *Danmarks kortlægning*, I (Copenhagen, 1943); C. M. de Sene, *Historisk Beretning om Norges geografiske Opmaaling*, Kristiania, 1878; K. Nissen, *Norsk geografisk tidsskrift*, IX, 185–209; S. Thorarinsson, "Islands kartläggning", *Ymer*, 1945, 115–29; N. E. Nørlund, *Faerøernes Kortlægning*, Copenhagen, 1944; *Finlands kartverk*, Helsingfors, 1892, and O. Savander, *Fennia*, 2, 1887, 187–205.

[2] F. Skrubbeltrang, *Agricultural Development and Rural Reform in Denmark*, Rome, 1953, 51.

[3] An idea of the effects of land reform on the village landscape and an appreciation of the quality of the maps for a selected area of Denmark can be obtained from H. Thorpe, "The Influence of Inclosure in Denmark", *Transactions, Institute of British Geographers*, 1952, 111–30.

[4] Cf. *Farming in Finland, op. cit.*, pp. 168–73. Norwegian materials are housed at Jordskifteverket, Norwegian Ministry of Agriculture, Oslo; but there is no comprehensive land register in Norway.

[5] An early appraisal of maps and the farmer in Norway is given in P. C. Asbjørnsen, *Norsk Landmansbog*, Christiania, 1868. Approximately fifty *tun*-type farms in West Norway are the subject of investigation by Miss R. Frimanslund of *Instituttet for sammenlignende Kulturforskning*, Oslo.

and C. J. Pontoppidan's standard works for south and north Norway from the 1780s also reflect the knowledge accruing from large-scale local surveys. A better example of this type of work, however, was the Atlas of Sweden compiled by Baron S. J. Hermelin (1795–9). For this, all the latest instrumental refinements were employed: though much of the basic work represented the reduction first to parish, and then to provincial level, of data initially collected on a farm or village basis. The ultimate scale in the Atlas was 1:540,000. The cult of the map was spurred by such bodies as the Cosmographical Society of Uppsala, founded in 1758: the science of survey found expression in such books of instruction as *Föreläsningar i topografin*, published by Tavaststjärna in 1807.

It was natural that town plans and urban maps should complement the rural surveys. Among finer atlas publications was the series of town maps of Sweden, by F. A. Wiblingen and C. P. Hagström (1792–1801) and of Finland, published by C. W. Gylden (1837–44). Large-scale maps of the urban areas of Denmark were begun in 1863; scale, 1:800. Other specialist maps were slowly prepared by interested authorities. Geological survey, for example, was promoted by the private exploitation of mineral resources, and each of the Scandinavian countries has pioneer documents. Among those in Sweden, few show as much diligence and enterprise as the materials of Daniel Tilas. His notebook from over two centuries ago is an excellent example of the type of field work undertaken by resourceful surveyors in his day.

The maritime world of Scandinavia has naturally cast an eye upon charts of the sea to parallel maps of the land. Ports, harbours and coastal "roads" have remained largely inaccessible save to the few pilots who knew them as they knew the backs of their hands. Wagenhaers there might be, but they were no substitute for local aid. The advice beside the Island of Jurmo in John Sellers' *English Pilot* epitomises this—"Here 4 farmers—

you may get a pilate here"! Eighteenth-century naval actions encouraged the preparation of new charts from the East Sea. British Baltic expeditions, such as those of Sir John Norris in the earlier eighteenth century, undertook chart revisions.[1] It is not easy to say how effective Admiral Nordenanker's new Baltic charts (1:500,000) were in aiding merchant mariner or naval strategist. They were originally published in atlas form,[2] incorporated interesting profiles and panoramas of the approaches to Bothnian harbours, and were improved upon by Erik and Gustaf af Klint. Although there were Russian hydrographical surveys in the gulfs of Finland and Bothnia during the earlier nineteenth century, progress was slow. Zachris Topelius, in his university lectures in geography, pointed out how ignorance of the coastal shallows grounded British men-of-war, which were reduced like Ingolf and Hjorlief, pioneers to Iceland a millennium earlier, to "probing the waves with lead". In the same breath, he pointed out that the urgency of Russian naval needs was spurring new charts. As the President of the Royal Geographical Society put it in his annual address at the time (1855)—"the war . . . has given an extraordinary impulse to geography".

Thereafter maritime survey proceeded apace. Norwegian and Swedish shipping was aided by the mid-nineteenth century publication of *Den norske Lods* (The Norwegian Pilot), the eight volumes of which were shortly afterwards followed by *Svensk Lots* (The Swedish Pilot) in four volumes.[3] The sprinkling of ships' captains who visited northern waters in the eighteenth century and who left comment on many of the whimsies which passed for sea-marks, were followed by a stream of merchant carriers who expected to be notified by the growing number of British consuls about the multiplying beacons and lighthouses ringing the northern coasts.[4] Bearing in mind the length and nature of the Scandinavian and Finnish coasts, it is not surprising that their hydrographic surveys make a substantial claim

---

[1] W. R. Mead, "Finland and the Landfall of British Authority", *The Norseman*, XVI, 1, 1958.
[2] *General charta till Sveriges sjö-Atlas*, Stockholm, 1797.
[3] Cf. C. A. Dahl, *Norges sjøkartverks historie indtil 1914*, Kristiania, 1914, and P. Dahlgren and H. Richter, "Swedish Hydrography, 1644–1944", *International Hydrographic Review*, **24**, 1947, 186–95.
[4] Consular reports of Foreign Office archives, P.R.O.

upon funds allocated for mapping. Indeed, there is a perennial tug-of-war between hydrographical and topographical demands.

This tug-of-war is an unavoidable consequence of an extensive land area with a relatively small population. Even Denmark has extensive Arctic and sub-Arctic dependencies to survey. Maps covering Scandinavia and Finland show a substantial variation in coverage on different scales from country to country, and they are also uneven in quality. Again, the extensive, thinly peopled and slowly developing areas are frequently cartographically neglected in favour of remapping the more limited, densely peopled and rapidly evolving metropolitan districts. The physical problems of survey have been relieved of some of their restraints. Thus, topographic mapping until the 1920s was largely by plane-table survey: but by the time of the Second World War half of the prepared maps derived from photogrammetric methods. At that time, Norway had no regular air survey: but today air-survey methods are employed almost exclusively. Sweden has complete air photographic coverage (scale 1:6,000): Finland[1] has virtually complete coverage—much of which has been sponsored for taxation purposes or for purposes of forest mensuration. Air photography has transformed the cartographic prospects of the Scandinavian countries and Finland. With photogrammetry to aid, complete and up-to-date coverage becomes a physical possibility for the first time in their histories. It is the most revolutionary discovery which they have experienced for summarising the nature of their lands and much of their resource.

THE DISCIPLINE OF DISTANCE

It is not intended at this stage to consider the network of communications which binds the Fenno-Scandinavian countries together. It is, however, impossible to appreciate the revaluation in their resources without reference to changes in "the discipline of distance".[2]

On land, by the introduction of railway (and subsequently automobile); at sea, by the replacement of sail by steam and timber by steel, changes in transport costs of a fundamental character were set in motion.

The discipline of distance was first relaxed at sea. It is difficult to realise that in sailing-ship days two or three round trips a summer—with over-wintering in British harbours or on tramp journeys between extra-Baltic ports—was the maximum possible number. Many cargo ships sailed only in summer—a single trip to the Mediterranean, with salt as a return cargo, was all that was expected. The exaggerated threat of the winter freeze[3] (cf. Fig. 23) and delays resulting from the treacherous coasts and pilotage also accounted for the remarkably small number of voyages per ship. The coming of steam-power automatically increased the number of journeys. At the same time it increased the manoeuvrability of vessels—especially during those late-season calms most likely to give rise to ice formation. Both points are frequently noted in consular reports from the Baltic to the Foreign Office in the later nineteenth century. Steel and steam also gave rise to the ice-breaker—first coming to the Baltic from North America in the 1880s. Greater security of travel resulted in falling costs of insurance.

The absolute reductions in freight charges which followed transport modifications were substantial, but the differential changes in freight rates were even more significant. For short distances freightage fell relatively less than for long distances. Reviewing freight quotations in early numbers of *Göteborgs Handels och Sjöfartstidning*, it may be found that the rates for timber from Göteborg to East Coast British ports in the earlier nineteenth century were from 30 shillings to 34 shillings per standard. The same produce from Bothnian ports cost 60 shillings to 100 shillings per standard and, for comparative purposes, from Canada 75 shillings to 85 shillings per standard. Pehr Malm, a Jakob-

---

[1] V. Erola *Publications of Finnish Geodetic Institute*, **46**, 1955.

[2] The phrase is from J. W. Watson, *Scottish Geographical Magazine*, Edinburgh, 1955, **71**, 1.

[3] It was as though ships' captains still heeded the warning of the author of the thirteenth-century *King's Mirror* (American Scandinavian Monographs, New York, 1917) who observed October 16th as the last date for high seas sailing. G. M. Jones, *Travels in Scandinavia*, London, 1827, observed in mid-October, English merchantmen waiting for deals off Viborg, "exceedingly anxious, fearing lest they might be frostbound for the winter". The *Copy-book of J. V. Snellman*, Oulu city archive, especially the letters for 1844, also has relevant observations.

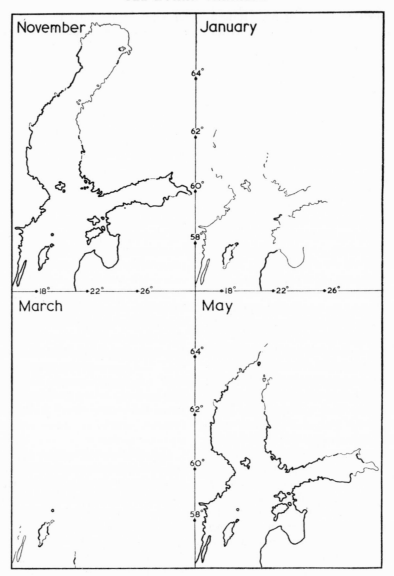

FIG. 23. Winter accessibility of the Baltic coast in sailing-ship days.
Those parts of the coast-line are drawn which are unaffected (heavy
line) or but little affected (light line) by ice accumulation. (After
Atlas of Finland, 1925–8.)

stad merchant, estimated in the 1820s that
nine-tenths of the cost of softwood products
exported from the Bothnian coasts consisted
of customs, freight and other charges.[1] Nor
must it be forgotten that the Sound dues added
their quota until 1857.   Steel and steam had
so profoundly altered transport costs that by

the 1880s rates from Norrland to Thames-side
had fallen to 30 shillings a standard.   Or, to
express it more significantly, they had declined
to a quarter of the F.O.B. value of the commodity.

Changes in the character of shipping rapidly
forced   structural   adjustments   in   harbour

[1] W. R. Mead, "The Discovery of Britain by the Finns", *The Norseman*, 1954, VIII, 4.

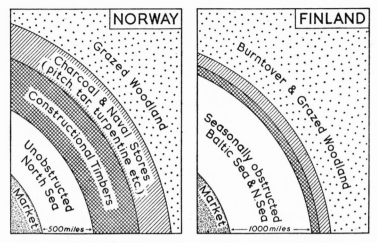

FIG. 24. Generalised diagram of zones of woodland exploitation in
Norway and Finland before softwood revaluation.

facilities. These were to be reflected in a new port hierarchy—some declining in status, some advancing, others striving to offset the disadvantages of local inaccessibility. "The demensions of ye ships" were a cause of worry to the eighteenth-century merchant Thomas Dunn.[1] The shallow (and, as has been noticed in Chapter II, shallowing) Bothnian coastal waters, prompted the rise of outports such as Holmsund for Umeå or Mäntyluoto for Pori. Other harbours, such as Kemi or Sundsvall, favoured an extension of lighterage in the shape of the Noah's-ark-like barge which is such a distinctive feature of certain Baltic roadsteads.

The sailing vessel, with complementary horse haulage and/or river-boat transport, gave rise to distinctive regional zonings of farmland and woodland use. Three general observations may be made. First, there was a sharp gradient in softwood timber values from coast and tributary waterway to the interior,[2] with corresponding differences in their use. In general, accessible woodlands tended to provide the bulkier, less-refined materials, while less accessible woodlands produced the refined more transportable commodities. Secondly, within any given area of softwood

exploitation, there were local variations springing from the capacity of farm produce to withstand transport costs to a market. R. Ajo has defined a series of producing zones for south-western Finland for the horse-transport period, basing them upon a price-parity system.[3] He calculates that a century ago planks could be transported 50 km., rye 140 km. and flax 200 km. according to price parity. Thirdly, within northern Europe, at large, there prevailed major regional variations in the degree and/or extent of softwood exploitation for different purposes dependent upon market accessibility. Fig. 24 presents a highly generalised picture of the situation prevailing around the Norwegian coast (500 miles, say, from the British and West European market) and that around the inner reaches of the Baltic gulfs (1,100 miles or more from the same market).

The outermost zone is that of board and lumber production. "Woody Norway" east of Lindesnes,[4] south-west Sweden and, to some extent, the south-east Baltic were the traditional sources of these. By contrast, Sweden and Finland became the specialised supply areas of pitch, tar, turpentine, distillations and resins. Pipe rolls in the Public

[1] Cf. his fascinating *Copy Buch*, 1717, Viipuri city archives, Mikkeli.
[2] Cf. H. Pontoppidan, "A choice mast-tree, which when standing may be estimated at 60, 100 or 120 rixdollars, cannot after it is cut down, be conveyed to the seaports for less than double the prime cost", *op. cit.*, p. 142.
[3] "Development of Traffic Areas in Finland", *Fennia*, **69**, 3, 1946.
[4] A. Bugge, *Den norske trælasthandels historie*, Skien, 1925, and "Handelen mellem England og Norge", *Historisk tidsskrift*, Oslo, **3**, iv.

Record Office indicate the antiquity, continuity and widely dispersed character of the medieval trade. Qualitatively a royal reputation was established for Norwegian deals by their demand for Windsor Castle, Holyrood Palace and King's College, Cambridge. Quantitatively speaking, the demand increased as British woodlands were progressively denuded. Calamity added to the demand; it is said that the Norwegians "warmed their hands by the Great Fire of London". Indeed, the Navigation Acts were especially relaxed in 1668 to permit freer timber import. The Swedes also shared the warmth. Among other testimonies to Swedish imports from the period is Samuel Pepys' account of his visit to Sir William Warren's timberyards in Deptford, where he was given a lecture on how the Swedes prepared their timber. From such eighteenth-century sources as the *Chancery Masters' Lists* of British merchants trading into the Baltic, it is possible to deduce that softwoods were coming into every British port of consequence—and to some, like Ravenser and Portus Romanum, which were in the final stages of decay. Forty-three ports were listed in 1798 and 759 vessels brought timber from Norway. With advancing years and, White Sea timbers apart, "Christiania deals" and "Drammen battens" became the first choice of all discerning timber merchants. Only when protected could timbers from the Maritime Provinces or the Gulf of St. Laurence compete with them. The Admiralty was peculiarly slow to admit that timbers other than Scandinavian were adequate for their purposes.[1] The higher price demanded for *Vik* boards naturally tempted the unscrupulous to pass off other timbers in their place or to smuggle them in as boards of lower value.[2] On the buying side, it is doubtful if merchants always recognised exclusive timbers or distinguished "floated" timber from what they called "bright timber" (i.e. that which had not moved coastwards by floatage way).

The second detectable zone of production was the territory of pitch-and-tar distillation, though it was not necessarily so uniformly broad as in Fig. 24. The significance of tar and pitch exports, brought out in Olaus Magnus's map (Plate 24), probably reached its peak about three hundred years later. At the time of the Crimean War, it was estimated that Finland probably had 3,000 tar distilleries; while there were single Bothnian dealers who were able to sell as many as 10,000 tons of pitch annually to a London wholesaler. The centres of export shifted, but there were times when one Bothnian port might supply a full quarter of the Swedo-Finnish export of "Stockholm tar". A primary source of information concerning tar shipments from the Baltic were (until their cessation) the Öresund accounts, though they were not always kept according to the same system of accounting.

Regionally complicating the idealised zoning of Fig. 24 were the charcoal burneries, which showed, in general, a pattern closely tied to that of mineral occurrence. Until modern methods of refining ore were introduced in the last third of the nineteenth century, charcoal was responsible for most refining in Scandinavia (and on a small scale in Finland).[3] Only since 1900 has coke been employed in quantities of economic significance. It has been estimated that a century ago a full quarter of Sweden's annual lumber crop was consumed in the charcoal burneries. The consumption had a very uneven distribution because of the poor transportability of charcoal. The average distance over which charcoal moved in the horse-drawn period was 5–15 km. Bulk movement was a great problem when six tons of charcoal were combined with three or four tons of ore to produce one ton of bar iron. Indeed, if there were not equal availability of ore and charcoal, it was more reasonable to transport ore to charcoal. Bearing in mind the character of forest ownership, it was common for smelteries in the pre-industrial period to purchase 35–40% of their charcoal. There resulted a highly decentral-

[1] Cf. G. S. Graham, "The Baltic Blockade and the Birth of the Canadian Timber Trade", *Baltic and Scandinavian Countries*, Torun, 1939. Specific examples can also be found in price lists, e.g. that issued by Messrs. Dempsey and Picard of Liverpool in 1821, in which Quebec deals were selling at £14 16s. per standard hundred with little duty, Archangel Reds at £18 10s. and Swedish deals at £17 plus a high duty.

[2] H. S. Kent, "Anglo-Norwegian Timber Trade in the Eighteenth Century", *Economic History Review*, VIII, 1, 1955, 62–74.

[3] G. Arpi, *Järnhanteringens träkolsförsörjning*, Stockholm, 1951.

PLATE 11. SUBURBAN HELSINKI

Post-war developments in Ruskeasuo (Brunnakär), where hospitals and apartment houses rise above the spruce woods on the north side of Helsinki.

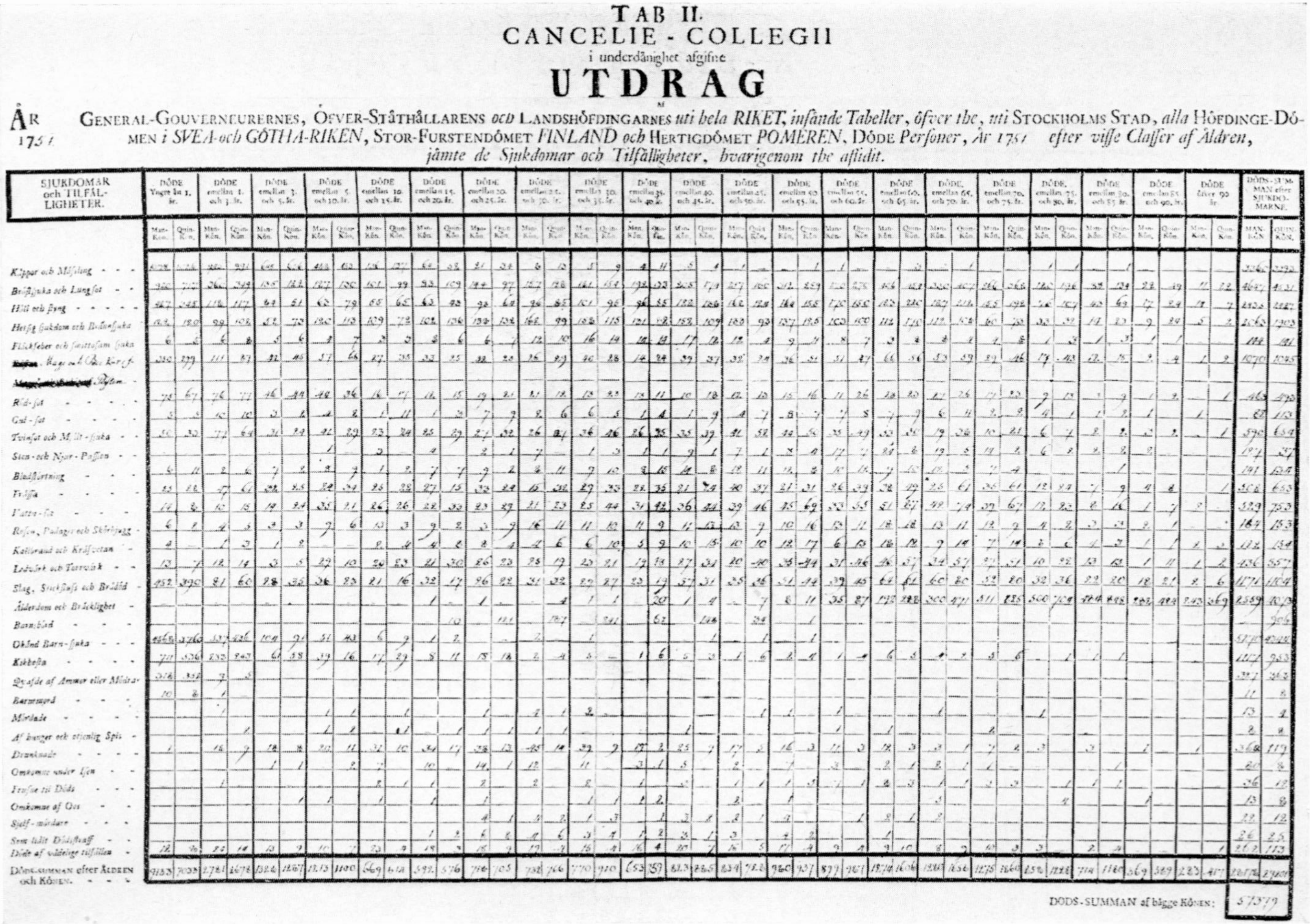

TAB II.
CANCELIE - COLLEGII
i underdånighet afgifne

UTDRAG

ÅR 1751 GENERAL-GOUVERNEURERNES, ÖFVER-STÅTHÅLLARENS och LANDSHÖFDINGARNES uti hela RIKET, insände Tabeller, öfver the, uti STOCKHOLMS STAD, alla HÖFDINGE-DÖMEN i SVEA- och GÖTHA-RIKEN, STOR-FURSTENDÖMET FINLAND och HERTIGDÖMET POMEREN, DÖDE Personer, År 1751 efter vissa Classer af Åldren, jämte de Sjukdomar och Tilfälligheter, hvarigenom the afledit.

SJUKDOMAR och TILFÄLLIGHETER.

Kopper och Mässling
Bröstsjuka och Lungsot
Håll och Styng
Hetsig sjukdom och Brännsjuka
Fläckfeber och smittosam sjuka
Hugg och Bröst-värk
Rödsot
Gulsot
Tvinsot och Mjältsjuka
Sten- och Njur-Passion
Blodstörtning
Frissa
Vattusot
Rosen, Pålagor och Skörbjugg
Kallbrand och Kräftsår
Ledbrut och Tandvärk
Slag, Stickflus och Bråddöd
Ålderdom och Bräcklighet
Barnsbörd
Okänd Barn-sjuka
Kikhosta
Qväfde af Ammor eller Mödrar
Barnamord
Mördade
Af hunger och otienlig Spis
Drunknade
Omkomne under Isen
Frusne til Döds
Omkomne af Os
Själf-mördare
Som lidit Dödsstraff
Döde af våldsamma tilfällen
Döds-SUMMAN efter ÅLDREN och KÖNEN.

DÖDS-SUMMAN af bägge KÖNEN: 57579

PLATE 12. THE COUNTING OF HEADS
A specimen page from *Tabelverket*, the Swedish census material of the late eighteenth century (cf. Chapter IV).

ised iron industry, consisting of small units fairly evenly scattered through the forest areas which overlay the iron deposits. Exhaustion of local softwood areas of supply was the greatest threat overhanging a smeltery. Charcoal thus had its own localised areas of production, overlapping and competing with other zones of utilisation.

The areas of softwood refinement—fingering their way upstream along valley and tributary lake and reappearing sporadically in association with mineral working—merged with the broad forest ranges of Norway and, in Sweden and Finland, with the great penumbra of burnt-over woodland. Though falling short of his idealised pattern, it would not be too great a stretch of the imagination to see in this threefold arrangement of zones some support for the theory of J. H. von Thünen. Clearly, land use and values (or rents) display here a tendency to respond to a market —or series of markets. Use and value are a function of the discipline of distance.

The new web of communications which relaxed this discipline changed the existing arrangement. Both the decline of established products and the rise of new ones made their contribution. Pitch and tar declined—the more so as a result of coal distillation and Trinidad pitch. Charcoal burneries were weeded out: burn-beating disappeared. The volume of sawn-timber exports from Sweden and Finland rose rapidly (cf. Fig. 25). New products, especially paper and pulp, capable of withstanding greater transport costs, multiplied location opportunities. And in the two-stage advance in land transport which in part accompanied and in part followed the development of new products, elasticity of location was further extended.

E.G.—8

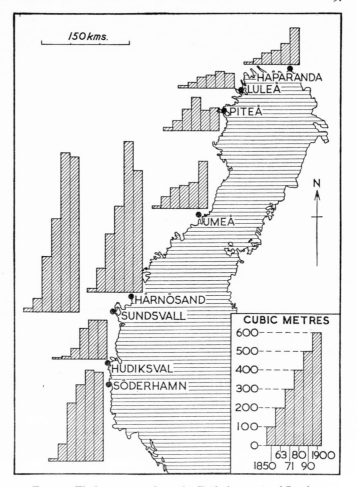

FIG. 25. Timber exports from the Bothnian ports of Sweden. (see also F. E. Söderlund, *Swedish Timber Trade*, 1850–1950.)

THE IMPACT ON THE LAND

(a) The Assault on the Woodland

The greater part of Scandinavia and Finland was originally covered by woodland, and woodland still dominates the vegetational scene of much of the mainland. Two forest forms prevailed—a deciduous tract of limited extent covering Denmark and the extreme south of Sweden, and a coniferous blanket to which in earlier times the adjective "limitless" could be applied. Any appreciation of the settlement and development of Scandinavia and Finland can only be considered within the frame of the forest. The same, of course, might be said historically of much of England and France; but the parallel is limited, because only a small proportion of the Scandinavian woodland bears ecological comparison. That part which shows similarity has been denuded almost as completely of its natural woodlands as most of England and France. But such a transformation of the vegetational scene is exceptional, and intensity of occupation shows marked contrasts between the coniferous forest and deciduous woodland zone. The removal of the softwood cover has only been as complete as the removal of the hardwood cover in extremely limited areas. In all senses of the word, it is one of the most *continuous* features of the northern scene.

The woodland has been attacked in a number of ways and for a number of purposes. First, there has been direct clearance with a view to reclaiming arable land. Secondly, there has been steady and regular denudation of woodlands around the periphery of settled areas through open ranging of animals, cutting for fuel and felling for constructional work (including fences). Thirdly, there has been exploitation of accessible timber for local industry. This industry, embracing also charcoal burning and pitch and tar manufacture, breaks the continuity of the timber cover. Finally, various methods of firing the woodland have made regional inroads. All of these systems of exploitation have had negative effects, but, save for Denmark and Iceland, the absolute scale of human attack on timber was not so great as to be of national consequence. Given new means of transport and new techniques, there remained abundant reservoirs for exploitation. Happily, too, those means arrived after the significance of woodland conservation had been realised. In other words, equilibrium between timber cutting and timber growth, though it had been disturbed regionally, had not been disturbed nationally in "coniferous" Scandinavia down to the softwood revaluation. Since the revaluation, the equilibrium has been jealously guarded.

While persistent pressure at the woodland margin is the ultimate manner in which land has been reclaimed for the plough, there have been a number of climaxes in which the attack has been regionally intensified. For example, as reclamation in fiord Norway approached its limits, the great "inner drama" of eastern Norway worked up to a crescendo when landtakers occupied Gudbrandsdal, Österdal and their tributary valleys. Several thousand *rud* or *rød* elements in place-names from these dales, identifying the clearings from the time, enable the reconstruction of this most energetic stage in the occupation of interior Norway.[1] Another significant climax in the regional occupation of a wooded territory was the Finnish colonisation of Swedish Värmland and Dalarna (Taalainmaa to the Finns) at the invitation of the crown in the seventeenth century. Again, a legacy of place-names has been left—a legacy which, stretching through the Norwegian border territory of Finnskogen, gives some indication of the extent of immigrant enterprise. Late nineteenth-century land-taking in north Norway and Sweden was another climax. Of different origin and order is the Finnish resettlement programme of the period 1944–51—perhaps the latest significant enterprise. It has been of unique consequence for the outside observer, who would see the past in the present and the impact of present techniques upon a traditional activity of the northlands.

In addition to the absolute denudation of timber, there have also been changes in woodland composition. Thus, selective cutting of timber has accounted regionally for the elimination of particular species. In the broad zone where deciduous and coniferous species mingle, deciduous trees have suffered the heaviest assault—weakening their regenerative powers in a community where, in any case, they are sub-dominant. The oak, in particular, has experienced reduction along the midland axis of Scandinavia. It was much sought for the construction of naval shipping—especially during the seventeenth and eighteenth centuries.[2] South Finland was also denuded for this purpose so that today there are place-names indicative of a former oak vegetation attached to areas which support a completely

[1] O. Heitmann-Andersen, *Det Norske Folks Busetning og Landnåm*, Oslo, 1944.
[2] Repeating here the theme of R. G. Albion, *Forests and Sea Power*, Cambridge, Mass., 1926.

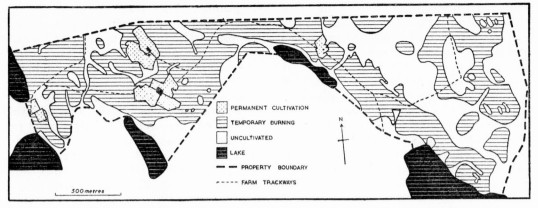

FIG. 26. A Finnish farm from Iisalmi parish, 1885, to show an area under rotational burning. (After T. G. Telen, *Charta öfver Follwäniemi Skiftetslagsäger, Iidensalmi Socken*, 1837.)

different tree community. (At the same time and with true irony the frontier of oak cultivation has shifted steadily northwards.) The beechwoods of south Norway have undergone a similar reduction. The peeling of birches for domestic birch-bark manufactures has produced local birch wastes, though as a resilient species the birch has suffered less than other hardwoods. The changing complexion of sample woodland areas has been effectively investigated for several tracts in Sweden. Halland is a good illustration of a mixed deciduous/coniferous province where the effects of exploitation have been carefully pieced together from past evidence.[1]

A changing vegetational pattern has also been produced by fire. The most extensive effects of woodland firing from recent historical times are found in Finland and north Sweden.[2] The original employment of fire as an aid to clearing, bearing in mind the extent of the woods and the small population, would have a limited impact upon the vegetational scene. The deliberate firing of the land in order to promote the growth of reindeer moss for pasturage in the tributary Lapp areas would also be of restricted importance. The effects of fire as a part of the rotational practice in land use, however, are likely to have been much more considerable. The repeti-

tion of firing over a given area had become part of an established agricultural process by a hundred years ago.

Firing the woodlands is a practice which has been variable in extent in time and place in Northern Europe. It is known as *svedjebruk* in Sweden and *kaskiapoltto* in Finland—the word experiencing minor changes in spelling according to particular nuances in the process. The objectives of firing have generally been to increase the harvest of grain or other crops from a given farm or territory without necessarily increasing the area of cleared land. Clearing, burning, sowing in the charcoal ash and harvesting have been undertaken in historical times both on an individual and a collective basis. The practice was given a special category in the land-use maps prepared in nineteenth-century Finland, and Fig. 26 indicates the areas rotationally under burning on a farm from Savolax during the 1880s. The rotational process was commonly long-term. As soon as the ash was cooled (and the greatest problem normally was not to produce the fire but to control its expansion), rye, barley, oats, turnips, flax or hemp might be sown in the clearing. Sometimes a fence would be cast around the clearing; sometimes the burned land might be temporarily divided among a group of farmers. The clearing

---

[1] E.g. C. Malmström, *Hallands skogar under de senaste 300 åren*, 1939, and also L. Toren, *Skogshistoriska studier i trakten av Degerfors, i Västerbotten*, 1937.
[2] The antiquity of the method in Northern Europe can be appreciated from J. G. D. Clark, "Forest Clearance and Prehistoric Farming," *Economic History Review*, XVII, 45–51. Firing in Jutland is the subject of a substantial essay by A. Steensberg, "Med braggende flamme", *Årbog for Jydsk arkæologisk selskab*, 1955.

would not be stocked of its roots, though a wooden plough might loosen the crust of ashes after rain. The land might support a succession of several crops before soil exhaustion was revealed by diminishing returns. It would then be allowed to revert to its wild state, degenerating through poor grazing land to colonisation by the more aggressive birch and aspen. Assuming complete occupation of the land and continuation of the rotational firing, the young bush growth might be burnt-over again after an interval of twenty-five years. Woodland burning cannot be considered without bearing in mind two other facts. First, the burned timber had no alternative use value—a fact impressed by an early British topographer, William Marshall, in 1767 during his journey through Vestrobothnia. Secondly, a general shortage of natural manure for the cultivated land forced a search for alternative fertilisers. Burning was a temporary solution.

How thoroughly firing could change the pattern of the original vegetation is perhaps borne out by the first woodland map of Finland produced by the land surveyor and forester C. W. Gylden just a century ago.[1] The enormous softwood timber deficiency in Karelia and the south-east coincides precisely with those areas which practised burning most intensively and relinquished it most slowly. The virtually unrelieved birch groves and poor softwood stands which characterise some of the wooded parishes of Mikkeli province are frequently a botanical reflection of the delayed disappearance of this practice. There is a widespread place-name legacy, from which the distribution of the practice can also be detected.[2]

Woodland burning has been subject to periodical and regional restraints. The comprehensive Swedish Forestry Act of 1647 acknowledged the impossibility of preventing the practice, but sought to restrain it by making permission necessary and by according fuller rights to the charcoal industry. Petty courts theoretically fined offenders, but frequently the juries were as deeply involved as the plaintiff. There is at least one interesting illustration from the Fredriksberg area of an ironworks which intruded upon an established area of woodland burning and where a compromise was arranged between charcoal burning and cultivation burning. Restraints upon burning were intensified with the dawn of forest rationalisation. Thus, Finland was brought into the orbit of stricter control by the law of September 9th, 1851, which prohibited burning for tar, bark-stripping for tanning and forest-firing in areas of oak or any other large constructional timberland. Restraints were also imposed in accordance with an ecological argument which emphasised the virtue of a heavy forest cover in ameliorating climate.

Yet, burning clearly had a place on the farm—and in the national economy. The burnt-over land was able to make a significant contribution towards keeping starvation at bay in much of Finland, Norway and Sweden. It was estimated by a newspaper correspondent who sought to support the practice that a century ago roughly a third of Finland's grain was derived from burned woodland. The last rye presumed to have been grown on burnt land was sown in Sweden in Dalecarlia in 1918; there may still be isolated areas in modern Finland where it persists in relic form.[3]

Woodland burning was regionally variable in its intensity. In general contrast to the low-value burnt-over areas were the high-value cut-over areas where timber shortage was an issue of consequence. "Timber shortage" generally implied a shortage of major constructional timbers, and it was one of the phenomena noted by the topographers—particularly in hardwood areas. Linnæus remarked on the timberless tracts of southern Sweden in his *Skåne Journey* (Stockholm, 1751)—even making reference to coal import from Great Britain to supply the lime-kilns of Malmö. Another Swede from the same period, Nils Reuterholm, declared that no country girl should wed before she had a hundred well-established hardwood trees as a dowry;[4] while above the door of the appropriately

[1] Reproduced in S. H. Jaatinen and W. R. Mead, *Economic Geography, op. cit.*, p. 32.
[2] Cf. *Geographical Studies*, 1954, **1**, i.
[3] Nor is it difficult to imagine that the Finnish steam-bath or *sauna* is a logical aftermath of woodland burning.
[4] G. Wieslander, "Skogsbristen i Sverige under 1600- och 1700-talen," *Skogsvårdsföreningens tidskrift*, Stockholm, 1936.

stone and brick vicarage which Pehr Kalm occupied in Maaria parish, near Turku, is inscribed the motto: "Save the woodland, the nation's wealth". Sometimes the response to this situation had pronounced landscape effects. The widespread wattle-and-daub buildings which characterise the older settlement pattern of Skåne are related to the coppiced willow and other deciduous species which abound. From such rural leaders as Rutger MacLean is derived roadside timber planting, so that parts of the Skånian scene resemble the avenued and tree-lined landscapes of France. All such comment and action were slowly to build up the idea that a balance must be struck between woodland and cropland interests.

The absolute consumption of timber at different periods is not easy to estimate; but it is clear that quantitatively it was never as great as today. Yet, today a balance between natural growth and consumption is maintained. The principal changes in the character of consumption are the use of the overseas markets, the relative decline of the domestic market and of charcoal consumption. Domestic fuel needs are remarkably persistent.

TABLE 8

CHANGING CHARACTER OF TIMBER CONSUMPTION

Employment of Timber Felled	1855	1895	Average 1926–30
Domestic fuel . . .	50·4	54	28·4
House, ship and bridge building	14·0	—	—
Charcoal	27·8	19·4	4·6
Manufactured exports .	6·1	21·0	32·2
Paper and pulp . . .	—	4·8	27·9
Other industries . . .	1·7	0·8	6·9

(Source: E. Heckscher, *op. cit.*, p. 324.)

Afforestation has never been of great consequence in the northern two-thirds of Fennoscandia, but in the deciduous zone—and to a certain extent in the transitional area—it has played a steady if unspectacular role. It has assumed several forms. First, there have been private plantations in parks, estates and experimental wood-lots. These have been especially numerous in Skåne and the Danish islands. There have also been public plantations in connection with reclamation—especially in the heathlands of Jutland. Indeed, the twofold aspect of Jutland's landscape partly derives its character from them—the accented relief of the eastern moraine country, embossed with residual leaf-woods, contrasting with the western outwash plains and their geometrically arranged plantations of conifers. Although western Jutland was probably wooded extensively with deciduous species in earlier times, long-period climatic change and the depredations of man and beast had already denuded them by the dawn of historic time. The contemporary plantations, a sample distribution of which is given in Fig. 27 (p. 102), are of varying age, though many are related to the initiative of the Danish Heath Society (1866). The conifers serve a variety of functions. As windbreaks and shelters, they are a means of checking sand encroachment from the dune coast as well as wind erosion from the exposed surface of the land. Their timber sales also provide an income from otherwise unproductive land.

In the past, so much of the woodland of Northern Europe has been regarded as wasteland—the *erämaa* of the old Finnish world, a territory at best used for hunting, trapping and extensive exploitation. Wasteland is a relative term, and the last century has seen a progressive and speedy contraction of the area to which it refers. The collective term *impedimenter*, which has no precise English counterpart, now embraces all those terrains where the plough will not operate and the tree will not grow. There are, however, broad marginal tracts which are difficult to classify. There are not infrequently boulder deserts where the plough may not go but which support tolerable timber stands. There are high fells which support little life and are above the limit of cultivation and the timber-line. They appear to be the true wastelands—yet, apart from scree and icefield, even parts of them may function as feeding grounds for reindeer.

The first "prize essay" of the Royal Finnish Agricultural Society, by B. F. Nordlund and published in 1874, was *On the effects of forest clearance on climate, culture and well-being, with special attention to the conditions in our*

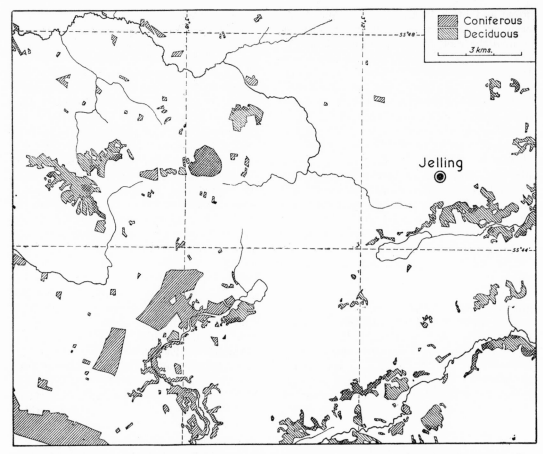

FIG. 27. Heathland plantations of conifers around Jelling in Jutland. (After *Geodetic Survey of Denmark*, 1:40,000.)

northerly located land. It summarised the arguments for an equilibrium in forest-farming relationships as they appeared on the threshold of the modern era. The dual personality of the forest as friend and foe was being slowly resolved. The natural enemy to be attacked in the struggle for extended living space might also be a friend to be protected in the eventual husbanding of resources.

(b) *The Creation of the Farm-land*

The old Scandinavian proverb that "meadow is the mother of arable land" is only true to a limited extent, for most of the cultivated area has been won from the woodland. The mirror image of the assault on the woodlands is, indeed, the creation of the farmland.[1] Some farmland represents the accumulation of piecemeal enterprise in the reclamation of swamp, heath and shore as well as woodland; but timber would have been the natural colonist of the improved swamp, heath or coastal track had not the land been tilled. The possibility of timber as a rotational harvest alternative to the rotation of field crops has only come within the recent economic horizon, but it has been latent botanically.

The expansion of farmland in Scandinavia and Finland has no more been a continuous phenomenon than in any other part of the continent, and there is a similar literature of stagnation, retreat and encouragement. Ex-

[1] Depth in understanding this process is also given by S. Bolin, "Medieval Agrarian Society in its Prime", *Cambridge Economic History of Europe*, Cambridge, 1940, Vol. I, 467–92.

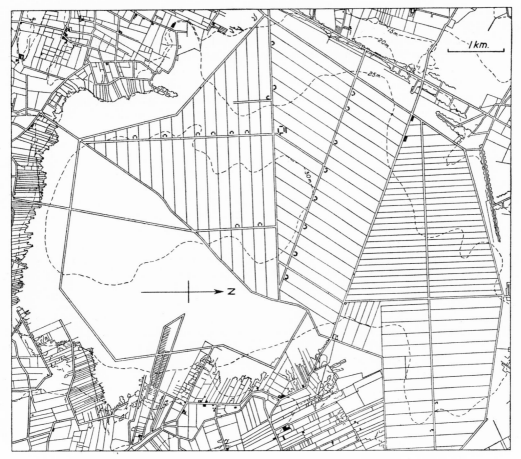

FIG. 28. Reclamation in Jutland. A sample area from the 1:25,000 Geodetic Survey Map of Store Mose, Brönderslev. The successive stages of occupation of the mossland can be detected in the settlement and field pattern of the area. M. K. Kristensen, *Vildmosearbejdet*, København, 1945, tells the story of an epic reclamation.

pansion and contraction of the arable area have followed each other with frequently bewildering speed, and have, indeed, proceeded simultaneously in different parts of the same country. The sequence in Norway following the late medieval expansion illustrates this. From a century later there is abundant documentary evidence of farms which reverted to the waste (*fell i audn*);[1] and testimony is continued by the Bishop of Stavanger, who observed (1521) "many farms now lie here deserted which were formerly occupied". Regional expansion in Trøndelag and Møre in the mid-seventeenth century were succeeded fifty years later by colonisation of the eastern fells. Almost simultaneously, Petter Dass was observing in Helgeland:[2]

"Where formerly men used both harrow and plow
Are wilderness, truly, and forest tract now,
Where wolves and the bear have their shelters."

A series of laws favouring colonisation culminated in the Act of 1752 which, granting settlers ten years of freedom from tax and tithe, encouraged south Norwegian colonists to look as far north as Troms. Retreat as well as advance has similarly characterised the

[1] This contraction of farm area is perhaps explained by price fall; cf. J. Schreiner, *Pest og prisfall i senmiddelalderen*, Oslo, 1948; perhaps by climatic change, cf. *above*, p. 46.
[2] There is an English translation of his remarkable poem, *The Trumpet of Nordland*, Northfield, 1954.

heaths of Jutland, where field, archæological and documentary testimonies to desertion may be found. Reference may also be made to a graphic factual statement from a letter by Ernst Creutz, dated April 26th, 1634, in the Finnish State Archives, "Many homesteads are now laid waste and are deserted"; or to the realm of fiction in Larin Kyösti's short story *Moss*, which describes vividly the process of decline of a colonial holding. Temporally and regionally there are many reasons for the contraction of the cultivated area.

Upon maturer consideration, of course, it is the limited extent of the cultivated area in former times which is the remarkable fact. A review of statistics of cultivated areas for the last century and a half shows that for the Northern Countries at large the figure is twice today what it was during the Napoleonic period. The tempo of reclamation mounted steadily between 1820 and 1860—Sweden, for example, having just over one million hectares in 1820 and more than twice this in 1860.[1] Oddly enough, reclamation displayed continuous vigour side by side with emigration at the end of the century. Thus, at a time when the general pattern of land reclamation in Great Britain and its continental neighbours had reached its virtual limits, the Fenno-Scandinavian agricultural area was expanding rapidly.

Domestic colonisation (*indre kolonisation*) was no simple matter. In Denmark, for example, where the agricultural area expanded by 3,000 sq. km. between 1870 and 1900, there was the urge to make up within what had been lost without in Slesvig-Holstein. Before the transformation, farmsteads were islands of cultivation in the heath; today, the heaths are islands in the cultivated area.[2] Fig. 28 shows the reclamation of a contrasting area of mossland. In Sweden, special assistance was given to Norrland. Following a general loan fund for cultivation in 1883, a new cultivation fund for the expansion and drainage of these northern territories was established at the turn of the century. Norway established a

society, *Ny Jord* (1912), to encourage colonisation within: although specific enterprises such as that in Saltdalen had already been set in motion. B. J. Hovde, indeed, has described the period as a second *landnám* or land-taking. Such "colonial" enterprise put the Scandinavian countries in a position midway between the older parent countries of Europe and their overseas domains in temperate latitudes. "Scandinavian rural society and the American frontier were similar" at this time, observed Hovde (*Ibid*, p. 309). The position of these lands was also unique in that the technical revolution in farming proceeded side by side with the process of taming the land in Norway, Sweden and Finland.

The warfare of the natural frontier—spelt in the carcass of the domestic beast and the pelt of the carnivor—was its accompaniment. And farmland was tamed from below as well as from above. In Denmark, families delved for marl—applying several hundred loads to the acre in the enthusiasm of a century ago; underground drainage pipes began to appear on Scandinavian estates in the 1850s.

The creation of farmland was one thing, its organisation another. Fig. 29 illustrates the general practice in the reduction of the open-field system. The form taken by strip holdings has varied regionally—and some parts of Northern Europe, as instanced by maps of seventeenth-century isolated settlements in Finnish Savo and Karelia, were free of the system. The widespread scatter of plots of land associated with the *tun* or family farm was distinctive to Norway.[3] The Norwegian family farm—or *tun*—community has been more persistent as a relic feature in Norway than the open-field system in the rest of Scandinavia (cf. Plate 16).

The reorganisation of holdings was already far advanced when invention and innovation began to make their impact. Daniel Wheeler —a Quaker peatland expert with Scandinavian connections—once wrote to Prince Galitzin of the "silent but certain diffusion of an improved system of agricultural manage-

---

[1] B. J. Hovde, *The Scandinavian Countries, 1720–1865*, Boston, 1943, 296.
[2] Cf. *Det Danske Hedeselskab, 1866–1916*, København, 1916; K. Sørensen, *Hedelandbruget, De Danske Heder*, København, 1943, and the journal, *Hedeselskabets tidsskrift*.
[3] An accessible description of the Danish position may be found in A. Skrubbeltrang, *Agricultural Development and Rural Reform in Denmark*, Rome, 1953, p. 46 *et seq*. Cf. also "The Old Norwegian Peasant Community", *Scandinavian Economic History Review*, Uppsala, 1956.

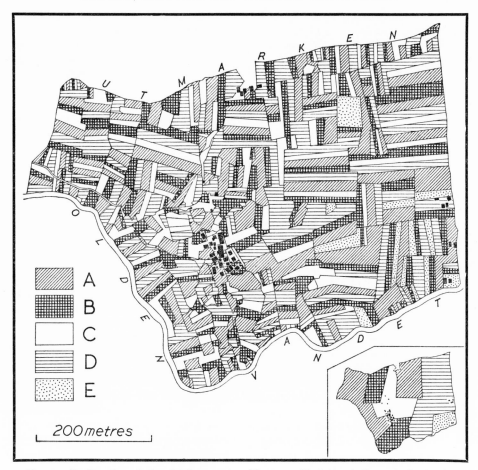

FIG. 29. Reallocation of a hamlet from eastern Norway. The letters indicate the land units of five farms. (From a reparcellisation map in the Norwegian Land Survey Office.)

ment".[1] The diffusion, which occurred apace and with even greater consequences to the old land than the new, is inseparable after 1850 from the transformation of communications. Commenting upon rural Härjedalen, Eli Heckscher observed that in the absence of a railway, it still possessed fifty years ago extensive tracts which followed a way of life three hundred years behind the time.[2] The farther one moved away from a railway-station, he continued, the deeper one moved into the past. Communications in a wider sense must also be remembered: for education and the ability to read spread rapidly. Popular farm journals began to supplement the dissemination of information already given

by the professional papers of the established agricultural societies.

The effects of "the diffusion of an improved system" were cumulative in both biological and mechanical fields. From the 1730s onwards, the potato began to fortify food stocks. It was averred that, through introducing it from Holland, Jonas Alströmer (1658–1761) "gave independence to a kingdom [Sweden] through one plant". Independence, however, was grudgingly accepted, and Linnæus was complaining two decades later, "People will not eat the roots". But eat them they must when famine prevailed and, through being forced to eat them, they came to accept them. The attitude to potatoes had already stabilised

[1] *Daniel Wheeler Papers*, Society of Friends' Library.

[2] A contribution to *Statens järnvägar*, Stockholm, 1906, 407.

in the latter days of Norwegian self-sufficiency (*naturhusholdning*), and it is summarised in Knut Hamsun's *The Growth of the Soil*:

"Potatoes were a new thing, nothing mystic, nothing religious: women and children could plant them—earth apples that came from foreign parts, like coffee. . . . Corn was nothing less than bread: corn or no corn meant life or death" (p. 28).

In Denmark, potatoes predate the arrival of the Rhineland heath colonists—although the colonists were in fact called *Kartoffel-tyskerne*, the crop giving them their nickname. Throughout the north, potatoes were preached from pulpits, and the wealth of "potato literature" written by natural husbandmen enables their dissemination to be traced. It was a long time, however, before the potato rivalled even the traditional turnip, a common harvest taken from the widespread burnt-over land.

The search for new tillage crops was extended by other protagonists to grasslands. Mountain pastures, salt-marsh grazings and heath-range lands were naturally outside this process of improvement; but meadowlands (*ängar*—like the *ings* of the East Riding of Yorkshire or Lincolnshire) were strengthened through seeding, and Linnæus was already actively encouraging the planting of hayseed in 1742. The possibility of grass seed as a rotation crop was strengthened by B. Bergius's introduction of species like Timothy from New York State via London in 1765. Improvement of grassland through manuring was to be an eventual consequence of progress in tillage; while grass was also to establish itself on reclaimed peatland. It was a crop which expanded with the victory over burning and paring of long-term drainage schemes and stable occupation. A great peatland literature bears testimony to this transformation, which was gradually extended to the margins of settlement by both public enterprise (as with the state railway schemes) and private enthusiasm (as with the prize essay of the Swede C. G. Indbetson and the great Norwegian folk-lorist P. C. Asbjørnsen's primers in peatland reclamation).[1] The in-

creased production of grass was intended to feed a growing animal population, the flocks of which were to be thickened in the fleece by marriage with imported "Cumberland, Iorkschire, Vallis, Lincolnshire, Leicester, Rumnei" and Merion breeds,[2] and the herds of which were to be improved in milk and meat by cross-breeding with such as the Shorthorn in Denmark or the Ayrshire in Finland.

Knut Hamsun's Isak "walked bareheaded, in Jesu's name, a sower". Grain was also to the men of Finnish Savolax a holy thing. It is clear that until the opening of the European railroads and the overseas temperate grain-producing lands, the Scandinavian countries and Finland devoted a disproportionately large area to grain. As a result, some unexpected trading occurred. Thus, in 1808–9 the Gothenburg Mails from which *The Times* drew its information, spoke of Swedish problems likely to result from the loss of the Finnish granary. In the 1840s, Denmark was not only the granary for much of Norway but also had a considerable and regular grain export to Britain. However, a situation in which Russian grain could cover a continent by rail and North America could claim a world market in iron-hulled steamships challenged—and reduced the need for—substantial Scandinavian grain production. Moreover, Scandinavian shipping took to grain transport so that specialised freighters like the Åland clippers established themselves upon the Australian run. Only in the mid-twentieth century has the accumulated inventiveness of Scandinavian grain research enabled the successful advance of cereal cultivation northwards. Yet, for travellers like Karel Čapek, Canaan was still Skåne[3] and, discounting northern grains, *The Economist* (October 29th, 1955, p. 4) wrote of

"the golden, wheat-laden plains of the south [which] cling like an invader to their precarious beachhead on the [Swedish] peninsula".

Among the striking developments in Denmark and southern Sweden was the increased use of clover and root crops in rotation. Clover slowly spread from the beginning of the nineteenth century. Sugar-beet began to ap-

[1] *Nyköping läns hushållningsselskap*, 1851, and *Farming in Finland*, Chapter IV.
[2] Jonas Alströmer, *Tal om Schäffernas nytta*, Stockholm, 1759.
[3] *Travels in the North*, London, 1939.

pear in the 1850s and, despite its low sugar content of 4·5%, soon made its mark upon the arable landscape of Skåne. In Denmark, between 1870 and 1914, the area under roots increased tenfold, to account for almost a third of the cultivated land. Of course, successes were balanced by apparent failures. Already, during the Napoleonic Wars, husbandmen like G. Begtrup were advocating the virtues of oil-yielding crops. The *Danish Polytechnic Journal* of 1826 (Vol. II, København) waxed lyrical over their possibilities, and academic dissertations were written on the crops to be anticipated—but without much material result. Nevertheless, seed breeding attracted the growing attention of scientists, and prompted private research stations like Weibulsholm and Svalöv in Sweden as well as government-sponsored institutions. Roots improved the soil, so did the new fertilisers. Guano came to Denmark in the 1840s, though the widespread use of artificial fertilisers awaited the turn of the century, with Norway developing a specialised industry in this field from which it not only supplied its neighbour states but also launched into a world market. The employment of new plants and fertilisers intensified the entire rotational system, reducing the marked regional differences which had hitherto prevailed.[1] A good cartographical summary of the frontiers of cultivation as they made their impact upon a foreign traveller is given by Arthur Capell Brooke.[2] His map, taken from a Swedish original by Colonel Hagelstam, relates to the "climatic productions" of Norway, Sweden and Finland, and emphasises the contrasts on the east and west sides of the Scandinavian peninsula.

The impact of farm machinery was retarded. The big estates naturally adopted the machines of the "new agriculture". Around Christiania, for example, families like the Ankers and Colletts kept abreast of the new ploughs and sowing machines (as well as making their estates models of English parks). Writing from the most advanced of the countries (Den-

mark) in 1860, the British Vice-Consul in Copenhagen observed:

"As Denmark is not a manufacturing country, its youth is not educated to look upon machinery with confidence as in England . . . the Danish farmer has difficulty in properly estimating the value of complicated agricultural machinery, the labourers in using it, the country mechanics in repairing it".

The need for machinery was seriously reported by such Consuls as H. R. Crowe, who in his annual report from Helsinki in 1863,[3] wrote:

"A large field is open here for the introduction of cheap and useful implements of agriculture as the peasantry in this respect are far behind other nations . . . an English agent would find it useful to visit this country for orders."

Machinery imports also resulted from study tours abroad which were increasingly sponsored by agricultural societies. Three almost revolutionary pieces of equipment were the saw, the separator and the steel roller for grain milling. The farmer's attack on the woodland was speeded by the manufacture and dissemination of saws. These were to replace the axes of lumber-jacks—slowly among professional foresters, and only following initial strike action among employees. The centrifugal milk separator was conceived jointly by a Swede, Gustav de Laval, and a Dane, L. C. Nielsen, in 1878. It was basic to the rise of commercial butter production in the north,[4] though its significance has been reduced with the development of the modern dairy network. The steel roller for grain milling, promoting the growth of the centralised co-operative mill beside the dairy, evoked a landscape change as well as a change in process. Some measure of the speed of its adoption is provided by the sudden disappearance of the windmill from the decennial statistics. This essential complement to farming was listed in its thousands in the 1890s, but a decade later it was regarded as effete. The profiles and panoramas of Scandinavian cities, hitherto incomplete without their windmilled eminences, lost within a generation all but a few museum pieces.

---

[1] F. Lägnert, *Syd och mellansvenska växtföljder*, Lund, 1955.
[2] *A Winter in Lapland and Sweden*, London, 1827.
[3] Cf. W. R. Mead, "The Rise of the British Consular System in Finland", *The Norseman*, 1957, **15**, 2. F. Skrubbeltrang, *op. cit.*, p. 215, lists the dates of arrival of machinery to a new Sealand farm.
[4] It is difficult to realise that less than a century ago, it could be written of Danish butter that "it has been principally sold under the name Kiel butter on account of the discredit earlier attached to the product of [Denmark]" (H. Rainals, *op. cit.*, p. 302).

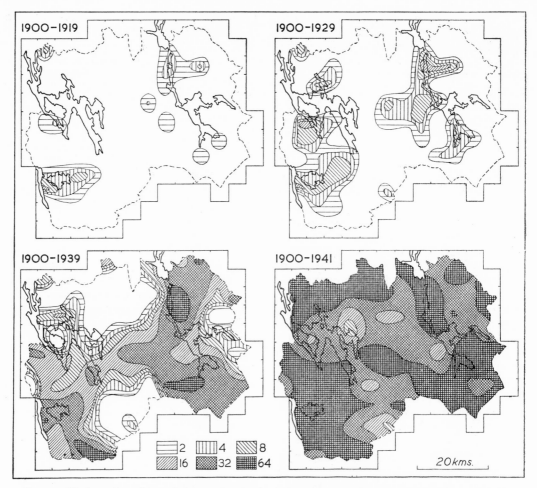

FIG. 30. The intensity of inoculation against bovine tuberculosis in a sample area from South Sweden. The isorhythms are based upon the number of dairy farms in the area. (Source: T. Hägerstrand, *Innovationsförloppet etc.*, Lund, 1953.)

When T. R. Malthus visited Scandinavia in 1799, he commented that there was much land under cultivation which would never be cultivated in Great Britain. It is not inconceivable that much of the land he saw was the product of new intakes and had about it an air of immaturity compared with the maturity of the long-cultivated soils of his home country. The diffusion of new techniques has done something to even out the disparity, and the ensuing generations of tillage have imparted a mature and trim air to much of what was obviously a raw and shaggy countryside. When Scandinavians contemporary to Malthus (Bishop Franz Michael Franzén, for example)

commented upon the garden-like character of rural England, it is not surprising that he should have felt the opposite of rural Scandinavia. Yet, there is a sense in which Malthus is continuingly right in his assertion. There is always a proportion of reclaimed land which is a failure and where the challenge is just too great for human effort. Failures remain as evident today as at any time.

Invention and innovation, aiding more thoroughly the occupation of the land and the integration of the settled areas, have simultaneously eliminated the picturesque self-sufficiency of the individual farm. This feature—called by Norwegians *naturhushold-*

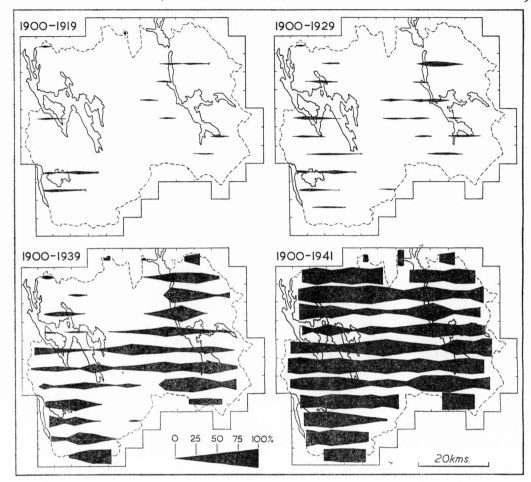

FIG. 31. A complementary map to Fig. 30 in which inoculation is expressed as a percentage of the total number of participating farms. The shaded zones represent transects through the area investigated.

ning—reached its climax during the Victorian age of discovery of Scandinavia. There are many abiding memorials of it written by British travellers and a film, *Havrå*, taken by Bergen ethnologists. Self-sufficiency meant the detailed husbanding of all sorts of food and fodder, and their storage in the multitude of specialised farm buildings which composed the historical centre of the farmstead. Fodder—food sometimes as well—fell to a minimum during the last few weeks of spring. This time of difficulty and skimped resources has contributed a special word to the vocabulary of Norway—*vårknipa* (the pinched springtime), so that today, one may refer colloquially to a slight or serious *vårknipa*. Before the coming of modern communications, such near-famine country jealously guarded its woodland rights as well as its *seter* rights. Leaf fodder was collected, while pulverised phloem from the alder tree provided that *ersatz* for dwindling grain stocks which the phloem of the conifer provided for the peoples of northern Sweden and Finland. It was not without prompting that the Norwegian poet Wergeland wrote a poem called *Famine* in 1839. *Naturhusholdning* was a system which all too frequently spelt insufficiency as well as duplication of effort. Today, production for consumption on the farm has been replaced by production for sale beyond the farm, and farm income is expressed essentially in cash rather than in kind. The period of transition was not without its difficulties, but the effects were no worse than the problems accompanying the system which it replaced. And when transformation was complete, a new stability was promised.

All these changes in the Scandinavian rural scene have been increasingly recorded. One of the first items which had to be agreed upon by the various national stocktakers was a resource classification—fundamentally a classification of land use. In this respect, the stocktakers had been anticipated by the surveyors, who had partly solved the issue in their maps. Over two hundred years ago, for example, the Swedish Land Survey Office had established its initial system of land-use recording. As national statistical offices took shape, they adopted the ready-made classification of arable, natural meadow, woodland, swamp, rock, outcrop and water. To this record of the land was added an increasingly elaborate classification of capital invested in livestock, in equipment and also in the soil.

Nor was the process of change to be neglected by investigators. One of the most fascinating but elusive topics for research is to trace the way by which ideas and inventions spread from a parent locality. An investigation by a Lund geographer, T. S. Hägerstrand,[1] employs this approach in his studies of Skåne and examines the dissemination throughout a selected area of mechanical inventions—such as the motor car, and scientific practices—such as the control of cattle for tuberculosis. His method cannot be fully described here, but Hägerstrand suggests that three stages may be detected in the spread of inventions or innovations—a diffusion stage, a condensing stage and a saturation stage. The saturation stage is reached when the innovation is universally accepted by the examined community. In Figs. 30 and 31 the isorhythm of TB control is reproduced and set within the frame of the area examined. The changes at intervals following 1900 are shown. At the same time, the percentage of farms submitting to the control are shown along a series of east–west axes. It does not necessarily follow that the pattern

of the "innovation waves", the propagation of which he has examined for Skåne, will be repeated for other parts of Scandinavia; but the method commends itself to historian and market research worker alike. Hägerstrand's work measures the methodological and material advances which have taken place in human geography since topographers first set a fashion for describing the rural scene.

THE LEGION OF MACHINES

Norwegian newspaper reporters attending the Great Exhibition in 1851 wrote home enthusiastically about "the legion of machines" which filled the Crystal Palace. The assault of this mechanical legion was eventually to restore the northern world to a significant status in Europe. New machines had been imported a century before the exhibition—sometimes even in the minds of men. Jonas Alströmer was alert to British invention during his eighteenth-century consulship, and where smuggling of equipment failed, bribery of technicians succeeded in bringing new inventions indirectly to Sweden. By 1851, machines were being imported conventionally —if their transport was sometimes unconventional. The local press of Turku, for example, describes the way in which major components for the Finlayson cotton-mill were trundled across country to be set up on Tammerkoski. "The progress of British industry is even sensed here in our northern wastes," Zachris Topelius wrote in the same city in July 1840; while out in the Finnish backwoods, the pedlars of Alexis Kivi's stories praised *engesmannin tavara* (the Englishman's goods). And when the seeds of invention were sown their fruits stimulated native talent. Swedish economic historians could quote the positive genius for invention stimulated in the barren marginal lands of Småland by the new ideas. So often, the Northern Countries had the resources but not the capital and enterprise to produce the equivalents of imported equipment. Their move forward from machine import to machine production, and from consumer goods industries to capital goods industries, measures

---

[1] *Innovationsförloppet ur korologisk synpunkt*, Lund, 1953, and the shorter paper, *The Propagation of Innovation Waves* Lund, 1952.

the progress achieved in industry in three generations.[1]

The market was the moving force and Scandinavia and Finland were drawn into the phenomenally expanding West European market. The reassessment of softwoods, for example, was due to new forms of demand as well as new means of transport. Thus, the extensive building programmes of the West European industrial communities called for large supplies of constructional timber, and Britain, the Low Countries and northern France all had very limited domestic resources. Simultaneously, the demand for mine timber and cellulose rose rapidly. The British market also grew in importance because of the reduction and/or elimination of timber dues (e.g. 1851, 1866). The great new market was born of the legion of machines at the same time as the legion itself began to appear in the Scandinavian world.

An immediate response was the relocation of industrial activity. Most striking of all was the shift in the centre of softwood production.[2] The resources of Norway and southern Sweden (which a little over a century ago funnelled a third of Swedish timber exports through Göteborg) were inadequate to meet the new demand. Sweden showed the most remarkable development. At the beginning of the nineteenth century, its total export was not much greater than the current output of one or two big mills. Fig. 25 shows the shift in production to Norrland—which area today supplies two-thirds of Sweden's timber exports. The lower reaches of Ångerman river were destined to witness such a concentration of activity that they were to be christened "The Lancashire of the Swedish timber trade".[3]

Behind the response to new demands and the application of new techniques to old resources, there were regional workshop traditions upon which to build. The metallurgical industries provide examples. Swedish Bergslagen, a manufacturing area of European distinction, claims special attention in Chapter XII. A tradition of similar origin to that of Bergslagen was developed in southern Finland. Such a metallurgical establishment as Fiskars rooted in the seventeenth century has all the external features of many Bergslagen plants, though Finnish steel plants had completely outgrown their local supply bases by the time the new technologies were becoming known. Likewise, in Norway, the resources at the old-established sites of activity were exhausted or at the point of exhaustion. One of the most remarkable of these relic sites is the old copper town of Røros. It is a museum piece in derelict scrubland, which has been denuded of its timber for mine and smeltery, and is fossilised in a form more than a century old. A score of Norwegian iron-working centres, which even used to export pig-iron to North America, have also declined or disappeared. The celebrated silver reducers at Kongsberg were again set in motion in 1815 by state authority, but without success. Kongsberg had a population of 8,000 in 1770, but less than half of that number in 1840. Nor were the iron-mines which were started by foreign capital in Nordland any more successful. The story of decline might be depressing, but one positive feature remained—all of these enterprises contributed a legacy of latent skills.

Similar skills could be called into play by the wood-working and textile industries. A full two centuries of experience with water-driven saws enabled an easy transition to the techniques of the steam-driven saw-mill. Sweden erected its first in 1848, Finland in 1857. At the same time, the change in the source of power was accompanied by refinement in equipment. The replacement of older and coarse-bladed by newer fine-bladed saws had a most positive effect upon deals and planks which merchants had hitherto protested were as "bristly as bears". In the field of textiles, the woollen goods produced domestically in Jutland, West Norway and West Sweden, and experience with linen and to a lesser extent hemp in Finland, assured a pool of labour for the new factories. The factories grew up

---

[1] As a result of the later impact of the change and the more simple process of technical change, the experiences of individual firms are often summarised with telling clarity in the technical museums of Scandinavia. Company museums aid the understanding of such organisations as ASEA or Stora Kopparberg.
[2] Cf. F. E. Söderlund, *Swedish Timber Exports, 1850–1950*, Uppsala, 1952.
[3] A. Montgomery, *The Rise of Modern Industry in Sweden*, Stockholm, 1939, 93.

mostly in smaller towns, rapidly added cotton to imported raw materials, and throve upon the values they were able to add to the raw materials through manufacturing. Forssa and Hyvinkää provide examples of such towns from Finland. The process was to be carried almost to its extremity in the Bergen area where, upon the foundations of an old woollen industry, there eventually arose a shirt-making industry based essentially upon imported cloth and capable of clothing all Norway. Places like Turku—little known to the outside world—were described as "Newfoundlands discovered by the genius of commerce" when the French traveller Xavier Marmier went there in 1842. Headstones in the local churchyards—Tampere, for example, with its Jenks, Howards and Smiths—tell of the technicians who accompanied the textile machines. Although Fenno-Scandinavia had a good supply of potentially suitable labour, it was not initially geared to receive the full benefits of "the legion of machines". The machines came commonly from lands where steam-power had supplanted water-power, and were received by a countryside where steam-power was generally subordinate to water-power.

Workshops continued to be set against the background of a multiplicity of manageable water-power sites, and showed a widespread dispersal. Lower Värmland and Dalarna provide good regional examples of this. Sometimes, where industry developed a strong orientation towards an immediate market, there was an especially intensive use of a particular river course. A good illustration is found in the intimate adjustment of workshop to waterfall along the course of the Akers river in old Christiania.

There was still a hope that adequate coal might be found. A century ago, Danish geologists thought it worthwhile to produce treatises on Bornholm's coal-seams and Swedes were optimistic of their Skånian deposits.[1] In the first stage of steam-power, however, Scandinavia and Finland were largely by-passed.

There was a second stage when they compromised over this fuel deficiency. In the latter half of the nineteenth century, Scandinavia and Finland offered a growing market for West European coal exports. Great Britain and Germany in particular came to look upon these Northern Countries as natural outlets, and coal travelled to and through them in a variety of ways. For much of Atlantic Scandinavia, British coal was virtually as cheap as on Thames-side, and gave rise to a measure of coastally located industry in southern Norway, Denmark and south-west Sweden. Newcastle coals had already ousted Bornholm fuels in the 1840s to become the basis of Denmark's "Steam à la mode". As a return cargo for timber, coal also encouraged a certain industrial redistribution around the Baltic coast of Scandinavia. It played a role in the locational succession of Norrland saw-milling during the crucial second half of the nineteenth century. This has been shown in a series of maps by Harald Vik.[2] A first stage in relocation of saw-mill sites from a scattered riverside distribution to a concentrated coastal grouping belonged to the period 1850–80 and was based upon return cargoes of coal. A secondary adjustment followed the passage of the railway through the territory between 1880 and 1890.

The spread of the railway network enabled easier inland distribution of coal and coke, and both fuels had (and continue to have) a surprisingly extensive market. Coal imports grew also as a result of the demand for coal-gas, which was a common feature of most northern towns by the 1870s. As an alternative source of fuel for steam, oil was absent—or effectively absent until the very limited resources of central Sweden were brought into play in recent years. With remarkable prescience, *Aftenposten* wrote in 1862: "Pennsylvania's steam oil will soon be one of the essential elements for our industry and welfare." Scandinavia's current interest in oil as a source of locomotive and industrial energy has expression in both the tanker fleet of Norway and the Danish perfection of the

---

[1] Cf. E. Erdman, *Laf ormation carbonifère de la Scanie*, Stockholm, 1873.

[2] *Sveriges sågverksindustri från 1800-talet*, Stockholm, 1950. There is a complementary Finnish study by N. Meinander, *Virkushållning och sågverksrörelse i Torne, Kemi och Simo älvdalar intill första världskriget*, Helsingfors, 1950.

PLATE 13. THE TOPOGRAPHICAL RECORD

An impression of the crater-like entrance to Nordmark mine in *Bergslagen*, from an engraving
by J. F. Martin in the 1790's.

PLATE 14. THE SURREY DOCKS IN 1827

An engraving by S. W. Cooke to show the type of wooden vessel engaged in trading with Scandinavia and Finland in the pre-steam age.

marine diesel engine. Oil import as a source of energy represents a third stage in the encounter with fuel deficiency. It is a stage beyond which Denmark cannot effectively proceed at the moment.

Industry was very clearly responsive to railway development—and, reciprocally, railway patterns were sometimes a response to industrial demands. Frequently railways suggested an industrial location, and an increasingly available supply of electric-power confirmed it. Eli Heckscher stated, for example, that the site of Sandviken was determined by the railway, and added that, for Domnarvet, the critical factor was the 64 km. *Bergslagsbanan* from Grängesberg. The localisation of sugar refineries in Skåne was also clearly influenced by the original railway pattern, and the relationship between railway and refinery remains vital. In Finland, Mänttä paper and pulp plant, considered below in Chapter XI, is a contrasting example of a localisation confirmed (but only just) by the coming of the railway.

Meanwhile, another source of energy was announced which was to enable the greater part of Fenno-Scandinavia to escape from its steam fuel deficiency. In the 1890s, Sweden first employed hydro-electricity for commercial purposes in a cotton-mill at Viskan, first extended a power transmission line between Hällsjön and Grängesberg[1] and first electrified a railway track. While the physical geography of Denmark denied to it the benefits of this new source of energy, it shared in the new series of techniques, new range of markets and new means of transport which were to enable the Northern Countries to overcome the time-lag in economic development which they had suffered.[2]

Among the new techniques none were more important than those which changed the value of Scandinavia's mineral resources. New metallurgical centres came into being, new concentrations of metal-working industries were initiated (cf. Fig. 89 which illustrates some of the changes in *Bergslagen*) and a north-

ward migration of the centre of gravity of large-scale mining took place.

The industrial archives of Sweden contain many materials for the study of the recent changes. A specific example is provided by those which cover the establishment of the Hagfors plant, one of the components of the Uddeholm Company north of Lake Vänern. The decision to create the plant at Hagfors was made on March 23, 1873.[3] It was the conclusion of a two-and-a-half-year debate behind which there had already been the still-born proposals of Engineer Cederblom. Considerations of site and of location proceeded simultaneously. There were a number of sites which met the two essential needs of the plant —a swift fall of regularly flowing water to drive the bellows and hammers, coupled with land which either belonged to the company or which might be easily acquired through purchase. Stjärnfors, Årås, Munkfors, Gustavfors and Dejefors were all equally suitable. Location was guided by a series of calculations based upon transport costs. Calculation A considered movement of ores, coal and charcoal over existing routeways (both water and rail) to potential plant sites. Calculation B considered their movement to potential sites over existing routes versus alternative routes which were to be constructed at company expense. Calculation C weighed in the balance alternative route systems A and B according to different scales of operation—1, 2, 4 blast furnaces etc. Calculation D considered costs A, B, and C in relation to the degrees of refinement of raw materials imported or products exported from the processing site. These various estimates were based on freight rates prevailing at the time and paid no attention to significant possible changes in the future. The ensuing growth of the plant around its original site can be traced from the succession of plans which began with the alternative layouts proposed in 1873. The integration of the plant with *Bergslagen's* system of communications can be followed from successive maps prepared since 1874. The transformation of the plant since

---

[1] P. Hjulström, *Sveriges elektrifiering*, Uppsala, 1940, p. 83 (map).
[2] The reduction of legal restraints upon the operation of industrial plants also assisted; cf. in Norway, 1839 and 1866; Denmark, 1857; Sweden, 1846 and 1864.
[3] The two principal manuscripts are E. G. Danielsson, *The most suitable place for the location of the new plant etc., 1870–1880*, Uddeholm AB. archive, 65 : 1/1 and E. G. Danielsson, *Diverse calculations etc.*, 1872, 26 : 1/2.

the establishment of the first electric oven in 1911 is covered in detailed records.

The northward shift of Swedish mining is a twentieth-century phenomenon. High-latitude mining has always commanded attention —sometimes out of proportion to its significance. Seventeenth- and eighteenth-century atlases make great play with the blast-furnaces of Kengis in North Sweden, while its contribution to the total national output was fractional. Although the major deposits of Malmberget, Luossavaara and Gällivaara were already known at that time and their surfaces were scratched with meagre commercial results in the ensuing decades, they only came into their own when their phosphorus-bearing ores could be smelted by less costly methods and could be transported with less effort. The Gilchrist-Thomas method provided escape from the former restraint, and the Narvik-Luleå railroad, effective successor to a number of ineffective proposals, finally eased the latter in 1902.[1]

The relative status and distribution of Scandinavian industry was being affected also by new ways of employing the new-found power. Norsk Hydro A/S[2] provides an outstanding example in this field, springing to existence with its whole range of electro-chemical preparations in the same period that Norway pioneered political independence. Electro-smelting and refining were not merely to multiply heavy industry in Norway; they were also to give rise to location in seemingly unaccountable areas. Moreover, electricity was to breed industries of its own accord, so that Sweden in particular gave birth to a variety of electrical engineering workshops.[3] Electricity rapidly became something more than an adjunct to existing industry.

New techniques in construction shifted the emphasis in building materials. Granites, for example, which were quarried for export as well as domestic consumption, were subordinated to less expensive materials. To the old-established lime-kilns which ringed the shores of Limfiorden were gradually added the giant cement works which are a twentieth-century feature of West European calcareous country.

Existing industries experienced two general effects. In the round, they reacted positively to the expanding demand; in detail, they experienced changes in relative status with an almost invariable concentration of effort. The glass and ceramic industries were caught in the general upswing, so that more than a score of Småland's glassworks and Copenhagen's Royal China factory (founded in the 1780s) experienced translation. A profound revaluation of sites occurred in the paper industry. In 1870, for example, there were eleven established paper-making factories in Finland, but by the end of the century only three of them were still in business. Concentration of effort is illustrated most strikingly in the Swedish iron and steel industry with the Domnarvet concern, for example, replacing a scatter of nineteen plants in Dalarna alone. The Danish brick and tile industry provides a second example—the thousand producing plants being reduced tenfold in the century after 1840. Shipbuilding also experienced concentration of effort—the multitude of small wharves yielding to the major yards with the speedy conversion of the merchant fleet from timber to steel. The Göta river, the Sound ports and Oslo became the focal-points. The Danish vegetable-oil industry showed both concentration and expansion. By the 1830s, there were thirteen soap factories in Denmark and twelve more in the Duchies; while a quantity of imported oils aided local hemp and linseed supplies. Major changes, beginning in 1871 with the establishment of the first palm-kernel compressors in Aarhus, were to transform the industry into one of the largest in Denmark.

The cumulative effects of the "legion of machines" began to be apparent by the turn of the century.[4] They can be traced in detail as well as at large. The process of development for a single town is given in Fig. 32. By 1900, Sweden's industrial production had surpassed its agricultural production, and the experience was soon to be repeated in Denmark, Norway and Finland.

---

[1] A. F. Rickman, *Swedish Iron Ore*, London (no date).
[3] P. Hjulström, *op. cit.*; e.g. the advertisement on p. 69.
[4] The onset of industrialisation can also be measured by the taxation value of agricultural and other property as a percentage of the total; cf. B. Thomas, *op. cit.*, p. 113.

[2] K. A. Olsen, *Norsk Hydro, 1905–1955*, Oslo, 1956.

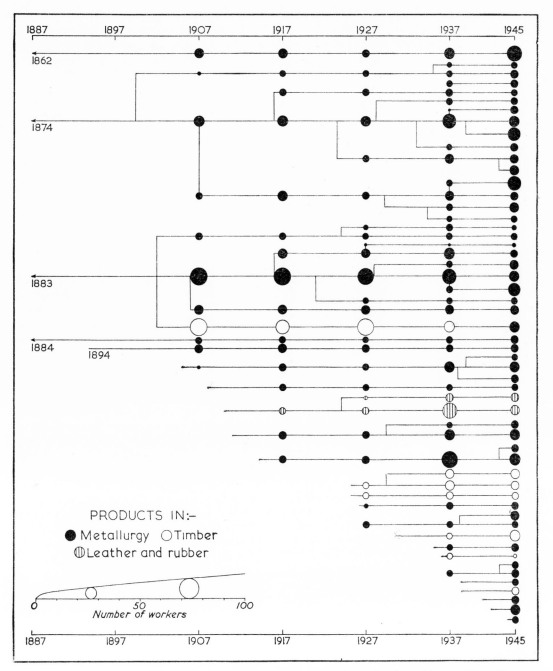

FIG. 32. The evolution of industry in Anderstorp, a small town in South Sweden. (Source: W. William-Olsen, *Halmstad-Nässjö Järnvägar*, Halmstad, 1950.)

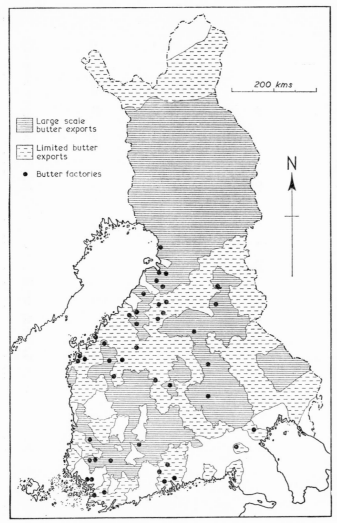

Large scale
butter exports

Limited butter
exports

● Butter factories

200 kms

N

FIG. 33. A dairy map of Finland. (Source: J. Wikberg, *Suomenmaan kartasto*, Helsinki, 1879.)

world with a reputation for social and economic experiment.

No single fact favours the urge to experiment. Limited size may not have been irrelevant for Denmark. In each instance the relatively small population may have been of consequence, while ethnographic homogeneity (Finland apart) may have aided. A course of history which has given rise to "economic egalitarianism" has probably been even more important, for extremes of wealth have not inhibited social experiment. Contrastingly, the limited domestic means at the disposal of small countries entering belatedly into the modern economy, have enforced co-operative or national action. Economic revaluation came from without, but the full benefit of it was often only realised through experiments within. The ideas frequently came from outside, too; but following import, they have been transformed out of all recognition. Edward Chamberlayne, in his *Present State of England*, a book well known in seventeenth-century Scandinavia, wrote that there were "few curiosities of art brought over from beyond the sea but are improved to a greater height". The same might be said of Scandinavia in the period of its social and economic transformation.

Co-operation is a case in point. The idea came from Lancashire, but the ground was fertile for its reception. In Denmark[1] the mood had been created by educational developments incorporating the practical philosophy of Bishop Grundvig and expressing themselves through the folk high schools. Co-operative movements—in gestation in the 1850s, born in the following decade—began to thrive in the 1880s. In Finland, eventually described as "the nation of co-operators",

THE SOCIAL LABORATORY

It would be possible to sum up the changes which the Northern Countries have set in motion in recent decades as a conscientious attempt to reduce uncertainty in an environment which is—regionally at any rate—below the optimum favoured by men making their daily living. The unremitting application of techniques to this end, more successful than in many areas, has provided the Scandinavian

---

[1] H. Ravenholt, *The Danish Cooperative Movement*, Copenhagen, 1947.

the movement was fostered by Hannes Gebhard (an economic geographer in the true sense of the word). J. L. Runeberg's *Peasant Paavo* was the sort of person likely to be sympathetic towards the creation of such bodies as the Pellervo Society (1899). This society was receptive to numerical arguments put forward by Gebhard about dairy cows per dairy and, through I. J. Inberg's earlier dairy map of Finland (Fig. 33), was able to appreciate distributional considerations.[1]

In contrast to England, co-operation in Northern Europe has been first and foremost a farmers' movement. There are several reasons. When co-operative ideas were introduced, all of the Northern Countries had a predominantly rural population, and neither town nor industry gave rise to their principal social problems. Secondly, a marketing organisation was required to take control of the change-over from subsistence to commercial farming, and no significant intermediary merchant group was available to collect and dispatch farm products. Thirdly, successful marketing implied a high-grade standardisation of product and the discipline of an acceptable organisation. This standardisation was first applied to milk marketing, and the first co-operative dairy was established at Hjedding in Denmark. In 1886, there were 176; by 1900, 942 dairies. The dairies were not only concerned with the receipt of milk but also with the swift return of skim-milk. To co-operative dairies were rapidly added cooperative bacon factories. These are generally on a larger scale and serve a wider area. Today, about nine-tenths of the milk marketed in the Northern Countries goes to the cooperative dairies and most of the pigs to the co-operative slaughterhouses.

Co-operation has an industrial and distributive expression as well as an agricultural form. In Sweden, for example, there are as many as forty co-operative industrial plants. The economies of large-scale distribution have meant that in Denmark about 40% of imported fodders and fertilisers move through co-operatives. In Iceland, up to a half of the flour and sugar may be handled by the co-operatives. An inter-Scandinavian wholesale buying agency is centred on Sweden. In the Northern Countries today co-operation expresses itself in a large number of small societies with a relatively small number of members, rather than in a small number of large organisations.[2]

This chapter began by emphasising the changing status of the Fenno-Scandinavian countries. Two hundred years ago, Gerhard Schøning attempted to review them prospectively and perspectively. "Long after the birth of Christ", he wrote, "the countries of Europe which we now regard as the best and most fruitful, were not a hair's-breadth better than Norway and Sweden today, and in many respects worse." There was a measure of truth in his comment—and it would be difficult to find in Europe today tracts of land which are more fruitful and rewarding than Skåne or much of Denmark. In the interval since he wrote, the transformation of much of the Scandinavian scene has been so remarkable that its component states have themselves become measuring-rods by which other nations assess themselves.

---

[1] H. Gebhard, *Co-operation in Finland*, London, 1916, with a distribution map of the co-operative societies.
[2] A good summary of the present status of co-operation in the north is given in G. R. Nelson (ed.), *Freedom and Welare*, Copenhagen, 1953, Chapter III.

Chapter VI

SETTING, RESOURCE AND SOCIAL REVALUATION

ECONOMIC CONTROL AND SOCIAL CONTROL

IN the continuing revaluation of the land-scape and its resources two interrelated, though essentially different, controls are operating from the human side. They are the economic controls and the social controls. To investigate either is to appreciate that there are two differing approaches to the problem of maximising opportunities in space. Economic controls, in the narrower sense of the word, predominate; but social controls may also be invoked in the management of space and resource. Although social controls seem to stand apart from economic controls, they are inseparable from them. In the frame of economic geography, the motive behind social controls is irrelevant; but the resulting arrangement or rearrangement of the features of the human landscape is of central interest. Genetically, then, the forces which give rise to a particular human land-scape, or to changes in it, may be spurred by social motives.

The face of the land offers a variety of ways by which man can reach his desired ends; but it also interposes varying degrees of resistance between the initiation and fulfilment of his enterprise. One way of looking at social controls is to regard them as a means of increasing the elasticity of human opportunity beyond the limits seemingly set by private economic controls. Thus, the investment resources of a private individual or organisation are likely to be substantially lower than those of a public authority. Social controls may therefore be a public means of overcoming costs of resistance too great for a private organisation. Social controls would appear to operate where the field of management of a resource or area requires broadening or intensifying beyond the economic limits set to private initiative. Such a condition is likely to arise

in a number of circumstances. Thus, capital resources in private hands may be inadequate to meet the scale of enterprise demanded. This is especially true in the opening up of extensive areas in northern Scandinavia and Finland, which the course of history had in any case placed in the hands of the state. The historical stage of development in a particular country at the time of economic revaluation may also favour the social approach. Independently of anything else, the political climate may encourage social controls. The reassessment of Scandinavian resources is by no means devoid of domestic or international politics. Often, too, the state has played the role of foreign investment organisations, favouring exclusion of foreign capital.

There is another way of looking at social controls. While they may enable the frontiers of physical resistance to be pushed back, social controls may at the same time impose their own system of restraints. Thus, the social revaluation of resources in the north of Scandinavia and Finland may, in fact, restrain the economic revaluation of certain resources and places in other parts of those countries. Social revaluation of resource, however, is more commonly presented as a long-term policy of economy in which a broad and unitary approach to resources and space is balanced against a narrower and piecemeal approach.

In age and degree, public ownership and development of resources are richly varied in Scandinavia and Finland. The control of the central authority may be or may have been total; again, it may have been significant only at a point in time. But whether the control is continuing or has been withdrawn, it will have made its mark in land development or in the localisation of enterprise. At an early stage the central authority directly encouraged and "arranged" location through loans or favouring tariffs (as in silver mining and smithing in south Norway) and through invitations to men of enterprise from abroad (such as the de Geer family in Sweden). Contemporarily, the state has acquired and developed existing concerns; sometimes it has bought them but not developed them (Dunderland Iron Company in Nordland, Ruotivare Mining Company in Sweden). Sometimes its enterprise is the result of resources being arbitrarily transferred to its hands in the distant past (State Forest Industry Ltd. of Sweden, founded 1941), or it may have accidental historical roots (the softwood resources for Elvenäs saw-mill on the Pasvik river). Sometimes it has bought up blocks of shares in established concerns, as in the disguised control to be found in Grängesberg-Oxelösund AB. of Norrbotten before its final nationalisation, and still to be found in Kemi Oy. of Kaarihaara/Veitsiluoto in north Finland. Sometimes it has injected capital into primary industry (Årdal aluminium plant in Sogn: Outokumpu copper mine in Finland, Finnish oil refineries), feeding private factories with its output. Sometimes industries are established for experimental purposes (Swedish Peat Company, operating in Kristianstad county), or for reasons of future economic security (Swedish Shale Oil Co.). Sometimes the state has created new plants of a major commercial character (Luleå Steel Works).[1]

Such state-acquired, assisted or sponsored activity is of geographical relevance for two reasons. First of all, it is likely to guarantee the persistence of the plants concerned so that they may well make a more lasting and perhaps more widespread impact upon the areas in which they are set. Secondly, taken as a whole, state-operated industries lie in relative isolation from most comparable private industry. They have often a marginal or submarginal setting in relation to private industry. As a result, their regional impact may assume an importance out of all proportion to their size.

Among other enterprises of the central authority throughout Scandinavia have been the state railways. The State Railway Commissions of the Northern Countries planned primary tracks which were to change substantially the relative values of land and resource, encouraging certain regional developments, retarding others. Among other responses was the creation of two significant state harbours—Esbjerg in south-west Jutland and Hanko in south-west Finland. Railways, with their related ports and workshops, were the first significant state enterprise to affect both the more mature and "colonial" territories of the respective countries.

In recent years, the phrase "developing areas" has gained wide currency, and it may be fittingly applied to much of Norway, Sweden and Finland. It will be increasingly evident that in these three countries a developed south stands in contrast to an underdeveloped north. The confines of the "north" are elusive, though Norway north of Hordaland, the provinces of Oulu and Lappi in Finland and the Swedish territory commonly known as Norrland,[2] are popularly described as belonging to it. These areas harbour a reservoir of resources and demonstrate statistically a higher proportion of "productive labour" than most others. Because they are poor in capital, public economic policy has favoured regional transfers of capital to them.[3] Such action, diverting capital away from the traditional investment areas, has been opposed. Supporters of the diversion claim that the state has long favoured industry located in the south by its system of customs protection.

THE NORTHERN DEVELOPMENT PLANS

Three motives have directed state attention to high-latitude planning. First, the resources of the north are worthy of fuller investigation. Until very recently the surveys of northern Sweden, Norway and Finland have been inferior to those of the south. Secondly, it is possible to argue that a greater regional

[1] There are twenty-six completely state-operated enterprises in Sweden (cf. R. Tersman, *Statsägda aktiebolag i Sverige*, Stockholm, 1956).
[2] More recently, the area has been officially titled Nordkalotten (Swedish Norrbotten, Finnish Lappi and Norway north of Hordaland). It has more than 25% of the surface area of the three countries.
[3] Cf. E. Browaldh, "Några synpunkter på Norrlands kapitalförsörjning", *Ekonomisk Revy*, 1944, 1.

balance in the distribution of invested wealth can make for a healthier domestic situation. Thirdly, in the interests of raising the lower income areas it is socially desirable to introduce industry into an under-industrialised area.[1] Fourthly, it is politically strategic to manifest an economic interest in an area which marches beside the U.S.S.R., and which, for this reason or others, is generally left wing in outlook.[2]

Interest in the northern areas has a different history in each of the three countries. In recent years, Sweden has led the way in surveying the character and possible contributions of its northern third. For Finland, the north has had a strategic importance as well as an economic significance, because it embraced the Petsamo corridor—a much-coveted outlet to ice-free water from 1920 to 1944. North Norway, a territory less wealthy in resource than its Swedish counterpart and less significant in the national framework than its Finnish equivalent, commanded relatively less attention until after the Second World War. Thereafter, the fundamental disturbance inflicted during the late months of the war made for closer parallel between Norway and Finland than between either country and Sweden. The high-latitude possession of Denmark—Greenland—has its own peculiar problems. Common to each of these northern territories is a group of people ethnographically different from the Scandinavians and Finns whose culture and economy (cf. Part 5) have been substantially changing with territorial revaluation.

(a) Finland and Historic Pohjola

Zachris Topelius recognised two realms in historic Finland—a "kingdom of life and a kingdom of death".[3] Pohjola, the northland, was the kingdom of death. It was never more so than during the months immediately following the peace settlement of September 1944. In this northern third of Finland, as in the northern third of Norway, state sponsorship has been integrally related to reconstruction. It will be recalled that North Finland was largely excluded from the programme of reception for displaced people from the ceded territories. Save for the effects of reception in such restricted areas as Toivala in the Kemi valley, parts of the Tornio valley and the western halves of the parishes of Salla and Kuusamo, North Finland did not share to the same degree as other parts of the country in the general intensification of settlement and rural investment. In the north, the motif of agricultural reconstruction was—initially at any rate—replacement; elsewhere, the resettlement programme forced on a whole series of new rural adjustments expressive of intensified land occupation.

Reconstruction has brought changes to north Finland of a different character from those initiated in north Norway. Thus, there have been attempts to seek in an underdeveloped north resources which will in part compensate for losses in the ceded lands. Secondly, these are sought in a territory which itself has been reduced in area by the loss of the Petsamo corridor and the eastern halves of the parishes of Salla and Kuusamo. In the promotion of north Finland, private initiative has jostled with state enterprise much more than in north Norway. Illustrative of this is the general battle for water-power sites—koskensota, as it is called locally. One of Finland's most serious losses by the peace settlement was developed water-power, and two organisations now rival each other to make good in the north what was lost in Karelia. Pohjolan Voima Oy. (1943), a privately sponsored concern backed by timber interests, has already harnessed the estuary rapids of the Kemi river at Isohaara and exploited the relief changes in Posio parish to create an isolated power-plant at Pumisko. It is also much concerned with the broader possibilities of the Kemi, Ii and Ounas rivers, as well as with those of eastern Kuusamo. Oulujoki Oy. (1941), an ancillary of Imatra Voima Oy., the state-sponsored power company, has simultaneously concentrated attention on the Oulu river, at Pyhäkoski, and five other sites now developed. Meanwhile, Oulu

---

[1] Cf. L. Wahlbeck, *Om inkomstnivåns geografi i Finland år 1950*, Helsingfors, 1956.
[2] S. Rydenfelt, *Kommunismen i Sverige, en samhällsvetenskaplig studie*, Lund, 1954.
[3] Föreläsningar, Mss., 6, p. 177.

city has built a barrage across its estuarine rapids at Merikoski. On the Pasvik river (*Finnish*, Patsjoki), the state also contracted with the Rajakoski construction company for a power-plant to supply energy for the nickel-reducing centre of Kolosjoki in Russian Petsamo. Power-lines in north Finland are stretching their tentacles eastwards and northwards into a full dozen areas of this wasteland.[1]

In part, power produced in north Finland will be exported to the power-deficient south; in part, it will be used locally by the growing rural community, by existing industry and by new plants. Among new industrial plants which look directly to the new sources of power is the state-sponsored ammonium and nitrogen plant. (Typpi Oy.) at Oulu. Here, nitrogen for agricultural use is produced in order to lessen north Finland's dependence upon imports. The location of the plant is the more important because of the nitrate deficiencies of the soils of Oulu and Lappi provinces, the distance of the area from alternative centres of production in the south and the growing faith of farmers in artificial fertilisers. At Otanmäki, near Kajaani, the state-sponsored exploitation of magnetite (37% iron and some vanadium) parallels Norwegian and Swedish high-latitude developments; though the projected 500,000 tons p.a. is a more modest output. The product is wholly exported in a crushed state from the new south harbour of Oulu.

North Finland, as with its Scandinavian neighbours, is acutely conscious of the inadequacy of communications, though these have not been the subject of any specific plan. Within the setting of the national plan for new communications,[2] the north, however, claims a distinctive place. Its claims on the state budget can be appreciated from the post-war statements (e.g. 1954, pp. 56–7) of the Finnish Highways Commission. They are frequently the highest for any province in the country—and are listed as *asutustiet*, or colonisation roads. Already the development is such that critics argue over the multiplication of highways in an area where the volume of traffic is the smallest in the country. The steady northward extension of the new interior arteries of the state railways and the multiplication of highways (as well as the equally important byways) within the state and community owned forests are two distinct developments promoted by other than private authorities.[3] Through them, the opening up of extensive and unexploited softwoods is directly promoted. It is also promoted indirectly, for better communications encourage a broader dispersal of settlement and, thereby, of labour supply for the maintenance and exploitation of the woodlands.[4] Yet this dispersal of settlement is much disputed, and counter-planners would cast the whole operation in a different frame—juxtaposing strong concentrations of population with extended stretches of uninhabited countryside.

Agricultural research as well as rural electrification and improved communications are calculated to stabilise the communities of Pohjola. There are several state-sponsored research stations investigating fodder crops as a basis for animal husbandry. Partly as a result of improved feeding, partly as a result of improved stock, milk production in good dairy herds in north Finland equals that in south Finnish herds. Peatland farming in this country of widespread boglands is the object of long-period research. It is, however, paradoxical that at the same time as the state is promoting all these schemes, it is regionally relaxing its ownership of the north. Thus, post-war resettlement and colonisation programmes have taken place primarily on state-owned land. An extreme example of the transference of state land to private ownership is found in the parish of Kuusamo.[5]

Nearly a century ago, Topelius was presenting his regional geography of Finland upon a river-valley basis. The new emphasis upon land drainage for forestry and farming, the reassessment of floatage routes, the regional planning of power-plants all redirect attention

[1] Cf. Map 6 accompanying *Valtakunnansuunnittelukomitean mietintö*, Helsinki, 1954.
[2] *Tielaitoksen kehittäminen ja sen rahoitus*, Helsinki, 1954.
[3] Cf. the map put forward for highway and railway extensions in connection with the forestry report, *Puun maakuletusolojen kehittäminen*, Helsinki, 1952.
[4] N. A. Osara, *Eräitä valtion metsätalouden ongelmia ja tavoitteita*, Helsinki, 1953.
[5] W. R. Mead, Finland's Rural Resettlement, *Tijdschrift Econ. Soc. Geog.*, **48**, 1957, 7/8.

to the river units. A greater concentration along the water-courses and withdrawal from the interfluves might even strengthen this position. Topelius recognised two valleys as of peculiar consequence—Auradal, in the south, for its persistence in the evolution of Finland; Kemidal, for its promise in the future. Something of this promise is being realised. For Topelius, the northland was "a field of experiment for Finnish civilisation"; it remains so for an enthusiastic group of septentrionalists today.[1]

(b) Norway and its "Arktandria"

Finnish and Norwegian development cannot be divorced from the impact of the war. The physical impact of the war was also greater on north Norway than on south Norway. From Hordaland to Troms most towns suffered much material damage; from Altafiord eastwards all forms of coastal settlement and most means of communication were obliterated by a German scorched-earth policy. Upon this *tabula rasa* the economy of north Norway had to be recreated.[2]

Reconstruction has not been piecemeal, but carefully planned over an extended period. In addition, reconstruction dovetails into the programme of development outlined for Nordland, Finnmark and Troms in the *North Norway Plan*.[3] A general system of needs and priorities was evolved for what was recognised to be essentially a problem area. Into the broad generalisations of the plan for north Norway are fitted the local details, and these are described in interlocking surveys which cover the lesser administrative areas. An instance of these surveys is found in the *Economic Analysis of Finnmark*.[4] This study, prepared according to the formula common for each province, is a virtual economic geography of Norway's northernmost administrative unit. It is also the type of document which lays bare the essential differences in the kingdom. Disraeli wrote of the two nations in Britain: Norway has two realms and the northern is *terra incognita* to the southern.

The three north Norwegian provinces embrace roughly a third of the land area of the country; in many ways, the least accessible third. It is clear from the plan that one solution to the difficulties of north Norway is to reduce as much as possible the differential of location. The north includes some of Norway's greatest stretches of dissected country—Troms, for example, is the most islanded province of the realm. Only 12% of the population lives in the three northern provinces; but the proportion which lives in scattered settlements is substantially greater than for anywhere else in Norway. In Troms, moreover, over half of the population lives on islands.

It is not therefore surprising that in northern plans communicational difficulties remain the foremost and probably the biggest single issue. The sea continues to be the main connecting-link, and most settlement is tied to it. The greater part of the movement upon it is individual, but the established express steamer route is followed by one boat every day in summer and six a week in winter. Accessibility of the land from the sea raises a variety of local problems in communication. This springs from the structure of the coastal forms of north Norway: in Finnmark, for example, the skerry zone is largely absent. Although there is sheltered harbourage in the fiord "bottoms" the fishing communities thrust their way seawards as closely as possible to the offshore grounds. These are relatively near—Fugløybanken, for example, is only eight nautical miles distant and four to eight hours away for an ordinary motor-driven fishing-boat from Finnmark's harbours. Considerable constructional effort is required to create a modern harbour. Vardö provides a good example of a problem port. It has largely outgrown its present harbour, and rather than straining to develop its limited island opportunities, a proposal has been put forward for the creation of a new mainland harbour at adjacent Svartnes. In Finnmark at large, strong official support is given to the

[1] *Föreläsningar, op. cit.*, 6.
[2] D. Lund, "The Revival of North Norway", *Geographical Journal*, CXI, 1947; B. R. Hellesnes (ed.), *Finnmark i Flammer*, Kragerø and Trondheim, 1949, 1950; Ø. Vorren (ed.), *Norway north of 65*, Oslo, 1960.
[3] *Utbyggningsprogrammet for Nord Norge, Stortingsmelding*, 85, 1951.
[4] *Finnmark, en økonomiske analyse*, ed. H. Luihne, Arbeidsdirektoratet, Oslo, 1952.

concentration of improvements in a few better harbours rather than to the widespread dispersal of energies among good and indifferent harbours alike.

The road network, discontinuous in south Norway, is even more so in north Norway. At the time of the First World War, Finnmark had only 400 km. of highway; today it has only a quarter of the density for Norway as a whole. A full quarter of the population of the three northern provinces has still no connection with express boat or arterial highway. For much of the rest of the population the contact is only seasonal. Kvænanger mountain in north Troms, for example, cuts off Finnmark from road communication with the outer world for a full five months; while in the not exceptional 1951, the first and last buses ran on June 20th and September 30th respectively. The highway programme forecasts several main features. First, a series of new highways will be constructed to enable express steamers to reduce their ports of call and new bus routes will provide substitute services to the harbours by-passed. In many cases, these highways will simultaneously link lesser harbours to the arterial Highway 50. In Finnmark, new interior highways are also projected;[1] for example, the trunk road from Skipagurra on the Tana river to Karasjok and then via Kautokeino to Nordreisadalen. This is regarded essentially as a winter way—following as much as possible the line of the fells where the snowfall is lighter. A third feature of the programme is the multiplication of second-class roads in a countryside where main highways are already disproportionately dominant. Fourthly, more attention will be directed to the maintenance of "open" communications.

The differential of location expresses itself in a general time-lag in the introduction of techniques. Sometimes the techniques of the south are unsuited to the north; but more commonly there is a capital shortage which has restricted their introduction. This applies especially to the fisheries. By improved techniques it would be physically possible to double the fish output. The full third of the male population over fifteen years

of age which is engaged in them represents about half of the fishing population of the country, and it produces about half of the total fish output by value for Norway. The main difficulty of the industry is, however, its seasonal character. In addition, there are variations in the quantity, type and place of catch. As a result, fishing is not a full-time occupation. An enquiry made in connection with the census of fisheries indicated that those gaining their living exclusively from it fished for an average of 32 weeks; those for whom it was a principal pursuit, 19 weeks; those for whom it was a secondary pursuit, 8 weeks. In Finnmark, the full-time fisherman is occupied during 4 to 6 weeks longer than his counterpart in Nordland and Troms.

The subsidiary occupation therefore becomes a feature of labour in the area and 52% of the fishers have farming as a subordinate activity; 17% of the farmers, fishing. Fishing and farming, in fact, go hand in hand, and a third of the farm area in north Norway is operated by fishers and their families. The most suitable farming areas are not always readily accessible to the fishing-grounds so that the communicational links between fishing harbour and interior farmland become the more important. Farm units are small. In Finnmark, where the fisher/farmer combination is most persistent, only 7% of the holdings have more than 50 decares of cultivated land. But the margins of cultivation have not yet been reached, and authorities declare a threefold increase of the cultivated area to be possible. North Norway is the most lively area of land-breaking in the country, and both the ease of cultivation and extension of cultivation are facilitated by the establishment of machine pools. On the other hand, any agricultural planning must bear in mind that the improvement of the existing area of cultivation is at least as important as reclamation. The *North Norway Plan* nominated certain areas for the immediate installation of underground drainage on the score of their relative fertility and proximity to consuming areas (for example, Pasvik area in Syd Varanger; Vesterelvsmyrene in Nesseby).

Farming is of a predominantly subsistence

Hans Luihne, *op. cit.*, p. 54.

character and is tied chiefly to animal husbandry. For example, only 30% of the holdings with over 5 decares which own dairy
cattle deliver milk to the dairy. In South
Norway, the figure is 54%. This fact is
representative of the general deficiency in
local foodstuff production. There is even
under-production of potatoes—which occupy
half the cultivated area. Vegetables, meat
and eggs all have to be supplemented from
outside sources—even at the present rate of
consumption, which is, from the nutritional
standpoint, below the optimum. Planning
authorities aim to meet at least the demands
for milk and milk products, pork and pork
products, from local sources. There is
another motive behind the encouragement of
local farm production. It calls forth greater
activity and, theoretically at any rate, reduces the underemployment which is characteristic of the area. Farming, however, can
never absorb more than a proportion of the
midwinter idleness forced upon fishers and
builders; because its winter season is also
slack. Farming in north Norway also lacks
one of the reserve outlets for winter labour
common to the greater part of Northern
Europe—the coniferous woodland. In this
northern third of the country are found only a
fifth of Norway's woodlands. Finnmark and
Troms have reserves of pine and Nordland's
resources are primarily spruce. The annual
increment is well below the average. State
ownership is absolutely dominant and the
average farm rarely has a wood-lot. Cutting
is rigorously controlled; improvement of the
woodlands—which are essentially in the interior of the country—is bound up with the
extension of motorable roads.

It is to industry that the *North Norway Plan*
looks for the amelioration of the economy. At
the time of the parliamentary statements in
1950, 1·7% of the total industry by value of
output for the country derived from North
Norway. The allocation of investment in the
area raises many problems. First, how can a
balance be struck between the claims of
communications, energy, the fisheries, farming and the creation of new industrial plants?
There must be a rigorous choice between
alternatives. Into any considerations of in-

dustrial expansion other facts must enter.
Thus, whereas farmers can expect to dispose
of their products in the local market, manufacturers cannot expect more than a small
proportion of their goods to be consumed
locally, and must assess the costs of long-
distance transport (albeit sea transport) to
markets. Again, industry demands trained
labour and, generally speaking, a steady flow
of labour. Unless special types of plant are
erected and workshop schools are established to
train labour in specialist or secondary skills,
industry is not likely to offer any substantial
corrective to the major problems of north
Norway—viz. seasonal unemployment or
underemployment. In fact, the potentialities
for industrial development in north Norway
are limited. In the first place, north Norway
is beset with a shortage of developed power and,
compared with other parts of the country, of
good potential power sites. Physical conditions for this supply of power are poorer in
that the head of water is generally lower (altitudes at large are lower), the volume of water
is lower (precipitation generally being smaller),
the regularity and reliability of flow are frequently less. On the distributional side, the
distances of transmission to points of consumption are at least as great and the consuming population much more widely scattered. At present only 15% of Norway's
hydro-electric power is generated in the north,
but despite physical difficulties in the distribution of energy almost all of the population
is supplied with electricity. As with the projected highways, development takes place
ultimately at the provincial level and, within
the framework of the provinces, a system of
priorities is laid down.

North Norway is not without a variety of
mineral resources—varying from the iron ores
of Syd Varanger to the slates of Alta. Development in the past has been sporadic and
the impact has been localised. State enterprise in north Norway is oriented to heavy
industry and mining. It takes two forms—
the granting of direct loans, e.g. to enterprises
at Sulitjelma and Bleikvassli, and the creation
of state-operated concerns, e.g. A/S Syd
Varanger and A/S Norsk Jernverk.

It is natural that industrial plans should

look to the fisheries. The season is here longer than in any other fishing area of Norway and the fishing-grounds are rich. Already, refrigeration facilities spread the marketing period in time as well as in space and point the direction away from canning. Activity centres upon two processing plants in Båtsfiord and Honningsvåg, each capable of dealing with 10,000 tons during the 180-day operating period. Another factory, established with Swedish capital in Hammerfest, specialises in deep frozen fish products for the West European market. Inland, meat processing plants and tanneries are associated with the reindeer slaughteries, and the summer profusion of berries is canned, frozen and even distilled. All this reflects a detailed attention to the resources of Petter Dass's province of Arktandria which would have gladdened his heart.

There are two other sources of stimulus to north Norway. First, its economy is powerfully influenced by the international contributions of N.A.T.O. Military bases, airfields and improved highways stimulate the economy indirectly as well as directly. Secondly, the tourist industry brings a spate of summer activity. This is impressively international in character. It also rejuvenates seasonally old-established provisioning bases such as Tromsø. Tromsø remains a point of departure for the Arctic. Its merchants and seamen continue to boast the fact in the titles *Ishavsreder* and *Ishavskipper*.

(c) Sweden and the Norrland Question

Norrland claims about 58% of the surface area of Sweden and somewhat less than 20% of the Swedish population. State concern about it and state plans for it are to be expected because extensive areas of it are crown lands. Interest in Norrland has intensified during the last generation. A geographical review of its status was sponsored in the 1930s[1] and the salient points of this have been underlined by the eight or nine official reports

published annually about the area from the 1940s onwards.[2]

In most of these, the tax of distance has been a steadily recurring theme, and plans for Norrland are greatly concerned with communications. Three different approaches to the problem may be identified. First, there is a multiplication of lines of communication— especially of the highways (cf. Chapter X). Secondly, there are attempts to shift the incidence of this tax to the state. In this connection, the Norrland committee has proposed that two special railway tariff zones should be introduced for higher latitudes. The one would hold for lines north of Umeå-Vännäs and the inland railway north of Östersund-Forsmo, beyond which 2 km. distance should be reckoned as 1 km. for tariff purposes. The other would hold for track to the north of Söderhamn-Bollnäs and Orsa, where 1·5 km. in distance would be reckoned as 1 tariff km.[3] In the third place, there is an indirect attempt to reduce the tax of distance by the reorganisation of established settlement patterns.

These solutions are aimed at alleviating a situation in which distance adds a sum variable from 5 to 10% to the cost of products moving in and out of Norrland. Exports have not only to absorb this tax, they have also to take account of the higher costs of living. In the Norrland area, the financial burden of local taxation is almost everywhere as high as in Stockholm, fewer inhabitants having to share the expense of maintaining services over an extensive area. New highways may ease the passage of the motor vehicle, but of the five price zones for motor fuel into which Sweden is divided, the highest is in the north, so that Norrland motor transport, although it enjoys an expanding network of roads, automatically operates at a higher cost than in south Sweden. Climate takes its toll in a variety of ways (cf. Chapter III, *above*). Thus, building costs are almost 5,000 kr. per room or 500 kr. more than for the rest of the land; stables cost 1,100 kr. per beast or 100 kr. *per capita* more than for the remainder of Sweden.

[1] [W. William-Olsen], *Norrlands Näringsliv*, Stockholm, 1943.
[2] Among the latest and most substantial of these is *Norrland Kommitténs principbetänkande, Norrlands utvecklingslinjer* 3 vols., Stockholm, 1949.
[3] The "Norrland tariff" has, in fact, been in operation in a variety of other ways in former times; cf. W. William-Olsen *op. cit.*, p. 68 *et seq.*

At least a part of this additional price is payment for insulation.

It is not surprising that such a situation should prompt regional exoduses from Norrland (cf. Chapter IV). It is also contributory to a frequent stultification of effort. As with north Norway, this shows itself in the low degree of independence in locally produced foodstuffs—30% for grain; 60% for meat (where a notable neglect in pork production has been observed); 90% for milk. In the case of the last two there is no reason why there should not be regional self-sufficiency.

Sweden has come to realise that perhaps the best solution for this problem area is not to fill its empty spaces so much as to reorganise much of the space which is already occupied. This applies at large and in detail. Thus, concentration is favoured for rural holdings—both in order to increase the size of farms (cf. Chapter VII) and to diminish the degree of population dispersal. To reduce the degree of dispersal is to lessen the cost of distribution for essential services such as education[1] and health. A concentration of effort is encouraged on farmland itself—with new cultivation and intakes being disfavoured and the improvement of existing farmland receiving priority. Of different character are the attempts to promote one or more large urban complexes in a province which lacks a commanding regional centre. Umeå and Luleå both aspire to such a position. In theory, a regional centre would not only provide considerable home markets for local production, but also encourage industrial diversification.[2] Luleå already begins to conform to the idea. Clustered around the Norrbotten ironworks other factories are coming into existence to complement the heavy industrial core—furniture, mechanical workshops, textile and clothing plants. Such a complex of industries not merely diversifies output, but creates a demand for a diversity of skills and talents. Among problems of the area are the lack of outlets for certain types of labour (e.g. female labour in urban districts) and a seasonal variation in the demand for labour. In the final place, all promotional activity tends to be cumulative, and behind the state initiative which creates new factories in the north is the expectation that additional private plants will subsequently be localised in their vicinity.

Swedish Norrland is the subject of a continuing battle between realists and romanticists. The realists hold that although it is an undeniable reservoir of raw materials which should be exploited and conserved with care, it cannot be considered more than the equivalent of a "colonial" land. The extremists of this school of thought facetiously describe it as void of that essential trinity of the cultivated south—"oaks, lobsters and nobles"! The romanticists regard it as the Cinderella of the kingdom; for them the northward course of empire holds its sway. According to their philosophy, it is only right that it should receive compensation for its delayed development and for the several generations of exploitation by the south.

(d) Denmark and the Problem of Greenland.

In Greenland, Denmark has a problem area which differs inherently from those of the other Scandinavian countries. Firstly, the northlands of Norway, Sweden and Finland are contiguous territories: Greenland is detached. Secondly, Greenland (2,200,000 sq. km.) is nearly fifty times as big as Denmark; though only approximately a tenth of it is ice-free. Thirdly, Greenland is country divided in itself to a greater extent than northern Fennoscandia. Its settlement possibilities are essentially peripheral, with East Greenland (accorded Danish sovereignty by the International High Court of Justice in 1932) living in complete detachment from West Greenland and with individual West Greenland settlements living in virtual isolation from each other except during the period of open water. Fourthly, Greenland is a territory inhabited by an ethnographically distinct people whose problem of adjustment to European life is even more acute than that of the Lapps in the rest of northern Scandinavia. All this implies that Greenland is not contemporarily a country of great economic con-

---

[1] 6,800 schoolchildren have to be found term-time accommodation because their homes are too far from schools (*Norrlands utvecklingslinjer*, III).
[2] Cf. S. Månsson, *Luleå stads generalplan—Nedre Luleådal generalplan*, Stockholm, 1950.

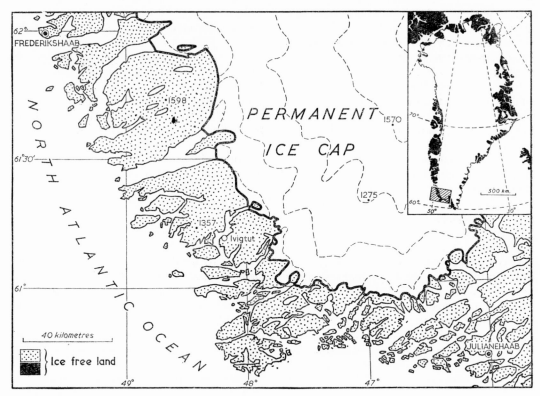

FIG. 34. The west coast of Greenland, with the fringe of settlements centred upon Ivigtut. (After *Army Map Service Series*, Washington; 1 : 500,000.) Inset: the outline of Greenland showing the location of Ivigtut.

sequence. Its significance, in fact, is strategic and academic. The new status of Greenland —like that of Iceland—springs from its world location in relation to changing communicational routes. Academically, it is a fertile and stimulating ground for primary exploration, a northern hemisphere territory unrivalled for glacial and periglacial investigation[1] and, as a result of its extent and situation, a key area for North Atlantic meteorological study.

It is very relevant to consider Greenland in this section because it has been and remains very much a country under state control. Since the revival of Scandinavian interest in Greenland with the missionary colonisation of Hans Egede in 1721,[2] the management of the territory has been more or less along mono-poly lines. During the last ninety years, side by side with the concentration of administration in the Greenland Department of the Ministry of the Interior, there has developed a system of regional trusteeship councils. Today, administration of the 34,000 Greenlanders, most of whom are of mixed Eskimo descent, is conducted from Godthaab on the west coast. Greenland, like the Færoe Islands, is an administrative county of Denmark. Godthaab is a town of 3,300 inhabitants, and is the largest of the half-dozen loosely concentrated settlements of west Greenland. The setting of Fredrikshaab and Julianehaab, two representative settlements between foreshore and ice-front, is illustrated in Fig. 34. There are approximately 170

[1] Through the *Commission for Scientific Research*, founded in 1868, scores of reports have been published. The Commission may, indeed, be described as a veritable Arctic Institute, founded long before that joint North American venture which is established in Montreal. The reports of the Commission are summarised in the index volumes to *Meddelelser om Grønland*. The Greenland Commission also publishes an annual report, *Grønlandske selskabs aarskrift* and *Grönland*, a monthly journal. A useful general account is V. Stefansson, *Greenland*, London, 1943.
[2] L. Bobe, *Hans Egede, Meddelelser*, Copenhagen, 1944, **129**, 1.

named settlement localities (*beboede pladser*, as they are defined in the *Statistical Yearbook*) around the margins of this semi-continent. Summer contact between many is maintained by steamship services.

From such bases, the majority of the Greenlanders pursue traditional activities about which two conflicting opinions have developed. The two policies are bound up with both ecological and economic issues. On the one hand, it is contended that the self-contained Greenland community, protected from outside interference, is the most satisfactory system for the Eskimo. Such protection implies that he is also shielded from the consequences of the fluctuating market for his products. On the other hand, it is asserted that the Greenland community must be slowly transformed in its culture and given opportunities to improve its material lot.

It is difficult to operate an independent and self-sufficient economy if its bases are the subject of trespass by outside agencies. Firstly, North Atlantic whale stocks have been so seriously reduced that the formerly frequent Eskimo whale hunts and strandings have been virtually eliminated. Secondly, and more seriously, opportunities for sealing have been affected by Canadian sealers from the coasts of Newfoundland and Labrador, who attack the migrant animals during their mating season. There are similar seasonal depredations by Norwegian expeditions to the east-coast ice-floes. Yet Greenlanders contrive to sell about 45,000 skins annually to the *Royal Greenland Trading Company*. Thirdly, there are the cod fisheries, which have now become the principal source of subsistence for the south Greenlander. The fisheries are an international attraction, and the speed of their natural replenishment is of concern for the local inhabitants, who lack alternative means of livelihood. If the ecological basis of existence is undermined, the peoples of Greenland become immediately dependent on the Danish state.

On the other hand, if the native Greenlanders are to adjust themselves to a changing ecological basis and to aspire to an economically independent existence, they must apply new techniques to old resources and develop new resources.[1] Examples of the former are found in the field of both fishing and farming. The Greenlanders' fish catch, hitherto oriented to domestic needs, is being transformed by the introduction of the motor-boat. More than 700 Greenlanders own motor-boats and operate in coastal waters. The banks fisheries are left primarily to international fishers, whom they attract by their increasing cod resources. The Greenlanders also catch and salt halibut and salmon. New enterprise at sea calls for adjustment ashore. The exploitation of shrimp and prawn beds in Disko bay, for example, has called for quick-freezing and canning plants on the adjacent coast. Replacement of *kayak* and *umiak* by motor-driven boats has given rise to repair yards and refuelling stations like Egesminde. An unavoidable commercialisation is in the air—a far cry from the barrel of blubber which was the standard token of exchange in the barter trading of a century ago.

Official encouragement has also been given to farm enterprise. After all, animal husbandry has a thousand years of history in Greenland. Sheep have been the focus of most attention during the last generation, the hardier Icelandic breeds having produced successful flocks. There were 22,000 sheep in Greenland (1961)—proportionately per head of population as many as in Iceland. The Julianehaab area is the centre of sheep rearing, with a slaughterhouse and processing plant (at Narssak) able to deal with several thousand carcasses a year (cf. Table 308, *Danish Official Statistics*). The biggest difficulty is to provide sufficient winter fodder for the flocks. Relics of medieval stables reflect the antiquity and relative size of herds and flocks in earlier times. They measure both the decline which occurred and the opportunity which is presented. It is an opportunity made the more accessible by new fodder crops which have been introduced to the limited cultivated "fields" of west Greenland. Fur

---

[1] P. P. Sveistrup, *Economic Principles of the Greenland Administration*, Copenhagen, 1949, and a recent statement in *Grønland*, 1956, **1**, 1–12. Other good reviews of the economy are "Erhvervsmæssige og Økonomiske forhold", *Grønlands-Kommissionen i betænkning*, Copenhagen, 1950, **5**, 2 vols., and W. Dege "Grönland im Strukturwandel von Wirtschaft und Siedlung", *Erdkunde*, 18, 4, 1964, 285–310.

PLATE 15. HIGH LATITUDE DEVELOPMENTS

Above.   The iron mountain at Kiruna with its old-established mining settlement in Norrland.
Below.   The new parish church in the reconstructed church village of Salla in Finnish Lapland.

PLATE 16. PANORAMAS OF FARMING

Above. An historic *tun* type farm from south Norway.
Below. On the "frontiers" of farming around Karasjok in Finnmark.

farming has also been debated, but is generally regarded as too precarious. New trends both in farming and fishing introduce new patterns to the daily life of the Greenlander. As in northern Scandinavia at large, these are most vital. The transformation of living conditions consists not merely in the introduction of new techniques and new enterprises, but also in conforming to new rhythms of activity which are their accompaniment. Personal independence is surrendered to a different set of controls, and the adjustment is not always easy to primitive peoples.

While farming and fishing can develop within the frame of protection, large-scale enterprise must invariably create problems. In these days of mineralogical revaluation it is dangerous to forecast the value of even the most barren territory and, although Denmark's energetic series of Greenland surveys do not consider mineral discovery as a primary aim, it is inevitably incidental to them. Certainly, Greenland contains precious metals, a range of base metals, marble, graphite and coal[1] (30,000 tons of which were mined in 1961 at Qutdligssat for domestic use). But the size of deposits, the frequent difficulties of extraction and the distance from markets has stultified enterprise. Within a "protected" setting, concession must be granted to outside authorities for such undertakings. The only significant example of such a concession (Pennsylvania Salt Company of Philadelphia) which is operating economically is the extraction of cryolite (with its aluminium and fluorspar content) at Ivigtut (see Fig. 34). The cryolite export (42,000 tons in 1961) from this settlement of several hundred inhabitants is the most significant commercial contribution to the trade balance of the territory. A policy of exclusion from outside contact also becomes progressively difficult to implement as international fishing fleets request rights of harbourage for repair, refuelling or even preparation of catch (e.g. the Færoese harbour, Færingerhavn, fifty miles south of Godthaab). All in all, it is surprising that the directors of the Greenland Trade who enjoy the exclusive rights of journeying to Greenland harbours

have been so successful in maintaining their monopoly.

But the Commission does not merely have to deal with matters economic and social. The new means of transport which have given the Danish state more effective control over this territory force on new compromises. Barely a generation has passed since the first aircraft began to explore Greenland. It was exploration for a variety of purposes, though from the initial flights of H. G. Watkins[2] and Charles Lindbergh, trans-Arctic commercial routes were being conceived. A step forward in the initiation was taken during the war years with the establishment of American military bases on Greenland as staging-points on the great circle route to Europe. Commercial routes have succeeded them, with Scandinavian air lines, oriented to such bases as Thule, as their logical successors. The Greenland administration must therefore face a twofold challenge—to the pressure for economic concessions within its territorial frame is now added demand for what are tantamount to political concessions.

(e) The Ultimate Restraints

The diversion of interest and capital to high latitudes represents an attempt to reduce the differential which exists between the north and the south. Independently of the regional reconstruction of devastated areas, it has been logical for the welfare states of Scandinavia and Finland to level up the standards of the neglected northlands. The resources of the north are, in certain instances, worthy of fuller exploitation on purely economic grounds, but there are also good social—and even political—reasons for investing in them.

Yet there are two ultimate restraints which tax human ingenuity, and both derive from location. There is first the tax of distance. Production is rarely cheaper in the northern than in the southern halves of Norway, Sweden and Finland; while transport from the seat of production to the point of consumption levies an additional charge, which may well average 25% (cf. state forest price-fixing regulations for timber). There is also a

[1] J. Humlum, *Danmarks minedrift*, Copenhagen, 1943.
[2] "The British Arctic Air Route Expedition" *Geographical Journal* LXXIX 1932.

domestic expression of the tax of distance. Within the compass of northern Norway, Sweden, Finland and Greenland, there is frequently less uniformity than might be expected in the problems which present themselves for solution. The coastal areas of Norway and Greenland and the broad valleys of Sweden and Finland have similar problems; but no simple formula can be applied to their solution, for the mixture of ingredients varies from area to area and from valley to valley.

There is a second physical levy—the tax of latitude—which exaggerates the impact of the seasons. It expresses itself in seasonal fluctuations of employment, and is not one of those impositions relieved simply by the introduction of solitary industrial plants. An economy which works so closely with the physical world as that of northern Scandinavia —and which seeks to profit from that association during a part of the year—can only with considerable disciplinary effort attach itself seasonally to another system. The element of human waywardness disturbs the neat estimates of the blue-print. And there is always the paradox that although life is sustained and insured by the introduction of state enterprise, there is both human resentment and resistance to the changes.

Human reactions in northern Scandinavia cannot be forecast on the basis of southern experience. Nineteenth-century geographers who sought a partial explanation of human character in terms of the influence of physical environment tend to stand in discredit, but the last word remains to be written. Climate has a very definite effect upon human reactions in high latitudes. No social policy can disregard it. But to explain the issue scientifically is not yet within the realms of possibility. Yet, as has been mentioned on page 81, technicians are encouraged to move north. In addition to the inducement of higher wages, a whole variety of subsidies is supported by the state. In Finland, for example, freight-rate assistance is given for bread grain, fodder, artificial manure, A.I.V. acid, agricultural lime and certain foodstuffs to a group of eastern as well as northern parishes. Parishes such as Suomussalmi and Ilomantsi, which border the U.S.S.R., suffer as much from

inaccessibility as the northern parishes. In Sweden, attempts have been made for a generation past to compensate for the influence of an unfavourable geographical environment. Six primary facts have been weighed in the balance when assessing such an environment—the relative lengths of winter and summer, the relative strength of winter cold, the extent of winter darkness, the topographical character of the countryside, distance from an urban centre and distance from a railway station. A so-called *kallortstillägg* (literally, "cold place subsidy") or *enslighets-tillägg* (isolation subsidy) has been paid to officials in unfavourable areas. In Norway, reference may be made to the high fell subsidy (*Höyfjells tillegg*) paid to certain government officials, to the special salary scales for teachers in Finnmark and Troms, and to the "Arctic" salary in operation for officials in Svalbard.

Different means of support have been initiated at different times by different authorities and it is natural that rationalisation committees should be at work to tidy up the anomalies which have arisen. An example is provided by the *Report of the Committee dealing with Marginal Districts* (*Syrjäseutulisä-komitean mietintö*, Helsinki, 1946). This committee has reviewed the diverse contributions made by such a range of ministries as those of the interior, agriculture, education, defence, trade and industry. It has subsequently compiled a simple formula for administering relief to individual settlements. This is based upon a set of measurable conditions—e.g. intensity of winter cold, population density, distance from railhead, distance from urban centres. In addition to having high-latitude applicability, the formula could also be applied to outlying island settlements.

Among the small stream of Scandinavians who move northwards, there is little to attract the scientist to more than a temporary residence. August Ehrensvärd, commenting laconically upon the dearth of scientists in the north part of the Swedish realm in 1767, remarked, "There are no Newtons in Lapland". Such men have been neither very willing to go there nor to stay there. The opening of a number of high-latitude research stations has encouraged a northward movement of scientists. More permanent centres of attraction are now the concern of Norway, Sweden and Finland. The establishment of institutions of university standing at Umeå, Tromsö and Oulu is at the same time an attempt to reduce the concentration of higher education in a few southern cities.

SAMPLE STATE ENTERPRISES

(a) The Iron and Steel Plant of Mo i Rana [1]

An outstanding example of state planning in the field of industrial location is provided by the new iron and steel plant at Mo i Rana (Fig. 35). The proposal for the plant sprang from the fact that before the war Scandinavia imported annually somewhat more than half a million tons of steel from Germany, of which more than 70,000 tons went to Norway to meet the deficiency in an annual consumption of 250,000 tons. Already, on the eve of the war, the Iron Committee of the Department of Commerce had recommended the creation of a plant with initial capacity of 55,000 tons p.a. and eventual output of 110,000 tons p.a. In the post-war period, the argument for establishing the plant has been strengthened by four supporting facts. Firstly, coal prices have risen and there is little prospect of a decline; the cost of developing hydro-electric power for smelting has not risen proportionately. Secondly, the enormous destruction of the war years guaranteed a large market at home and abroad for a long time to come. Norwegian demand for iron and steel remained 200,000 tons p.a. above the output of home plant in the post-war period, although production had risen to 100,000 tons by 1950. Thirdly, Germany's capacity to supply steel for the Scandinavian market under conditions as favourable as before the war was subject to

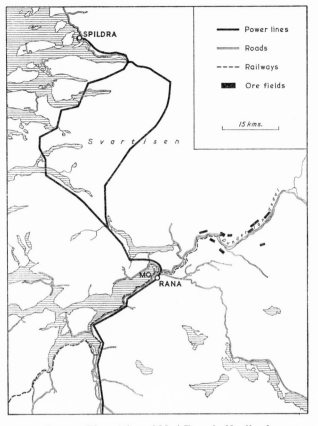

FIG. 35. The setting of Mo i Rana in Nordland.

considerable doubt. Fourthly, the European Steel Cartel had been dissolved, so that each country was freer to produce than before the war (though it must be noted that the prospect of the European Iron and Steel Federation had not yet emerged). Against these favourable elements in the climate of the time was set one negative fact—world experience suggested that technically and economically iron and steel production favoured units of increasing size. Even here, however, publications from the British Iron and Steel Federation pointed the case for the establishment of more modestly sized plants in the so-called "under-developed areas".

Domestic arguments could also be mustered in support of the project. Thus, a substantial

[1] This section is based upon *Innstilling fra Statens Jernverkskommisjon . . . sammendrag av utredninger og planer vedrørende et eventuelt nytt norsk jernverk*, Oslo, 1946; "Om A/S Norsk jernverks utbyggning og produktsjonsprogram", *Industri, håndverk og skipsfartsdepartementet*, St. Meld, Nr. 2, Oslo, 1949; U. Styren, "Norsk jernverk", *Teknisk ukeblad*, Oslo, 1951, 19. I am grateful to A/S Norsk jernverk for critical comment on this section.

proportion of the raw materials were available. A number of orefields of suitable quality occur in north Norway. Of these, Syd Varanger with its open-pit workings at Bjørnevann, has estimated reserves of several hundred million tons. In its post-war form it aspires to a capacity of 2 million tons p.a. The ore, which is a magnetite with an average 33% iron content, is crushed and magnetically separated at Varanger to form briquettes with 66% iron content (·01% phosphorus and ·01% sulphur) before export. About the same quality as Varanger ores and second in size of reserve are those of the Dunderland Iron Ore Company—formerly British, now Norwegian state-owned. The company has a proposed long-term output of 800,000 tons p.a. The Rana Mining Company, also in Dunderland, owns magnetite and hæmatite reserves. Norwegian state geologists aver that North Rana, South Rana and Elsfiord have the largest orefields in Norway. There are also the Fosdal magnetites (40–41% iron content) near Malm, with a capacity of a quarter of a million tons of concentrate annually. Another possible source of supply are the so-called "purple" ores of Grong. A pre-war scrap production of slightly less than 100,000 tons p.a. also makes a contribution to the raw-material pool. Limestone and dolomite are available at Spildra, Mo i Rana, Steinkjer, Orkanger and Larvik.

These resources would be of relatively little consequence but for developments in technology which make their employment possible. The *sine qua non* of 90% of the world's iron and steel plants is the coke-oven. In the commonly employed smelting process, coke is used both for the refinement of the ore and the reduction of the pig-iron. For refining the Varanger and Dunderland slag, 800–900 kg. of coke are required per ton of parent material. A Norwegian electric furnace (the Tysland-Hole furnace) has been developed over the last thirty years which requires only 400 kg. of coke in association with 2,500 kWh. per ton of pig-iron when limestone flux is used. There is no means of dispensing with coke imports (in spite of successful coking experiments with Svalbard coal), but the new electrical method of smelting is sufficiently economical

to make processing possible. Experience in the use of this type of furnace has been gained through Norway's largest integrated steel concern—*Christiania Spigerverk* (which began, as its name indicates, as a nail factory). As a result of high cost of electricity in the Oslo area, pig-iron production has been transferred to Årdal in Sogn. The new type of furnace is based upon the undeveloped hydro-electric power potential in Norway; though it is anticipated that iron-ore exports to Germany and the United Kingdom may offer favourable transport of complementary coke on a return freight basis.

One further fact has induced the establishment of a new iron and steel complex in Norway. Such a plant might not only reduce steel imports and save foreign exchange, it might even produce an export surplus. The best prospective markets were Denmark and Sweden—two neighbours with whom Norway has had a negative trade balance. Denmark produces about a third of its annual needs of 400,000 tons and looks traditionally to Germany and Great Britain to meet the deficiency. In spite of Sweden's expanding steel production, it still has a domestic deficiency. One Norwegian argument suggests that special ships' steels might be sold to those concerns most closely connected with the construction of ships for Norway.

Given this encouraging background, the search for a suitable locality for the new plant next engaged attention. A pre-war plant would probably have been located either on Skaggerak coast or at Narvik, where the stream of shipping favoured cheap movement of essential raw materials. It is revealing to follow the successive steps taken in localising the plant, for the printed records provide a unique example of planning for the student of economic geography. Although the capital sums given in the tables were substantially exceeded, it has been felt worthwhile to include them. Granted hydro-electric energy as an essential means of reduction, the source of power became the primary localising factor. It is estimated in the rugged countryside of Norway that for distances in excess of roughly 100 km. the cost of power transmission becomes in general greater than the cost of trans-

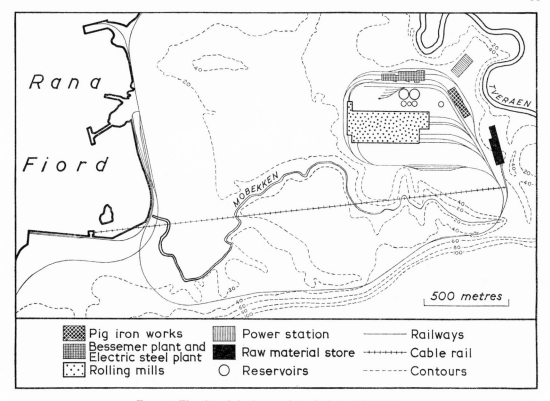

FIG. 36. The site of the iron and steel plant at Mo i Rana.

porting ore. Cost of power development and transmission was therefore the first of the variables considered in the six alternative sites for development.

TABLE 9

Alternative Sites	Cost of Power in Ore per kWh.	
	Initial Development	Ultimate Development
Glomfiord and Røsåga falls for Spildra site .	0·47	0·91
Glomfiord and Røsåga falls for Mo i Rana site	0·54	0·74
Røsåga fall alone for Mo i Rana . . .	0·89	0·82
Namsvassdraget in Steinkjer	1·20	1·04
Aura in Orkanger . .	1·10	0·65
Tokke in Larvik . .	1·20	1·20

Glomfiord with the Røsåga falls, in fact, belonged to the most easily harnessable types of fall in Norway, and could be ready for production in two to two and a half years, as distinct from the minimum four years required for the Aura site.

The second localising fact was the primary source of raw materials—the semi-refined slag. On the basis of power plus ore, eight possible combinations were proposed:

	Site	Power Source	Slag Source
1.	Spildra (Meloy)	Glomfiord	Fosdal
2.	Mo i Rana	Glomfiord	Fosdal
3.	Mo i Rana	Glomfiord	Dunderland
4.	Mo i Rana	Røsåga	Fosdal
5.	Mo i Rana	Røsåga	Dunderland
6.	Steinkjer	Namsvassdraget	Fosdal
7.	Orkanger	Aura	Fosdal
8.	Larvik	Tokke and local net	Fosdal

It is natural when considering these alternatives that other schemes of development should be borne in mind. The site of Orkanger, for example, was strongly and convincingly recommended in a minority report.

The third step to be taken in assessing the

TABLE 10.

	Capital Needs in Millions of Kroner				
	Spildra	Mo i Rana	Steinkjer	Orkanger	Larvik
1. *The Primary Variables*					
(a) Harbour and quay	4·9	6·3	7·8	9·4	5·3
(b) Rail and road	4·3	8·4	6·8	9·1	7·5
(c) Preparation of site . . .	10·1	2·5	9·7	8·6	5·7
(d) Water supply and drainage. . .	1·5	1·8	1·8	1·6	2·4
(e) Transport of raw materials . .	0·2	1·4	3·7	0·2	0·4
	21·0	20·4	29·8	28·9	21·3
2. *The Secondary Variables*					
(a) Acquisition of site	2·7	1·4	1·5	2·3	2·5
(b) Construction of buildings . . .	10·0	10·0	10·8	11·1	10·4
(c) Interest during construction period .	3·0	2·5	4·0	4·0	2·7
Total Cost . .	15·7	10·9	16·3	17·4	15·6
Total capital costs of the complex including constant costs	217·0	207·0	226·0	231·0	213·0

(Based on Table I, *Nytt norsk jernverk, op. cit.,* p. 26.)

most favourable location was to juxtapose the variables for five competing sites and to compare the estimated cost for each site. The variables could be divided into two categories, which might loosely be described as primary and secondary. The primary variables are rooted in geography, for they are associated with the modification of land-form and its adaptation to a particular use. The greatest range of costs within them was tied to transport and to the preparation of the site. The advantages of Byparken at Mo i Rana (Fig. 36) were particularly strong in this respect. It could offer a low plateau some 610 decares in area, 48 m. above sea-level and only 2 km. from the seashore. It had a small river providing the necessary 72 cu. m. per minute of fresh water required by the plant. Harbour and quay installations also entered into the costs of preparation of the site, for the bulk of raw materials enter by water and are carried by light railway to the plant. Most finished products are likely to move out over the same route, although favourable freight rates on the single-track railway which follows a circuitous route southwards may encourage overland movement to the domestic market. Possible icing in severe winters was levelled

against the harbour of Mo i Rana, though it is doubtful if it would ever be worse than could be dealt with by the type of ship entering.

The fourth step in the assessment was to juxtapose potential running costs and capital costs. Within the framework of this picture, always assuming price stability, there were certain identical and certain differing costs for the five selected sites. The differing costs were most closely related to the geographical differentials. Three representative items were electrical power, freightage of ore and slag (See Table 11, p. 135).

Supplies to be freighted to Mo i Rana to meet the needs of iron and steel plant were to be brought in by ship and rail. Only limestone comes overland (66,000 tons p.a.). Semi-refined ore (230,000 tons from Fosdal), pyrites (60,000 tons), coke and coke breeze (92,000 tons), manganese ores (4,000 tons) and other ore (2,000 tons), together with 14,000 tons of waste deriving from the steel- and rolling-mills are the estimated annual requirements. A precise programme of output from the integrated plant was also put forward based upon the steel imports of the post-war period and computed for future needs.

TABLE 11.

Item	Running Costs in Millions of Kroner				
	Spildra	Mo i Rana	Steinkjer	Orkanger	Larvik
1. Electrical power . .	2·7	3·2	7·0	6·4	7·0
2. Freight of ore, etc. .	2·1	2·1	·4	1·5	1·7
3. Slag	·5	·3	·3	·5	·6
Total in Kroner per ton .	316	316	340	340	340

In the eventual decision to build at Mo i Rana, a number of imponderables had to be borne in mind. The highly variable selling price of steel—with depression price probably 50% below boom price—was balanced against possible production costs. The need to keep the end-product of the mill in flexible form was impressed. The establishment of a settlement to meet the needs of 1,400 employees called attention to the desirability of the area in relation to other sites. In this respect Steinkjer, with its fertile Trøndelag hinterland, was favoured, though the committee advanced the claim that the district around Ranafiord offered some of the most developable land in Nordland—agriculturally as well as industrially. In contemplating the future, an eye was cast upon the ore reserves of North and South Rana with Elsfiord—among the country's most extensive deposits. Criticism of the scheme has come from a number of directions. Domestically, other industries have complained of the state subsidy which lies behind it. Shipbuilders, glancing at the projected output of ships' plate, feared that they might be compelled to meet their needs from Mo i Rana rather than have the option of buying (perhaps more cheaply) elsewhere. In fact, they are asking for a special plant to meet the growing need for ships' steel in Norway. Renewed emphasis has been laid on the point that "Electric-power pig-iron furnaces have never been competitive with coke blast-furnaces, although the low-cost power in Norway may make them able to compete".[1] As an extension of this, electrical engineers have been afraid that, as has been the case in the ferro-alloy industry, power supply may be disturbed by seasonal fluctuations in run-off. The Economic Commission for Europe has declared that a fully integrated iron and steel plant cannot operate effectively with an output of less than 2 million tons p.a. Nevertheless, the idea of the mid 1930s has taken shape. To creation has been added operation, and *Norsk Jernverk* functions with the conviction that its possibilities are not essentially inferior to those of Sweden's largest private plant at Domnarvet.

It is a far cry from *Det Store Jernkompagnie*, which was founded in Copenhagen in 1624 to promote iron production in the northern half of the dual kingdom, to the situation which prevails in Norway today. Yet, in one respect it is not. For Mo i Rana represents a shift in a centre of gravity which parallels that of the seventeenth century. The opening up of Norway's earliest mines was to be separated neither from the well-being of the nation state nor from international policies. Out of *Det Store Jernkompagnie* emerged charcoal-smelted "Norway iron", with an international reputation for quality but an output insufficient to meet demand. From Mo i Rana emerges an annual output ten times greater than the total yearly production of Norway a century ago.

Mo i Rana has a Swedish parallel, for the iron and steel plant at Norrbotten (N.J.A.) is a similar state experiment.[2] Its location in Luleå represents a marked shift in the centre of gravity of heavy industry; for the plant, which like Mo i Rana is the largest single unit in the country, lies many hundreds of kilometres from the Bergslag iron and steel complexes. The Norrbotten plant embraces three

[1] "European Recovery Plan", *Iron and Steel Community Study*, Washington, 1949.
[2] S. Grunström, "Norrbottens järnverk", *Svensk geografisk årsbok*, 1946, **22**, 125–40. The decisions to establish the plant were taken in 1938 amid much debate (*Tackjarnsutredningens betänkande*, August 1938, 12).

primary elements: electric and coke blast-furnaces (with a capacity of 500,000 tons of pig-iron annually), Thomas converters and electric steel furnaces (for ingot steel production) and rolling-mills for the lamination of ingots (capacity 450,000 tons annually). The factory has 2,500 employees and is located in the established port, Luleå. It is intended that labour for the industry should be recruited primarily from Norrbotten—and special technical courses have been instituted to train local unskilled labour. Two indirect effects are anticipated as a result of the establishment of the plant. First, it is hoped that secondary industries may be born through the plant—and that they may even be diffused outside Luleå. Secondly, it is hoped that recruitment of labour from rural sources may draw farmers away from the smaller properties and facilitate a compacting of under-sized holdings.

Although there are differences in emphasis, the arguments favouring the establishment of the Norrbotten iron and steel plant closely resemble those favouring Mo i Rana. Firstly, Sweden's pre-war production of pig-iron was slightly less than three-quarters of a million tons, and fell short of domestic requirements by somewhat more than half a million tons. Sweden's overseas market for quality steel is steady. In particular, it has an expanding domestic market for rolled steel. Demand increases at somewhat more than 5% annually, and the government bill (*Proposition*, 1946, 302), which planned development in Luleå, anticipated a demand sustained at least at this level. As with Norway, an export surplus is also expected. Secondly, the creation of heavy industry in Norrland was favoured. Thirdly, it was pronounced undesirable that almost all Lappland ores should be exported before processing (*Proposition*, 1939, 70). In the fourth place, changing techniques aided the establishment of the plant. The so-called "sponge-iron process", substantially economising in coking coal, is perhaps the most significant of these. Electric power is available. Although it is more distant than at Mo i Rana, improved long-distance transmission eases the journey. The Porjus site, harnessed first in 1910 to meet the needs of the electrified ore railway, was ex-

panded during the First World War to supply two electric furnaces (at Porjus smeltery), and now directs a full third of its output to Luleå. Harsprånget, generating twice as much as Porjus and now the largest single power-plant in Sweden, has a site of Norwegian magnitude (with 106 m. fall) and is blessed with great lake reservoirs.

The partial substitution of electricity for coke in the sponge-iron process has fundamentally altered the thermal economics of the Scandinavian iron and steel industry. Both Mo i Rana and Luleå reverse the classical nineteenth-century rule that ore has gone to coal in the localisation of the iron and steel industry. As an extension of this, Luleå is favourably situated for the freighting. Admittedly, it is closed for an average of six months each year, but ships arriving during the open period commonly enter in ballast. On the basis of low return freight charges, it is argued that they can profitably bring coke. Limestone in relatively large quantities and manganese ore in relatively small quantities must also be imported. In addition, Norrbotten has an historic source of fuel absent from Mo i Rana. Charcoal smelting—or, more precisely, the partial reduction of pig-iron by charcoal—is possible. The State Forestry concern (*Statens skogsindustri*) has a timber distillation plant at Piteå with a maximum capacity of 160,000 cu. m. of charcoal annually.

The last and most significant fact for the existence of the Luleå plant is iron-ore. Quantitatively and qualitatively, its sources of supply are superior to those of Mo i Rana. At the present rate of production, it is estimated that Norrbotten ores are adequate for 200 years. They are, in contrast to those of Mo i Rana, at a peak of commercial development. Admittedly, they are distant from Luleå, but the down gradient of the track and available power give to them ease of access. Moreover, one-third of the production of Kiruna automatically moves through Luleå, which is a natural break-of-bulk point.

Theoretically, the picture is satisfactory, but it must assume the continued existence of a lively market. Traditionally, iron and steel activities have flourished not only when the market has been good but also when they are located near to the consuming centres of their products. Past experiences in Norrbotten have not been encouraging. The presence of ores and generous charcoal resources gave rise to small-scale charcoal bloomeries a century ago—with ores, for example, moving by reindeer sleigh from Luossavaara to Junosuando furnace. These smelteries died out in the 1880s. Largely basing the argument on cheap return freight, Luleå iron-works came into being with two furnaces, bent upon the export of pig-iron in 1904-6. It ceased to operate in the 1920s. The combination of an improved market, a new scale of operations, technical and transport improvements may offset unsatisfactory past experiences.

The visitor to the sites of these high-latitude industries has two abiding impressions. The first is their complete detachment from the ultimate market for their products. The impression is peculiarly strong at Mo—where an industrial panorama is spread beneath the shadow of Svartisen glacier (cf. Plate 22). At Luleå, shades of Duluth and its plant detached from the main American market spring to mind.[1] The second impression is the determination of the respective promoters that these plants shall function for social reasons if they do not operate as economic propositions. Although each plant is in its incipient stages of development (Mo furnaces warmed to action as the deep snows thawed in April 1955), their respective impacts on Helgeland and Norrbotten are already widespread and considerable.

(b) Esbjerg and its State Harbour

In the localisation of the Norwegian state enterprise at Mo i Rana, the steady crystallisation of ideas can be traced through a series of debates in which advantage and disadvantage are proposed and disposed. The element of social control is never far removed from an argument in which economic possibilities are always posed as marginal. There were clearly less economic settings than Mo i Rana for the enterprise, but there were possibly more economic settings. There were conceivably more economic outlets for the investment involved.

In the foundation and localisation of the Danish port of Esbjerg, there was the same process of debate, but official authority was backed by strong economic motives. There was little or no risk of Esbjerg being a commercial failure and calling for heavy subsidisation. Esbjerg harbour was state-financed partly because of the relative urgency to open a western window and partly because there were inadequate private resources.

The creation of Esbjerg called for three separate acts. The first one was to construct the harbour. Plans, which had already been made as early as 1864[2] and were shelved during the war, were eventually formulated into a law in 1868. Secondly, steps had to be taken to establish the town. According to the population statistics of 1860, thirty people were living on the site of Esbjerg. The first town plan was put forward in 1870. Thirdly, port and town had to be tied to the state railway system, which had been initiated a generation earlier. A single track eventually linked the harbour with Vamdrup in 1874.

A combination of circumstances gradually focused attention upon Esbjerg bluff. In the first place, developing trade relations with Great Britain and Western Europe called for an outlet on the Atlantic coast to reduce sailing time from Denmark and to lessen the hazards of journeying round the Skaw. Secondly, a new set of hinterland relations was introduced for the Jutish coast through the railways. British interests had already demonstrated an interest on land (in their search for railway concessions across the Jutish isthmus)[3] and at sea (in the commercial steamers which on their own initiative had penetrated the channels of the Slesvig archipelago in search of harbourage). British shipping first appeared in Danish North Sea waters in the 1850s, emulating small-sized Danish vessels which as early as 1847 had attempted to use the limited facilities of Ballum, Hjerting and the Limfiord as loading-places for export cargoes. Indeed,

[1] Cf. L. White and G. Primmer, "The Iron and Steel Industry of Duluth", *Geographical Review*, XXVII, 1937.
[2] C. Carlsen and C. G. Bruun, *Om anlæget af en havn ved Graadybets Fastlandkyst*, Copenhagen, 1866 (including a map).
[3] "Dansk Jernbanepolitik, 1850–65", *National Økonomisk Tidsskrift*, Copenhagen, 1898.

the British Vice-Consul in Copenhagen was constrained to write:

"If the Gudenaa or even the East Coast line of railway were extended to Ballum and a harbour wese built there, a considerable direct trade with England must be the consequence . . . at the same time the politico-commercial question of too close intercourse with Hamburg or Germany would be evaded."

The third decisive factor was the Dano-Prussian War of 1864, which reduced the surface area of Denmark by a third and precipitated an economic revolution. The new boundary reduced the Atlantic coast of Denmark to an equal extent, both simplifying and complicating the problem facing the state authorities responsible for creating a harbour. The number of alternative port sites was immediately diminished. The reduction occurred at the same time as the urge to maximise agricultural resources became most insistent.

The harbourless North Sea coast of Jutland had been christened "The Iron Coast" in medieval times. It displays a treacherously broad and sandy foreshore backed by a dune cordillera of varying amplitude. The sand which menaces the mariner's keel is matched by that which threatens to advance upon the farmer. In earlier times, Limfiorden had a natural North Sea outlet, but by the twelfth century this was silted up.[1] North Sea commerce, however, was centred essentially on the south-west, where the cathedral port of Ribe fulfilled a significant medieval role. Ribe, at the junction of the *watten* and *geest* zones, was one of the termini of the cattle trails along which exports moved on the hoof to North European and Netherland markets. It was the first urban centre of consequence south of the breach made by the North Sea in the outer dune rampart.[2] Behind the island arc of this relic cordillera is found a broad area of tidal flats (*vader*) called *Vadehavet* by the Danes and experiencing a tidal range of from 1 to 2 m.[3] To this, Ribe was oriented, and its export routes largely followed the tortuous channels through the mud-flats southwards in the lea of the islands. Its decline, from the sixteenth century onwards, was due principally

to the physical deterioration of the site, with the silts of the Ribe river and the shifting channels of the tidal flats reducing access to its riverside wharves. It was not an indispensable port, for others along the Slesvig-Holstein coast to its immediate south could continue to function. Changed political boundaries and changed commercial routes, however, called for a new Ribe, and Esbjerg became its logical successor.

In 1851, a Dutch engineer was invited to make recommendations for a harbour north of the Eider mouth, the coastal problems involved in harbour construction being considered common to Denmark and the Netherlands. Weighing all available evidence, engineer Beyerinck limited the alternatives to Strandby, Husum and Tønning. Tønning was rejected as being too far south in relation to planned landward routes of export. Esbjerg was favoured on strictly geographical grounds—its location on the most direct route between the broadest Jutland hinterland and the overseas markets; its relatively favoured high and dry site with adjacent deep water; a tidal range sufficiently small to dispense with lock gates; the approach of the Graa Deep and comparatively good sailing conditions in relation to marine currents.

In the succeeding evolution of Esbjerg, four interrelated developments must be mentioned —those of the harbour, its transport agencies, the trade and the town.[4] The development of the state-owned harbour, with its five miles of quays, is given in Fig. 37. The original undertaking was the dock harbour—completed in 1874. Lateral developments have since encased several miles of foreshore in concrete walls. The increased size of vessels has called for dredging, and approximately a million cubic metres of sand are removed annually from Graadyb, to give it an 8-m. channel at high tide. One of the most significant harbour developments has sprung from the natural shelter afforded by Esbjerg to fishing vessels. Indeed, the creation of Esbjerg may be said to have given birth to a new North Sea fishing industry for Denmark. A Fishery

[1] There is a channel piercing the obstruction at Thyborøn today, but it admits only small vessels.
[2] G. Neufeldt, *Ripen und Esbjerg*, Copenhagen, 1937.
[3] N. H. Jacobsen, "Skibsfarten i det danske Vadehav", *Meddelelser fra Skalling Laboratoriet*, 1937.
[4] *Esbjerg, 1868–1943*, Esbjerg, 1944.

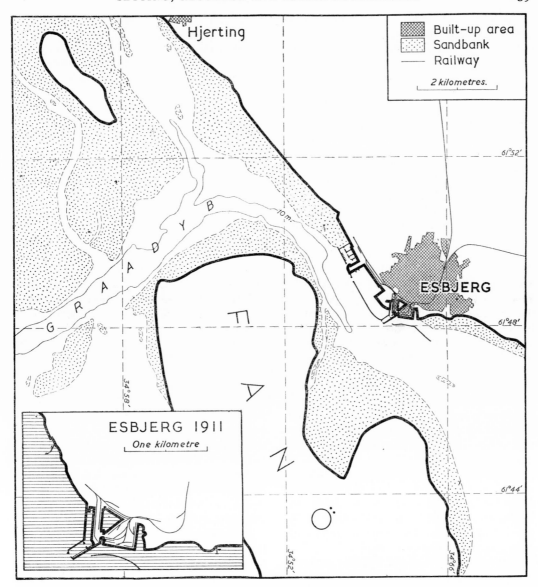

FIG. 37. The setting of the port of Esbjerg.

Society was in existence in 1878, and dock facilities were developed in the 1880s; but the specialised west side fishery harbour (1897–1902) led to a change in the scale of operations. Simultaneously, the first screw-driven motor fishing vessels came into use. From a very limited local and seasonal activity, fishing was transformed into a large-scale, long-distance, continuous undertaking. Up to 600 fishing-boats can be accommodated in Esbjerg har-

bour. Icelandic and North Atlantic fishing has been added to that of the North Sea, and today Esbjerg is unrivalled in Denmark for the receipt, processing and dispatch of "sea food".

Transport relations have changed simultaneously. In 1860, the British Vice-Consul could write that the great drawback to Husum or Tønning exports was "that the Jutland farmer, having no railways, is obliged to drive his lean cattle for a long distance to be fatted on the marshes, at a loss of £1/10/- per head". Subsequently, Denmark developed an almost uneconomically intensive rail network. The appearance of the motor lorry has exaggerated this. Moreover, the lorry is privately or co-operatively owned, and therefore is in competition with the state-owned railways. Already, a full third of the agricultural products moving over Esbjerg journey by road, and improved highways are not likely to reduce the proportion. Seaward, the multiplication and intensification of Esbjerg's contacts have been swift. The English routes were the most commercially rewarding—Esbjerg, indeed, was the hinge upon which exports swung from Danish rural producer to British industrial consumer. Newcastle and Thameshaven were the initial importing harbours before the completion of the Parkestone Quay (by the Great Eastern Railway in 1880). It was in the establishment of regular routes followed by fast vessels that the success of Esbjerg lay. Needless to say, a steadily mounting import trade complemented the export trade—especially in fuels to meet the essential needs of shipping and transport in a fuelless land. In one peculiar respect the harbour of Esbjerg has a unique advantage, and may be intermittently transformed from Denmark's fifth harbour (after the capital, Aarhus, Aalborg and Odense) into its first. That is, when the impact of winter is sufficiently severe to close the Kattegat ports. Esbjerg was aware of its unique role for the first time in 1893 and, more recently, in 1929 and 1940.

The trade of the harbour, fulfilling all hopes of expansion, must be regarded as a series of variations upon an essentially agricultural theme. In 1851, the English-born Lowestoft–Hjerting line carried from Denmark over 1,000 animals and 100,000 kg. of meat—a commodity traffic which continued directly the medieval character of that of Ribe. Within ten years of the completion of the dock harbour, the volume of Esbjerg's exports of meat, butter and eggs was second only to that of Copenhagen. Animal husbandry continued

to provide the export trade, but the range of its constituents was being steadily broadened and the proportion between them substantially changed. Thus, meat exports were to be rapidly affected by refrigeration, which meant severe competition from the cheaper grazing lands of Australia and South America. But the same device enabled Denmark to secure successful European markets for its dairy produce and, on the strength of its qualitative improvements, to meet subsequent overseas competition. Esbjerg as a bacon-exporting harbour is unrivalled—another specialist variation upon the agricultural theme. A small export of root crops intermittently accompanies animal products. The stream of trade to the harbour has been summarised in a series of flow diagrams prepared for the *Atlas of Denmark* (by A. Aagesen). They show Esbjerg to be first and foremost a Jutish export harbour, though the archipelago hinterland is also partly served. Freight rates from Esbjerg to Great Britain are thought to be about half those from the East Jutland ports to Great Britain; a considerable "depth" in road or rail transport can therefore be added complementarily.[1] The hinterland was affected only to a very limited degree by opening of the Kiel Canal in 1896 (a descendant of the unbuilt canal which Christian III planned to link the Nipsaa and Königsaa). This protected water route from the outer sea to the archipelago naturally offered an alternative means of communication for the transport of Danish exports.

Above the harbour a chequerboard plan of late nineteenth-century brick residences and twentieth-century suburbs house roughly 60,000 inhabitants (cf. Plate 8). Three periods of development may be defined: from the time of the first settlement until 1894, when Esbjerg became an independent commune; Esbjerg the administrative commune, 1894–8; Esbjerg as a merchant town (Købstad) with its own administrative charter. Esbjerg is an independent administrative unit, but because the town is so much the harbour, its existence can never be considered independently of the state-owned port.

---

[1] Cf. R. Schou, *L'Agriculture en Danemark*, Paris, 1900, Map 23, which shows the relative hours to British markets from Danish ports other than Esbjerg.

The state harbour of Esbjerg is not without parallel in Northern Europe, for an artificial harbour was similarly called into existence in Finland. The birth of Hanko (Hangö)[1] was a generation later than that of Esbjerg. But whereas in south-west Jutland the problem was to overcome a harbourless coast, in south-west Finland the problem was to create a satisfactory ice-free terminal. Hanko is a winter port. Its origin is inseparable from the link struck with Finland's state railway network in 1872-3 and from the continuity of overseas trading made possible by the iron-hulled steamship. Hanko peninsula, in Uusimaa, has always been a commanding feature of the coast, and within its protection potential harbourages already existed. The final design for harbour works and town represents the outcome of a series of alternative proposals, together with the inevitable accretion which encumbers rather than enhances any original plan. Hanko, in fact, has been a specialist port in two senses of the word. It has been a harbour with a seasonal activity in almost inverse ratio to the other ports of Finland; it has also been so removed from the main export industries of Finland that in its incipient stages its trade was not truly representative of an inherently "wooden" economy. It was, in fact, the principal centre of export for agricultural products, with a trade structure extraordinarily akin to that of Esbjerg. Although the battle with ice has revealed for Finland that there are other winter ports, the seasonal monopoly of Hanko is always a strong possibility. The contemporary problem of Hanko is one of flexibility, for its requirements cannot be forecast in advance. Seasonal demands upon it may be the anticipated normal or they may be exceptional. In order to accommodate itself to this short-period problem of adjustment, it is perhaps natural that Hanko should be underwritten by the state. In fulfilling its role as a critical winter port, social fact may have to take precedence over considerations of economics.

THE RANGE OF PLANNING

In considering setting, resource and social revaluation, the accent has been placed upon high-latitude lands and the central authority. It would, however, be wrong to assume that the old-established parts of the Fenno-Scandinavian economy have suffered neglect while attention has been concentrated upon "filling the empty quarter". The northern sector is the controversial sector, and is accordingly inclined to overshadow less controversial development elsewhere.[2] In the established areas, total sponsored enterprise is probably greater. In the north, the debate is more frequently centred upon the theme "to be or not to be"; elsewhere it is more commonly a question of starting from the assumption "to be" and then debating the detail of the ways and means. Much the same principles are at work in the south, though differing social and economic restraints appear. A fundamental difference springs from the more thoroughly humanised landscapes. In the south, new lines of communication, new industrial and agricultural forms must adjust themselves more thoroughly to the articulations of the old.

The central authority can still be deterministic. In a crisis, it can direct industrial distribution, as with the relocation of Karelian industry after its displacement from south-eastern Finland in the autumn of 1944. In detail, its operation can be traced from such reports as the Swedish government publication on the location of economic activity of 1951.[3] For example, a new central clothing factory was projected, in part to meet military needs and in part financed by military resources. Economic considerations favoured a location at either Kramfors (in West Norrland) or Degerfors (in Örebro county). It was, in fact, guided by the Ministry of Labour to Storfors in Värmland on the score of a surfeit of employable labour.

Social controls operate at a number of levels, and it is principally through the intervention of civic authorities that they assert themselves in the metropolitan territories of Scandinavia. Local authorities use an increasing variety of means when bargaining site advantages and site prices. Such bargaining

[1] A. Wesen, *Hangö hamn*, Helsingfors, 1911.
[2] e.g. Ottar Brox, *Hva skjer i Nord-Norge*, Bergen, 1965.
[3] *Näringslivets lokalisering*, Stockholm, 1951, 6.

may be an integral part of urban planning and development schemes. Sweden provides instances of the many forms which can be taken by indirect promotional activity. Sites may be offered to industries by local authorities at peppercorn prices; as, for example, at Luleå (for a factory in 1941), Söderköping (for a machine-shop in 1946), Hässleholm (for a pharmaceutical factory in 1945). Oskarshamn gave a substantial mortgage to a copper works to construct a new quay in 1949. The free installation of essential services to possible plant sites may be a significant inducement. In 1945, Nyköping provided a road, gas, electricity and water supply and a branch railway with a transformer station to an industrial site. Skövde, Köping and Lund have provided similar facilities. Assistance can take the form of restitution of local taxes as in the localisation of a timber-plant at Eksjö. Sometimes the authority (e.g. Karlskrona) may take out shares in the plant equivalent to the value of the site offered. All such measures are strong enough to encourage private organisations to compromise in their choice of plant location.

The biggest problem is to discourage trends in industrial distribution. This has become of singular consequence in respect of all the capital cities of the Northern Countries, but nowhere more than in Sweden. The disproportionate development of industry in the neighbourhood of the principal population concentrations is a natural tendency. Here, market, transport and frequently labour conditions provide a favourable setting. To enforce the dispersal of industry into the tributary region rather than to permit its development within the existing urban area represents only a limited solution.

Formal planning, indeed, has been forced on apace by the growth of cities. Already in the early 1920s there were town planning acts in the North and they were both anticipated and accompanied by specialist plans, of which Eliel Saarinen's 1918 plan for Helsinki is an example. Garden suburbs in the tradition of England's Welwyn were built around Stockholm a generation ago; today they have been swallowed by concentric suburban accumulations and supplemented by yet remoter satellite cities of self-contained character, such as Vällingby (cf. Plate 10) with its anticipated 100,000 population. The planning of towns has been a particular concern of post-war years. Stockholm's master plan, prepared 1945–52, is perhaps the most elaborate of all. A measure of catastrophe, as in the bombed towns of coastal Norway, has prompted formal development as it occasioned past planning in, for example, Swedish proposals in 1750 and 1782 or the Finnish Ordinance of 1856 with its principles for laying out a town against fire hazards. To the same category of planning belong the virtual new towns of Finland which have been grafted on to the older towns to accommodate displaced people. The new halves of Valkeakoski and Lahti provide examples.

Although town planning is a tangible phenomenon, a more broadly integrated regional basis is sought.[1] In the north, regional plans are incorporated within the broader scheme of total development. A hierarchy of plans is detectable. In Sweden during recent years comprehensive regional programmes have begun about the foci of Göteborg, Borås, Örebro, Karlskrona, Kalmar, Sundsvall, Örnsköldsvik and Umeå, as well as the capital.[2] The concept of the "harmonious region", in which rural and urban interests are balanced and blended, is the objective of such programmes. Projects along parallel lines have been conceived in south Finland. Along the length of the Kymi valley, for example, eleven communities and nine industrial enterprises have submitted their development proposals. It is implicit that regional planning bureau and city planning office gather together in their hands the reins of employment opportunity at the same time as they collect those of space development.

There have always been people who have formulated plans for the land and written names on the map. There was an age when state plans were conceived by monarchs or projected by sagacious if despotic ministers. The Bothnian ports of Finland testify to this—

[1] J. Humlum, *Landsplanlaegnings Problemer*, Copenhagen, 1966 provides illustrations from Denmark.
[2] F. Forbat, "Raumordnung und Landesplannung in Schweden", *Raumforschung und Raumordnung*, 1955, **13**, 1.

Oulu (Uleåborg) was created in 1605, Vaasa in 1606, Uusikaarlepyy (Nykarleby), Kokkola (Gamlakarleby) and Tornio (Torneå) all in 1620, Raahe (Brahestad) and Kristiinen-kaupunki (Kristinestad) in 1649, Pietarsaari (Jakobstad) in 1653. There was a time when central authority relaxed and industrial settlements like those of Swedish *Bergslagen* or east Norway were created by *baroner och patroner* (barons and patrons). In turn, aristocratic initiative was succeeded by the astute directors of joint stock companies, who created factory towns like Notodden[1] and Høyanger in Norway. Now new settlements and new patterns of distribution are again planned by central authorities. Their motives and objectives are clearly defined in the beginning, though they may be confused in the end. The ultimate process of creation is not very different from that in the past—nor is the manner in which it gives rise to forces at variance with established ways.

[1] J. C. Hansen, "Notodden", *Norsk Geografisk Tidsskrift*, **19**, 1963–4, 273–90.

PART 4

SOME PRIMARY ECONOMIC ACTIVITIES

Chapter VII

THE CONTRIBUTION OF FARMING

"They have carried the ploughshare beyond the Arctic circle."

Xavier Marmier, *Letters*, 1843

THE DISTRIBUTION OF THE CULTIVATED LAND

In Northern Europe, the pattern of soil fertility has guided the historical occupation of the land and, in general, soil quality explains the varying intensity of cultivation.[1] The good soils derive first from sedimentary bed ocks which, in Northern Europe, are very restricted in area. Instances are provided by the loam-yielding calcareous rocks of Denmark and the extreme south of Sweden; by the intermittent limestones, picked out strikingly in the agricultural florescences of Siljan and Dalälven in north central Sweden and of Norwegian Trøndelag; by the very limited occurrences of mica shales, giving rise to troughs of great fertility in such eroded features as the remarkable Flåm valley of western Norway. In the second place, fertile soils may be of marine or lacustrine origin. Reference has already been made to the differences in fertility between the "sub-aquatic" and the "supra-aquatic" areas of Sweden and Finland. Clays and sands of marine or lacustrine origin are the most common background to the old-established arable areas of Sweden and Finland. In Norway, too, with its restricted lowland, the areas of marine transgression are readily detectable. Everywhere marine transgression has had a fundamental effect in modifying, redistributing and reassorting material of glacial origin. The interplay of ice and sea, and of human ingenuity in the detection of good soils reaches its most subtle expression in western Norway. Thirdly, soils improve or deteriorate in response to climatic conditions. It is not therefore surprising that Denmark, having the most uniformly favourable climate, should have the most uniformly favourable soils. Fourthly, good soils may be created either through generations of human effort or through the heavy investment of capital over a shorter period of time. Such transformation is seen to most effect in the humus soils of the peatlands—contemporarily regarded as the most rewarding for reclamation. Peatland reclamation calls for heavy investment in soil drainage.[2] The transformation of inferior soils has proceeded most thoroughly in Denmark, where "pressure on the land" is most noticeable and climate most helpful. Danish farm statistics list the millions of loads of sand which are moved to the peatlands and the millions of loads of peat humus which are reciprocally moved to the sandy lands. Some improvement results, but the inherent fertility of the better soils can never be matched by those artificially improved.

The cultivated area established against this background consists of arable land (*åker*) and improved meadowland (*äng*), and Table 12 gives some idea of the absolute extent of these types of land use. It indicates the small percentage of cultivated land to be found in all of the Northern Countries except Denmark. It is so small in Norway, in fact, that the re-

[1] A valuable aid to the understanding of Scandinavian agriculture is *Landbrukets driftsøkonomi* (ed. N. Westermarck and L. Hjelm), Stockholm, 1956.

[2] There is an interesting survey of drainage in Finland by T. Juusela and T. Wäre, *Suomen peltojen kuivatustila*, Helsinki, 1956.

TABLE 12
LAND USE (1,000 HECTARES)

Country	Total Area	Arable and Orchards	Meadows and Pasture	Woodlands	Hectares per man employed in agriculture[1]
Denmark . .	4,303	2,698	325	473	8·4
Finland . .	33,703	2,868	140	19,780	5·4
Iceland . .	10,300	88	2,300	—	—
Norway . .	32,422	846	161	7,026	3·2
Sweden . .	44,979	3,184	525	22,505	7·6

(Source: The comparative tables from the *Yearbook of Nordic Statistics*, Stockholm, 1967.)

turns for it are made in decares instead of hectares. In Iceland, meadowland is not recorded in the same way, but is referred to as manured grassland. Fig. 38 illustrates the distribution of cultivated land. The map, showing the absolute extent of cultivated area, displays an expected southern concentration, a contrasting northern void and a most widespread dispersal of improved land in Norway.

Four observations may be added to these introductory statements. First of all, while the absolute area of improved land appears to be small, it must be recalled that compared with much of Europe, the population of the Northern Countries is not large. On a *per capita* basis, the extent of cultivated area naturally varies from country to country. Simple mathematical equations provide misleading conclusions. But if it be argued that the average Englishman requires two acres of cultivated land to support his present standard of consumption, due allowance being made for the differing physical circumstances, it may be assumed that the average Scandinavian needs no less. Paradoxically, the purely agricultural surpluses are largest from Denmark, which is one of the smallest constituents.

Secondly, while it is possible to summarise the distribution of cultivated land in Table 12 and on Fig. 38, it is almost impossible to define satisfactorily the land area from which the farming community obtains its livelihood. For there exists an old-established distinction between intensively cultivated and extensively employed land. This is summed up in their basically differing nomenclature. *Innmark* or

infield stands in contrast to *utmark* or outfield. Historically, infield has been held in scattered parcels divided among the inhabitants of the community; outfield has generally been held as common land (*almenning*), though there have been (and remain) significant divergences from this rule. The outlands have experienced differential reduction. Common pasturages or grazings have yielded most thoroughly to enclosure and improvement in Denmark. As represented by the *seter* economy of Norway, the outfields remain a widespread feature of the fell and fiord farming scene. Outland grazing, however, is not confined to *seter*, heath and salt-marsh, for it remains a significant practice in privately owned woodlands. In Finland and Sweden particularly, forest grazings continue to fulfil the role of the *seter* of Norway. The infield has been historically fenced against open-range animals, though it is increasingly employed at the present time for controlled grazing.

Thirdly, the relation between cultivated or improved and uncultivated or unimproved land is unstable. It will be evident from Chapter V that there has been an historical succession of advances into and retreats from the wasteland. Reclamation remains lively regionally, though it is usually prompted by particular local or national forces. Axel Schou identifies "one of the last incomplete phases of land occupation in Denmark", in the formal assault on the tidal mud-flats of south Jutland which is mustering the energies of scientists and technicians.[2] Yet despite such endeavours, Denmark is losing farmland to

[1] From F. Dovring, *Land and Labour in Europe, 1900–1950*, The Hague, 1956.
[2] N. Nielsen, *British Association for the Advancement of Science*, Bristol, 1955, and *Geografisk Tidsskrift*, 55, 1956.

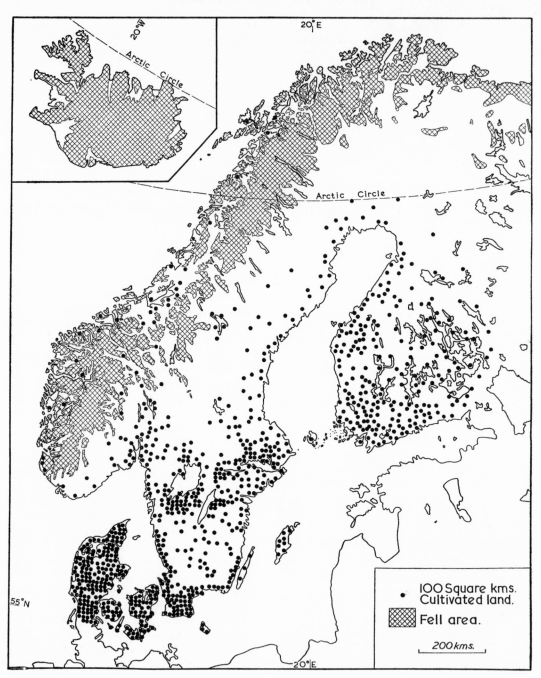

Fig. 38. Distribution of cultivated land in the Northern Countries. (Based upon W. William-Olsen, *Economic Map of Europe*, Stockholm, 1951.)

building more quickly than it is reclaiming new—a situation which gives to it a unique status in the Scandinavian group. Iceland has three times as much cultivated land today as fifty years ago and *landnám* is still proceeding.[1] The most intensive reclamation in Scandinavian history has, in fact, occurred during the last decade. 35,000 new farms have been carved out of Finnish woodland and wasteland to accommodate principally the farming families who elected to leave territories ceded to the U.S.S.R. in September 1944. This contemporary epic in pioneering has had a marked effect upon the distribution of cultivated area in Finland, for by it roughly half a million hectares of new land have been brought under the plough. Such an attack on the woodlands has been a social necessity. The irony is that, simultaneously and in the interests of its softwood economy, Sweden has been discouraging the expansion of its cultivated area. Swedish policy may be argued upon increasingly rational premises today. Given opportunities for measuring the relative yields of land, it should be possible to determine whether a potential intake is likely to produce a greater return under timber or under a particular crop. In Sweden, for example, it might be held that where the yielding power of land falls appreciably below 1,000 crop units per hectare (which is the average for the country), it is often more profitable to leave it under a timber cover.[2] All of the Northern Countries have their protagonists of cultivable land, but their estimates are subject to substantial variation. In Norway, for example, the Peatland Society

estimates a cultivable peatland area which is two or three times as great as that recorded by the farmers. Yet simultaneously, Norwegian farm economists are faced with the retreat of farming from long-occupied and cultivated tracts in the fell zone, the maintenance of which might be less costly than reclamation of peatlands.[3] By and large, entrenchment rather than expansion is a scientifically supported tenet for the management of the arable areas.

Fourthly, while it would appear that there is ample space in Northern Europe for the farming community, there is distinct regional pressure on the land. In Norway, for example, population distribution per square mile of country is frequently meaningless. Ice, rock and slope conditions (with the threat of avalanche, scree fall or flooding) eliminate so much of the surface area from habitation that population per square mile of cultivated territory is the only satisfactory criterion. In many western fiords the figure rises to 500 persons per square mile. Complete occupation of the land exists and has existed for generations. Land only rarely enters the market. The family farm, frequently bearing the same name as the occupying family, is the basic unit; it is legally protected by *odel* law in their name. Where there is an expanding non-agricultural population, even the acquisition of settlement sites calls for ingenuity.

THE DIFFERENTIATION OF FARM PRODUCTION

If the fertility of the soil is the primary criterion of its occupation, the possibilities of

TABLE 13
CROP YIELD
(*in 1,000 short tons*)

Country	Wheat	Rye	Barley	Oats	Potatoes	Sugar-beet
Denmark	292	276	2,045	800	1,938	1,694
Finland	249	137	265	830	1,079	371
Norway	41	2	224	161	1,130	—
Sweden	1,031	308	364	880	1,465	2,002

[1] *Jordpolitiken i Norden*, Stockholm, 1956, chapter on Iceland.
[2] One *crop unit* is the equivalent of 1 kg. (2·2 lb.) of wheat, rye, barley, peas, etc.; 1·2 kg. (2·64 lb.) of oats; 1·1 kg. (2·42 lb.) of mixed grain; 4 kg. (8·8 lb.) of potatoes or sugar-beet; 10 kg. (22 lb.) of fodder beets; 2·2–2·5 kg. (4·84–5·5 lb.) of hay, and 3·5–5·0 kg. (7·7–11·0 lb.) of straw.
[3] Cf. "Effektiviteten av ulike driftsformer i fjellbygdene", *Norges Landbruksøkonomisk Institut*, Oslo, 1953.

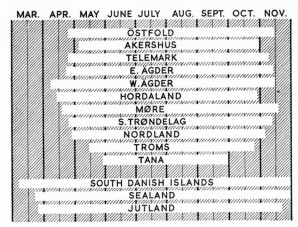

FIG. 39. The length of the growing period for sample centres in west Scandinavia.

the prevailing climate differentiate the pattern of crops borne upon it. The crowding together of the physical and economic frontiers of cultivation of so many familiar West European crops is one of the noticeable features of the Fenno-Scandinavian scene. This negative fact much impressed early observers. Consider the virtual litany of marginal remarks on the map accompanying Arthur Capell Brooke's travels in 1827:[1]

"The plum bears as far as Gefle"; "The Oak is planted as far as Sundsvall"; "Wheat succeeds as far as Ångermanland"; "Peas, vetches and beans north of this [63° N.] do not ripen every year"; "Cabbages cease to come to a head" [64° N.]; "Rye ceases to recompense the labour bestowed on account of the frost [at the Polar Circle]"; "Barley reaches almost to the boundary of the pine woods [69° N.]".

It was the general paring down of opportunity which impressed him as he travelled northwards; though regionally and locally he was aware of facts offsetting the incidence of latitude or distance from the Atlantic. And restraints upon the range of crops were accompanied by increasing uncertainty of yields as the margins of cultivation were reached.

The physical facts operate inexorably. Save for possible long-period changes in climate, the growing period conforms approximately to the patterns of Figs. 39 and 40 for

Norway and Sweden respectively. The Swedish picture is especially striking from this standpoint because the number of growing days in the deep south is almost twice that of the high north. Yet the contemporary approach to the boundaries of cultivation is essentially positive. The boundaries are regarded very much as a challenge. While recognising that there are ultimate limits, it is apparent that the range of opportunities within those limits has never been fully explored—let alone exploited.

New crops, new varieties of old crops, new combinations of established crops, bend if they do not break the absolute boundaries of cultivation. There has, for example, been a transformation in the pattern of wheat cultivation in the north. Not merely is more wheat grown today in Sweden, Finland and Norway than in former times, but the distribution of cultivation is more widespread. The Northern Countries consume more wheat than ever before; but they, nevertheless, aspire nearer to self-sufficiency. New varieties have carried the safe boundaries of cultivation northwards to the Siljan area of Sweden.[2] An August journey from Bergen to Oslo emphasises the contrast between green western grass country and golden eastern grain country—and today the eastern grain is frequently wheat.[3] Advance in wheat cultivation is even more strikingly illustrated by comparing a series of crop maps from successive editions of the Finnish National Atlas. Progress in wheat cultivation cannot be considered independently of demand for wheat. In the final place, the new boundaries of cultivation have not been established independently of a change in the national diet from rye bread to wheat bread. In the field, wheat overtook rye in Sweden for the first time in the 1930s; it is sown about equally as a spring and winter crop. Norway had more land under rye than wheat in 1917; today rye, covering about 10 sq. km., occupies less than a thirtieth of the area under wheat.

[1] And the first plant geographical map of all Sweden of C. A. Agardh and C. E. Dahlman, *Ankologisk och fysisk karta öfver Sverige*, 1:1,250,000, 1857.
[2] Cf. B. Fullerton, "The Northern Margin of Grain Production in Sweden in the Twentieth Century", *Institute of British Geographers, Transactions*, 1954, **20**, 181–91.
[3] Cf. A. Sømme, *Jordbrukets geografi i Norge*, Oslo, 1954, Fig. 151.

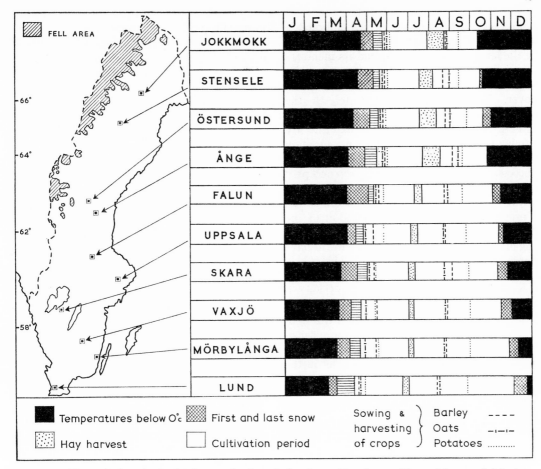

FIG 40. The agricultural calendar for sample places in Sweden. (Based upon *Ekonomisk-geografisk karta över Sverige*, Text, Stockholm, 1954.)

Improved varieties of rye, oats and barley have entered the picture simultaneously, but they have not caught the northern imagination to the same extent, though their absolute importance may be nationally (as in the case of oats) or regionally greater. Oats retain a position of considerable importance in the grain statistics of Sweden, though there has been a relative decline in the total area devoted to them. Barley has fallen steadily in popularity, but as a component of the mixed grain crop for fodder, it is among those grains which stand in competition with the improved grasses. Table 13 shows average yields.

Grass is the least spectacular of crops, but the most fundamental in northern latitudes.[1] It is, today, the principal crop on the improved lands of Scandinavia—having established itself a place in the rotational system. The grass constituent in the rotational system is a ley of varying length. The length of the ley may be as brief as three years in the south of Sweden, for example, and as long as ten years in the north. The yield of cultivated grass, at approximately 3,000 lb. per acre, is not merely greater than that of any corresponding grain crop with the possible exception of winter wheat, but the harvest is a much more certain one. Most grasses are more tolerant of precipitation and temperature

[1] O.E.E.C., *Pasture and Fodder Production in N.W. Europe*, Rome, 1954, and *The Breeding of Herbage Plants in Scandinavia and Finland*, Aberystwyth, 1940.

conditions than grains. Moreover, the word "grass" is a collective noun which embraces a wide variety of plants. *N.O. Graminæ* is one of the largest plant families, and its members offer infinite opportunities for intermarriage as well as for combining together in a plant cover. Timothy, above all, interests the Scandinavian farmer; cocksfoot, the rye grasses and fescues to a lesser extent. By taming grasses and by giving them a place on reclaimed land, man has achieved a major success. Grass, hitherto a farm crop accepted from the circumscribed meadows or associated with the extensive outlands of Northern Europe, has entered into the domain of the fenced land. And in the contemporary breeding of new species, few parts of the world have been more energetic than Scandinavia.

Grass includes clovers, and it is this component which has given to the crop its significant value in rotation. Whereas hardier grass species will grow and overwinter throughout Northern Europe, clovers are more sensitive. The establishment of clovers in a temporary ley becomes increasingly harder in the higher latitudes, not only on the score of killing winter temperatures and poor resistance to diseases like crown rot (*Sclerotinia trifoliorum*), but also because of their relative sterility and their inability to seed in the absence of long-tongued insects. Clover, more than almost any component of the ley, has done most to eliminate fallowing from the rotation. The red and alsike (named after the Swedish village Alsike) clovers are the sown species; white clover enters as a natural subsidiary to the grass community. Lucerne enters the picture only in the south.

Permanent grass, in the English sense of the term, is not a common feature of the northern farm.[1] Most improved grassland is fostered through the plough, though the more "Atlantic" parts of Scandinavia can maintain a permanent grass sward. Western Norway continues to provide examples of what Erik Pontoppidan called the "liberal blessing of grass". Of Devik, in Nordfiord, he wrote that it was "not above half a Norway mile in circumference . . . yet it feeds very near 200 people and 1,200 cattle of different kinds" (p.

109). The permanence of west Norwegian grass is sometimes emphasised by the virtually permanent hay racks (or *hesjer*) which are erected. There are continuing experiments to test the effectiveness of permanent grass and its stock carrying capacity in Finland.

The importance of the potato in northern farming has already been stressed. It has not merely brought much-needed variety to the limited range of roots, but also brought a new crop which could be cultivated on almost any land under tillage at the time of its arrival. Today, it forms the third of the trinity of essential crops—grass, grains, potatoes. It is, of course, sensitive to frost in higher latitudes and higher altitudes, but the risk is widely taken—and assuming the absence of summer frosts, its yields in the northern third of the territory can exceed those in the southern third. It is an invaluable adjunct to the crop pattern of the wetter western lands—as well as to that of the higher latitudes. In Dalarna, for example, where the cultivation boundary rises above 600 m., no single crop shows a more even distribution.

Sugar-beet and fodder-beet are tied essentially to the southern third of the area. Both are fairly exacting of soil conditions and prefer warm to cold soils. There is, therefore, some differentiation between the loams and the clays. In Sweden and Denmark the yields of beets have risen spectacularly since their introduction; today they average 15 tons p.a. or three times that of potatoes. Turnips are also grown, though by no means as widely as in former times. While linseed (or flax) has been a traditional crop, oleaginous crops have never ceased to interest the Scandinavians— so that winter and spring rapeseeds are popular in the south (*c.* 200,000 acres in Sweden). Newer varieties of rapeseed make their vivid yellow impact upon the early summer landscape of Finland as far north as the Oulu valley. Collectively, oil crops in Sweden cover as extensive an area as spring wheat and almost twice as extensive an area as that under rye. Field peas continue to claim substantial space—frequently in association with oats for fodder.

The extending range of crops and species

---

[1] Cf. the interesting comments for Sweden by S. Laing, *A Tour in Sweden*, 1838, pp. 190–1.

introduces a new elasticity in rotation possibilities. Contemporary rotations show a substantial regional variation. A Norfolk rotation (or variations upon it) is commonly encountered in southern Sweden; the prevailing grains-and-leys of central and southern Sweden is popularly called the "alternate rotation".

The predominance of the leys northwards has already been mentioned. Fallowing still occurs in Sweden and dominates the central zone of grass and leys. The more intensive cropping of the south reduces fallowing; the widespread grass component of the north eliminates it. This series of rotations emphasises that almost everywhere in Scandinavia a mixed husbandry is favoured over single-crop enterprise. Mixed husbandry has been traditionally related to the self-sufficiency which long prevailed among the northern farmers, but there is an essential difference between the diversified production of the past and the present. Today, mixed farming has a market orientation.

The blending of the improved plant constituents in the new husbandry and their more effective yields are not due to developments in seed material alone. They often spring from other continuing processes of improvement.[1] Independently of the new mechanical methods of tillage, the transformation of the soil proceeds in two ways. The soil-water relationship is being widely changed through underground drainage; the chemical structure of the soil is being widely changed through the application of artificial fertilisers.

Among these processes, none is more fundamental to soil improvement (and crop yield) than drainage. The replacement of primitive open-ditch drainage by improved underground drainage belongs essentially to the twentieth century. There is a landscape contrast between open-ditched farmland and deep-drained farmland. A fraction of the cultivated land is naturally drained; but, taken collectively, the bulk of Scandinavia's farmland is seamed with open ditches. Deep drainage, with clay pipes in the clay soils and wooden-box drains (to counteract buckling) in the peatlands, tends to be most fully employed on the better farmlands of Northern Europe and to be restricted on those soils which require it most. This paradox arises from the generally greater abundance of capital on good as distinct from poorer farms. Underground drainage is most extensive in Denmark; least extensive in Norway, Finland and Iceland. There is a very uneven distribution of subsoil drainage in all of the countries except Denmark. In Sweden, half of the cultivated lands of Skåne and Östergötland have underground drainage; only a tenth of those in Norrland. A similar contrast prevails between south-west Finland (locally, as much as 25%) and north-east Finland (less than 5%). The extent of subsoil drainage is also related to farm size, being more common on larger than on smaller farms. In Sweden, for example, the highest degree of subsoil drainage is found on farms in excess of 100–120 hectares. Subsoil drainage is increasingly encouraged today by ditching and tile-laying machines. It helps especially to improve cold clay soils, speeding vegetative growth on

TABLE 14

ANIMAL POPULATION

(*in* 1,000s)

Country	Horses	Cattle	Sheep	Pigs	Poultry
Denmark	45	3,386	111	8,127	20,270
Finland	184	2,027	199	558	4,085
Iceland	34	60	847	3	95
Norway	61	1,041	2,096	568	5,105
Sweden	109	2,250	220	1,884	8,778

(Source: The comparative tables from the *Yearbook of Nordic Statistics*, Stockholm, 1967.)

[1] The *Danish Statistical Yearbook* lists annually "the soil improvement works according to law No. 33 of 26 February 1937", and provides local detail of drainage, watering, marling, liming, diking, moor and bogland improvement.

them in spring. Subsoil drainage also aids the employment of mechanical cultivators. It is, at the same time, a means of expanding the cultivated area; for in some places as much as a fifth of the surface area of a farm is wasted in open ditches.

Improved drainage of its own accord slowly changes the chemical structure of the soil, but transformation, swifter in some respects, may also take place through artificial fertilisers. To their increasing availability has been added a growing range of fertilisers. Phosphorus and potassium were already being employed quite generously at the beginning of the century; the use of increasing quantities of nitrogen distinguishes more recent developments. In Sweden today, for example, the consumption of nitrogen per hectare exceeds by a third that of potassium. The degree of self-sufficiency of the Northern Countries in their supply of artificial fertilisers is widely variable. All have substantial supplies of lime, though its distribution varies widely from country to country. Finland has the most uneven distribution of lime and it is a long haul for this commodity from the producing plants in the south, e.g. Parainen (Pargas) to the lime-hungry soils of the northern provinces. Phosphates have been steadily produced from Swedish apatite (for example, at Vitåfors, Malmberget). The nitrogen group of fertilisers are most widely obtainable from Norway. In the interests of national self-sufficiency, Finland has established a new plant at Oulu; but there remains an overall national deficiency of fertilisers.

The interest of the Northern Countries in soil science has also given rise to a geographical representation of data. Chemical soil mapping as a means of demonstrating the needs of the land has reached an advanced stage in Sweden, where roughly a fifth of the arable area has been tested. On the more advanced Scandinavian farms, it is an established practice through detailed soil analysis to prepare a deficiency map of the arable area in order to plan chemical application. In order to bring artificial fertilisers to the most marginal farms of Norway, they are sold at the same price throughout the country. While artificial

manures claim more attention, it is important to recall the even greater contribution of animal manures to field husbandry. In the final place, it is perhaps not so much the employment of chemical fertilisers as their association with the carefully husbanded animal manures which distinguishes current farm policy.

Mixed farming implies an association of stock with crops, and Scandinavian crop production today is orientated to stock. There exists what might be called a stock control of farm activity. "A Norwegian farm," Axel Sømme writes, "is better classified by its livestock population than by its arable land."[1] In Sweden it is estimated that three-quarters of the crop production is converted into animal products. In the field, it is not possible to distinguish between grain, potatoes or sugarbeet intended for human consumption or industrial processing and those intended for animal consumption. Fodder precedence on the cultivated area, however, presents an interesting contrast to former times. Animal husbandry is deeply rooted in Northern Europe. It was evidently associated with the economy of Bronze Age Denmark (c. 2000 B.C.): it was an integral part of the economy of Dark Age Finland, as Kalevala folk-lore attests. The animal population of Scandinavia, which has shown a substantial increase since the 1860s achieves regional densities today which give to it a world stature. Table 14 (p. 151), giving the absolute animal population, shows cattle and pigs to take precedence. The relative decline of sheep is one of the most striking features of the last century. In Denmark, for instance, they took second place to cows as recently as the 1880s, and only yielded numerically to pigs in the 1890s. Sheep, having a more even distribution than other animals, show several marked concentrations; for example, in western Norway, the Atlantic islands and Swedish Gotland. Oxen, which still claimed a place in cultivation forty years ago, have been eliminated.

Horses have shown a relatively sharp decline, though there is still export from Norway and Finland. Goats are of little consequence save in Norway. For a brief period, fur farm-

A. Sømme, *Geography of Norwegian Agriculture, op. cit.*, p. 369.

ing presented considerable prospects, but they have not been realised. The yield of domestic pelts has never assumed the importance formerly held by wild pelts. Batteries of empty cages tell locally of the failure of the silver-fox market, though mink is still bred. By contrast, poultry are of great commercial consequence—entering the international as well as the national market. The rise of commercial poultry-keeping is not unrelated to improved crop production. In northern latitudes it assumes a correspondingly greater outlay on winter housing.

The winter byre, indeed, with its variety of separate pens housing the individual groups of farm stock, is a better way of appreciating the mixed character of animal husbandry than are the pages of the farm censuses. The byre is an architectural reflection of the animal population of the farm. Increasingly unitary in structure, it aspires to bring together crop and stock in order that a minimum of effort may be spent in maintaining beasts during the "dead" season. The Scandinavians have a special word for the complex of farm buildings distinct from the dwelling-house; no unit is more precisely named *ekonomibyggning* than the three-storied building—fodder above, beasts intermediarily, manure and urine tanks beneath, silage tank incorporated, lit by electricity and fed by running water—which is the focal-point of the farm. It is functionalist in the fullest sense of the word—and, in more accidented localities, the farmer's eye appears to be invariably alert to the site upon which it is erected in order to maximise the value offered in detail by slope or rock formation. To graft such a building on to the side of a hillock provides a natural access to the upper story. At the same time, the employment of sites awkward in contour or rock outcrop subtracts nothing from the limited area of arable land.

Per head of population and per hectare of agricultural land, the number of animals stands high.[1] The dairy cow has absolutely the widest distribution, though the greatest concentrations of stock are in the extreme south. Each country has its own particular breeds, which have been modified regionally and, in part, by imported stock. Milk production is widespread beyond the range of milk marketing, a fact which complicates output statistics. Milk yields are widely variable—from region to region rather more than from country to country—with Denmark displaying the least variation from the mean. According to the statistical estimates of the Swedish Cow Testing Association (which tend

TABLE 15

DAIRY PRODUCTION
(*in* 1,000 *short tons*)

Country	Milk	Butter	Cheese	Margarine
Denmark.	4,967	166	95	90
Finland .	2,901	99	35	19
Iceland .	106	1	1	2
Norway .	1,442	17	40	90
Sweden .	3,311	79	50	120

(Source: The comparative tables from the *Yearbook of Nordic Statistics*, Stockholm, 1967.)

to take their material from the better farms), the range of butter fat per cow in 1950–1 varied from 389 lb. in Halland to 264 lb. in Norrbotten. Variation shows a similar decline northwards in Finland and Norway. The steady increase in milk yields during recent decades results from planned breeding[2]—and planned feeding. The change which has taken place in the feeding programme reflects the broadening range of cultivation in itself. The Swedish Cow Testing Association estimates the following percentage distribution of fodder units for its registered herds: concentrates (oil, 4·8%; bran and mash, etc., 17·2%); succulent feeds (including silage), 14·8%; pasture and green fodder, 35·0%; hay, 22·6%; straw, 5·6%. Yet in spite of considerable planning there is still a marked seasonal fluctuation in the supply of milk reaching the creamery. This is partly explained by the large number of small producers, whose fodder management still lags behind the smoothly regulated supply of the larger holding. There is some breeding for store purposes, but high-grade beef cattle interest only a minority of farmers.

[1] And livestock units complement fodder units; cf. *Denmark, F.A.O. Report*, 1955, 1 livestock unit = 1·05 bulls = 1 cow = 1·4 bullocks = 1·75 heifers = 2·65 calves = 1 horse = 1·33 small horses = 3·33 foals = 2 sows or boars = 25 sucking pigs = 2 hogs = 6·25 sheep = 50 chickens.
[2] The changeover to calving during the indoor period of the winter months is one established aspect of this.

In meat production more attention is paid to the pig than to store cattle. The bacon pig, in fact, has become the natural complement of the dairy cow. Like the dairy cow, from the point of view of the small farming budget, it provides a more "regular" flow of returns than beef stock. The distribution of pigs conforms closely to that of dairy cattle. Given contemporary feeding methods, they become as sensitive to the distribution of dairies as the milk cows—the sale of fresh milk from the farm being counterbalanced by purchase of skim milk and whey. The number of pigs per holding is modest, but in the areas of greatest concentration—Denmark and Skåne—remarkably even from farm to farm. The pig population adds to the essential uniformity which characterises rural distributions. Bacon production in Denmark has transformed pig rearing into a virtual industry. In some respects, it might be said that commercial processing has imposed upon the Danish and south Swedish farm scene a marked standardisation. The 60-lb. "side" of bacon—ultimate product for the consumer—dictates the precise weight of the pig which must be delivered, and implies accessibility to the factory itself, independently of anything else. Meat canning has widened the range and field of pork production for the market—the co-operative slaughterhouse in more northerly latitudes setting up its ancillary plants to cope with seasonal variations in supply. Seasonal variations in supply also affect egg delivery. Here, too, cold storage does much to smooth out the seasonal peaks and troughs of production.

Animal husbandry in Scandinavia, claiming a world status, cannot escape from the control of the world market. International changes in price level will be directly reflected in the price offered for pork, butter and cheese. The number of hogs, for example, has shown a greater tendency to vary than the number of milk cows. Again, although Danish butter prices tend to be the highest offered in the world market, they are not established independently of butter supplies from other sources. Denmark is especially sensitive to the agricultural policies of other countries. Price guarantees enter into the picture of crop and stock distributions in Scandinavia as in other countries, though support received by Danish farmers is very modest.

The mixed-farming system of modern Scandinavia displays a new diversification and a new pattern of rural organisation by which the farmer has exchanged a direct dependence upon his physical background for a dependence upon a market. Old uncertainties were shed through improved farming, but new uncertainties have been bred in the process. Old uncertainties expressed themselves in the physical frontiers of production; new uncertainties announce themselves in the economic frontiers of production. The biologist, who challenged the former, has left one type of imprint inscribed on the face of the land. The political scientist (or administrator), whose task is to stabilise the latter, inscribes his mark in a different but no less detectable manner.

THE CONTRIBUTION OF THE OUTFIELD

The contribution of the outfield to Scandinavian husbandry has diminished progressively with advances in contemporary farm management. Its contribution has been essentially seasonal; its character, extensive; its fullest expression, relatively recent. Its decline has been differential as its development has been regional. And the same facts have not accounted for its growth and decay in different areas. Both Finnish and Swedish farming have displayed regional examples of summer grazing. Their outfield systems have tarried into contemporary times and have been analysed by human geographers with an interest in this pastoral way of life.[1] Transhumance to summer grazing (*fäboder*) sites lingers in a relic form in Swedish Dalarna and Jämtland and, although it has largely disappeared from the Finnish mainland, it is encountered sporadically in the skerry zone. Revaluation of woodland has done much to destroy the practice in Sweden and Finland. For the most part, Norwegian summer pastures—or *setrer*—lie above the timber-line or in detachment from the more heavily wooded

[1] J. Frödin, *Skogar och myrar i Norra Sverige i deras funktioner som betesmark och slåtter*, Oslo, 1952; S. Solheim, *Norsk sætertradisjon*, Oslo, 1952.

parts of the country. Their decline, persistence—or even resuscitation—is largely a matter of accessibility. But they are such a distinctive feature of the Scandinavian scene that they merit a brief excursus.

The broad hunting-grounds of the fells, uninterrupted by woodland such as clothed and closed much of the lowland interior, had attracted attention to them in the earliest period of Norwegian settlement. In historically recent times, their yield of game (from hunting-pit as well as from the chase) made some Norsemen esteem the mountain farm above the valley farm. Not infrequently, therefore, the giddy farm site—pinnacled 2,000 ft. up, for example, in Aurland or Nærøy—had more reason than might appear at first glance. It was near to the open hunting-lands; it was probably protected against attack from pirates cursorily entering the fiord; it was also on the threshold of the grazing country. From such places, upland grazing rights were staked out as a part of the property of specific holdings at an early period, and the customs appertaining to their employment did not cease to be elaborated down to the end of the nineteenth century.

The pattern of *seter* management varies widely. The *seter* may be duplicated, even triplicated, for spring and summer grazing in different places and at different altitudes. Two- or three-stage transhumance may be governed by common laws, so that spring grazings may have to be left upon penalty by June 20th and vacated until August 6th in the interests of pasture recovery. The *seter* will also be at varying distances from the home farm. In the fiord areas it is rarely more than 7 or 8 miles, and it may be as little as half a mile; in the interior, for example Gudbrandsdal, where it may be as much as 20 miles, appropriate overnight chalets and grazings have been an integral part of the system. Travelling time is not necessarily proportionate to the mere distance to be covered—for altitude and rough trackways take their toll. The *seter* season is also variable in length. In the west country, three months is a good average; while in the east, a full six months may be spent in the outfield. Aspect as well

as altitude may determine this—the incidence of sunshine being highly important for early snow melt and grass growth. Pasturing of animals is an individual matter, with different types of animals allocated to different kinds of grazing. Dairy cows are most strictly controlled and are herded near the buildings for milking. Their grazing lands, originally an open space called by the oldest word in the *seter* vocabulary—*støl*, may be ring-fenced and, where shared, they may be precisely allotted. Although no boundaries are visible within the ring fence, owners know the exact extent of their properties.[1] Bullocks and bulls are separated from the milking herd and are grazed more distantly. Sheep are taken to the areas of marginal grazing (today, in south-west Norway, often by motor lorry); while goats are found—theoretically if not actually—at the timber-line, where fuel may be obtained to heat their milk for cheese. *Seterdrift*, the economy of the outfield, has contributed a unique vocabulary to the language of Norway's economic geography. This distinct *seter* vocabulary, with verbs like *buføre* (to go to the *seter*) and nouns like *budrott* (the output from the *seter*), quite without English counterparts, has much engaged the attention of philologists. Place-names, too, spring out of *seter* conditions—like Nonshaugen (Noon Height) or the occasional Middagsvarden (Dinner Beacon), solar timepieces before the days of watches.

Some indication of the regional distribution of summer pasturing at the height of its development can be seen in the encyclopædic work of Lars Renton.[2] In detail, the distribution of *seter* may be gleaned from the 1:100,000 topographical map of Norway, though there is no indication of their extent and the wide range of publication dates on the individual sheets reduces their effective comparison. Maps in the *Atlas of Norwegian Agriculture* (pp. 58–61) provide a contemporary picture of distribution which emphasises the persistence of this outfield practice as well as illustrating the changes which have occurred. Oppland, with over 5,000 *seter* sites, and Sogn with Fiordane, listing over 4,000, show the greatest abundance. Oppland, too, has been least

[1] F. Isachsen, *Norsk geografisk tidsskrift*, VIII, 1940, 73–84.   [2] *Sæterbruk i Norge*, Oslo, 1955.

affected by the general decline since the First World War. The degree of persistence is related to three facts. There is, first, the availability of *seter* labour, for both the *budeie* (or *seter* girl) and the *driftekarl* (or drover) decline. There is, secondly, the quality of the *seter* product—today measured regularly against the standards set by the co-operative dairy. Persistence is, thirdly, affected by changes in the character of the transport network. Motor access to the *seter* is usually a guarantee of its persistence; in some areas it has actually led to a revival of neglected *seter*. The railway has kept others alive, special trains sometimes being chartered for movement, as in the case of cattle from Voss. The peak of *seter* development was reached about fifty years ago, when over 40,000 *setrer* were listed; today, with 20,000, the number is still probably greater than a century ago.

The picturesque practice of *seterdrift*, however, belongs to the romantic period of Norwegian life, and its limited contribution to modern Norwegian farming must not be exaggerated. It remains a debated activity. Rural Norway cannot afford *seterdrift*, but it cannot afford to go without it. So much open range or ranching land cannot be allowed to go completely to waste, but as currently managed it is wasteful of effort. Rationalisation —through consolidation of dairy range lands, co-operative road building, concentration of milk cows on communications and stock beasts in peripheral areas of accessibility—have been the lively concern in recent years of agricultural economists.[1]

THE FOREST COMPLEMENT

Over extensive areas of Scandinavia, forestry is inseparable from farming. This is most true of Finland and Sweden; regionally, of Norway; rarely, of Denmark. It is impossible to assess the income and activities of most Swedish and Finnish farmers without regard to the contribution of the woodlands. Farming and forest are increasingly integrated, increasingly interdependent. While the contribution of the outfield has shrunk, that of the woodland has become increasingly spectacular.

Traditionally, the forest lot (which may or may not be held in juxtaposition with the farm holding, and may, in itself, be subject to severance) has had three functions. First, it has provided constructional timber—not merely for building projects but also for fencing. Both might have called for alternative heavy capital outlay in an area which demands prolonged indoor protection for its animals in winter and their outdoor control in the grazing period. Timber does not last long, but it provides easily replaceable constructions. This may be a disadvantage in some respects, but it can be a virtue in time of swiftly changing technology. Secondly, the wood-lot has provided the substantial volume of fuel demanded. Thirdly, the woodland has provided a natural, open-range grazing area. As has been mentioned earlier, it was formerly subjected to rotational burning for cropping.

Consumption on the farm is now supplemented by (or challenged by) demand from outside sources. The wood-lot is therefore not only a resource for various domestic uses, it is also an exchangeable commodity in its own right. It has become a source of income, not merely to supplement but to complement the farm exchequer. In the first place, lumbering has enabled the farmer to work with greater risk-bearing plans in agriculture. Timber frequently provides him with ready money or with the funds for a substantial investment in building or machinery. His liquidity is not so greatly pressed when a substantial wood-lot stands near to hand. Next, price variations for lumber do not necessarily follow the same pattern as those for farm products. Income variation from cultivated land tends to be greater—on the climatic score alone—than income from timber; relative uncertainty of yield is balanced against certainty of yield. But, in the longer period, farm prices tend to greater stability than forest prices. Over a fifteen-year period

[1] The following literature is directly relevant to *seterdrift*, maps and diagrams making their contribution where language presents a barrier: F. Isachsen, *Norges geografisk tidskrift*, III, 1930–1, 165–84; IV, 1932–3, 488–513 (examples of routes followed); VII, 1938–9, 302–339 (winter *seter*); VIII, 1940–1, 73–84 (specific treatment of a spring and summer *seter* above Sandane in Nordfiord); K. Østberg, *Seterbruket i Norge*, Oslo, 1942; A. Sømme, "Recent Trends in Transhumance in Norway", *Proceedings of the 16th International Geographical Congress*, Lisbon, 1951; M. Cabouret, "La transhumance du mouton dans le sud-ouest de la Norvège", *Norsk Geografisk Tidsskrift*, **21**, 1967, 3–38.

in Sweden, for example, forest prices demonstrated a 40% variation from a given mean, while agricultural prices showed only a 20% variation. Whether the farmer appreciates it or not, the wood-lot has assumed a national stature. For the bulk of the woodlands in Northern Europe are not merely privately owned but owned by the farming community.

The woodland is also important in the farm labour programme. Forest operations are essentially seasonal. Moreover, they enter the activity cycle at a time when agricultural activities fall to a minimum. Apart from carting manure, there are no field operations of consequence on most Swedish, Finnish or Norwegian farms for six months of the year. Admittedly, the stabled animals require attention, but that task is often left to the womenfolk. Building and repairs may engage some attention, but climate sets a strict limit here. Under-employment—or even unemployment—is therefore offset to a great extent by lumbering. It is, of course, not merely lumbering in the farm forests, but also in the company wood-lots or the state forest lands. The supply of employed winter labour will naturally tend to come mostly from the smaller farms. In some months and in some districts of Finland, for example, 20% of the labour force of dwarf holdings may be spent in forests owned by others.[1] The reservoir of such labour will be variable according to many facts, such as the price paid for farm products or the character of the harvest. A combination of forestry and agriculture leads to a levelling of the annual work programme (cf. Fig. 41). In all senses of the word it imparts a continuity to rural output and income.

FARM SIZE AND SHAPE

The smallholder—*bonde* in the Nordic tongue—is the symbol of Scandinavian farming. It must be emphasised at the outset that he does not conform to the British or American concept of a peasant and that farm conditions in Northern Europe cannot be described as

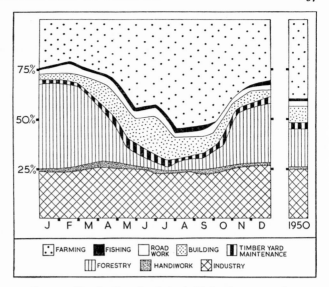

FIG. 41. The rhythm of activity in Finland as summed up in the number of working days according to different pursuits. (After L. Heikinheimo, *Metsäkäsikirja*, Helsinki, 1956.)

those of a peasantry. Tables of statistics which present categories of holding by size do not necessarily convey a satisfactory impression of the complex of farms which composes the rural picture. Superficially, the statistical summary of British farms might lead to the conclusion that Britain was at least as much a land of "peasant" farmers as any of the Northern Countries. When reviewing farm size in Scandinavia and Finland, the most that can be said is that large farms are extremely rare. Where they do occur, they are commonly associated with richer soils or with the forest zone where the woodland element bulks large in them. The Scandinavian countries and Finland have striven to establish a system of small-holdings, and they have with equal energy tried to eliminate large estates. In Denmark, for example, the Partitioning Movement in the early years of the present century, culminating in the Acts of 1919, reduced sharply such large holdings as remained from the enclosure period. In Finland, large estates were also subjected to a series of land reforms over the same period. Large estates persist in Sweden, but they are not commonly owned by individuals. It is a fairly frequent

[1] Cf. the studies of L. Heikinheimo, *Use of Rural Manpower in Finland*, Helsinki, 1955.

practice for industrial companies in rural areas to own and operate a highly developed farm. The pattern has been repeated in Finland, though the company farm, like the large private farm, has suffered severance as a result of the land acquisition laws in the 1940s.

Farm size in Scandinavia and Finland is therefore an expression of ownership conditions. The concomitant of the small-holder is a land-owning farm community. An old Norwegian saying—*eget bu er best om enn lite det er* (your own holding is best however little it may be)—sums up a situation in which tenancy is extremely rare. More than 90% of the Norwegian, Finnish and Danish farms are owner operated; the corresponding figures for Sweden and Iceland exceed 80%. Such a pattern of ownership has not been achieved without an elaborate system of farm loans and credit facilities. The perennial debate upon farm size sets the social desirability of ownership against the economics of scale.

Of the Northern Countries, Denmark and Sweden have the largest-sized holdings expressed in terms of arable area. More than two-thirds of their agricultural land is held in units of 10–60 hectares. In Finland, about half of the agricultural area is shared by farms of 10–50 hectares in size. The bulk of Norway's agricultural land is held in units of less than 10 hectares of arable land. If an arbitrary figure of 2 hectares be chosen for holdings which are not true farms (or are merely part-time holdings), the average cultivated area per farm in Denmark is 14·1 hectares; in Sweden, 13·7; in Finland, 8·8 and in Norway, 5·1. It will be appreciated that the apparent deficiencies of Norway and Finland are balanced by their fisheries and forests.

It is obvious that the most favourable farm size cannot be divorced from the type of farming. Bearing in mind the range of physical conditions in Scandinavia and Finland, it is equally clear that the same size of holding will not be ideal in all areas—even if the type of farming is the same. The absolute area of land required to carry a given number of stock will vary from region to region. Besides these spatial differences, the optimum size of holding will respond to changing techniques. This is perhaps one of the most important aspects of contemporary farming in Scandinavia. The five Northern Countries are not in identical situations and do not therefore react precisely the same.

Bearing in mind the historical priority of farm size to contemporary technique and recalling the relative inflexibility of the former compared with the latter, it is natural that the technical research worker should look for a different approach. He may perhaps most profitably consider the adaptation of machinery originally constructed for bigger farms to the needs of smaller farms. The tractor[1] provides a specific example. It is not long since it was widely held that the tractor was economic only on farms of 50 hectares or more. In Scandinavia there has been a concerted effort to adjust tractor size to farm size. This need was initially met by import; but, side by side with it, the assembly of small tractors has begun to prove commercially successful in Sweden and Finland (e.g. Volvo, Valmet). The tractor is now widely owned by farmers with less than 50 hectares of land and, in such areas of restricted farming as the Åland islands, it is not unusual to find tractors owned by farmers with less than 15 hectares. Today, the fundamental problem of mechanisation has been pushed down to the level of the farms with 5 to 15 hectares of cultivated land.[2] Many Scandinavian farms of this size are tractor-owning,[3] but it is evident that sometimes they represent investment for prestige rather than for economy. It must not be ignored, of course, that to own a tractor makes available the hectare of land which might otherwise be used for maintaining a horse. The steam plough—making its first appearance in Northern Europe in the 1860s—caused Karl Marx to forecast the elimination of the small-holding by the large estate. The refinement of equipment (and the refinement of the means of measuring effectiveness) tell a different story nearly a century later.

---

[1] *The European Tractor Industry*, Geneva, 1952.
[2] This issue was debated by the O.E.E.C. conference at Stuttgart, 1954.
[3] Cf. H. Lönnemark, *Kungliga lantbruksakademiens tidskrift*, **90**, Uppsala, 1951, 113–49, and N. Westermarck, *Acta agralia scandinavica*, 1955, 293 *et seq.*

Although technical adaptation takes place, it is nevertheless clear that adjustment ought to be a two-way process, and Sweden has recognised fairly and squarely the role played by farm size in farm efficiency. Legislation within the past decade has initiated correctives so that the local agricultural authorities must now be consulted when there is any risk of the existence or suitability of a farm unit being impaired.[1] Authorisation to purchase "may be refused if it be found that the property is considered essential to a more convenient composition of units . . . both as to size and layout". In so far as a farmer proposes to devote himself personally to the land acquired and "there is no reason to presume that the property could to greater advantage be joined to some other farm", it may be freely acquired. Contrastingly, however, "where the property is of more than unimportant extent . . . the resulting agricultural unit (must not be) larger than the farmer and his family can manage . . . without having to rely on assistance". The integration of the farm in its local setting is constantly to be kept in mind and, in so far as the estate is to be given a new lay-out, this must be the subject of consultation. Action to prevent the diminution of properties through partition is of especial consequence in the northern half of the country—where, theoretically, farms should be larger than in the south. Dwarf farms, long distances from markets, suffer from comparatively low incomes. Economic opportunities for smaller farm units are more favourable in the south on the threshold of the industrial markets. Yet, even here, farm economists can point to a unit of irreducible minimum size to support a rural family. The figure of 30 hectares, for example, is given for Denmark, and an increase in farm size is favoured. The Finnish situation has been aggravated by the resettlement operation; for, at a time when theory favours that farm sizes should be increased, they have been widely reduced. There is, moreover, no significant check upon division on inheritance in Finland. A substantial school of thought in Finland

favours the transference of capital investment away from dwarf farmsteads and new holdings (where they are clearly unsuccessful) to older and larger units.

Farm size in relation to investment economies must also be remembered. Relative to the general capital outlay, building capital is approximately twice as great on smaller farms as on those with 100 hectares or more of cultivated land. In Denmark it has also been estimated that expenditure on fodder is about four times as great under the same circumstances.[2] Farm size in relation to the effective application of farm labour introduces another point for consideration on the dwarf holding.[3] To attempt to reduce considerations of farm size and lay-out to a series of mathematical formulæ is a revealing exercise, but in the final place it does not fit in with the mentality of the farming community.

In the forest zone, farm size makes its impact upon the rural economy in a second way. Fragmentation of land ownership extends into the forests and becomes the greatest single obstacle to rational forest management. Solutions to it are virtually impossible. Exchange of land between owners is difficult to put into practice. At the same time, there are restraints imposed upon timber companies which seek to compact their timber stands by purchasing forest land in the open market.

To the perennial problem of farm size is added that of farm shape. The series of territorial reorganisations which Northern Europe experienced in the eighteenth and earlier nineteenth centuries gave unitary form to most holdings. The unitary farm is most common in those areas where uninterrupted tracts of cultivated land are most extensive. Farms consisting of more than one unit are most commonly farms where the separate units fulfil different functions. Thus, the forest-farm of the northern half of Scandinavia is as likely as not to consist of several units. In Norway, discontinuity frequently results from grazing—the summer pastures standing in detachment from the home farm. Consolidation is regarded as desirable on 5% of the

---

[1] And the range of provisions is summarised in Laws Nos. 272 and 273 on Farm Property, June 3rd, 1955.
[2] F. Skrubbeltrang, *op. cit.*, p. 300.
[3] Cf. especially the investigation of T. Ristimäki, *Use of Manpower on Dwarf Farms*, Helsinki, 1955.

agricultural area of Sweden and Finland to-day.[1]

The shape of holdings was a direct concern of the surveyors who reorganised Denmark's farms. "The land of each farm shall have the best possible shape, the length of the main plot shall not exceed three or four times the width," runs item 4 of the Act for the Abolition of the Commonfield System. Sometimes, too, rather than disperse an established nucleated village, a compromise was struck in a star-shaped consolidation, with the farm units radiating from the home in the village to the outer fields. And in this rational ordering of the land, the lay-out of the holding was not neglected. The priest, with his broad experience on the vicarage farm, was also ready with his advice. The vicar of Gentofte parish produced a prize-winning essay entitled *A guide to a well-arranged holding for farmers and cottagers who have had their land consolidated*. The arrangement of the units of land and their size grows increasingly important in a mechanised age.

In addition to severance through ownership, there may be physical discontinuity of the farm land within the frame of the farm. Eric Pontoppidan, writing of west Norway in 1752, commented: "The cultivated land consists of small parcels here and there among the rocks, so that they could not commonly be ploughed but must be dug." This extreme situation, where spade perforce takes precedence over plough, is still found in western Norway. *Impedimenter* are a common feature of farmland—especially of newer areas of reclamation. Large-scale land clearance equipment can be of positive assistance in reducing stone and boulder interruption, as in Mikkeli province for example. Where the bedrock is an intrusive feature it commonly controls land use. Physical discontinuity may be raised to a vertical plane by sharp variations of contour, as in western Norway. It is estimated that about 15% of Norway's farms cannot satisfactorily employ machinery because of unfavourable terrain. Cable ploughing represents an extreme adaptation to sloping farmland.

Considerations of farm size raise social issues as well—and the economic may not agree with the social. The Northern Countries have been haunted by the fear of a *bondeproletariat* (a small-holding proletariat). In the past, this threat derived from the abundance of cottagers and labourers, in addition to the small-holders; today, the emphasis has shifted to the small-holders. Equality in size of holding may be desirable socially, but if it means the reduction of holdings to the level of uneconomic units it defeats its own object. It is undeniable that many Scandinavian farms fall short of the agricultural economists' minimum-sized unit. But the problem does not stop there, for the farmers may fall short of the qualifications required to operate a modern holding. Provision for technical training must run side by side with the Folk High School. Personal shortcomings, independently of other issues, afflict some farmers in Finland, for example, who took up new forest holdings after 1944 and who are neither justifying their farming existence nor the considerable subsidy which their continued activity as farmers demands. The outward signs of the *bondeproletariat* are seen in rural slumdom. Rural slumdom is a very real issue in northern Scandinavia, and it is hardly surprising that radical thinking should be its accompaniment.

MEN AND MACHINES

Tendencies towards a rural proletariat have been partly corrected through migration and emigration. Given the present circumstances of production, it is clear that limited migration from the land need not be undesirable; for there has arisen a natural redundancy of labour with the steady rationalisation of farm work. The harvesting of grain provides an example. Grain cutting by sickle can still be seen in some of the remoter tracts of Scandinavia. It demands about 50 man- (or woman-) hours per hectare. The first step forward came with its replacement by the scythe which required about 20 hours per hectare. The side-delivery reaper, where it can be introduced on economic or physical grounds, en-

[1] F. Dovring, *op. cit.*, p. 43; cf. also K. Skovgaard, "Consolidation of Agricultural Land in Denmark", *International Journal of Agrarian Affairs*, Oxford, 1952, p. 9 *et seq.*

ables the same work to be completed in 3 hours. The binder, succeeded by the contemporary combine-harvester (now modelled increasingly on a smaller scale in the process of adaptation to farm size) reduces labour needs essentially to those of the well-trained machine operator (and maintenance man). The speed of change has been such in Finland that the binder stage in the sequence has been by-passed. The potato harvest has been simultaneously eased by the introduction of the simple digger or the complete harvester— the former saving 130 man-hours per hectare, the latter, 180 man-hours. The excavator has transformed digging, so that Iceland alone digs 800 km. of ditches annually.

These, however, are items of equipment which apply at a particular phase within the annual round of activity. The tractor and its attachments have much more fundamentally affected land and labour relations. The degree of substitutability of tractor power is high. The tractor age is upon Scandinavia, but it has by no means reached its peak of expression. In 1961, more than half of Denmark's holdings had tractors; more than 80% of Iceland's. It is a point of interest that the number of horses has not shown a uniformly corresponding decline. Indeed, in Norway and Finland the decline has been only nominal; there remain 125,000 at least in Denmark (and they require 125,000 hectares of arable land to feed them!). Tractors effect their economies in a variety of ways—8–10 hours per hectare are saved on ploughing operations alone. It is estimated in Sweden that, depending upon the size of the farm, from $1\frac{1}{2}$ to $2\frac{1}{2}$ man-days per hectare are saved at harvest-time by the employment of a tractor.

To express these economies on a comparative basis is not easy, because of the absence of precise figures; but K. U. Pihkala estimates that over the last generation (since 1920) the labour of 4–14 persons per hundred hectares has been saved by the employment of machines in Finland. The decrease of rural labour in more recent years has been more marked in Finland and Norway than in Sweden—and in Sweden than in Denmark. In some respects this is indicative of the time-lag in development or of the speed of development which has characterised these two countries during the last generation. The rise in labour effectiveness, in so far as it can be estimated, is greater on the larger holdings of Finland and the smaller holdings in Denmark.

Investment in machines is a more simple matter where the farm holding is an exclusively agricultural enterprise than where it is based upon a combination of farming and forestry. On such a combined farm, where the flow of labour is alternately diverted from field to forest, similar diversion of machinery cannot take place so readily. Machines developed for farming are not generally adaptable to forestry. Thus, the substitutability of the tractor for the horse in the woodlands is extremely limited. It is rather more likely that a division of labour will take place—the horse persisting in the earlier stages of logging operations, the tractor in the latter. Farmers who seek to employ their draught animals and equipment during the winter months are likely to establish a new division of labour. Forestry meanwhile calls for new machines in its own right. The mechanically propelled saw is an example. The extent of its efficiency is not yet proven, though it has already a considerable distribution—not unrelated again to its prestige value.

It is sometimes lamented in Scandinavia that the countryman has shed many of the accomplishments of former times. Yet reflection upon the relation between men and machines recalls the many new skills which have replaced them. No less than in other progressive agricultural regions, the modern farmer is a rural technician.

MUNDAL, AN OLD NORWEGIAN FARMSTEAD[1]

Mundal Farm is among the ancient family farms of west Norway, which may either have

[1] In the preparation of this section I am greatly indebted to Mr. Anders Mundal of Fjærland. It is interesting to compare the holding with that described by P. Munch,"Gard, the Norwegian Farm", *Rural Sociology*, **12**, 4, 1947, 256–363. A. Sømme, *Atlas of Norwegian Agriculture*, Bergen, 1954, has farm maps from Norway. Norwegian farms have also seized the imagination of W. Kirk and F. M. Synge, "Farms of Verdal, Norway", *Scottish Geographical Magazine*, **70**, 3, Edinburgh, 1954, and H. J. Savory, "Farming in the North Trøndelag", *Geography*, **39**, 4, 1954.

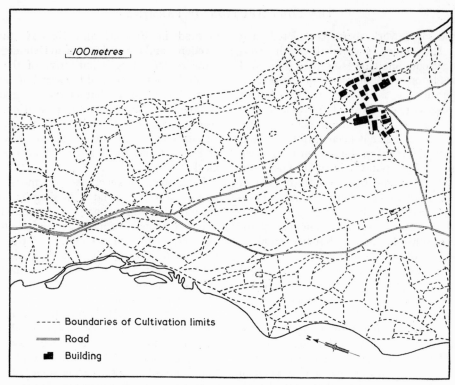

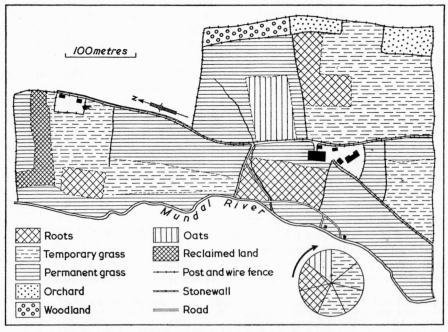

FIG. 42. Mundal farm in Fjærland. Field and plot division of the cultivated area at the time of the break-up of the old *tun* or family farm. (From *Matrikel* 59, 60, *Tjugumsthingslag, Sogns fogtteri*, 1881.)

FIG. 43. The contemporary farm map of Mundal.

given its name to the outermost spur valley of Fjærland or have taken its name from it as the primary settlement within it. Its old community structure—the *tun* form as outlined in Fig. 42— has been shed; it has taken on a reduced shape and is operated by a single owner. The farm consists of 150 decares of cultivated land (or *innmark*) and 1,000 decares of open-range grazing (or *utmark*). The *innmark* is held as a unitary holding; the *utmark* falls into several parts, only one of which is contiguous with the *innmark*. Fig. 43 is a plan of the *innmark* with its land use in 1953. For most Norwegian farms, however, such a two-dimensional outline conveys an inadequate impression; the third dimension (Fig. 44) is therefore given above.[1] It will be seen that the *innmark* occupies a valley flank bounded on the one side by the Mundal river and on the other by the scree and rubble of the adjacent wooded *utmark*. The southward-facing valley, lying near to sea-level, is entrenched between fells averaging a height of 3,000 ft. Its eastern boundary rises to the upper rock precipices of Hestskredknipa (4,400 ft.), while *utmark*, beyond the river, extends above the tree-line. The valley has a deep infill of material primarily of glacial origin, but much redistributed and reassorted by marine and sub-aerial forces. Thus, the three upper benches of the farmland are testimony to former shore-lines, while the lower terraces are modelled by stream erosion. Land emergence and the corresponding downcutting of the Mundal river provide much of the surface detail against which the farm is set. Although within its limited frame the farm area is considerably modulated, it is not broken

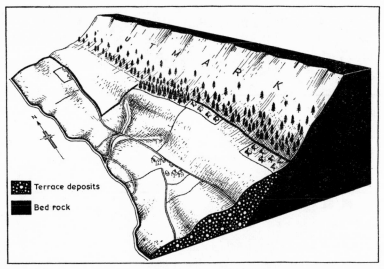

Terrace deposits

Bed rock

FIG. 44. A block diagram of Mundal farm.

down into that elaborate arrangement of slopes which characterises so many holdings.

Slope is important for soil development. There is a range of soils within the small area of the farm—from the silts and clays of the valley bottom, through the terrace sands and gravels to a 3-ft. peat development in the less-readily drained area of the north enclosure. Stone-fall from the weathered precipices above litters the higher areas of the farm. For the most part, the land is drained naturally, though on the northern margins it has been necessary to ditch and underdrain. The erratic behaviour of water-courses which cross the farmland means that soil wash and soil erosion affect farm practices. Mundal farmland, as with all occupied agricultural land, is assessed according to one of the five categories of fertility for purposes of taxation.

In Norway at large, mixed farming dominates, with stock farming taking precedence over crop farming. It is natural that the wetter west should concentrate on grassland husbandry and that the drier east (or southeast) should specialise more as the country's granary. As a western farm, Mundal is devoted to animal husbandry, and the seven-

[1] Slope considerations have not generally entered into the catalogue of farm assessment, though they are fundamental to its practical operation (cf. A. Sømme, *Jordbrukets geografi etc.*, p. 331). One of the classificatory columns of the farm lots allocated to displaced Finnish farmers offered five specific topographical categories—varying from "level plainland" through "gently sloping" to "accidented". But the problem of reducing these to measurable and scientifically assessable concepts was not tackled.

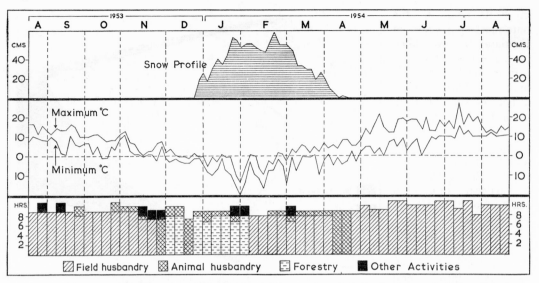

FIG. 45. The annual rhythm of activity at Mundal farm set against the background of the climatic rhythm. (Based upon a diary kept for one day a week by Anders Mundal. The material has been simplified into four primary categories. It does not represent total labour input on the holding.)

year rotation on its crop land is oriented to their fodder needs. The land is for four years under temporary grass and for three in "open ground", when it carries turnips, potatoes, kohlrabi, oats or barley. As is often the case on the Westland farm, the crop land is bedded in grassland. The management of the rotation engages much of the attention of the farmer-owner.[1]

Two crops of hay are commonly harvested from a mixture of clover and timothy. The first, yielding 1,000 kg. per decare, is spread over a period of 3–4 weeks from mid-June; the second, 200–300 kg. per decare, is harvested in mid-August. The hay is commonly dried on harvest lines; some grass is ensiled in early June and mid-August. Of rotation crops, turnips give the heaviest yield (3,000 kg. per decare); potatoes yield an average 2,500 kg. There is a subsidy on potatoes grown on the first 12 decares of land, so that almost all holdings support this crop. Such harvests are attributed largely to a heavy application of artificial fertiliser (c. 6,000 kg. p.a.) in addition to stable manure. Among chemical fertilisers saltpetre is regarded as the

most important to meet soil deficiencies. Granted good harvest weather, wheat would yield 250–300 kg. per decare and barley 350–400. Ploughing precedes the November snows—which may cover the ground until April and reach a depth of more than a yard in February. Today, ploughing is commonly done by tractor from a small machine station established in Fjærland. On old-established and level cultivated land, 2 decares per hour may be turned by the plough.

From the end of May until mid-September when the *setrer* are employed, the farm is a different unit for all practical purposes. The spring *seter*, 3 km. distant and at 150 m. altitude, is used from June 1st to July 31st and for a short period from mid-September onwards. It has 200–300 decares of fairly intensive grazing. The summer *seter*, about twice as far, lies at 400 m., and its *støl* has 300–400 decares of pasture. Nearer at hand on the scree slopes are 2,000 decares of woodland—about three-quarters of which are moderately productive of firewood. They are mostly birch and alder, but several thousand spruce seedlings are planted each year.

[1] The analysis of labour output on farms in Norway has been the subject of an increasing number of investigators in recent years. P. Borgedal, *Intensitets problemet i det norske jordbruk*, Frederikshald, 1926, includes investigations into the seasonal rhythm of work on farms in eastern Norway (cf. p. 269), while current work—especially on fell farms—by Landbruksøkonomisk Institutt has concerned itself with the under-employment of farm labour.

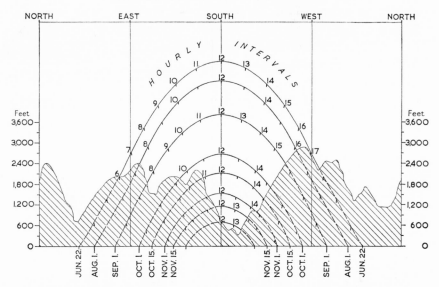

FIG. 46. Sunshine potentiality at Mundal, showing the surrounding mountain profile and the angle of inclination of the sun in relation to it at different times of the year.

Activity on Mundal Farm centres on fourteen cows, which are a crossbreed of native south-west Norwegian type and Ayrshire or Jersey. These dual-purpose animals, calving after their second year, have an average milk yield of 3,500 litres annually, with a fat content of more than 4%. For the most part, they calve during their autumn and early winter period of indoor stalling. This guarantees that the flush of milk shall be readily available without the problem of transport from the *seter*. Milk prices, varying seasonally, also encourage this. In order to sustain winter output, a substantial and concentrated diet is needed. The daily feed per cow is estimated as 6 kg. hay, 15 kg. silage, 20 kg. turnips and 2 kg. grain. Milk may be marketed in Vik (some fourteen miles distant by boat) to be re-exported to Bergen or Høyanger or converted into cheese or butter. It may also have its fat content removed in Fjærland co-operative dairy and be brought back as skim-milk for feeding. Some cheese and butter is made on the summer *seter* under the care of the *budeie*. Five or six bullocks are also kept, according to the price of beef.

The rest of the farm stock embraces thirty sheep, forty lambs and two or three horses.

Sheep are of the native breed, heavily-fleeced Merino types being unsuited to the damp climate. The work diary (Fig. 45) indicates that April is the principal month in the sheep economy; it is both the time of lambing and shearing. Pigs and poultry are kept for domestic use only. For all these animals, the farm is generally self-supporting in fodder-stuffs. In the outdoor feeding programme, 3 or 4 decares of *innmark* are reckoned to be the equivalent of at least 10 decares of open-range grazing. Milk yields are correspondingly lower on the *utmark*—10–12 litres per day, as against 15–20 from the enclosed pastures. About two-thirds of the farm income derives from the dairy herd.

Mundal Farm is representative of the independently operated, compacted holdings which have escaped from what A. W. Brøgger once called "the totalitarianism of the individual farm", but which are still subject to all of the restrictions and restraints of the fiord "bottom" lands of west Norway. It is lifted above the level of the subsistence holding by its market orientation, but the range of its operations and opportunities is restricted. The reorganisation of land and buildings, the introduction of contemporary methods of

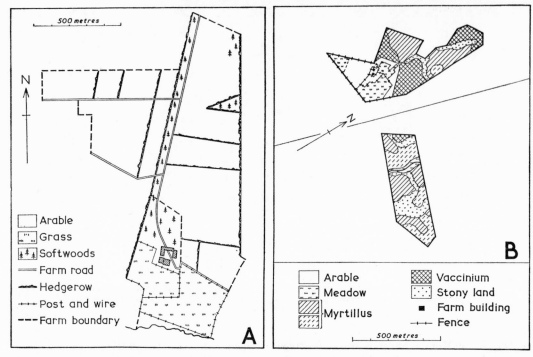

FIG. 47. The farmsteads of Juho Judin, Lapinlahti, Finland, (B) and Anders Olsen, Skovlund, Jutland, (A). The representative Danish smallholding provides a useful comparison.

scientific husbandry[1] and, above all, the multiplication of steamer contacts, have changed its self-sufficiency. The measure of that change can be appreciated, if only in literary terms, by comparing the holding of the Erlingsens in Harriet Martineau's *Feats on a Fiord* from a century ago.

T $(876^{23}1^{12})^5$, A NEW FINNISH HOLDING

This is the official number of the land holding of Juho Judin, a displaced farmer from Suistamo parish in Ladogan Karelia, who was precipitated into a pioneer existence in Lapinlahti (central Finland) after the Russo-Finnish wars of 1939–44. His holding, which still lacks the dignity of a named farm, is one of a colony of new holdings carved out of extensive company-owned woodland (Plate 5). It belongs to the type of holding called a "cold farm" (*kylmä tila*), because on occupation it lacked any form of improved farm land or buildings. The farmer and his family literally began life anew with an axe. The forces

which prompted this were political, but the assault on the woodland demonstrated the continuation of the tradition of woodland colonisation in Finland. The family was familiar with the art of reclamation, and came to a territory where the steady winning of land for cultivation had never ceased. Yet, in carving out the holding, little aid was forthcoming in the early stages from the large mechanical equipment which was eventually to spur the process of resettlement forward. Juho Judin occupied his land in 1948, three and a half years after leaving his Karelian homestead. In 1956, he became the formal owner of 25 hectares of land, held in two units.

The holding is accessible by cold farm standards. It is situated on the eighteenth-century post road between Iisalmi and Kuopio, and the nearest railway station is 5 km. distant. The holding was prospected in spruce land which was capable of cultivation, and the detailed appreciation of the soil as assessed by survey officers is given in Fig. 47.

[1] Cf. *Jordbrukets produktions- og rationaliseringskomité, 1946*, Oslo, 1949.   A. Sømme—*Jordbrukets geografi*, p. 175— illustrates the changes in form on Moene holding, Ørsta herred, Sunnmøre, which have resulted from rationalisation.

Fifteen different units of land were identified on the home farm at the time when deeds of ownership were acquired: twelve units in the wood-lot, which is 4 km. distant. The site of the parent farm is on a gently sloping lake shore, the reasonably well-drained clayland of which has a limited boulder content. Most of the farmer's neighbours have had to consider three stages in the creation of their cultivated land—deforestation, boulder clearance (frequently by dynamiting) and drainage. Here stone clearing has been largely unnecessary. Drainage, as almost everywhere in this tract of resettlement, is by open ditches. The farm also commands a view of mature farmland and old-established farmsteads, whereas most cold farms sit in isolation or at most have a prospect of one or two equally raw homesteads. "I could count twenty lights from my Suistamo farm," declared a neighbour of Judin. "Here, I can see two." The accessibility of the new Judin farm also ensured available electricity, though limited capital has prevented its installation.

The growth of the farm is a saga common to 10,000 similar holdings in other parts of Finland. Half a dozen essential tasks clamoured for simultaneous attention in the early stages. The *sauna* or bath-house was built first—a small cabin which was the initial home. From this shelter, the other buildings were erected—first the barn for animals and next the farmhouse. Deforestation of the potential arable land has been undertaken in three spells. With the destruction of the stumps, the fencing of the fields and the establishment of a permanent crop cover, the land bears a new appearance of stability. In the interval between arrival and the emergence of the farm as a working concern, the farmer has supported himself in two principal ways—by the timber sold from the cleared land and by the successive bounties given by the Resettlement Board as successive hectares of land have been brought into cultivation. As the frontiers between forest and farmed land have stabilised, it becomes apparent that on this farm, as on so many Finnish farms, a substantial contribution must derive from the woodland. And, as the farm is established, a new and more regular annual rhythm of activity establishes

itself. Figs. 48 and 49 show the annual work rhythms of a number of colonial settlers in Lapinlahti parish. Field and forest become much more prominent as maturity is reached.

In so far as this small-holding engages in farming, it looks first towards animals. The bulk of the area is therefore under grass or fodder crops (oats, roots, clover). One or two heifers are maintained with their weaning calves, one horse, one sow and half a dozen chickens. In summer there is some woodland pasturage, but this is commonly discouraged in the interests of timber growth. Except for the horse, the care of the animals is invested in the farmer's wife. A limited amount of farm income derives from the animals, most of their produce being consumed by the family. It is, in other words, a marginal subsistence venture; capital for the development, if not the maintenance, of which comes at best from the wood-lot or from direct outside subsidy.

PROGRESS IN PRODUCTIVITY

To distinguish between the human and the natural contribution to the harvest is a well-nigh impossible task. The physical setting, with its varying annual weather conditions, complicates attempts to measure the human contribution. It remains undeniable, however, that if yields increase without a proportionate increase in costs, the productivity of labour as well as of land must be rising. It has been estimated on a 100-hectare arable estate, for example, that a 10% increase in yield has been obtained with an increase in the application of labour of less than 5%. In dairy production the productivity of labour has probably risen much more sharply. A hundred years ago the average annual yield of milk per cow in Denmark and Sweden was below 1,200 kg. Today it is 3,200 kg. for Denmark, 2,900 kg. for Sweden—and for Norway and Finland, with their smaller cows, 2,480 kg. and 2,320 kg. respectively. Naturally, a greater consumption of fodder has accompanied increased output, and this calls for increased human effort in its production. Nevertheless, it remains undeniable that the net productivity of labour has risen sharply in the dairy industry—perhaps as much as 25%

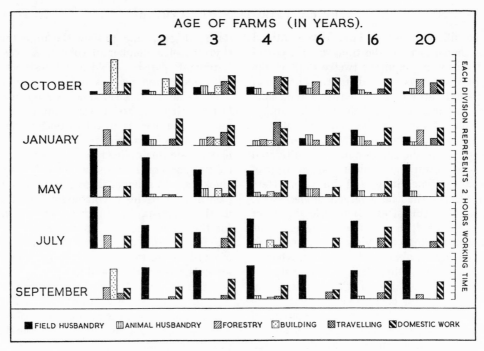

FIG. 48. Progress in Finnish rural settlement as illustrated by diaries kept by displaced farmers. Different types of activity on farms of different ages in Lapinlahti.

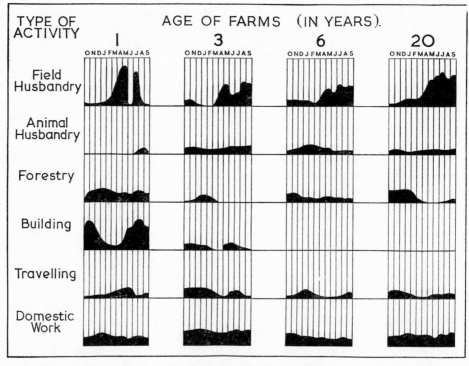

FIG. 49. Work rhythms on four sample "colonial" homesteads in Lapinlahti, compiled from farm diaries.

in a generation. On the basis of much more precise accounting, substantial increases in the total net productivity of labour can be claimed since the immediate pre-war period. Almost everywhere the figure seems to be between a quarter and a third greater. Labour effectivity nevertheless remains below the optimum in the Northern Countries.[1]

These statements on labour productivity are part and parcel of the general growth in net income from farming. In the absence of similar statistical data, between the constituent countries as well as over any extended period of years, it is not possible to draw very precise conclusions. However, attempts have been made to estimate the increase in *per capita* net incomes derived from farming. Already in the 1920s this income was about twice as great for Denmark and Sweden as it was in the 1860s. In Norway, a rise of 1·87 is calculated on the figures for 1925–9 when set against those for 1950–2; in Finland, of 1·90 between 1926–9 and 1950–4.

These general observations upon productivity appear to carry the wheel full circle. No matter what may be done with the soil, its natural endowment appears to be the prime determinant. It seems to be an established fact, based upon wider experience than that of the Scandinavian countries, that the better land tends to respond more satisfactorily to new techniques than the poorer land. There is even some evidence to support the view that the increase in productivity is greater on the superior land—larger net returns resulting from otherwise equal costs. Such an experience implies that technical improvements may well widen the margin of advantage between the better land and the poorer land rather than even out the differential. Scandinavian experience shows that though there has been a rise in productivity almost everywhere, it continues to be greater in the two most favourably located countries—Denmark and Sweden. Within the extended frame of Sweden, the greatest relative increase during the last fifty years has been in the extreme south (though the transformation of forest values in Norrland has given a fillip to its

farmers and a new criterion for comparative assessment). Within the narrower frame of Denmark, considerations of relative productivity are no new line for argument. Precisely where to direct capital investment in the land has long taxed Danish administrators. In 1866, E. M. Dalgas—urging the foundation of the Danish Heath Society—directed attention to the need for investment in western Jutland, "not only for the sake of the dead earth . . . but for the living people". Simultaneously, the practical farmer, Jorgen la Cour urged that capital and labour would yield a greater return if continuingly invested in the country's good soils. Transferred to the inter-Scandinavian level, the difference in yields between more favourably located Denmark and Sweden and the less favourably located Finland and Norway give rise to a potential economic conflict. Through their consumer organisations, the Scandinavian countries aspire to a common price level for essential agricultural commodities; through their labour organisations they aspire to a common level for rural wages. The latter situation is strengthened by the existence of the common Scandinavian labour market. In theory, Finland and Norway stand at a distinct disadvantage. Within the constituent countries, the systems of rural taxation are compiled with direct reference to differences in fertility.

Progress in productivity can be measured by relative as well as absolute standards. An important fact is that production has been increasing more rapidly than population. At one time in the past the individual farm strove for self-sufficiency. Although overall production may have out-paced population growth, there are continuing deficiencies besides the essential surpluses.[2] Regional deficiencies have two causes. First, there is the purely physical cause which restricts cultivation (unless under exceptional circumstances, as with the greenhouse cultures based upon the hot springs of Iceland). As a result, fruit and vegetables will normally be exported from southern Norway and Sweden to their sub-Arctic halves;[3] while Denmark may be called upon to supply Finnish deficiencies of these.

[1] Cf. F. Dovring, *op. cit.*, p. 86.   [2] They are strikingly defined in the *Atlas of Sweden*, Maps 73–4.
[3] Cf. A. Sømme, *Jordbrukets geografi i Norge*, Fig. 15.8, and *Jordbrukets atlas över Sverige*, Stockholm, 1952, pp. 103–5.

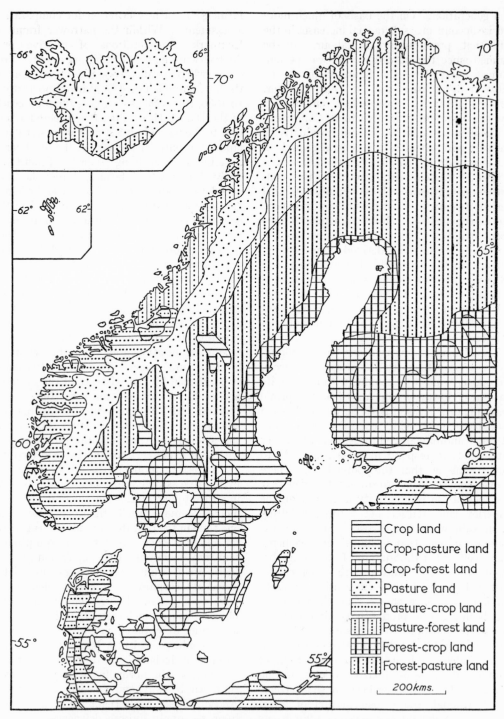

FIG. 50. Agricultural regions of Scandinavia and Finland proposed by Olof Jonasson.
(Source: *Economic Geography*, **1**, 2, 1925.)

Legend:
- ▬ Crop land
- ▬ Crop-pasture land
- ▦ Crop-forest land
- ⦂ Pasture land
- ▬ Pasture-crop land
- ▥ Pasture-forest land
- ▦ Forest-crop land
- ▦ Forest-pasture land

200 kms.

Secondly, there is the essentially human aspect—that insufficient effort may have been made to explore and encourage local production. The north Norway plan makes great play with this fact, while areas of agricultural under-production in north Finland are the cynosure of farm economists. Deficiencies in farm products are met, to a certain extent, from outside the area. Thus, a Finnish deficiency of 30% in bread and fodder grains is met largely by import from the U.S.S.R., while an 80% sugar shortage is offset by imports from the tropics. In 1939, its maximum year of grain production, Norway consumed six times as much bread grain as it produced and bought twice as much in weight of fodder concentrates as it produced of coarse grains. The Norwegian State Grain Monopoly, however, calls attention to the fact that barley and oats are widely consumed as food. It will be appreciated that, to a certain extent, the general increase in crop productivity has been achieved through the import of artificial fertilisers. To this extent, a dependence on external sources of food supply is disguised. The same disguise is imparted by the raw materials of fodder concentrates which not infrequently enter as industrial raw materials for the vegetable-oil factories. Denmark's deficiencies are the most serious.[1] All its nitrogen (78,000 tons p.a.) and potash (140,000 tons p.a.) must be imported. Phosphates are produced, but solely on the basis of imported raw materials. There is a net import of 800,000 tons of grain a year, and the equivalent of 680,000 tons of oil-cake and meal. It is, indeed, a reflection that agriculture is an industry.

Nor must it be assumed that agricultural distributions in Northern Europe are free of those elements of artificiality resulting from various forms of protection.[2] If the international commodity market were free, the deficiency in the production of certain crops might be appreciably greater. In Sweden, for example, three types of measure stabilise the rural pattern—a complex of import duties, guaranteed price controls for the harvest and state insurance against crop failure. Such measures are intended to maintain farm incomes in relation to those of wage earners engaged in other activities.[3] There are also various forms of regional assistance. Thus in Finland, higher milk prices are paid in areas where natural conditions of production are difficult. These areas of difficulty are defined as the skerries, Lapland and the eastern border tracts (*Law* 49, 1955). It has been the concern of a recent government commission (*Syrjäseutulisäkomitean mietinto*, 1956) to define these problem areas according to more scientific principles.

AGRICULTURAL REGIONS IN THE NORTH

Geographers, looking at these agricultural distributions, have been tempted to read into them a pattern of agricultural regions. The first synoptic view of North European agricultural regions (Fig. 50) was published by Olof Jonasson of Göteborg more than a generation ago.[4] Since then, a number of regional patterns have been presented for individual countries, but no comprehensive picture. In Norway, Axel Sømme had distinguished agricultural regions within the frame of the major natural provinces,[5] while the Central Statistical Bureau of Norway has made an attempt to define a series of farming regions for administrative purposes. Regions enter Swedish and Finnish atlases to summarise agricultural observations; while Aage Kampp has proposed seven agricultural regions for Denmark.[6]

Different criteria have been selected for the compilation of these regions. The broad pattern of Jonasson's regions pays appropriate regard to combinations of crop (or resource) in its delimitation. Kamp's approach adopts a number of criteria, and at the same time employs a statistical approach. His calculation of yields per hectare for a number of important crops over a number of years provides a basis

[1] F.A.O. *Report on Denmark*, Rome, 1955.
[2] Cf. *International Journal of Agrarian Affairs*, II, 3, 1957.
[3] E. Höök, *Befolkningsutveckling och arbetskraftsförsörjning*, Stockholm, 1952.
[4] *Economic Geography*, **1**, 2, 1925. Contrast with N. Westermarck and L. Hjelm, *op. cit.*, Fig. 23.
[5] "Types and Regions of Norwegian Agriculture", *Compte rendu du XVIème congrès international de géographie*, Lisbon, 1949.
[6] *Geografisk tidsskrift*, 1944–5, and also *Geographische Rundschau*, **8**, 11, 1955.

for his proposed agro-geographical regions. The formula of Kampp moves along the lines of John Weaver's "crop combination regions".[1] At the same time, it pays regard to productivity—a fundamental fact in the definition of regions. Regions might also be built up in quite another way—through regional appreciation of seasonal time-use. The Scandinavian countries might be an area where the annual round of activity is sufficiently varied on the score of climate to offer another criterion for regional detection.

The steadily changing use of the cultivated area tends to convert any series of regions into historical expressions. Yet there are components of seemingly permanent consequence which emerge from Jonasson's classification. Is it coincidence—or merely his design—that the essential "cross-road" areas in Northern Europe (the central Baltic area focused on Stockholm, and the Öresund) stand out as two areas of greater variety and abundance in production? Certainly an economic geographer with an eye to agricultural appreciation finds in Northern Europe farming contrasts which offer much scope for speculation and experiment in method. And the field scene is backed by a generous statistical storehouse to which agricultural economists make their independent contribution and upon the basis of which Scandinavian geographers have prepared their syntheses.[2]

[1] "Crop Combination Regions in the Middle West", *Geographical Review*, **44**, 2 and 4, 1954.
[2] R. D. Narain, *Methods of Collecting Current Agricultural Statistics*, F.A.O., Rome, 1955.

Chapter VIII

THE NORTHERN FISHERIES

"There is no country in Europe fitter for the study of Ichthyology."
Eric Pontoppidan, *The Natural History of Norway*, London, 1755

THE RESOURCE AND ITS INTERNATIONAL SETTING

THE ocean waters faced by Atlantic Scandinavia contain some of the richest fishing-grounds in the world. It is not surprising, therefore, that the Northern Countries collectively assume a world status in this field. The response of Atlantic Europe to the fisheries was considered in a classical work some two decades ago;[1] the standing of the individual Northern Countries in relation to the principal world producers is summarised below.

TABLE 16
FISH CATCH, 1964
(*in* 1,000 *metric tons*)

Country	Cod	Herring	Total Weight
Denmark	221	370	871
Færoe Islands	118	19	139
Iceland	367	544	972
Norway	625	746	1,622
Sweden	39	185	372
Finland	—	53	63
U.K.	648	138	974
U.S.A.	179	778	2,638
Japan	786	399	6,334
U.S.S.R.	908	1,821	4,475

(Source: *F.A.O. Yearbook of Fishery Statistics*, 1965).

The prominence of Norway in Table 16 is the most striking fact. It takes fourth place in world fish landings by weight—after the U.S.A., Japan and the U.S.S.R.; while its production is substantially greater than that of Britain. Norway, with one of the longest salt-water coasts in Europe, also has the largest number of fishermen of any European country. The proportion of the population engaged in the fisheries is, however, higher in Iceland and the Færoe islands. Swedish fisheries are tied largely to the Bohus coast, with the Baltic production closely resembling that of Finland. Finnish aspirations to share in the ocean fisheries were thwarted with the loss of its Arctic harbour. Danish fisheries have experienced a substantial shift in their centre of gravity and a change in their status in recent times from the "Scandinavian Sea" to the outer ocean. The fisheries of Northern Europe have displayed curiously differentiated development, examples of radical advance and conservative persistence existing side by side. They are a source of wealth which has shown markedly different change from country to country.

The medieval north virtually bartered stockfish as money. In the 1890s, Thomas Cook's *Guide* spoke of Norway as a land where everything was valued in terms of fish—worth "two cod or four herring". The symbol of the cartouche on such a map as that of Joannes van Keulen from the mid-seventeenth century lives on in the codfish printed upon Færoese paper money. Fish, fundamental to diet—with Icelanders and Norwegians consuming 50 kg. *per capita* each year—are therefore fundamental to the economy as well. And the limitations which may restrict the Scandinavian economies ashore are relaxed afloat.

THE NATURE AND BEHAVIOUR OF THE RESOURCE

A variety of physical facts contributes to the abundant and available fisheries of the Scandinavian foreland. First, there is the sheer length of the coast-line. Secondly, the coast-line is scarcely rivalled in its range of littoral forms—with deep fiords in which warm surface drifts mingle with glacial melt-waters

[1] *Handbuch der Seefischerei Nordeuropas*, ed. H. L. Lübbert and E. Ehrenbaum, 10 vols., Stuttgart, 1936–8. A useful book which places the Northern Countries in their world setting is R. Morgan, *World Sea Fisheries*, London, 1956.

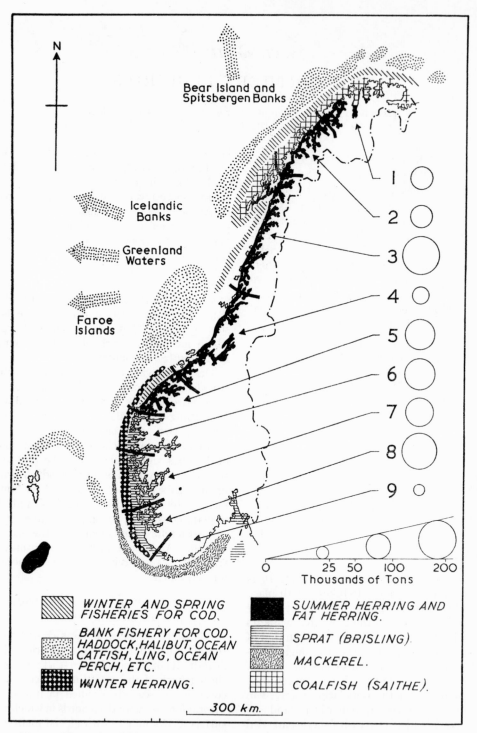

FIG. 51. Norwegian fishing-grounds and their regional yields. (Based upon the official statistics of Norway.)

standing in contrast to the shallow strandflat ringed with pastures of seaweed or kelp and seabedded with stone or fine sand. Thirdly, there is the broad continental shelf with its succession of offshore banks. The relatively shallow conditions which prevail on the banks provide some of the most fruitful fishing areas in the northern hemisphere—raising the sea-bed to the level of the dense plankton layer and giving particularly favourable conditions for demersal fish (i.e. flat fish, which occur mostly on the sea bottom). Fourthly, there are the peculiar temperature conditions of the water, which derive in part from its maritime currents. The rich fishing banks are charac-terised by a stratification of waters of three different consistencies. At the lowest level are the saline Atlantic waters; intermediarily are the so-called bank waters; superficially the less saline coastal waters. Surface salinity varies regionally—according to the volume of fresh-water drainage; the south coast of Nor-way is particularly affected by the flow of brackish water from the Baltic. The water strata are liable to periodical temperature variations which directly affect their micro-organisms and, in turn, the quantity of fish. It has been demonstrated, for example, that the mingling of cold and warm streams of water can have a positive chemical effect in introducing nutrient salts, thereby stimulat-ing the growth of minute vegetative organisms.

The distribution and behaviour of the fishery resources of Norway have their direct reflec-tion in the form and activity of the local coastal economies. Fig. 52 (below) gives a general impression of the distribution of the principal fishing-grounds of Norway. Four distinct types may be recognised: the coastal fisheries, the offshore fisheries, the banks fisheries and the deep-sea fisheries. The coastal fisheries might more precisely be called the fiord fisheries. In respect of specific production, they offer 3–5-year-old summer and fat herring (Clupea harengus), between Altafiord and Sunnmøre; and from Nordfiord to Lindesnes, sprat or brisling (Clupea sprattus) which are 1–2-year-old fish. Oslofiord also has brisling fisheries. Offshore fisheries embrace coalfish or saithe (Gaddus virens) from Varangerfiord to the southernmost Lofotens coupled with an outer zone of winter and spring cod fisheries (Gaddus morrhua) which extends south to Ranafiord. There is a southern zone of winter and spring cod fisheries off Møre and Romsdal.[1] Winter herring, occurring from Møre and Romsdal south to Lindesnes, are among the oldest fisheries and are described in Egil's ninth-century saga. They are succeeded seaward by mackerel (Scomber scomber) in an arc which broadens from the latitude of Sognefiord to the approaches of Oslofiord. In general, the banks fisheries offer a greater range of catch. Probably their most specialised fishing is the most southerly—the North Sea summer or fat

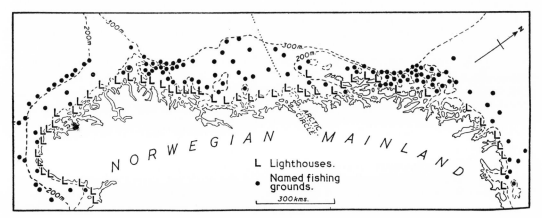

FIG. 52. The distribution of the principal inter-visible lighthouses and named fishing-grounds of Norway. (Based on a model in the Fishery Museum, Bergen.)

[1] The details of which are given in Norway in Maps, op. cit., Fig. 54.

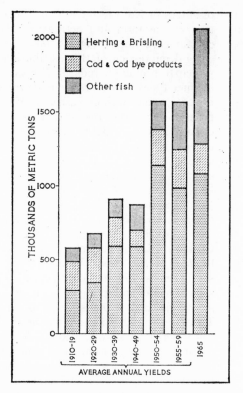

FIG. 53. Principal fish catch for Norway, 1910–65.
(Source: *Fiskeristatistik*, Bergen, 1966.)

coast and relates them to the major submarine contours. The banks are as fundamental to the fisherman as his "capes and bays".[1] "In the course of a few minutes . . . a young man of 27 was able to name and locate on a map up to thirty fishing-grounds inside the fiord", Robert Paine records from Revsbotn in his study of Coast Lapp Society (Tromsø, 1957). Fig. 52 also shows the fifty-six major lighthouses, each of which commands a distance of over 30 km. and is normally visible from the next to north or south. By such lights and more than 2,200 ancillary beacons, it is possible to steer to the fishing-grounds by night as well as by day.

Distribution maps must be complemented by both quantitative and qualitative considerations. The absolute output of the Norwegian fishing industry between 1910 and 1950 is summarised in Fig. 53. The graph is divided according to the herring and brisling catch, the cod catch and the harvest of other fish. Herring and cod account for about nine-tenths of the catch. The herring is pelagic by habit and, in its varying stages of development, is the most widely distributed fish. Harvesting is a reflection of shoal behaviour. Thus, the winter herring fisheries are a response to the herring immigration of January–April, when spawning takes place in offshore waters. Having spawned, the winter herring migrates to distant waters—probably as far as Jan Mayen or Iceland; while the young herring may either drift seawards according to prevailing marine currents or, as it was picturesquely put in James I's Act for the Better Preservation of Sea Fish, "it lieth in still [coastal] waters where it may have rest to receive nourishment and grow to perfection". In any case, the immature fish finally leaves for the open sea to return as a part of the winter spawning shoals when from four to seven years old. A date is fixed annually which divides the large herring (or *storsild*) season from the spring herring (*vårsild*) season.

herring. The banks fisheries for cod (a variety of species), haddock (*Gadus æglefinus*), halibut (*Hippoglossus vulgaris*), catfish (*Anarrhicus minor*) and ling (*Molva molva*) fall into three main groups which are located off west, central and north Norway. For Norway, the development of the central banks fishery dates from about sixty years ago. Deep-sea fisheries carry Norwegian enterprise to the islands of the Viking Empire—to Icelandic waters (for cod, halibut and herring) and to Bear Island, Spitsbergen, Greenland, the Færoes and the banks of the Wyville-Thompson ridge (for cod and halibut). To Norwegians these are the *fjerne farvann*.

Long experience has shown that fish are so persistently associated with certain areas that they may be mapped with fair precision. Fig. 52, based upon a map in the Bergen fishery museum, shows the location of over sixty of the named banks along the Norwegian

Cf. *Fiskerilære*, Flisa, 1953.

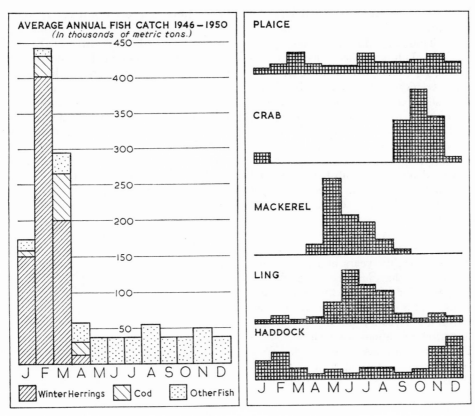

FIG. 54. Seasonal rhythms in the harvest of the sea.

The cod are of two main types: coastal cod regularly associated with the fiord and off-shore waters, and cod of sub-Arctic (largely Barents Sea) origin, which migrate seasonally to north Norwegian waters. The migration of mature cod (6–15 years old), or *skrei* as they are commonly called, is primarily to the Lofoten area, though some move farther southwards. Contact is usually made with the migrating shoals in January and February; spawning takes place in March. Cod are caught in the Icelandic waters in spring; in summer, on the Arctic banks of Bear Island and Svalbard.

Lesser fish in the general picture are the saithe, caught principally in summer and autumn off the north Norwegian coast. Mackerel fishing begins in May or June, about 20–30 miles off the south coast, retreating shorewards later in the season. Halibut is primarily a winter-caught fish. Nor must

salmon be omitted, the traps for which are a distinctive feature of littoral or river-bank scene. Salmon is most abundant in the northern rivers—where private angling can still be a source of considerable revenue. The present decade, for example, has seen Alta river rights offered at over £3,000 sterling. The establishment of nurseries in part offsets the obstruction of hydro-electric power dams, while aerial inspection of fishing tracts keeps a check on poaching—an ever-present threat to the increasingly valuable salmon catch.

From the seasonal distribution of the fish catch and of some of the minor harvests shown in Fig. 54, it will be evident that the different types of fishing activity are not comple-mentary. There is no physical counterweight to the winter herring and cod fisheries, and where there are summer peaks of other varieties, they are frequently geographically distant from the main centres of operation. The major operations in the fishing industry are treated administratively as great unitary activities. Thus, in ordinary parlance, *"Lofotfisket"* (the Lofoten fishery) has immediate meaning for Norwegians as a cod harvest; likewise, *"skreifisket i Finnmark"* (the Finnmark cod fishery) and *"brislingfisket"*. Sometimes, they also have a legal expression in territorial waters; for example, the maritime divisions of the Lofoten (Fig. 58).

Seasonal periodicity in the industry is complemented also by a substantial annual variation in the fish catch. Fig. 53 (p. 176) gives a good indication of its character (though the trough during the war years is due to conditions other than physical).[1] A statistical record of fish catches has now been made for eighty years and gives some perspective to its changing character. Variation is a particular feature of the herring and cod shoals, and a change of several hundred per cent. in a few years is not exceptional.[2]

Long-period variations as well as short-period variations are also observable. They may be of a cyclical nature, such as the 3–5 year flushes of Arcto-Norwegian cod, or of historical consequence, such as the celebrated regional migrations which historians claim to have had such an influence upon the shifting fortunes of cities in Atlantic Scandinavia. The Paris manuscript of Sanudo's fourteenth-century map of Europe bears over the south Baltic basin the inscription: *In hoc mari est maxima copia aletiorum*. Both the foundations of Hanseatic trading and the early wealth of Copenhagen are ascribed to this fact. The herring shoals were already deserting the Great Belt and the Sound when Olaus Magnus recorded:

"There is such plenty and they come in such huge shoals to the shores, that not only the fishermen's nets are broken; but in that great troop, an axe or spear thrown into the thrung of fishes will stay there."

Göteborg and the Bohus coast have also enjoyed periodic flushes of herring. *Sillfiskeperioder*, as the Bohus men call them, are believed to recur every century. It was one of these flushes which was encountered during the visit of the English traveller, E. D. Clark, and which prompted him to record that Göteborg was, after Bergen, the fishing city *par excellence* of Northern Europe. Simultaneously, Limfiorden rejoiced in a flush of fish. Gunnar Rollefsen comments that "the periods of the fishery near Bohuslän and in west Norway have shown a clearly alternating character".[3] Fortunes have been made and lost by the ebb and flow of the shoals. It was this essential problem of distribution which caused Petter Dass to write:

> Og skulde du Herre forkorte din Hand
> Og stænge Skrei-Torsken og Fisken fra Land
> Da lagdes vi hastelig øde.
>
> (And should thou, Lord, withhold thy hand
> And keep the cod and fish from land,
> So should we speedily be laid low.)

Statistical records enable the longer period variations to be more scientifically appreciated. It is known, for example, that cod is now caught with less effort in the Barents Sea and Icelandic waters than fifty years ago. It is estimated that a trawler today may catch nearly three times as much in these waters with the same effort as at the beginning of the century. Simultaneously, a change is seen in the Baltic fisheries. The migration of the herring from the Baltic Sea occurred towards the end of the Middle Ages; contemporarily, there is an invasion of cod and sprat. But the Baltic cod catch is very variable and although cod appear to have entered the Gulf of Bothnia for the first time, it would be unwise to predict their persistence.

Possible explanations of this change in resource distribution are geographical in the fullest sense of the word. No single science can offer an explanation, but the results of a number of fields of research when set together offer grounds for an hypothesis.[4] Observations upon surface and deep-water layers by oceanographical expeditions such as those of Fritjof Nansen's *Fram* (1893–6), Russian high-

---

[1] Other examples of statistical diagrams illustrating the industry are found in G. Rollefsen and T. Sund, *Norsk fiske, Norsk geografisk tidsskrift*, X, 122–56; G. M. Gerhardsen, *Våre fiskerier*, I, Bergen, 1946, 77.

[2] The measure of change is seen by a glance at an early volume of fishery instructions, e.g. *Beretningen om Norges fiskerier, 1868*, Christiania, 1870, and the first volume of statistics, *Tabeller vedkommende Norges fiskerier*, Kristiania, 1879.

[3] "Fluctuations of Fish in Northern Waters", *Conseil permanent international pour l'exploration de la mer*, Copenhagen, 1949, CXXXV, 33–5.

[4] Outlined more fully by A. Lee, *The Listener*, May 6th, 1954, 779–81.

latitude mariners (especially 1927–35) and by the present-day research ships *Ernest Holt* of Great Britain and *Ernst Sars* of Norway, indicate minor temperature increases. It is suggested that an increase began to occur in the decade following 1912. There have been at least two effects—the dwindling of sea ice in the Arctic (as is demonstrated in the north-east passage) and an increase in fish larvæ produced in the spawning grounds. Even so, this does little to explain the improved stocks in the nursery and feeding grounds. It is clear that migration can be eased or hampered by water movement, so that anything which speeds or retards ocean currents will tend to aid or hamper the movement of fish fry. Given a stronger current, larvæ will not merely be carried to feeding grounds more swiftly, but will also be carried more distantly to the new pastures brought into being by slight temperature increases in the sea-water. Given a weak current, overpopulation by larvæ of the restricted feeding ground will occasion high mortality. Oceanographical research has recently revealed that twelve times as much water may be flowing when a current is strong as when it is at its weakest. Simultaneously, meteorologists have demonstrated an increased atmospheric circulation in the Arctic —particularly in the northward movement of air masses over the Norwegian Sea. An increased southerly or south-westerly component in the wind-rose may have a marked effect upon oceanic circulation, and indirectly upon the zoning of salinity in the affected area.[1] Cod seems to have stabilised on its northward course at a maximum latitude of 72–73°.

While these major physical facts may affect the micro-behaviour of the fish population, human action is operative at a different level. Although it has only been acknowledged for two generations, overfishing can clearly have an effect upon the harvest of the sea—and this has been amply shown in reverse by the substantial recuperation in the North Sea fisheries following the respites of 1914–18 and 1939–44. As an international activity, the regulation of

sea fishing has called for a rather more fundamental, yet at the same time simpler, type of control than that which might be applied at the national level. Norway, like other countries fishing in the North Sea, has been concerned by the decline of the trawl catch of demersal fish. Investment in new equipment or improved trawlers failed to result in an increased catch. A simple and convincing explanation prompted international action at a conference in April 1954. Observations on the structure of the catch of plaice, haddock and cod in the North Sea demonstrated an increasing component of smaller fish. In order to maintain fish stocks and at the same time output, it was suggested that the younger fish must in some manner be left and the larger and older harvested. This form of selection would also guarantee a more generous recruitment to the fish stocks. At the international level, it has been agreed to substitute a larger mesh in the North Sea trawl fisheries, which will be selective in favour of larger and more mature fish. In such action, technique and biology work hand in hand to maintain a distributional pattern and prevent the disturbance of an established economic activity.[2]

THE UTILISATION OF THE RESOURCE

The utilisation of the resource depends largely upon the organisation of the fishing industry, and this is inseparable from the relationship of fishing to the rest of the economy, the characteristics of the fishing fleet and the nature of the processing industry.

(a) The Relationship to the Rest of the Economy

The Scandinavian fishing industry is characterised by an extreme dispersal of activity— both geographically and personally. Dispersal recalls the ubiquity of opportunity presented by the industry. Where there is water there are usually fish. It suggests the countless little boats with lines lowered into fiord waters, the rickety wooden structures at the fiord edge or protruding from the river sand-bank which are the salmon traps, the

---

[1] Cf. also A. J. C. Jensen, who gives a similar explanation of the Baltic situation, *Conseil permanent international pour l'exploration de la mer*, Copenhagen, 1954, CXXXVI.
[2] R. J. M. Beverton, *The Listener*, June 3rd, 1954, 966–7.

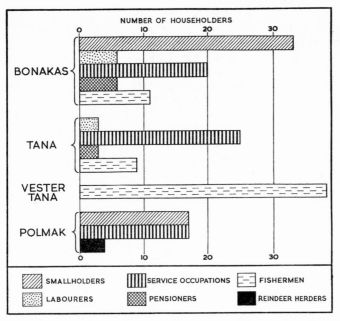

NUMBER OF HOUSEHOLDERS

SMALLHOLDERS SERVICE OCCUPATIONS FISHERMEN
LABOURERS PENSIONERS REINDEER HERDERS

FIG. 55. The integration of fishing with other activities in Tana valley, North Norway. (Based upon data in the *Adressebok* for Finnmark province.)

Fig. 55 gives an idea of the structure of some small Finnmark communities. In the country at large, the number of those engaged in fishing with farming as a subordinate activity is greater than of those engaged in farming with fishing as subordinate. About 40,000 engage in the joint pursuits. It is an interesting reflection on the absence of woodlands from the coast that only several hundreds of the fishermen listed have lumbering as a subsidiary activity. Work in the woodlands, in any case, proceeds simultaneously with the major fishing operations. Even in Denmark, nearly 5,000 "occasional fishermen" are listed besides the 12,000 fully occupied in the activity. The problem of the fishery industry is not merely the uncertainty of the catch, but also the certainty of some seasonal unemployment. For those who are only part-time or occasional fishers, the adjustment is relatively easy. But if the 21,000 Norwegians for whom fishing is the sole occupation be investigated, it will be discovered that they work an average of only twenty-four weeks per annum (1964), with a possible four additional weeks repairing and maintaining their gear. The theme of underemployment repeats itself.

Although it is still quite possible and common for fishermen of moderate means to acquire and operate their own boats, the growing specialisation of the activity is encouraging a professionalism which may make for increasing differentiation between fishermen and farmers. The good fisherman must be master of as many skills as a good farmer. A glance at the Fisherman's Almanack (*Norsk fisker-almanakk*, published annually) or the elaborate guide to the coast of Norway (*Norsk kysthånd-bok*, Oslo, 1950) indicates the range of practical matters to be understood and physical conditions to be familiarised. Growing capital outlay on equipment encourages its more intensive employment. An instance is found in the cod fisheries, where the added mobility given to

shoreline byres the sunward and windward sides of which are strung with herring drying for animal fodder, the lattice of fish-drying frames on the crystalline rocks of Lopphavet. These features identify the industry as a personal activity. At the same time, they are an expression of the fact that fishing does not necessarily absorb the whole energies of the fisherman. They often have the air of improvisation. The part-time fisherman, to whom they frequently belong, makes a statistical count of employment in the fishing industry a complicated matter. The total number of fishermen is accordingly divided into those whose livelihood derives exclusively from it, those for whom fishing is the main occupation and those for whom it is a supplementary activity.

In Norway, there are somewhat more than 50,000 persons engaged in fishing, approximately three-quarters of them fall into the first two groups. The proportion of the population directly dependent on the sea for a living increases progressively northwards. In Troms, a half; in Finnmark, two-thirds of the population look economically to the ocean.

vessels through motorisation enables would-be fishers to follow the cod northwards at the end of March until they are far away from Lofoten at midsummer.

The efficiency of the activity cannot be considered independently of this extreme decentralisation and frequently part-time character. Measures of efficiency in the industry suggest, however, that no simple criterion can be adopted. The annual output per fisherman has been proposed, but bearing in mind the marked international differences in the collection and expression of fishing statistics and the equally important differences in the definition and classification of fishermen, output per man is likely to be wide of the mark. Iceland and Great Britain have a relatively efficient industry measured by the criterion of man output. In both instances it is the consequence of relatively high capitalisation, though Iceland's lead is partly guaranteed by the fact that its modern fleet operates on its doorstep, whereas British trawlers must journey hundreds of miles to their grounds. Most Norwegian fishing takes place in coastal waters so that, theoretically, fishing time is employed more effectively than in the British industry. Ton output per man, however, is little more than half that of Britain and less than a third that of Iceland. Ton output per unit of invested capital may, however, be substantially greater. Local conditions must affect the criterion adopted. Thus, for Norway the most socially desirable—as well as nationally economic—methods of fishing may be those which employ more labour and which make do with less capital than methods employed in Iceland or Great Britain. Norway is likely to retain a range of different types of fishermen—from the professional, who aspires to repeat British or Icelandic performances, to the part-time operator, who best fills his time and balances his budget by taking to the waters. The structure of the national economy calls for this range.

(b) Characteristics of the Fishing Fleet

Unlike the British fishing fleet—and increasingly that of Iceland—the Norwegian fleet consists of a large number of small units. It is composed effectively of over 40,000 registered and powered vessels. They are mostly built of wood and half are under 20 years old. It is still reasonably true to write today, as Samuel Laing[1] noted over a century ago, that it is within the reach of every seaman to have a boat of his own, whereas in England "it costs as much to make a herring boat as it should require for a coasting sloop". The bases of the fishing fleet, as related to statistical districts, reflect accessibility to fishing-grounds, coastal character and possibly alternate shore pursuits. The number of registered craft diminishes on the north coast east of Alta and to the south-east of Rogaland. A full twelfth of Norway's decked motor-boats is, in fact, based on Lofoten. The decked boats of the cod fisheries are usually manned by crews of from three to six; the crews of the herring fleet are commonly smaller. The motorisation of these vessels is the most significant fact about Norwegian fishing in the present century. For a brief period, certain fishery interests sought to prohibit the use of the internal-combustion engine. Professor Brøgger has commented on the differences in two generations, the first of which cried out for its prohibition and the second of which has been "born to the beat of its quick measure".[2] It might be said that for Norway the internal-combustion engine has been more important in its effects on sea than on land. The change began at the turn of the century; the motor caught up with sail soon after 1910 and had almost replaced it by 1920.

There is no pronounced tendency towards a general increase in size of fishing vessels, and the appearance of trawlers of several tons with twenty or thirty crew is exceptional.[3] Trawling in Norwegian territorial waters was forbidden by law in 1905, so that such vessels are tied largely to the distant fisheries. The first was brought to Kristiansand from England in 1930, and the fleet today is based chiefly on Møre and Romsdal. In 1964, there were twenty-eight trawlers operating in excess of 300 registered tons. They undertook a total

[1] *Journal of a Residence in Norway*, London, 1836.   [2] *Norsk geografisk tidsskrift*, VII, 96.
[3] Cf. T. Iverson, "Norske båttyper og fiskefartøyer", *Geografiska Annaler*, 21, 1939.   R. Morgan, *op. cit.*, Section II, has interesting parallel observations on fishing craft.

of 586 journeys. There were also 69 smaller trawlers. In contrast to the time economy of the inshore fisheries, the trawlers spent hundreds of days plying between the home port and the trawling waters.

Some of the more developed herring fisheries also call for larger vessels. The type of boat is related to the type of net employed and the type of net used has been steadily changing. Thus, with the "purse seine", which may be up to 200 fathoms in length, vessels of more than 100 ft. in length and crews of up to twenty men may be employed. Here, the parent vessel works in association with motor dorries which set and subsequently "purse" the net. Depending upon the size of the shoal netted, the parent vessel may require the aid of an auxiliary boat to carry the catch ashore. Independently of the cost of capital outlay, accessibility of fishing-grounds to the coast has eliminated the need for the possible employment of factory ships, though the "purse-seine" type of fishing has carried the activity several scores of miles seawards. The "purse-seine" has also been employed with some success (and, of course, following permission) in the Lofoten cod fisheries.

Although for many reasons the size of vessel may not therefore be subject to marked changes, equipment used on the commercial fleet is making for substantial advance in efficiency and economy. Power installations aid the handling of nets and long lines. Electrical devices, like searchlight beams to attract herring by night or the echo-sounder to detect fish shoals, are widely used. Radio position-finders facilitate ease of movement; radio telephone keeps the more important vessels in touch with factory bases on shore, so that delivery and unloading can be streamlined. Today, for example, when vessels have the option of a number of delivery points, they are notified by radio which processing plant can best handle their catch. Such an arrangement is only possible, however, where appropriate co-operation exists between fishing vessels and a uniform price prevails. Hitherto, the first ship to put in at a factory had the best price, while the man who landed his fish at a quay might get a higher price than he who sold it to a factory. Today, a central co-operative agency receives all payment, and fishermen are reimbursed on a hectolitre basis. A guaranteed price makes for stability among the fisher-folk, though changes in the type of vessel and the type of equipment prompt continuous changes in emphasis on landing-places and trading-places.

(c) The Nature of the Processing Industry

After the introduction of the motor-boat, industrial processing has probably produced the most marked changes in the fishing industry during the twentieth century. Processing aids in many ways a country which must seek an overseas market for its surplus production. Historically, Norway has sought beyond its shores a steady outlet for dried and salted commodities (the Mediterranean, the Baltic, Britain and the Netherlands), and the higher priced luxuries of the seal and walrus hunt. Seal pelts for apparel, walrus hide for thongs and ropes (capable of withstanding the strain of sixty men, observed the anonymous author of the thirteenth-century *King's Mirror*), walrus and narwhale ivory for commodities as exotic as croziers, reliquaries and unicorn horns, were traded for northern necessities. Iceland paid its Peter's Pence in sea ivory in 1327—a harvest from the Outer Ocean almost as precious as Baltic amber. Today, it is the mass product of the ocean for the massed consumer of the Atlantic coastlands which interests Scandinavian fishers. Norway, for example, is concerned with the annual disposal of a million tons of herring and a quarter of a million tons of cod—at the bare minimum. Even sealing takes on the character of a mass assault and 100,000 pelts from Vesterisen (the Greenland ice-edge) or Østerisen (the Svalbard ice-edge) may not be unusual. Industrial processing has modified the distributional pattern of a significant part of Norwegian industry. In changing the form of raw material from the sea, industry gives to it increasingly wider currency.

In contrast to the general picture of industrial distribution in Norway, there are more fish-processing plants north of Trondheim than south of it. The distribution of different kinds of processing plants shows substantial regional variations. Salteries and smokeries are fairly evenly scattered. There is an absolute preponderance of herring-oil factories and canneries in the south and south-west. The areas with the greatest concentration of processing plants are Møre, Romsdal and Nordland. The contemporary rate of increase in plants is rather greater in the north than in the south. Processing is important for Norway not merely because it increases the range of end products, but also because it introduces a greater uniformity of opportunity to Norwegian fish producers. Processing increases the range of marketing in space and time; this, apart from the transport differential, giving to the northern half of Norway similar opportunity to the southern half.

Three of the oldest processed exports are saltfish, stockfish and klippfish. The first is cured for thirty days in brine, the second is cured with lye, and the third is salted and dried over a period of six weeks, mostly by natural means. Dried fish and salted fish have been sold abroad since medieval times—there is a canto on "the commodious stock-fish of Iceland" in *The Libel of English Policy*. Klippfish has been exported since at least the seventeenth century. Stockfish, in particular, are a favourite motif in the cartouches of map-makers who drew Norway in the seventeenth and early eighteenth centuries. Both klippfish, flayed open across acres of bare rocks, and stockfish, suspended round or half-open on their frames or racks, make a distinct contribution to the landscape. Klippfish took precedence over *tørrfisk* as an export just over a century ago, and its peak period was the generation before the First World War. Norway still produces a fifth of the world output, third only after Newfoundland and Iceland. Over 80% of the Finnmark catch of cod has been disposed of as klippfish in more recent years. Dried fish has shown a relative decline in the export table in the present century, but the traditional orientation to the Iberian market (evidenced by Portuguese and Spanish consulates in the leading fishing-ports) is maintained. To it has been added a Latin-American and, more recently, a West African market. Klippfish is a commodity which will withstand both the heat and moisture of tropical climates.

Salted herring are a traditional product which also retain their export status, but they are no longer a single product. Through the degree of salting, the form of the salted fish and the mixture of ingredients in the pickling process, herring are transformed to meet the demands of specific markets.

Most significant but, in some respects, most simple of the changes in the export trade has been the growth of the fresh—or wet—fish market. Already, two centuries ago through such firms as Lund of Farsund, "live" fish were being sent to the London and Amsterdam markets. The coming of the steamship and the railway gave an appreciable impetus to Norwegian ice-packed exports of "live" fish. A whole new market opened up beyond the littoral fringes of Europe; this market in depth (as it might be termed) was, moreover, a market in which the population was rapidly expanding. In Great Britain and Germany, with their city concentrations of consumers linked effectively by rail to the coast, Norwegian exporters found a ready and steady market. In Great Britain, Norwegian wet-fish imports are at least as much complementary as competitive with British landings. Herring, for example, are landed in spring (for kippering), which is the off-season for British drifters; while other landings are subject to a 10% import duty. The elaboration of refrigeration and freezing techniques has added to the ability of north Norway to share in the live fish market. Accessibility to the ice-plant or the deep-freeze chambers becomes more important than distance from the market. The quality of the marketed product is related to the speed (today reduced to a few hours) with which it can be gutted and packed in ice or transported to the refrigeration plant and converted into frozen fillets. Bearing in mind the frequent (seasonal) ubiquity of fish, the problem resolves itself into one of multiplying ice-plants. Around the coast of Norway, nearly two-thirds of the freezing plants are located north of Trondheim.

Another means of prolonging the marketability of fish products is by canning. The fish-canning industry began in the Stavanger area in the 1880s, and the main focus of this activity remains there today, though there is a wide dispersal of canneries around the coast of Norway. Principal among more than a dozen categories of canned fish are smoked and unsmoked *sild* (sardine) and brisling—with annual production averaging well over 30,000 metric tons. With its world-famous laboratories and waterfront factories, Stavanger has the wealthiest "Cannery Row" of Norway. The swing-over to the cheaper and lighter aluminium can represents another form of technical development.

These varying processes, however, by no means account even for the bulk of the fish harvest. Nearly two-thirds of the herring catch, for example, is converted into oil and meal. The production of herring oil dates back two centuries;[1] but the evenly distributed factories which are concentrated south of Trøndelag have as their precursor the plant established at Brettesnes in Nordland in 1884. Such processing enables the fish to be delayed in time before consumption. Although the resulting quality of the oil may suffer, it is nevertheless possible to keep herring for three weeks before disposal. The first of a number of floating herring-oil factories—"Glupea"—is in operation. It provides a means of increasing the speed of transformation of raw materials and for bringing the converting plant to the site of the fishing-grounds. The multiplication of uses for herring oil has called forth a great expansion of output in recent years. A similar expansion has occurred in the cod-liver-oil industry. Its centre of gravity is in high latitudes, and it is a much more seasonally conducted activity than that of herring oil. There is also a by-product of fish-meal from the cod processing. The minutiæ of the fish-processing industry, of relatively little consequence, are nevertheless of considerable interest. Herring scales provide an example—yielding guanin, an organic substance sought by artificial jewellery manufacturers for the production of "pearls" and used as a component in the manufacture of lacquer.

This rich maritime resource has given rise to an elaborate coastal culture. Oscar Sund once attempted to map all the components of the fishery economy in the Gildeskaal area. With a slight modification of symbols, his work is reproduced in Fig. 56 as an economic map worthy of emulation.

THE LOFOTEN FISHERY—A SAMPLE REGION[2]

Lofotfisket has been a phenomenon in the economic life of Norway for the better part of a thousand years. At the peak of the season, several thousand boats and more than 20,000 men may be operating in Lofoten waters. This activity, scarcely equalled throughout the fishing world in its concentration and organisation, takes place within a well-defined maritime area. *Lofotfisket* is a term which has immediate meaning for a Norwegian in respect of both time and place. The distinctiveness of its form and setting gives substantial evidence for regarding it as a particular type of economic region—a region which has its *raison d'être* in the sea. Within the sea area there is a nucleus about which it is only possible to draw a temporary—perhaps momentary—boundary. The nucleus may consist of 40 sq. km. of cod, 50–150 m. in depth, concentrated in shoals of varying density. The individual constituent of this mass may be a cod averaging seven pounds in weight. An interesting attempt to define the cod shoals was made in the *Annual Report of the Lofoten Fishery* (1939, p. 115), when the distributional pattern of the fishing fleet was plotted for a sequence of eight days in March. The operation at sea has a complementary expression on the surrounding land: an expression of increasingly involved character. Both offshore and onshore activity display a succession of patterns tied closely to the changing seasons. *Lofotfisket* is a regional phenomenon; its impact is the more impressive because it is also a seasonal phenomenon.

Three primary features characterise the Lofotens topographically. First, there is a mountain backbone roughly tangential to the main Scandinavian range which stretches south-westwards for 180 km. into the Norwegian Sea. This is commonly called the Lofoten Wall (*Lofotveggen*); but both visually

[1] Ct. Hans Strøm, description of Sunnmøre, 1762—"7–8 tons of herring are reduced to one ton of oil".
[2] For help in connection with this section, I am indebted to Hans Bjørnstad, legal officer in charge of the Lofoten Fishery District.

FIG. 56. The Gildeskaal area of Nordland and its related fishery picture. (Compiled from observations by Oscar Sund, *Die norwegische Seefischerei,* Stuttgart, 1938.)

Key

1. Ice-house.
2. Klippfish drying area.
3. Purse-net area.
4. Seine-net area.
5. Seasonal residences of fishermen.
6. Salmon netting.
7. Spring-cod grounds.
8. Herring grounds.
9. Redfish grounds.
10. Coalfish grounds.
11. Plaice grounds.
12. Halibut grounds.
13. Shellfish grounds.
14. Shrimp and prawn grounds.
15. Telephone centrals.
16. Steamer quays.
17. Mooring place.
18. Ice in February and March.
19. Lighthouses.

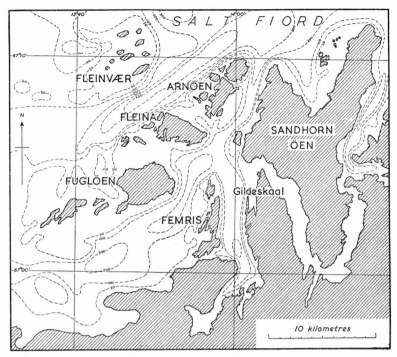

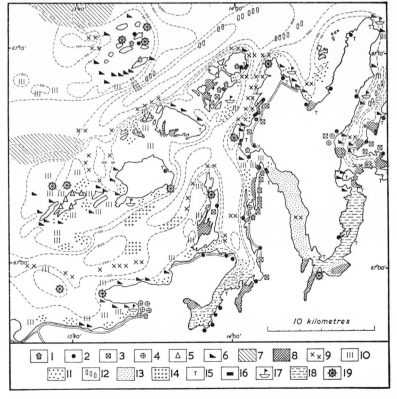

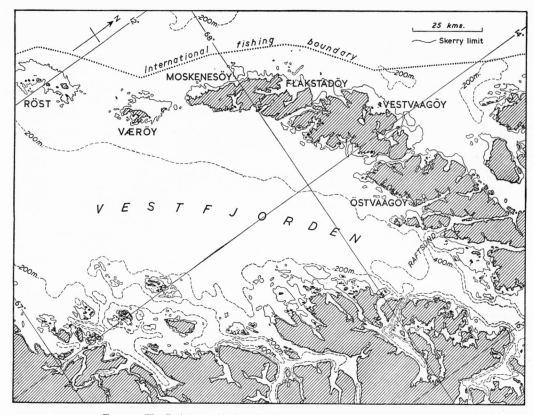

FIG. 57. The Lofotens.   (After the Norwegian Admiralty Chart, 311.)

and cartographically it is more suggestive of the skeleton of some vertebrate monster. Its outstanding Syenite or Gabbro peaks and horns (*tinder* or *nykker* as they may be called locally) attain altitudes exceeding 1,100 m. on East Vågøy and rise sharply from the continental shelf. Their remarkable cirques dip virtually to sea-level and the continuity of the Wall is broken longitudinally by sounds of varying width, such as Raftsund and Moskenes Sound. The second characteristic is the strandflat—a low shelf of land, much water-worn and recently emergent—which surrounds the cirqued peaks and stands in complete contrast to them. This "cincture of rocks", as a nineteenth-century cleric called it, is fully developed on both sides of the Lofoten Wall. Wall and strandflat, composing inhabited islands which vary in size from East Vågøy (526·7 sq. km.) to Røst (3·6 sq. km.), also define the third feature of the Lofoten

area—the great Vestfiord. The outlines of Vestfiorden and its submarine contours are given in Fig. 57. Landwards, Vestfiorden takes its origin from a number of ancillary fiords, the most noteworthy of which is Ofotenfiord. The focus of Vestfiorden and the vital centre of the fishery resource is the Hølla Deep between East Vågøy and Skrova, extending into Øysteinsfiord. The tidal rush of waters in Moskenes Sound gave rise to the legendary maelstrom, generously retailed in Purchas's *Pilgrimage*, decoratively displayed on many Renaissance maps and a stimulus to the literary-minded from Anders Arrebo's epic poem *Hexameron* (1661) to Edgar Allan Poe's *Tales of Mystery and Imagination*.

The Lofotens, the ten constituent civil parishes of which total 1,227 sq. km., are administered from Bodø as a part of the Nordland province. Their resident population, of about 30,000 *nordlendinger*, shows a tendency

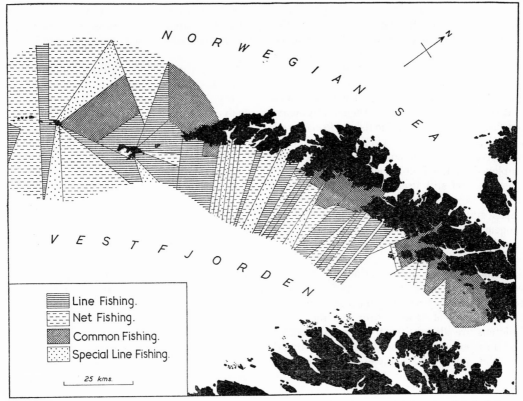

FIG. 58. Boundaries of the Lofoten fishing area. (Based on material supplied by the Chief of the Fishery Inspectorate, Svolvær.)

to concentrate on the inner side of the Lofoten Wall, where the strandflat provides a full dozen good harbours. The dissected ocean face provides sites for another half-dozen harbours. Apart from these nucleated settlements, farms are dispersed over the three islands which have the most cultivated land— West Vågøy, Gimsøy and Flakstadøy. At one time, the migratory fisherfolk added a widespread coastal scatter of cabins to the Lofoten scene; today, their temporary accommodation (still totalling over a thousand cabins or *rorbuer*) tends to be increasingly tied to the harbours. The shift in the distribution of fisher-cabins is part and parcel of a general redistribution of settlement in which many permanent fisher-farms have been deserted and many former fishery sites (or *vær*) have disappeared but for the name on the map.

Lofotfisket takes its character from the annual ebb and flow of cod. The advance guard of fishers arrives preparatory to the cod soon after Christmas; their season officially ends on April 25th. Fishermen may come from as far north as Varangerfiord and as far south as Vest-Agder. The extent of their migration is rivalled only by that to the Ålesund herring fisheries off the Vestland coast between January and March. Two sources may be considered for an appreciation of the Lofoten scene. Administratively and statistically, its character is summarised in the succession of year books concerning *Lofotfisket* which have been issued with increasing detail since 1859. Descriptively, there are few better sources than the files of the independent newspaper *Lofotposten*, which blends local colour with its day-by-day analyses of the region as seen from Svolvær.[1]

[1] It has been published since 1900, and *Lofotens Tidende*, published in Kabelvåg, was its predecessor. There is also a good descriptive Norwegian work edited by Kåre Fasting, *Lofotfisket* Trondheim 1946.

The annual report of the Lofoten fisheries embraces a weekly report covering the activities of the main fishery administrative districts. Its general tables list the participating boats first according to their form: open or half-decked with motor, open or half-decked without motor, decked with motor—and secondly, according to their equipment: net fishers (*garnfiskere*), line fishers (*linefiskere*) and handline fishers (*juksafiskere*). Most primitive of the elementary fishing methods employed in the Lofoten area are the hand-lines (*jukser*) still used by a quarter of the fishers. More elaborate lines, stretching perhaps a mile with 2,500 baited hooks, and arrangements in which 120 or more nets are strung together may be owned co-operatively by the six to ten men of the bigger motor-vessels. The most recent introduction to Lofoten waters is the "purse seine"—and it promises to be the most revolutionary advance since the coming of the motor engine. The Lofotens are also visited by merchant boats, and an average of 150 of these may be based on the ports of Svolvær, Henningsvær, Stamsund, Steine and Balstad during the peak month of March. Fish merchants ashore, measured by dozens in the local telephone directory, may total several hundred during the season and are drawn from far afield.

The intense concentration of activity calls for a correspondingly elaborate organisation of the fisheries. Three phases of development may be recognised historically. The right to fish was first based upon littoral ownership, and a few acres of barren rock in Lofoten were sometimes esteemed above their equivalent in fertile fields upon the mainland. From 1816 onwards, fishing rights—especially in Vestfiorden—were precisely defined according to compass points, and the exclusiveness of the activity even more rigidly impressed. The contemporary phase of development dates from the reforms urged by Ketil Motzfeldt, sometimes known as the father of the Lofoten fishing law, and introduced in 1857.[1] Waters are no longer divided according to littoral ownership, but on the basis of fishery practice.

The fisheries are open to any Norwegians in so far as they apply for permission and abide by the restraints imposed upon the method of fishing.

Today, the coastal waters of Lofoten are divided into: (1) common waters for all fishery practices (*felleshav*); (2) waters exclusively employed for line-fishing (*linehav*); (3) waters exclusively used for netting (*garn-hav*). There are currently over fifty divisions. They are based on landmarks on the Lofoten spur and commonly run with parallel lines at variously defined intervals "so far into Vestfiorden as there are fishing waters" (see Fig. 58). Towards the ocean terminus of the Lofoten spur, the pattern changes and the boundaries between the differing permitted practices radiate from Værøy and Røst. Here they embrace the outer ocean as well as Vestfiorden. The boundaries are subject to periodical revision, and amendments to them are published in the various fishermen's calendars as well as in the annual Lofoten report. The districts are tied to a readily recognised system of points and lights. There are two types of fishing which are not bound by these formal divisions. The hand-line fishers (*juksafiskere*) have complete liberty of movement; they are the free-lance agents of the fishing fraternity. The purse-seine fishers (*snurpenotfiskere*), already regarded as outlaws by the other fishers, have liberty of movement between the hours when the line-fishers and net-fishers have not set their tackle.

Principally because of the size of the fishing fleet engaged and the congestion in the waters, fishing is commonly restricted to daylight hours. The daily duration of activity varies according to the length of daylight (e.g. January 16th, 7.30 a.m. to 4 p.m.; March 15th, 6 a.m. to 8 p.m.), and ordinarily changes at fortnightly intervals. Indeed, the legal organisation of this area is so precise that the Lofoten fishing district has been called by some "a state within a state".

The intensity of fishing is represented in Fig. 59, which shows the weekly concentrations of boats at the principal harbours in 1952. The returns emphasise the concentration of

---

[1] Simultaneously, more detailed charts of Vestfiorden were undertaken. In 1869, five special "fishing maps" of the inner reaches of the fiord were published.

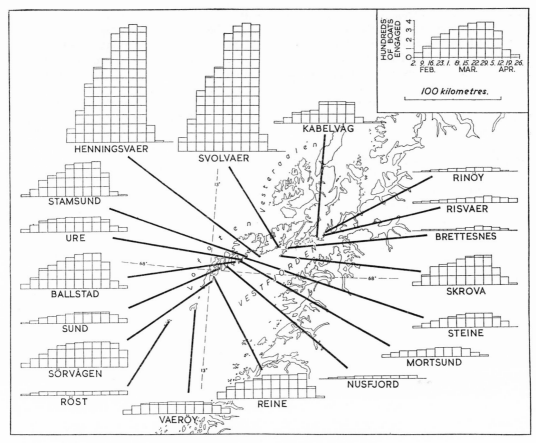

FIG. 59. Distribution of the fishing boats during the Lofoten fishing season, 1952. Based upon *Lofotfisket*, Official Statistics of Norway.)

the catch in time as well as space. Although they are not shown here, the statistical tables also display the various methods by which the catch has been made on a port basis. The variability of fish catches for Norway at large has already been stressed and Lofoten is no exception to this rule.[1]

Variation, however, is at least as much a matter of weather conditions as of fish availability. Within the fishing season, weather is liable to wide and frequent changes. Both fish and fishermen may be there but not the weather. The Lofoten fisheries are found in partly protected waters, but the proverbial storminess and the relatively small size of the fishing-boats affect the number of operational days. The number of what are called *land-liggedager* (weather-idle days) usually diminishes from January (one-third to one-half) to April (perhaps nil), and almost invariably from the West Lofoten to the East Lofoten fishers (by two or three days per month). Thousands of fishermen may be shorebound in Stamsund, Henningsvær or Svolvær on a weather-idle day. It is not uncommon for activities to be hindered either partly or wholly for a full quarter of the days within the fishing season.

Lofotposten offers grounds for appreciating the opportunities and restraints which characterise the fishing region. Man-power, boats, equipment, sales mechanism, land and

[1] A good illustration of the variation is given by Oscar Sund, "Fiskets gang og utbytte", *Report of Norwegian Fishery Investigations*, Bergen, 1938, 12.

sea problems pass in regular review. While the national employment statistics demonstrate that a fifth of the males over fifteen years of age in Nordland and North Troms engage in the Lofoten fisheries and that 77% of the population of islands like Værøy live by fishing, the employment columns of the press underline the tyranny of seasonal operations and the degree of specialisation in the activity. Winter vacancies (*vinterplasser*) are advertised for netmen (*garnmenn*), filleters (*fiskeflekkere*), motormen, hand-line fishers (*juksafiskere*), fish-oil workers (*trandampere*), klippfisk driers, ships' cooks and *bestmenn* (who are, in fact, ships' captains). Most fishermen as distinct from shore workers will be employed on a percentage understanding (*prosentfiskere*). The influx of seasonal labour attracted by such advertisements is tabulated on a township basis in the *Annual Fishery Report* of the Lofotens, and a total of 5,000 is not unusual.

A range of boat types is employed: formerly they were largely described according to the number of oarsmen which they carried (for example, *fembøringer* or five-pairs of oars; *åttringer* or eight oars). During a contemporary season there are advertised for sale or hire dorries, cutters (*fiskekuttere*), decked-boats (*skøyter*), *krysser*, *klipper*, *sjarker* and a variety of others which defy precise translation. In them, sail and oar are today usually superceded. The degree of mechanisation is generally related to the size of the vessel, but the variety of equipment to tempt the ship-owner—from new-type radio telephones to diesel engines, from echographs (a joke a generation ago, an essential today) to aluminium floats, from nylon lines and nets to fishermen's plastic clothing—illustrates changes in detail. The increasing employment of the heavy purse-seine emphasises changes in the scale of activity proceeding simultaneously. Shore equipment keeps pace with equipment afloat. There are diesel-driven propellers to speed *klippfisk* drying, and mills which, grinding ice at 10 tons per hour, enable advertisers to offer "ice delivery anywhere in Lofoten".

The purchaser's scales on the quayside divide the function of fisherman and processor. The sales mechanism no longer operates in a state of unlimited competition, though there might be some nightly bargaining between skipper and wholesaler around the larger harbours. Minimum prices are fixed at the national level—per kilo for cod, per litre for liver and roe. In addition, nine price zones have been recently introduced around the coast of Norway—based upon a system of transport differentials. Stabilisation of price enables producer and processor alike to plan their investment more carefully. In the transformation of shore establishments, new and old plants as well as new and old processes exist side by side. In Stamsund, for example, can be found single processing establishments as well as completely integrated plants. Here, too, stock fish holds its own. The drying racks (*fiskehellerne*), crowded as near to the harbour as possible, support a thickening canopy of cod until early May. A rough rack, 150 by 20 ft., with cod suspended in pairs by their twisted tails, may be worth over £1,000. Liver-reduction and fish-meal plants absorb the steady output of offal; while a relatively increasing proportion of the catch is filleted and fresh frozen on the quayside. In the old days, the merchants who handled the products were popularly known as *neskonger* (kings of the headland). The factory processor today, with his substantial home on the commanding peninsular point, is the contemporary order of monarchy.

The intensification of fishing operations has raised new problems in the strandflat settlements. Dwellings (their foundations blasted from the bedrock), factories, wharves, boats, fishracks—all call for the import of timber to a timberless countryside. Harbour improvements are increasingly demanded—to meet the congested seasonal needs, to accommodate ships of growing size and to protect shore establishments from the intermittent high seas. Next, the strandflat suffers an Ancient Mariner's nightmare of fresh-water deficiency, though relatively long-distance piping can help. During an average winter in Rinøy, for example, "snow had to be melted all winter long for washing and drinking water. Some residents had storage tanks to catch the rainfall from their roofs . . . but it is rendered very unsanitary by the sootfall from the chimneys".[1] Not merely is there increased demand for water with the influx of the fishing population: there is also the added demand for freshwater in fish processing. Places like Henningsvær display this difficulty, so that water may be strictly rationed to several hours a day during the fishing season. Elsewhere, water supply and electricity supply stand in competition at the peak season, with the limited flow of the power channel being necessarily diverted into the water-pipes. Svolvær Electricity Company, for example, has been forced to advertise week-end power cuts to make more water available for the fishers. State-established fresh-water plants for supplying fishermen show a concentration in Lofoten—in common with other skerry sites near to major fisheries.[2] The problem of power distribution, always assuming its availability, will be evident from a glance at the map of the islands. Similarly, there exists the problem of overland communication—in a country of crowded contour, juxtaposed land and water and of heavy winter snowfall.

The urgency of such matters belongs to the present: they did not disturb the readers of *Lofotens Tidende*, published in Kabelvåg sixty years ago. Kabelvåg was then the historical centre of the area. Then, too, motor-boat and fast steamer had not appeared to modify the commercial character of the fisheries—it was in 1902 that Lofoten heard the throb of the first motor-boat. The annual taxation record was still published in the local press to give with its list of professional titles and incomes a picture of the community upon which the fishermen made their impact. Property advertisements could offer "a fine situation for engaging in both the outer and inner fisheries" or salting places for up to 150,000 fish. Fishing telegrams were just beginning to even out prices between the neighbouring ports, while fishing intelligence about the Humber ports, Newcastle and London came regularly from an agent at Prince's Dock, Hull. Exports went to Trondheim, Kristiania and Altona. Surpluses and shortages were summed up in the advertisement columns—British steamship coal, hemp and cotton yarns for fish nets, barrels, planks, joinery items, oilskins, hay, margarine-butter and potatoes. "Lisbon salt" recalled that 7–8 tons were required to salt 1,000 cod. Bread grain was short in supply, though amelioration was expected when the Russians opened the Murmansk railroad. There was editorial comment on "English sea robbers" around the coast of Iceland. And, in the final place, it was a precarious world. As Sir Edmund Gosse had written in his *Northern Studies* (1890): "A whim of the codfish, a hurricane in the sky or a cold spring is sufficient to plunge [the fishers] into distress and poverty." Every issue of the press carried life-insurance invitations from British, American and German houses for those who sought to assuage the toll of the northern waters, the promise of free land in Canada for those who wished to escape their dangers and the cure-all of Dr. Gronwold's universal plasters for those who sought to salve the wounds of the trade.

The measure of change in technique but of persistence in phenomenon is illumined by reference to the rhyming topography of Nordland—*Nordlands Trompet eller Beskrivelse over Nordland Amt* (Bergen, 1739) by the poet-priest, Petter Dass (1674–1707). Its Lofoten lines speak of the fishermen as migratory birds of passage:

> Det har sig med dem, som med Fugler i Flugt
> De planter ej, pløjer ej, høster ej Frugt
> Og sanke ej Sæden i Lade

who neither plant, plough, harvest nor set their seeds in store. When they depart, there is neither hunting vessel, nor sail nor mast and the land is lifeless as a desert:

> Man ser der ej Jægter, ej Seiler, ej Mast,
> Ret ligesom Landet var øde.

The Lofoten migrant's life is summed up with poetic exaggeration as being bound to the fisherman's hook:

> Hans Plog, og hans Ager, hans Avel og Aag,
> Det hænger altsammen paa eneste Krog.

The hook is a peculiarly persistent symbol, and the Lofoten fisheries are, in part, dis-

---

[1] *Lofotfisket*, 1952, p. 59.   [2] Cf. *Die norvegische Seefischerei*, Fig. 203.

tinctive because of the tenacity with which their operators cling to outmoded methods. It has been estimated that with the employment of contemporary techniques perhaps the same results could be achieved with a third of the presently employed man-power. Enough has been said elsewhere, however, to emphasise that social equilibrium and economic efficiency are often antipathetic.

The independent Norwegian fisherman has been described by Anthony Martin as shaking his fist at the smoke-stain left by the trawler;[1] he may be pictured as metaphorically fingering his cod-knife when he views his other rival— the purse-seiner. The big boat is a challenge to the freedom of action of the local fisherman. He sees it as a threat to his future as well as carrying with it possible overproduction or, indeed, overfishing. It is a scapegoat to which all ills are ascribed. But the Lofoten fisheries have previously shown similar resentment to innovation, and through their adjustment to it have emerged the richer. Any feature which can assist in the recovery of the seasonal bounty of the sea must surely ease the lot of the fishing community. Large-scale rationalisation may, indeed, be on the threshold. The extent to which it can be a rationalisation tied to the community of the Lofoten strandflat is, however, debatable— bearing in mind the freedom of other Norwegians to fish in Lofoten waters. Nor, indeed, can such rationalisation solve the seasonal problem of overactivity and under-activity. *Rikstelefonkatalogen* informs that telephone exchanges like those of Risvær and Steine are "open only in the fishing season". These human nerve centres emphasise the continuing control of a fish crowned as a monarch in at least one Norwegian coat-of-arms. It is unlikely that the immediate future will see the establishment of any complementary activity to engage the Lofotens when the monarch is absent from his court. Furthermore, to modify a behaviour pattern inherited from the centuries might be almost as hard as to depose the authority of King Cod himself.

THE RESOURCE AND ITS INTERNATIONAL RESTRAINTS

Fisheries are the cynosure of economists and politicians as well as biologists, and the peaceful pursuits of the biologists cannot be divorced from the contentious activities of the others. Fishery disputes have always exacerbated otherwise peaceful relations between states, and the whole range of inventions which have transformed the harvesting and marketing of fish have sharpened rather than softened international reactions. Settlements at the international level have been demanded on two scores. First, the increase in the fish catch has made for signs of regional or specie exhaustion. Secondly, multiplication of fishing fleets has increased the intensity of competition, and the threat of trespass upon the established rights in the rich coastal waters of the Atlantic world of Scandinavia. Restraints have accordingly been imposed. In the whaling industry there is restriction upon the absolute size of the catch; on the European "shelf" there is the International Fisheries Convention of 1946, to which the Scandinavians subscribe; in the Atlantic fisheries there has been intermittent redefinition of territorial waters.

(a) The Regulation of the Catch

The prehistoric interest of Norwegians in whaling is engraved in a Stone Age rock drawing at Strand in South Trøndelag.[2] More recent developments, however, fall into two periods, and each is tied largely to a different hemisphere.[3] The first dates from the late Middle Ages until the latter part of the last century, and has as its setting the North Atlantic fringes. Its harvest was the Greenland, sperm and Northcaper whale; its technical equipment consisted of the sailing ship, the rowing boat and the hand harpoon. Whaling in Norwegian coastal waters has been vividly described by sixteenth- and seventeenth-century travellers, while whale strandings and landings have been graphically described by Renaissance topographers like

---

[1] "The Lofoten Fisheries", *The Norseman*, VII, 3.
[2] J. G. D. Clark, *Prehistoric Europe, op. cit.*, Fig. 32.
[3] The authoritative works on Norwegian whaling are published in the series *Chr. Christensens Hvalfangstmuseum*, Sandefiord. Historically, reference should be made to B. Aagaard, *Den gamle hvalfangst*, Publications 13 and 61.

Johannes Schefferus.[1] Until the age of reason restrained imagination, the cartographical vacuities of the Norwegian and Barents seas were generously filled with a variety of whales such as never entered a zoological textbook. Their recurrence in successive atlases stamped Norway a whaling land as surely as Ahab in *Moby Dick* became a symbol of New England whaling. And there was international competition for the harvest of these high latitudes. The Dutch, especially, during their transitory visitations scattered their artefacts—and their place-names—along the littorals of what were later to be recognised as Norway's Arctic outlands.

Norwegian operations in the northern hemisphere have sunk to a modest place in the whaling scene, though a relict industry, located principally on the west coast, retains something of the original flavour. A special statistical section in the annual fishery reports gives some indication of the importance of an activity which is also limited to the season May–September. Blomvåg, in the skerries north of Bergen, with its three catchers operating from a shore base, is one of the three remaining stations.

The shift of interest among Norwegian whalers to the southern hemisphere is usually dated as 1905, when the first floating factory was dispatched to the Antarctic.[2] Already the so-called shell harpoon had been invented by Svend Føyn of Tønsberg and had been in use nearly forty years. It made possible the hunting of whales of the baleen type—and speeded the exhaustion of stocks in Atlantic coastal waters. New equipment—the electrically-operated harpoon, steam-driven catchers (perhaps up to several hundred tons in size) in the proportion of seven or eight to one factory ship of several thousand tons, and spotter aircraft—heralded a new age. Norway has established shore stations in Antarctica, such as Husvik Harbour, South Georgia, to accommodate the fleet which

moves south during December–April. The dominant rivals in the Antarctic scene are Japan and the U.S.S.R. In the 1930s, an average of about 30,000 whales per season were being caught, yielding substantially over 2 million barrels of oil, with the Norwegian percentage of this steadily declining from 50% in 1932–3. The depletion of whale stocks during the last decade has forced a series of international agreements, which now restrict the catch of blue whale units.

With the creation of the *Bureau of International Whaling Statistics* at Sandefiord, expeditions are now required to report in detail their weekly catches. In 1955–6, the hunting season was restricted to fifty-six days. The size of the catch will naturally be affected by the length of the season, and Norway's production does not consequently increase. The growing concentration upon immature whales means a lower return per unit of effort. Norway employed four factory ships in 1964 and 6,000 whales were caught in Antarctica. It supplies about 1,000 operatives for whaling fleets of other countries.

Seal hunting is a lively enterprise, based on the ports of Vestlandet. 73 expeditions were mounted in 1964, principally in April and May. They resulted in a total of 200,000 Greenlandic sealskins. Polar bear are also hunted on the same expeditions.

(b) The Definition of Territorial Waters

In a world which is given to the redefinition of territorial waters for political purposes, Norway's extended claims have an essentially economic motive.[3] There is also a second contrast. Whereas redefinition in the New World has sprung essentially from interests in the bed-rock resources of the adjacent portion of the continental shelf, Norway is moved by the content of the waters above the sea-bed. Scandinavian waters have been much subject to trespass by the fishing vessels of their North Sea neighbour states. Before the First World

---

[1] K. Williamson, *The Atlantic Islands*, London, 1949, provides an interesting contemporary parallel from the Færoes, and the remoter background to the activity is provided by J. G. D. Clark, "Whales as an Economic Factor in Prehistoric Europe", *Antiquity*, 1947, 84–104.

[2] The *Norwegian Whaling Gazette* (Norwegian and English) gives a monthly picture of activity and output.

[3] Cf. S. W. Boggs, "National Claims in Adjacent Seas", *Geographical Review*, 1951, XLI, 185-209. The Norwegian case is succinctly summarised in H. Giverholt, *Den norsk-britiske Fiskerigrensetvisten*, Bergen, 1953. Directly relevant data is also found in H. S. K. Kent, "The Historical Origins of the Three-mile Limit", *American Journal of International Law*, 48, 4, 1954.

War, there was scant appreciation of high-latitude fishing and ignorance concerning the behaviour of its associated pack-ice; but British long-distance trawlers had already been operating off Iceland in the 1890s, and a decade later appeared in Barents Sea (still called by some the White Sea). Between the wars, trawlermen advanced to the very margins of the permanent ice-cap, and developed, against heavy capital outlay, a highly specialised activity. In 1954, for example, the British trawler fleet totalled nearly 300 vessels of some £18 million estimated value. Based primarily upon the Humber estuary, this fleet of vessels which average several thousand tons, makes journeys of three to four weeks' duration to the "waters of the midday night" to fish competitively with the Norwegians and Russians.[1] Hitherto the land areas most geographically proximate to the Arctic fishing-grounds have been among the least adequately equipped to deal with the catch. Although north Norway has been revolutionising its fish processing, beyond the Lofoten group there are few sights as impressive as, for example, the mile-long panorama of fish barrels at Hull —some 1,500 miles from the fishing-grounds which flash beneath the "old feathery" of the Aurora Borealis.

"The norskies", as the Humber trawlermen refer to their little-known competitors, are very vulnerable to the superior equipment of British fishing vessels; while both the U.S.S.R. and East Germany compete increasingly in the Arctic fisheries. Norway's claim for a re-definition of territorial sovereignty was based upon the averred necessity of protecting coastal fishermen, with their limited equipment and restricted opportunities of alternative income, from this competition. A second argument for the exclusion of alien fishing vessels has been fear of exhaustion of inshore fisheries. Though less generally convincing, this argument has specific meaning for fishermen who are sensitive to short-period changes in quantity. In 1951 at The Hague, Norway claimed the limits of her territorial waters ran parallel not with the coast, but "with straight base-lines drawn between

fixed points on the mainland, on islands and on rocks". This completely changed the contours of the old "three-mile limit from the low-water mark", with its provisions for bays of less than ten miles wide. Alien fishing vessels were now prohibited from extensive areas which they had formerly fished.

The significance of this prohibition will be appreciated by glancing at the topographical sheet for Tromsö (1 : 100,000) or the sketch-map of the Lofoten area (Fig. 57, p. 186), in which the outermost islands of the spur are too small to be indicated, but not too little to have meaning for the agreement. In 1959 Denmark sought to impose a 12-mile limit for all foreign fishing vessels. In 1960, Great Britain recognised a six-mile limit from the Norwegian base line: as from 1970, it is to be a 12-mile limit. Since 1964 Britain has recognised a 12-mile limit from the base lines of Iceland, while agreement has also been reached to extensions in Færoese waters. In the process the international attitude to territorial waters has passed under the review of the United Nations Organisation in Geneva.[2]

"THE THREE LEGS OF A COOKING POT"

Christian Molberg, an eighteenth-century author, in his book on fisheries gives a picturesque example of fishing by landmark:

"We sailed WNW from a promontory on Sunnmøre," he wrote, "rounded so far from the shore that the terribly high peak called Romsdalshorn went so near under water that it did not show higher than the three legs of a cooking pot (*gryte*). My mate therefore called the place *Gryttingen på store Eggen*, the cooking pot on the large bank, and said it was sixteen miles from shore."

The three legs of the cooking pot provide a convenient symbol for the three related facts in which are rooted the outstanding problems of the Scandinavian fishing industry. First, the commercial realisation of the resource has outstripped its biological appreciation. Next, the resource—which may be a variable quantity—has yet to adjust its claims on and contributions to the national economy. Thirdly, the management of the resource is a very personal and individual matter and calls for the integration of many minutely differen-

[1] For a fine personal account of these trawlers, see A. Martin, *The Norseman*, 1954, XII, 3, 4, 5.
[2] cf. L. M. Alexander, *Offshore Geography of Northwestern Europe*, London, 1966.

tiated local economies. As with fishing by landmark, these three facts at least must be brought into continuous focus. Enough will have been said already to demonstrate that the solution of most of their related problems calls for the combined investigation by a number of different scientists and humanists. For their complete understanding few activities emphasise so fully the unity of knowledge as the fishing industry.

Chapter IX

SOURCES OF ENERGY

"And furthermore, that stream Castalia
Which people talk so much about,
With fall on fall, at lowest reckoning
Must mean a thousand horse-power good."

Henrik Ibsen, *Peer Gynt*, 1867

THE DISTRIBUTION OF ENERGY

MOST of Fenno-Scandinavia's rivers are un-navigable, but this vice conceals a virtue. From early times the obstacles to their navigability have been locally employed for the production of energy. Water-power has thus a long tradition in these northern lands. The transformation of running water into hydro-electric power, however, has given rise to a scale of operations so great as to defy comparison with the water-wheel days. And side by side with the multiplication of hydro-electric plants and their increase in size, a new elasticity has been given to the energy produced. Mere water-power made a limited contribution to a modest workshop régime which was fixed by crankshafts to the site of the energy; hydro-electric power, fundamental to the contemporary industrial structure of the area, imposes few direct restraints upon plant location. An added importance accrues to hydro-electric power because in the Northern Countries it is without a serious rival.[1]

Water-power potentialities in any area are a direct expression of its physical character. From the power point of view, relief and land forms are the "topographic constants". They account for the complexities of drainage in Finland and Scandinavia and the generous distribution of surface water. Precipitation —and evaporation—are significant variables. The quantity of precipitation, with its west Scandinavian maxima and east Scandinavian minima, is inseparable from the quality of precipitation. The low-temperature condi-tions related to the prolonged winter affect the quality appreciably. Run-off directly trans-mits them to power generation. Fenno-Scandinavia, in fact, shows considerable regional variations in its river régimes. Lake reservoirs, a distinguishing feature of Scandinavia and Finland, play an important role in regulating their flow. Schemes for artificial regulation are multiplied continuously.

The political divisions superimposed upon the physical features of Fenno-Scandinavia imply a very uneven distribution of hydro-electric power. Denmark, the least varied in relief and one of the least rainy parts of Scandinavia, is virtually devoid of resources. Norway, with its contrasting altitudes and heavy rainfall, can claim the richest resources of any single European country. Finland, low-lying and falling within the rain shadow of the Scandinavian Keel, has more limited opportunities; while Iceland has a potential development comparable with that of the northern provinces of Norway. As in so many respects, Sweden shares the hydro-electric characteristics of all four neighbours. The uneven distribution of resource between the several countries is repeated within them, so that the main centres of demand do not coincide with the main sources of supply— and potential supply.

Of all resources, hydro-electric power lends itself least to satisfactory statistical expression. Figures showing developed power are often substantially outdated before they find their way to the printer. The changing methods employed in harnessing the resource

---

[1] *The Transactions of the World Power Conferences* provided much basic data for this chapter. A standard unit to which reference is continually made is the kilowatt-hour (kWh.). "Ten 100-watt lamps require a kilowatt to keep them alight and burn 1 kilowatt-hour (kWh.) of electrical energy in one hour" (The Earl of Verulam, "The Geography of Power", *Geographical Journal*, 1953, 251–66).

call for a continuous restatement of estimates.[1]

THE THEORY OF
HYDRO-ELECTRIC POWER

Three primary technical developments have favoured the present-day management of running water. The turbine or dynamo has enabled the conversion of moving water into energy. Its effective employment in Scandinavia belongs to the last sixty years. Secondly, the capacity to control the flow of water has been eased by contemporary constructional methods. The modern techniques of damming, which employ ferro-concrete as a primary material, offer a mastery over power sites which was impossible in earlier times. Thirdly, the cable has reduced the control of the supply points and has given rise to growing ease in the distribution of power. Each of these basic inventions is subject to continuous improvement, and its modern expression is far removed from its original form. Improvements have also enabled a continuous increase in the scale of operations at the site of construction and a steady reduction of the coefficient of loss in the distributional system. Such improvements frequently permit a new flexibility in the siting of power-plants—electricity, indeed, becomes a ubiquitous resource. Relief, precipitation and distance still impose their tax, but the incidence weighs less heavily and the tax assumes an increasingly indirect character.

Given this technical equipment, what are the simple criteria for the assessment of power resources? The two essentials are the head of water and the flow of water. They will be expressions of the character of the catchment basin concerned—its area, its elevation, its precipitation and its run-off conditions. The capacity of a water-course is therefore a variable quantity and its value may well be assessed according to its constancy of flow.[2] Indeed, a fundamental aim in the management of a waterway employed for power is to regularise the capacity. Potentialities are commonly discussed in terms of low-water and high-water capacity. The amount of energy which can be theoretically generated on a given water-course may therefore be variable according to the degree of technical control which may be exerted over its capacity. To build for the maximum capacity of a given fall carries with it higher installation costs; to build for the low-water capacity—with a run-of-stream plant—may imply a substantial waste of power. The régime of a water-course may accordingly play a considerable role in the priority given for development and in the scale of installations, though it may also be noted that installation costs diminish with increased capacity.

In assessing the value of a particular source of supply, considerations are therefore extended beyond the site of the power-plant. They must take into account the behaviour of the entire river system above and below the point or points of development. For example, every water-course has greater or lesser possibilities of water storage in its upper reaches. Frequently the regularisation of tributaries assumes greater importance than the control of the main stream in this respect. The elaborate succession of hanging valleys tributary to the Skien water-course of south Norway provides a specific instance of this. Examples of the development of valleys as unitary wholes are provided by the Dalälv and Indalsälv of central Sweden. Not infrequently, of course, the organisation of a catchment basin for power production can imply artificial enlargement or alteration—as at certain west Norwegian sites, where high-level water-courses have been conduited through watersheds and their heads of water increased by short-circuiting the natural drainage channel. In the management of the river as a unit, the control of the capacity cannot be divorced from the control of its other functions. The design of projects cannot ignore multi-purpose development. Irrigation does not enter into the Scandinavian picture (save in a purely local manner and in detachment from power development), but the floatage of timber is a complementary function

[1] This is well illustrated by reference to the classic work on Scandinavian hydro-electric power from a generation ago, A. Ludin, *Die nordischen Wasserkräfte*, Berlin, 1930.
[2] *Hydro-electric Potential in Europe, its Gross Technical and Economic Limits*, Geneva, 1953, or, for an engineering approach, J. J. Doland, *Hydro-power Engineering*, New York, 1954.

which enforces structural and organisational adjustments. Navigation does not enter seriously into the management of any Scandinavian river system. Nor can the picture stop short at national boundaries, for the coincidence of political frontier and watershed is a rare occurrence. In brief, for the purpose of power production, each river system is a problem unto itself—a composite problem, in fact, the various solutions of which call for growing ingenuity.

But, given the contemporary scale of operations and flexibility of exploitation, no single unit can be ultimately considered out of its national context. Assuming that there are limited supplies of capital available for investment, the development of one water-course will be balanced at the national level against the development of possible alternative waterways. The various solutions offered to the problem of any one given river cannot accordingly be considered in isolation. That this situation is real and not hypothetical is admirably illustrated by the case of Sweden, fuller details of which follow below.

The increasingly unitary character of power production at the national level in Norway, Sweden and Finland is inseparable from two facts. First, within the national frame, areas of surplus and of deficient power must be steadily balanced.[1] In Norway, the south has essentially greater power potentialities than the north. In Sweden and Finland, the demands of the south not merely exceed the resources of the south, but the southern resources have been developed almost to capacity. The northward shift in the centre of gravity of power supply is a continuing characteristic of both countries.

This shift, however, is inseparable from the second fact—the invention of new forms of transmission.[2] In 1950, it was estimated that the transmission distances in the Scandinavian area were as follows: Denmark, 60 km.; Finland, 170 km.; Norway, 90 km.; Sweden, 250 km. New forms to aid this may spring from improvements in overhead transmission of alternating current or from conversion of power into direct current before transmission. While the maximum distance that alternating current can be effectively and economically transmitted is 600 miles, direct current can be transmitted 1,000 miles. External evidence of this technical improvement makes its mark on the landscape. No less than 75,000 tons of steel structures and cable carry the cross-country lines which link Sweden's high-latitude supply sources with their Stockholm market. Three thousand work-sites have been employed between the intermediary transformers of Harsprånget, Midskog and Hallsberg. And the scale of operations makes experiment in technical alternatives an economic proposition. Thus, in the binding together of Swedish power regions, new steel-aluminium cables replace former copper lines. They are 30% lighter than copper cables and 30% stronger. All of these features are basic to a new integration of the northern lands.

It is, moreover, difficult to see this integration stopping short at national boundaries. For the precise coincidence of political frontier and watershed is a rare occurrence in Norway, Sweden and Finland. The course of events in Scandinavia during recent months is such that the various solutions offered to the problem of any given river can no longer be confined even within the frame of the state concerned.

THE IMPACT OF INTERNATIONAL BOUNDARIES

International boundaries interfere with the unitary development of natural resources.[3] They impinge upon the production of hydro-electric power directly by dividing the control of water-courses; they may also affect the distribution of energy produced. Fig. 60 shows the interplay of watershed and international boundary for the area under consideration. The relationship between the two assumes three different regional expressions.

Give-and-take characterises the Norwegian-Swedish relation. The situation is most

---

[1] Cf. F. Hjulström, *Sveriges elektrifiering*, Uppsala, 1942, pp. 150-1, the first Swedish attempt to unify two régimes—the Klarälv and Norsälv—took place fifty years ago.
[2] *Some Technical Aspects of the Transmission of Electric Power*, Geneva, 1952.
[3] Economic Commission for Europe, *Transfer of Electric Power across European Frontiers*, Geneva, 1952. Cf. also *Legal Aspects of the Hydro-electric Development of Rivers and Lakes of Common Interest*, Geneva, 1952.

complicated in the south-
east, where certain Norwegian
waterways not merely penetrate into Swedish territory
but return again to the Norwegian side of the boundary.

This aroused original problems in their employment as
floatage ways (cf. p. 236, *below*). A whole series of agreements between the water-
boards of Norway and Sweden
now cover the beheaded water-
courses of the frontier zone.[1]
These have been of growing
importance for Sweden, because with the shift in the
centre of gravity of its power
production to higher altitudes,
the head waters of many of its
rivers lie in Norwegian territory. The course of Klarälven
in Finnskogen on the Värmland border is a specific issue.

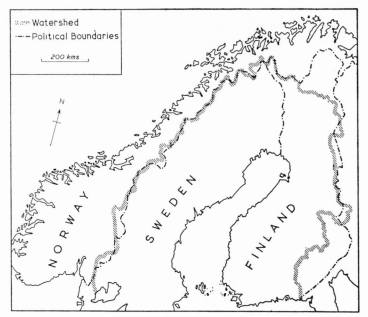

FIG. 60. Watershed and international boundaries in Scandinavia and Finland.

In the high north, watershed and boundary show a different relationship, for three of the major rivers form international boundaries. The Torneå is the established boundary between Sweden and Finland for half of its length. Little power is developed on it, although its course is as rich in possibilities as those of many Scandinavian rivers. The Tana river is the boundary between Norway and Finland for some miles; it has not been harnessed for power. The post-war boundary commission of 1947 was much taxed in finding the centre points which should form the inter-national division between Norway and the U.S.S.R. on the Pasvik river. The river has been virtually eliminated as a routeway, but there have been Russo-Norwegian negotiations over joint power production at Skoltefoss and Skogfoss. Norway would be much interested in joint power development to meet the de-ficiencies of Kirkenes mining (cf. Chapter XII). Higher up its course, two Russian power-sta-tions have been constructed by Finnish en-gineers at Jäniskoski. They are located in the

former Finnish "corridor", and supply the needs of the Russian nickel smeltery at Nikkeli in Petsamo. Lake reservoirs regulating their needs lie in Finnish territory.

A third relationship is encountered in Fin-land, where although the headwaters of most Finnish rivers lie within the frame of Finland, there are extensive areas in the east of the country which drain into the U.S.S.R.[2] Eastern Finland has one of the most confused watersheds in Europe. The situation has been complicated by the Karelian bisection, for the whole of the Saimaa lake system has its outlet through Russian territory—and the Soviet power-plants on the lower Vuoksi river are exclusively dependent upon the supply of water from Finnish sources.

There is thus an unavoidable interchange of water between the Northern Countries. Given the present situation of power surpluses and deficiencies, it is natural to anticipate an interchange of energy. In keeping with Europe at large,[3] the present extent of this is extremely limited, though the technical

---

[1] Already prepared for in the Treaty of Karlstad (by which Norway and Sweden were separated in 1905), **Articles**
1 and 2.
[2] Cf. a convention between Finland and the U.S.S.R. of October 28th, 1922, *League of Nations Treaty Series*, **19,** 193.
[3] *Annual Statistics of Production, Consumption and Exchange of Electrical Power*, UNO, 1955.

obstacles diminish daily. Not merely is over-land transmission less difficult, but extended underwater transmission is increasingly simpli-fied. Swedish export to Gotland, from Västervik to Visby across 115 km. of sea, has proved successful. The export of power from south Norway across the 70 miles of the Skaggerak has been debated, and the projected interchange of power between Norway, Sweden and Denmark around the "Scandi-navian Sea" has been sketched.[1] Already in the 1930s, Swedish and Danish power systems were linked by two cables beneath the Øre-sund—ostensibly for the export of Swedish water-power surpluses to Denmark. Not in-frequently the flow of steam-generated power from Denmark to Sweden has taken precedence in the exchange. A 380-mile undersea cable from south-west Norway to Berwick on Tweed has also been discussed.

Prospects for the interchange of energy are complicated by differing national aims and policies. As a country with a theoretical sur-plus of power, Norway is a possible exporter, but there is an immediate investment prob-lem. Investment in water-power can only claim a limited amount from the available pool of capital—and the additional power which this provides barely keeps pace with expand-ing national demand. Joint Scandinavian exploitation of Norway's water-power has therefore been raised in discussion. "We stand in many respects to Sweden as a whole as Norrland stands to the rest of Sweden," it has been said in Norway.[2] A large-scale development programme spread over ten to fifteen years has been put forward. Norway, Sweden and Denmark would contribute to it financially in the proportion of 50%, 25% and 25%, and would draw out corresponding sup-plies of power. Meanwhile, practical agree-ment has been reached over the Nea project, near Trondheim. In the construction of this plant, approximately three-quarters of the capital will be raised by Swedish loan, and it will be redeemed by Norway over a span of fifteen years by the export of power from Nea

to Stockholm. It is an interesting reflection on the integration of the two countries that Swedish "power" politics can balance develop-ment in Norrland against a western extension of its supply into Norway.

The export of power from Norway seems natural, and it is averred that regular exports could be guaranteed for twenty years without prejudicing domestic supplies.[3] But there is a measure of caution in its promotion. In the first place, it may be more profitable to "pro-cess" power before export; for example, by converting it into exportable electro-chemical and electro-metallurgical products. In this respect, the indirect transfer of power by Norway to Sweden is particularly significant. Finally, Norway is only just beginning to fore-see its own domestic power needs, and it is not easy to forecast the extent to which they will consume its developing power supplies. The electrification of Norwegian railways alone creates a growing need. To undertake long-period export commitments might well give rise to domestic embarrassments. Upon such arguments rests the widespread opposition to the international development and integration of Norwegian hydro-electric power.

NATIONAL VARIATIONS IN SUPPLY

(a) Finland

Finnish waterways have a greater uni-formity than those of either Norway or Sweden. A general similarity of physical conditions throughout the country, by elimin-ating variety in their courses, restricts oppor-tunities of equalising regional variations. Finnish rivers are uniform again in their low heads of water.[4] Reflecting the prolonged winter freeze and the continental late summer precipitation, Finland's rivers experience a rhythm of flow which expresses itself in two maxima and two minima. High spring and low autumn maxima balance intermediary summer and winter minima.

Resources are found principally on the relatively short rivers which drain the lake

[1] The Earl of Verulam, op. cit., Fig. 3, p. 255.
[2] F. Vogt, "Kraftforsyning og eksport", Teknisk Ukeblad, July 8th, 1954.
[3] Transfer of Electric Power, op. cit., p. 120. And "Power Report from Norway", Teknisk Ukeblad, 1950, 277–330; 403–13.
[4] P. Harve and B. Nordquist, "National Resources of Fuels and Water-power in Finland", Transactions, 4th World Power Conference, London, I, 1952.

plateau to the coast or along the more extended courses of the Oulu and Kemi rivers. The chief rivers flowing from the lake plateau are—the Vuoksi (outlet for Lake Saimaa, largest of the Finnish lakes), the Kymi (outlet for Lake Päijänne) and the Kokemäki (outlet for the western lake system of Näsijärvi). Between these there are a number of smaller rivers, while to the north of the Kokemäki a series of parallel rivers strike in a north-westerly direction to the Bothnian coast. The volume of energy derived from this southerly group is limited by the relatively low altitude of the lake plateau and by the relatively small volume of rainfall received. Within the Finnish lake system, there is also a series of rapids and low falls which have provided local sites for development. Among them, the earliest to be seized upon—and to give rise to the greatest industrial city of the interior—was Tammerfors. The virtual boxing in of its stretch of rapids remains one of the most remarkable urban features of Finland.

The southern water-courses are characterised by rapids rather than falls. The Vuoksi, a former *Baedeker* sight, was one of the first to be harnessed, and provides the largest single power potential of any river in southern Fin-

land. Given contemporary facilities for maximising low heads of water by a series of dams, the Kymi river experienced a transformation. Industry located itself along the lines of these three southern rivers in the early electrical period and has been persistent at its original sites. Almost each rapid along the Kymi, for example, has been picked out by an industrial plant; or, alternatively, each rapid has been seized upon as a source of tributary power to supply existing plants. The familiar pattern of industry outgrowing its local power supply is repeated throughout the lake plateau, with industrial concerns casting around for supplementary sources of energy. Mänttä is a representative example (cf. Chapter XI).

Table 17 (p. 202) gives some indication of the distribution of power—actual or potential—on the principal Finnish waterways. Power is developed at approximately 100 sites.

During the last generation, industrial development in Finland has been running ahead of hydro-electricity. This position has been seriously complicated by the loss of power on the lower Vuoksi to the U.S.S.R. in 1944. Developed power as well as potential power has been reduced. In the resulting plans for a more thorough exploitation, two measures are

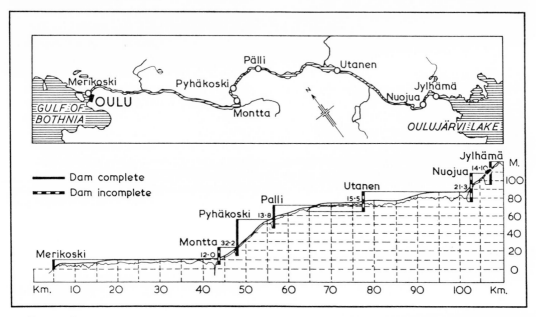

FIG. 61. The Oulu river system with its post-war power developments. (After *Voima ja valo*, 1954.)

TABLE 17

FINNISH POWER POTENTIAL

River Systems	Actual kW. Generated 1954	Projected kW.	Energy in kWh./PA Projected
Vuoksi .	209,870	126,000	523
Kymi .	152,360	89,900	507
Kumo .	168,400	19,630	31
Oulu .	242,800	203,000	1,115
Kemi .	76,000	700,500	3,543
Others .	27,095	9,740	42
Total	876,525	1,148,770	5,752

(Source: *Voima ja valo*, **3**, 3, 1954.)

being effected. There is, first, a general integration of the power systems into a national grid; secondly, the harnessing of latent resources in the north to meet the needs of the south. The centre of gravity of power production is shifting north even more irrevocably in Finland than in Sweden. Eighty per cent. of the power in south Finland is already tapped; in the foreseeable future north Finland will provide two-thirds of Finland's power instead of the third which it currently produces. Indeed, among Finnish river systems none has developed more power than the Oulu. The balance between northern surpluses and southern deficiencies will be struck preliminarily through the contribution of Oulujoki—the successive heads of water of which are shown diagrammatically in Fig. 61.

The Kemi is Finland's least exploited and most powerful river system. Its drainage basin includes the greater part of Finnish Lapland. The first site tapped was at the mouth, where the demands of the large paper and pulp plants of Kaarihaara and Vetsiluoto have spurred the costly damming of the lower falls. Fig. 62 illustrates the range of sites at which generation is possible and the succession of constructional works which are steadily marching upstream.[1] Exploitation of the Kemijoki is of significance for several reasons. Above all, it represents investment in an under-capitalised and under-developed part of Finland (cf. Chapter VI). Construction and maintenance work provide alternative income for rural communities precariously tied to farming, as well as a new continuing flow of exports from a region of hitherto limited production. The more elevated relief of north Finland bestows upon the Kemi system greater power resources than upon most other Finnish waterways.

(b) Iceland

The first hydro-electric power-station in Iceland was constructed in 1902, and half a century later there were approximately fifty generating plants in the island. The country is relatively rich in resources. Major enterprises have been developed in the neighbourhood of the capital and in northerly Akureyri. The great bulk of Iceland's power is of hydro-electric origin; less than 10% deriving from thermal installations. A state plan, established in 1942, proposes a national grid and

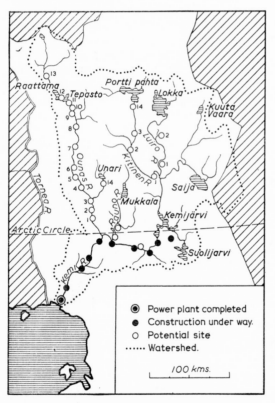

FIG. 62. Hydro-electric power developments in North Finland. (Source: *Voima ja valo*, 1954.)

---

[1] Cf. also W. R. Mead, "Finland and the U.S.S.R.", *Geography*, XLI, 3, 190.

government ownership or control of plants. The hot springs in the south-west of the country provide a limited source of alternative heat, making a significant contribution to greenhouse cultivation and to domestic hot-water supply in Reykjavik. Production of electric energy was 678 mill. kWh in 1965.

(c) Norway

Norway, a classical land of waterfalls to nineteenth-century tourists, has become a virtual paradise for twentieth-century water-power engineers. A high percentage of steep gradients, often combined with an equable rate of flow, give to its water-courses virtues not commonly encountered. The shining falls of John Murray's Blue Books are now scientific-ally recorded according to their heads of water. It is estimated that Norway has over 600 falls, with a head of water exceeding 300 m.; while the average utilised head is not far short of 250 m. The most spectacular head—exceeding 900 m.—is at Indre Ålvik on the Hardanger fiord. These stand in marked contrast to those of Sweden and Finland.

Moreover, these heads of water are fre-quently backed by lake reservoirs. Where reservoirs are missing, modern engineering methods can often employ drainage diversions to maximise a head of water or to regularise the volume of flow. The régime of Norway's waterways varies from west to east and from south-west to north, but the Atlantic in-fluence is sufficiently strong to guarantee a strong "pluvial" predominance. In general, the rivers of Norway do not conform to the relatively simple rhythms of most of the waterways of Finland and Sweden. One reason for this is the greater range of altitudes at which their collecting basins are likely to be situated. Moreover, while temperature vari-ability is more likely to affect the behaviour of many Finnish and Swedish rivers, rainfall variability will most certainly be a primary influence on the western flank.

At its most simple, the Norwegian power potential may be grouped into four primary districts.[1] The first is western Norway (also em-bracing for this purpose Vest- and Aust-Agder). Here, modest plants which have been installed for two generations beside low-level falls are juxtaposed with increasingly elaborate under-takings, which exploit the marked altitudinal changes in level. In size, these modern in-stallations commonly exceed 10,000 kW., and may be as much as 100,000 kW. More than a score are either in process of construction or already in operation. Their greatest con-centration is on the Sogn (for example, Høyanger) and the Hardanger (for example, Tyssefallene and Ålvik). Here power sup-ply occurs beside deep, open water and has directly favoured heavy industry. This in-dustry, strictly localised in area, provides a marked contrast to the older established work-shop industries, originally located in response to water-power, and subsequently expanded with conversion to small-scale electrical power. The difference between the two is illustrated by the heavy electro-metallurgy of Ålvik and the textile workshops of Sogn and Fjordane. Hordaland and Rogaland are the richest fiord *fylker* in energy, but in spite of large-scale developments, not more than 10% of their potential power has been so far exploited.

Norway's most extended rivers occur in the eastern dales—a second definable district. On the map, the broad valleys of Gudbrands-dal and Østerdal, with the Lågen and Glom-ma rivers respectively, make the greatest impression. Yet Oppland and Hedmark—the *fylker* with which they are respectively most closely associated have relatively little energy —both potentially and actually. It is es-sentially in the dales of Buskerud and Tele-mark to the west and in Østfold with the lower Glomma to the south-east that ex-ploitation has been most active. In the Måna valley of Telemark, the Rjukan power plant at Vemork led the way to the expansion of large-scale enterprise. Two additional water sites have been subsequently added to Rjukan I: they are Såheim and Møsvatn, both in the Måna valley. The five Rjukan plants (with their great underground generating chambers and tunnels) are oriented to the needs of Norsk Hydro and are basic to its electro-chemical industries. Telemark, with current developments at Tokke, still leads the way in large-scale enterprise.

[1] Norwegian power resources are reviewed systematically in A. Solem (ed.), *Norske kraftverker*, Oslo, 1954.

Trøndelag, divided into a northern and southern half, lies at the fulcrum of Norway, midway between south and north. It claims some of the broadest, open valley landscapes of the country, and is accordingly less rich in resources than many parts of Norway. In potential and degree of development, it may bear comparison with the valleys of Gudbrandsdal and Østerdal.

North Norway, the final region, presents two contrasting halves. Nordland has reserves rivalled only by Sogn and Hordaland; but their exploitation has been much delayed. Glomfiord and Røssåga are the two principal sites harnessed, and their output is directed largely to the steel plant at Mo i Rana. In Finnmark and Troms rivers are shorter, altitudes lower, lakes fewer, precipitation smaller and the impact of winter icing more pronounced. Indeed, their resources are the smallest and least developed of any in Norway.

Viewing the Norwegian power picture as a whole, 80% of the resources are located to the south of the Trondheim depression—thus offering a primary contrast to the Finnish and Swedish situations. Unlike those of Sweden, Norwegian power-plants are not nationally integrated, though there are fourteen regional grids. In contrast to Finland, integration is no easy matter. The nature of the terrain makes not merely for difficulties in the construction of power-lines, but presents equal problems of maintenance. The advantages of integration must be seriously balanced against the costs of maintenance. As in Sweden, the growing size of power plants, their elaboration (as in the ninefold plant of the Tokke project) and/or the increasing remoteness of their location concentrates their construction in state or municipal hands. In Norway, with so many outstanding alternative sites and only about a fifth of its supplies harnessed, there is a hard tug-of-war between rival schemes.

(d) Sweden

Sweden was the earliest Scandinavian country to make notable efforts to harness hydro-electric power, and it still leads the way in the intensification and integration of pro-

duction. The sequence of development of hydro-electric power in Sweden and the swift expansion of the area served by this resource are shown in the appendices to Filip Hjulström, *Sveriges elektrifiering*, quoted above.

Sweden's resources, which are unevenly distributed, can be divided geographically into three areas. Peninsular Sweden, to the south of the great lakes axis, has a considerable number of exploited water-courses providing relatively small-scale supplies of energy. They were easily harnessed in the early stages of hydro-electric power and were speedily seized upon. The Lagan provides an example of a river originating in the Småland plateau which has experienced full-scale modern development. Secondly, along the great lakes axis of Sweden, major and minor enterprises have grown simultaneously. Trollhättan falls on the Göta river were the initial development in the west; Klarälven provided power sites on the northern edges; while in the east the lower reaches of Dalälven witnessed hydro-electric control following the industrial concentrations which occurred there during the late nineteenth century. Intermediately, the long-exploited local power sites of Bergslagerna swung over from water-mill to turbine.

The third resource area is north Sweden, and its rivers may be subdivided into a southerly and northerly group. To the southerly group belong those of Jämtland, Medelpad and Ångermanland. The southern area focuses on Storsjön, commands the Trondheim depression and drains by way of the Indalsälv, one of the most highly developed of Swedish rivers.[1] To its immediate north is the Ångerman river, and immediate south, the Ljungan. The second division consists of the well-defined complex of Norrland rivers, principal among which from north to south are Kalix, Lule, Pite, Skellefte, Vindel and Umeälv. Their valleys, striking in a northwest to south-east direction have four distinct sections: (a) a mountain gathering ground; (b) a piedmont lake zone falling to (c) an entrenched plateau tract interrupted by falls and rapids, differentially excavated but not uncommonly 100 ft. or more below the level of

---

[1] F. Hjulström, "Elektrifierings Utveckling i Sverige", *Ymer*, 1941, 107–41; H. Nelson, *Indalsälven, Svensk geografisk årsbok*, 1946, 141–71.

the surrounding country; and (*d*) a broad, boulder-strewn, much-braided estuarine tract across the emergent coastal plain. Four-fifths of Sweden's hydro-electric power resources occur in this region.

Swedish rivers at large have a relatively low head of water—more than half of the water-power sites offering a head of 10 m. or less. The rivers also present regional contrasts in their régimes. From Torneälv to Dalälven, they display a "mountain régime" and react strongly to the prolonged winter freeze. Their peak flow succeeds the snow-melt in May, when problems of water control affect power plants as well as the agricultural flood-plains. High-altitude tributaries guarantee a regular summer flow, but low water marks the winter. The seasonal variation of flow is less pronounced in the rivers of southern Sweden, where a more distinctly "pluvial régime" balances the "glacial régime" of the north; but the south is more sensitive to drought conditions. As Sweden has outgrown its southern power, it has thus geared itself to the more pronounced rhythms of northern supply.

Sweden's water-power resources have been called into operation in a fairly distinct chronological sequence. The exploitation of southern resources has preceded that of the northern partly because of their proximity to centres of demand, partly because of their more easily negotiated form. There has been, of course, some simultaneous development in the north and in the south. For example, limited industrial and domestic demand called for power development in the northern half of the kingdom before the advance of the large-scale industry to Norrland or the emergence of the long-distance power-line. Again, the early need of transport for electricity resulted

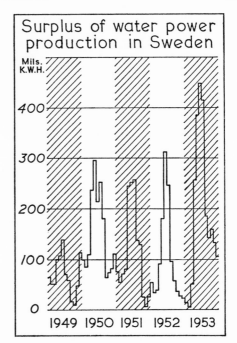

FIG. 63. Variations in Swedish water-power supply. (After *Svensk vattenkraft föreningens publikationer*, 1954, 11.)

in an almost precocious appearance of power plants in Swedish Lapland. The state-sponsored power plant at Porjus, on Lule river, built before the First World War, illustrates this point. It is, however, a difference in the intensity of exploitation which distinguishes the several parts of Sweden. Over most of southern Sweden, a maximum exploitation has already been achieved. There are also certain regional differences in the size of plants. Of the 1,100 stations listed in the annual statement of the Water Power Board, the northern half of the country claims the smallest percentage, but most large-scale

TABLE 18

IMPORTS OF FUEL (1965)

(*in* 1,000 *metric tons*)

Country		Coal and Coke	Crude Petroleum	Motor Spirit	Other fuel oils
Denmark	. .	4,486	3,396	1,130	5,548
Finland	. .	3,352	2,308	27	2,884
Iceland	. .	13		58	352
Norway	. .	1,047	2,754	498	2,326
Sweden	. .	3,110	3,824	2,423	12,288

(Source: The comparative tables from the *Yearbook of Nordic Statistics*, Stockholm, 1967.)

plants occur there. Increase in size of plant and in the attention paid to northern power sites proceed simultaneously.

In northern Sweden policy appears to be directed towards a river-by-river assault. So far, the main regional developments have occurred on Indalsälvern with fifteen neighbouring rivers and upon the Luleälv. A cluster of nearly a score of plants, including major stations such as Krångede, Midskog and Stadsforsen makes the Indals area the largest single concentration of power production in Sweden. It is at the same time the largest single exporting centre of power in Sweden. The largest exporting plant, however, is now found in Arctic Sweden, where six miles below the Porjus plant, Harsprånget has been called into existence. Harsprånget has a capacity of 350,000 kW., and is capable of producing one-tenth of the national power output. It has called for the construction of a barrage 164 ft. high and 2,500 ft. broad across the Lule river; it claims to have generators surpassed in capacity only by those of the Grand Coulee, and its ultimate average yearly production will be identical with that of Donzère-Mondragon. The assault on the Umeälv is imminent.

THE ROLE OF THERMO-ELECTRIC POWER IN SCANDINAVIA

The energy picture of Europe shows a broad east–west zone of thermal power sandwiched between a northern zone of hydro-electric power and southern—Alpine—zone of hydro development.[1] Denmark lies in the thermo-electric area; so, too, does much of southern and south-western Sweden. But the distribution of thermo-electric plants in Scandinavia and Finland is much more widespread than maps suggest. Thermo-electric installations are complementary in the fullest sense of the word to hydro-electric installations, and the zone in which they are marginal has a natural tendency to broaden. There are wide variations, but a common tendency for the two types of power to expand side by side. Thermo-electricity is based principally upon coal and varying kinds of oil.

Thermo-electricity is most important in Denmark—where hydro-electric energy provides about 1% of the power. The steam turbine dominates; the diesel motor is subsidiary. As with water-power plants, there is a marked tendency towards a concentration in larger units, and plans are to reduce them to eleven. Although there is regional small-scale employment of peat, Denmark's power is based essentially upon imported coal and oil. Pre-war Denmark had the largest *per capita* consumption of coal of any country in the world; during the war, it used up to 6 million tons per annum of peat substitute. In 1960, it consumed only 100,000 tons of peat and lignite.

Within the hydro-electric area, thermo-electric plants exist to fill in permanent regional deficiencies. Finland provides a good illustration. It has a coal import of several million tons per annum, most of which is directed to heating plants (gas, in fact, as well as electricity; with the gas stove making an unexpectedly widespread appearance in Helsinki kitchens). One-third of Finland's generated power derives from thermal sources. Its dependence upon thermo-electric power has been increased by the loss of major sources of

TABLE 19

PRODUCTION OF ELECTRIC ENERGY, 1965
(Millions of kWh.)

Country	Production		Consumption
	Total	*Of which water power*	*kWh. per inhabitant*
Denmark . .	7,379	25	1,710
Finland . .	14,515	9,354	3,535
Iceland . .	678	644	2,917
Norway . .	48,950	48,858	11,283
Sweden . .	49,093	46,431	6,243

(Source: The comparative tables from the *Yearbook of Nordic Statistics*, Stockholm, 1967.)
Cf. "Transfers of Electric Power across European Frontiers", *op. cit.*, Maps 1 and 2, and F. Hjulström, *op. cit.*, Map 20.

supply on the Vuoksi river (e.g. Rouhiala) in 1944. In addition, thermo-electric plants make a primary contribution to the power supply of the Göteborg and Stockholm areas; though only one twentieth part of the energy produced in Sweden derives from thermal sources.

Thermo-electric plants may also make a local auxiliary contribution. At times of seasonal deficiency—for example, during summer low water or winter low water as in north Norway (cf. Chapter VIII), they may be temporarily employed. Imatra power plant, in east Finland, has a steam auxiliary at Vanaja. Many of the larger timber mills or paper and pulp concerns have a thermo-electric installation as a standby in case of emergency. Imported coal provides an October–April supplement for Mänttä mills (cf. Chapter XI); while its cost for the paper industries in south Sweden is brought out by Olof Lindberg (cf. Chapter XI). A 7,500 kWh. steam turbine plant serves as a reserve for Reykjavik's supply. In isolated islands, e.g. the Westman islands of south Iceland, small diesel electric installations are a great boon. To attempt to ensure against cyclical water deficiency in contrast to seasonal shortage is almost impossible. Cyclical deficiencies even occur in Norway, where it is ironical to find from time to time that under-production and power rationing are serious national problems.[1]

In the long-period planning of electrical output in Scandinavia, thermal plants play an integral part, and their substitutability as well as complementarity is an unexpected feature. In Norway, for example, there has been prolonged discussion as to whether to build up hydro-electric plants sufficiently to guarantee an adequate supply in dry years or whether to ensure against the threat of drought by the construction of thermo-electric installations.[2] In both cases, heavy capital investment is entailed, but the latter may be the more economic alternative. Sweden is also seriously concerned with long-period planning of thermo-electricity. For some years past, exploratory glances have been cast at a future in which

Swedish demands exceed hydro-electric potentialities. Two supplementary sources are suggested.[3] In the first place Sweden has a great wealth of peat; though only about a tenth of its resources are in the south. It is estimated that Sweden could employ the peat equivalent of 5 million tons of coal per annum without much difficulty (it was, in fact, employing $1\frac{1}{2}$ million tons of peat per annum during the war in an emergency organisation). Secondly, the oil shales of the Swedish midlands—focused on Närke with poorer extensions in Östergötland and Västergötland—offer an alternative source of energy. The Longström field at Kvarntorp, where oil reduction from shales takes place through electrical heating, has a proposed production of 700,000 tons per annum by 1960.[4] Iceland's simultaneous experiments with natural steam for the production of electricity are logical.

The presence of and proposals for thermo-electrical developments in classical territories of hydro-electricity speak volumes of economics. Admittedly, the source of their energy is neither free nor regenerative; but given normal access to coal and oil, a flow of energy can be derived from them at lower installation costs than those involved in most hydro-power sites. This flow is not affected by variations of discharge, and is adaptable to demand. Each Northern Country has a hydro-thermal cost ratio, and development programmes must pay increasing regard to it. The ratio has become the more critical with the growth of oil refining in Scandinavia.

Substitutes for electric power are not restricted to thermal sources. Atomic power plants naturally interest Scandinavia. The extent of this interest will vary according to the availability of existing potential water-power. Norway, for example, discounts large-scale atomic development. The cost of building atomic power plants in Norway is estimated to be much greater than that of building hydro-electric power plants—at the current rate of costing, three or four times. It is a reflection upon comparative costs that

[1] O. Strand, "Norsk vattenkraftpolitik", *Svenska vattenkfraftföreningens publikationer*, 1949, 406, 4.   See also J. C. Pugh 'The floating power stations of Scandinavia", *Geography*, **47**, 1962.
[2] E. Blomquist, "Dagens kraftfrågor", *Norske kraftverker*, 1953.
[3] *Svenska Vattenkraftföreningens Publikationer*, 1952, 428, 7.
[4] F. Ljungström, "Skifferöljefrågan", *Teknisk tidskrift*, 1951, 33–9.

while Norway hopes to export power at three-tenths of a penny per unit from the new plant near Trondheim to Stockholm, the cost per unit of electricity from atomic plants is provisionally estimated at twice that figure. Sweden, however, contemplating exhaustion of its resources by 1980, is already operating atomic energy plants. Finland is constructing its first plant near Kotka.

THE DEMAND FOR POWER

To guarantee a uniform supply to a uniform demand would present few problems for the producing plant; but to resolve a continuous disharmony is a task which calls for action at a number of levels. First of all, there is a steadily increasing demand; though the rate of increase differs regionally. This implies action at the state level. In order to keep pace with this increase, most of the Northern Countries aim to expand their annual output by 10% of their currently generated power. Remembering the differing impact of the war years upon the component states, it is unfair to regard the development during 1938–52 as fair for purposes of comparison. During that period, it was natural that Sweden should approach most closely to its objective; but even Sweden only achieved 7%. The rate of production in Norway has gathered swift momentum in recent years—the 100,000 kW. addition per annum between 1945 and 1947 having been increased to 250,000 kW. by 1952–6. Following the rapid decline of the war years, the average annual rate of increase has quickened in postwar Finland to 10%.[1]

In the second place, demand is subject to substantial seasonal variations. These seasonal variations result principally from changing domestic requirements. Though there may be some degree of complementarity between the peak demands of industry and the home during the round of the day, there is a marked winter peak and summer trough. This rhythm is initiated by a domestic consumption which calls for a quarter of the Swedish electricity output and a third of the Norwegian. The peak demand occurs when power potentiality is below its maximum. It is partly offset by storage lakes and dams on the supply side. Indeed, much of the capital investment in power sites represents an attempt to cope with maximum demands—and it is a primary cost which must be carried at all periods (i.e. the greater span of time) when demand is not at its peak.

Domestic consumption represents such a large proportion of the total partly because of distributional policies and partly because of population densities. In most parts of Denmark, for example, density of rural settlement favours widespread rural electrification. Elsewhere, it is consistent with the "welfare state" to carry electricity to as wide a section of the community as possible. Rural electrification has a history going back to the turn of the century, and the results are striking. Thus, Norway estimates that in the south-east of the country, 99% of the population is supplied with electricity; while only 4% (or 150,000) of the inhabitants are not served. In Denmark, 95% of the farm population is served; in Sweden, 93%; in Finland, 75%. Even Iceland claims that electricity is within the reach of three-quarters of the population.

Bearing in mind the size of the demand and

TABLE 20

WATER POWER IN 1965

Country	Capacity, 1000 kW.		Energy, million kWh.	
	Potential	Developed end of 1965	Potential	Produced in 1965
Denmark .		9		25
Finland . .	3,600	1,925	18,000	9,354
Iceland . .	4,730	127	35,000	644
Norway. .	16,424	5,990	143,874	48,858
Sweden . .	20,150	9,300	176,500	44,700

(Source: The comparative tables from the *Yearbook of Nordic Statistics*, Stockholm, 1967.)

its character, it is not surprising that the capital requirements of electrical undertakings in the Northern Countries should be high. A quarter of the total national investment in Norway and Sweden is absorbed by them.

POTENTIALITIES IN THE NORTHERN COUNTRIES

To plan for future demand calls for an assessment of potentialities. Such assessments can be so variable that the maximum potentials listed a generation ago have already been exceeded by today's developed power. The concept of potentiality is not static. First, it is subject to a threefold interpretation; there is the gross potential of the resource, the technical potential and the economic potential. Each of these is liable to change. The economic potentials as summarised by engineers in Finland, Norway and Sweden are given in Fig. 64. The total economic water-power potential is outlined against the background of the major power regions, and a very approximate dispersal of potential site development is added.

In the midst of changing potentialities, the relationship between the individual countries is not likely to show marked alteration. To-day, Norway has twice as many kWh. available *per capita* as Sweden, five times as many as Finland and nine times as many as Denmark. Denmark, indeed, is one of the small number of European countries with a low energy potential stated in terms of domestic resources. Energy availability has an economic expression. Thus, the average price of electricity will remain much less in Norway than in Finland—with all the attendant advantages for industrial production. In Norway, the cost of power to the consumer is a sixth of that to his Danish counterpart—and with coal costs rising more sharply than water-power costs, the difference is likely to be increased.

Potentiality changes largely as a result of technical progress and, more than anything else, technical progress has promoted an increase in the scale of operations. On the physical side, this permits the harnessing of resources hitherto beyond the technical scope

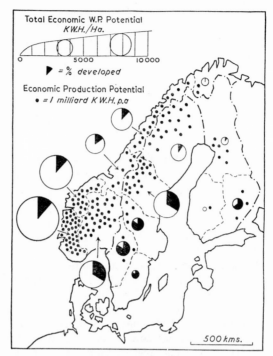

FIG. 64. Potential hydro-electric power in Scandinavia and Finland. (Source: *Hydro-electric Potential in Europe*, Geneva, 1953.)

of engineers.[1] On the economic side, there are two consequences: first, an undeniable tendency for cost of output to diminish; secondly, increase in the size of operations calls for a scale of investment possible only for the state or the large corporations.[2]

Potentialities change in another way. As prospects of direct exploitation are narrowed down, the more efficient use of available resources is encouraged. The drive towards efficiency will tend to be stronger in countries, e.g. Finland, where resources are not abundant. To conserve water run-off more effectively, to maximise heads of water by underground work (tunnelling now costs a third of its pre-war price), to reduce losses in transmission, all aid in an economic climate where conservation succeeds to exploitation. Denmark and Norway are especially concerned about the potentialities of North Sea gas and oil. Their claims have also been resolved with those of their neighbour states.

[1] *Prospects Opened Up by Technical Advances in Electric Power Production*, Geneva, 1952.
[2] M. Rousselier, "The Size of Hydro-electric Power Plants" *Transactions of the 4th World Power Conference.* 1952, 4.

Chapter X

THE NETWORK OF COMMUNICATIONS

"Ursa major and minor with Orion serve them as a compass ... in the long winter nights".
Elias Lagus, *Svenska vetenskapliga handlingar*, 1772

WHEEL AND RUDDER

IN his *General and Classical Atlas* of 1804, Edward Paterson wrote beside the map of Scandinavia: "The ancients knew very little of Sweden and Norway, which they imagined to be vast islands." Not least in the matter of communications, they have behaved as if this were a fact. Historically, movement by water has frequently offered less resistance than movement by land, in the same way that the sea has frequently been easier to "handle" than the soil. Water has been fairly easy to negotiate; land has commonly been difficult. Water routes, moreover, have generally been more direct than those overland. Movement by water remains of continuing significance for the domestic economies of the north independently of its national contribution through the mercantile marine.

Water control and administration have also been interrelated. Thus, the outlines of many Scandinavian and Finnish parishes indicate that lake, river or fiord have been central unifying features and that administrative boundaries have slowly crystallised in the intervening no man's land. This intervening area may have been forest, bogland or fell. At a higher administrative level, the historical outlines of the northern kingdoms tell of the possibilities offered by water communication and the technical mastery of them. The medieval realm of Norway was an expression of water routes; the Renaissance empire of Sweden was a sea state based upon technical and political mastery of the Baltic.

If relative accessibility by water is the first transport feature, relative inaccessibility across land is a contrasting second characteristic Over the greater part of Scandi-

navia and Finland the communicational network remains as thinly spread as almost any where in Europe. Inaccessibility has frequently been due to vegetation. There is, for example, much historical evidence of the role played by the woodland as a barrier in international as well as domestic association. The fells of Norway bore the traditional military routes, lifted above the forest obstruction of the valleys; the open heath of Jutland was the traditional country of movement. But although Scandinavia and Finland present a low-density picture of communications when viewed in their entirety, there is naturally a differential intensity of communications. This is eloquently expressed in the contrast between the northern part of the Scandinavian peninsula and the Swedish midlands. In Fig. 65 the black areas represent territory more than 5 km. from a motorable highway.[1]

In most countries lines of communication fall short of the ideal, rarely in Europe more than in some of the Northern Countries. The growing appreciation of Scandinavian wealth enables deficiencies to be overcome so that in few parts of Europe today is the struggle with transport problems more lively. Old means of transport and new means frequently expand side by side. The expansion of highways and the multiplication of motor vehicles upon existing highways have by no means reduced the need for railways over much of the area. Railway expansion continues in Norway and Finland. It is usually single-track, in keeping with the principle of quantitative coverage. From the outset railways have tended to be centralised in Scandinavia, and have generally lacked the competitive patterns promoted where private construction has operated. As a result, competition in trans-

[1] A supplement to this picture is given in the detailed accessibility diagram for Norrbotten prepared by G. Hoppe, *op. cit.*, Plate IX, and cf. also A. Jonasson, *Befolkningen och näringslivet i Mellansverige, 1865–1940*, Göteborg.

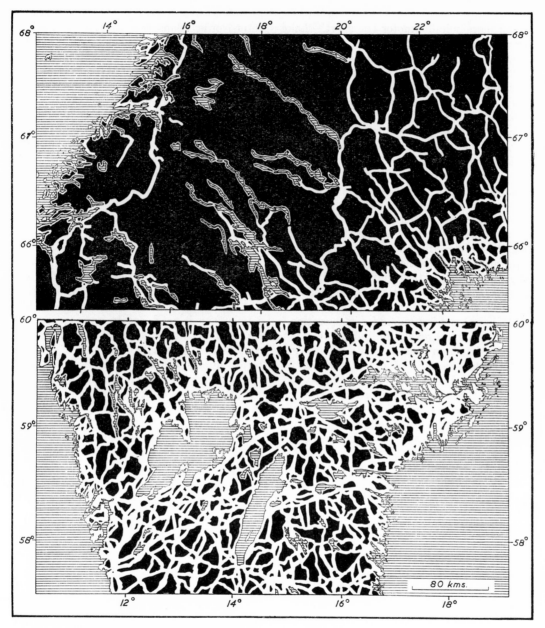

FIG. 65. Contrasts in accessibility—South and North Scandinavia. The degree of accessibility is in relation to motorable highway or navigable waterway. (Based upon the highway pattern of the 1:1,000,000 map of Northern Europe.)

port services has emerged relatively recently; though there has been a frequent tug-of-war between the several interests which have tried to attract transport routes through particular districts.

Complementarity as much as competition characterises the four primary means of transport in Scandinavia and Finland. Certain railway tracks in Sweden have been closed, though this is to be explained as much by changing resource background as by the rise of more suitable motor transport. Lake steamers in Finland have been reduced in numbers, and the skerry steamers in the Turku archipelago have lost pride of place over extended areas to bus and lorry services.[1] Again, there have been changes in the regional importance of fiord steamer and automobile in west Norway. The railway organisation, however, sets out to create its own complementary system of buses, to link separate sections of the line or to extend routes beyond existing railheads. Steamer and land services are similarly integrated in Norway.

The increasing proportion of national investment absorbed in the transport systems of Scandinavia and Finland reveals the degree of adjustment felt to be necessary. In Sweden, for example, 10% of the country's total investment is absorbed by the transport network and somewhat more than 8% of the country's total labour input is required for its operation.[2]

The mechanical revolution in Scandinavian transport has been possible only by accepting an increased measure of external economic dependence. The coming of the railway resulted in the increased import of coal; the coming of the automobile, the import of oil. Seaway and airway are similarly dependent. The search for alternative means of energy to maintain primary transport services has led locally to the use of birchwood fuel and intermittently to the employment of peat briquettes. More significantly, it has resulted in the extensive electrification of Swedish railroads and the increasing electrification of Norwegian railroads. In few countries in the world is there such a high degree of electrical development as in Sweden. Although Swedish railways have reacted more sharply to the motor vehicle than those of Norway or Finland, their comparative strength lies in their domestic source of energy.

As might be expected, the tradition of co-operation has encouraged integration and, where possible, standardisation between Scandinavia and Finland. Characteristic of inter-Nordic plans was that formulated for highways in Stockholm in 1950. Sweden, however, continues to use the left-hand side of the road!

TERRAIN AND TRANSPORT

Movement across the land is locally and regionally hampered by at least five physical facts—the intricate association of land and water, the pronounced changes of relief in the short distance, the wide variations of rock and soil type within the small area, the extensive forest cover and the frequently marked seasonal variations in the character of the terrain produced by winter conditions.

The intricate pattern of land and water is one expression of the dissection of the terrain. Anyone familiar with the map of Northern Europe will be aware of the spread of surface water, but the extensive boglands which supplement it (and are in some respects a legacy of its former broader extent) are not commonly appreciated. Features of historical interest in British transport evolution, such as Chat Moss, are insignificant compared with the expanse of Scandinavian mossland to be traversed or circumvented. It is not surprising to glean from the late nineteenth-century proceedings of the offices of communication for Sweden or Finland that the railway authorities were among the first promoters of large-scale drainage. With the growing weight of motor vehicles, peatlands take increasing toll of road construction.[3] The pattern of land and water has one expression in the shield area, a second in the fell and fiord land, and a third in the peninsular and islanded kingdom of Denmark.

In each instance it calls for transport adjustments. These take the form of ferries and bridges. Zachris Topelius, alert to Finland's communicational needs a hundred years ago and experienced in post-chasing over its roads, once pointed out to his students that there were eleven ferries between Oulu and Tornio. Without perhaps knowing his

[1] A. A Santti and O. Ihkinen, *Über die Wandlungen verkehrsgeographischer Verhaltnisse im Schärenhof vor Turku seit der letzen Jahrhundertwende*, Turku, 1954.

[2] C. W. Petrik, *Svenskt transportväsende*, Stockholm, 1952, and cf. L. Wahlbeck, "Investeringarna i vårt kommunikations-system och planerna för vägväsendets utbyggnad", *Ekonomisk samfundets tidskrift*, Helsingfors, 1956, 9.

[3] Cf. The distribution of "weak" places on the road map of Värmland in A. Westling, "Skogbruket och vägarna", *Svensk Skogsvårdsföreningens tidskrift*, 1956, **2**, 119.

sister Scandinavian countries so well, he was prompted to suggest that there was no country in Europe with so many bridges and ferries proportionate to the length of its roads. River, lake and salt-water channel continue to take their toll in the cost of construction and maintenance of bridges or in the delay in time imposed by ferries—Finland has over 100 ferries today. Written ferry laws in Norway go back to that of Magnus Lagabøter in 1274 and remain a persistent feature of highway regulations. Ferries imply a direct tax on movement as well as an indirect tax on time taken in movement. The 100 km. between Hundested and Grenaa in the Danish archipelago imposes, for example, 20 kronor on cars and 32 kronor on lorries. In order to overcome the communicational obstacle of the Great Belt, five rail ferries, completing twenty-five return journeys daily, and three car ferries completing nine return journeys daily are needed.[1] The major rail ferries of Denmark, which link Sjælland with the west, are among the longest of their kind. Plans to bridge the Øresund between Saltholm and Flinthamn (altogether 18 km. with the tunnel from Saltholm to Amager) are not likely to replace in the near future the rail ferries between Malmö and Copenhagen. The west coast of Norway, although it has an increasing number of suspension bridges, must remain a region of ferries.[2]

Today, there are approximately eighty major traffic ferries operating in Norway. The greatest water traverses are in the counties of Møre with Romsdal and Sogn with Fiordane. The heaviest bus traffic on Norway's fiord ferries is in Møre with Romsdal (23,000 vehicles, 1953) and Nordland (14,000 vehicles). Numerically, more lorries move over the ferries of Troms than over those of any other province.[3] Such ferries do not take into consideration the numerous regular water routes which tie together the more than 2,000 inhabited islands of Norway. Although the Scandinavians are bridge-builders by experi-

ence, with Norway numbering railway bridges alone by the thousand and Denmark's Storstrømmen bridge between Masnedø and Falster as the longest in Europe, most of the fiord and sound interruptions are unbridgeable. Nor need it be added that every bridge built or new highway opened in Norway's Westland occasions fierce debate. It will have an immediate effect on established water communications, and it will frequently have to be supported out of taxation to a greater extent than the existing subsidised water routes. Established bridges, moreover, have to be continuously renewed because of the growing weight of motor vehicles. In Sweden, for example, the marked increase of the 4–6-ton lorry over the 2–3-ton vehicle illustrates the problem.[4]

The dissection of the terrain also gives rise to abrupt changes of relief in the western half of the Scandinavian peninsula. An extreme example is provided by the Flåm railway, which descends nearly 900 m. to sea-level over a distance of 20 km. Moreover, abrupt changes in relief are exaggerated in their obstructiveness because they are accompanied by land and water intricacies. Relief forces diversion of routeways as much as water—or necessitates tunnelling which may outcost bridging. Norwegian railways, for example, have over 700 separate stretches of tunnel and they include one of the longest in Europe in West Agder. Tunnelling remains a lively topic in railway planning.[5] Though we may dispute the clinometric vision of Mr. Forrester, an English traveller to Valdres in 1818 who declared the pitch of the roads to attain sixty degrees, Norway has fought the battle of gradients hard in the interval. It is calculated that only about a fifth of Norway's track contrives to avoid gradient, but it is worth mentioning that most of its major upland lines support more gentle gradients than the major Alpine routes. The Dovre railway, for example, has a gradient of 1:55 against the Mont Cenis 1:33 and St. Gotthard 1:38. It

[1] W. Herchend, *Nordisk Järnbanetidskrift*, 1951, **77**, 8, 245-7.
[2] Some idea of the discontinuity of the highway pattern is provided by the maps accompanying Sigurd Malmo and Tore Sund, *Bergen's Communications with its Neighbouring Counties* (Bergen, 1954).
[3] Statistical data are given annually in *Norsk vegtidsskrift*.
[4] A. Westling, *op. cit.*, pp. 107-22.
[5] Cf. references to the contemporary Bergen-Tunestveit tunnel in *Innstilling fra Jernbanekommisjonen for 1949*, Stavanger, 1953, 204-15.

goes without saying that gradients will affect speeds and engine types. Gradients in Swedish Norrland, for example, do not permit the same speeds as in southern Sweden. Much of the level track also suffers from unavoidable curves. And in addition to all these problems of slope, avalanche, landslide and stonefall exact a regular toll from the Transport Ministry of Norway in particular.[1] A kilometre-long wooden canopy as a protection against snowfall in Setesdal may be instanced. Recalling winter snow conditions, the contemporary engineer scents his way across high-level routes with almost animal cunning. He may call in the aid of a whole range of unexpected specialists. Among them, the botanist is not the least effective; for plant morphology as well as ecology may be a valuable key to snow depth and snow duration.[2]

The nature of the land automatically affects construction costs. The railways of Sweden cost about twice as much per kilometre of construction as those of Denmark; those of Norway about three times as much as those of Denmark. And, within the compass of the major Scandinavian peninsula, there is a latitudinal tax which causes a substantial difference between constructional costs in the south and the north. In Norway, for example, the Ofoten railway cost two and a half times more per kilometre of track than the railway from Meråker to Trondheim. From current accounts kept for the construction of the new Finnish lines to, e.g., Taivalkoski and Juankoski, it is possible to compare the relative costs of clearance, drainage, stone removal and other operations. A German economic geographer has an appropriate phrase for such a terrain—"*eisenbahnfeindliche Landesnatur*".[3] It defies succinct translation, but sums up the totality of natural obstacles to railway construction.

THE PERSISTENT WATERWAY

Inland waterways have been of particular consequence for Sweden and Finland; coastal waters have been more important for Norway and Denmark. This is not to imply, of course, that coastal waterways have been unimportant for Sweden and Finland or that inland waterways have not been of regional consequence for Norway. The rivers of Scandinavia—although frequently of considerable length and volume by West European standards, are not generally navigable—save for small boats over limited stretches and, perhaps, for a restricted period. The lake systems, however, are eminently negotiable during open water. They assumed a peak of importance following the introduction of lake steamers and before the revolution in land transport. Regionally, they have remained of consequence until the intensification of automobile transport.

The discontinuity as well as the continuity of the water systems attracted attention from the first. Testimony to it is borne by early travellers, who were struck by elaborate portages or impressed by the skilful rapid shooting of native rivermen (still a tourist attraction on Torni river). It is hardly surprising that points of obstruction should be the object of early consideration. Over 200 years ago, a commission was appointed to deal with the improvement of Sweden's natural waterways. The canal fever of Great Britain was transmitted, in part, to Northern Europe; though the more far-sighted administrators realised that the needs of the north differed from those of England. The initial accents were on short interlinking waterways between major water-bodies or upon the type of canal advocated in Robert Fulton's *Treatise on the Improvement of Canal Navigation, exhibiting the numerous advantages to be derived from Small Canals* (London, 1796). The cost of lock construction was regularly quoted. H. G. Porthan, for example, noted that thirty-six falls or rapids on Kokemäki river would have to be eliminated before it became navigable for shipping. It was suggested in some quarters that wheels might be fitted to

---

[1] Cf. in this connection the alternative routes for the Bergen railway to avoid winter snow. The maps are in the historical collection of *Norges Geografiske Opmaaling*.
[2] R. Nordhagen, "Hvorledes vegetasjonen i høgfjellet registerer snødekkets tykkelse og varighet", *Norsk vegtidsskrift* 1952, 2–4.
[3] M. Rudolph, "Geographie der Landstrassen und Eisenbahnen von Norwegen", *Petermanns Mitteilungen*, Gotha, 1929, XLIV.

boats to enable them to be dragged by ob-structions. Canals, too, implied towpaths and draught horses.

And to what end were these improvements directed? In Britain, coal, lime, clay and bricks were carried to industrial markets. None of these commodities entered the prospective canal traffic of the north—except possibly iron ore on a canalised Lule river (as proposed by the Gällivare company in 1864). Contrastingly, timber and tar could be satisfactorily moved with the existing means available. Two points were made. First, the construction of canals might ease the movement of farm products from interior districts to coastal points of consumption or export. Secondly, famine conditions in the interior could be ameliorated if occasion arose. It was to be some decades before a complaint raised by Porthan in respect of Finland (but equally applicable to its northern neighbours) was met —that the full employment of lakes, rivers and streams awaited the preparation of satisfactory maps.

The introduction of steam navigation to the Scandinavian lakes and the development of deeper draught canals ran side by side. In Finland, for example, the first lake steamer was assembled at Siikaniemi wharf by Hackman and Co. of Viipuri in 1846; lake survey maps were begun in the 1860s, and by 1875 more than a hundred steamers were operating on lake routes. Canals, as Gabriel von Bonsdorff put it,[1] meant that the entire lakeland interiors of the Northern Countries would become great *skärgårdar*, with the inhabitants enjoying all the benefits accruing to the coastal skerries. Nature had, in fact, directed the way and its "finger-writing statesmen could not overlook". With the Suez in mind, he engaged in what the geographer Edmund Halley would have called a piece of "fulsome panegyrick"—"Päijänne is our Mediterranean: the Baltic our Indian Ocean!" The importance of all these water routes was impressed by the first map of Finland's communicational system in *Tidning för Finlands Kommunikationer* (May 1st, 1874). The canal accompany-

ing these developments was the Saimaa Canal, which linked Finland's largest system of inland lakes directly with the Gulf of Finland in the hinterland of Viipuri. The waterway, stepping up 76 m. in twenty-seven locks, was calculated both to eliminate the 30-mile overland portage between Lappeenranta and the coast, and to increase the absolute traffic. It had been projected for 350 years and petitioned for thirty before its opening in 1856. Supporters submitted calculated arguments in its favour. Thus E. von Rosenkampff demonstrated that a quarter of a million man-days per annum could be saved on transport alone. The canal reached its maximum importance between 1920 and 1940, bearing half of Finland's canal-borne commerce and contributing to the fact that Viipuri was Finland's chief export harbour. In 1944, by the Russian peace settlement, the canal was severed and salt-water access for a full quarter of Finland eliminated. The re-opening of the canal through Russian territory represents a new chapter in Finnish-Russian cooperation.

More ambitious than the Saimaa Canal was "Sweden's blue ribbon"—the Göta Canal— which had been a vision fondly nourished by twelve generations of enthusiasts before it became a reality.[2] Lakes Vänern, Vättern, Hjälmaren and Mälaren, with their related waterways, were regarded as a potential link between the Baltic and Skaggerak. J. Oddy's *European Commerce* (London, 1805) anticipated the canal keenly for commercial reasons. And, for a fee of five guineas a day, Thomas Telford came to Sweden in August 1806 to examine the engineering possibilities. Among Swedish protagonists and pamphleteers, none was more energetic than Balthazar von Platen, and in some ways he was the father of the scheme. The eventual series of canals, which created the shipway enabling Sweden to avoid Danish waters and payment of the Sound Dues, was completed after twenty-two years in 1832. It was never a complete financial success; though the western portion of the system; from Lake Vänern to the Skagerrak coast has carried a substantial

---

[1] *Helsingfors Tidningar*, 1857, I, 2.
[2] S. E. Bring, *Göta Kanals Historia*, Uppsala, 1922–30. It gave rise to an interesting set of plans—*General kart öfver Göta kanalen*, Stockholm, 1808, devised by C. G. Forsell, containing the maps, plans and profiles belonging to Telford's designs.

commodity traffic. This "State Ditch", as it was widely called, remains a picturesque folly, better known by tourists than industrialists today.

Canals, of course, were to encounter vigorous competition with the ensuing interest in railways. When it was debated whether canal or railway should be constructed to link Helsinki to the interior lakes, J. V. Snellman pointed out that railways would be available for transport for ten or eleven months of the year, whereas canals and waterways could be used only for five or six months.[1] Speed and mobility, however, were to win a victory for rail over water. "Time is money" was a Victorian proverb framed on walls even in nineteenth-century Scandinavia.

Coastal navigation is also a persistent feature of the North European transport system. In many instances, coastal routes provide the only links between settlements. Precise figures concerning shipping engaged in domestic movement are not readily available on a comparative basis for the Northern Countries. However, Norway probably has 250,000 tons, Sweden, 100,000 and Finland 70,000 tons engaged in cabotage. It is an activity which has felt the transforming touch of the steamship.

The time-table is an excellent means of reviewing the changing tempo of transport. A succession of Norwegian time-tables may be taken by way of illustration. Time-tables were first published by the *Marine and Post Department* in the early 1870s—every Thursday in summer. By then, *Nordenfjeldske* and *Bergenske Steamship Company* boats were running regular schedules from the southern Norwegian ports to Tromsø and Hammerfest. From here, there was an independent service to coastal settlements of Troms and Finnmark. A glance at the 1871 time-table shows that from March to August there was a fast steamer weekly; but no regular passenger communication at all in December and January. On some occasions in the 1870s, there was what might be called a "Christmas ship", which left Trondheim in mid-December and continued all the way to Varangerfiord.

Winter services had improved by the end of the century, but even down to 1914 there was no substantial modification. By 1910, some special goods routes had come into operation to meet the seasonal requirements of the fisheries. The Murmansk trade was also being conducted by regular steamships; north Norway had a weekly summer route to Archangel and there was a monthly winter service to smaller settlements along the Russian Arctic coast. By 1914, express steamers had reached their maximum speed—covering the distance from Vadsø to Trondheim in roughly four days. There is a daily express steamer on the Trondheim–Kirkenes run throughout the greater part of the year at the present time.[2] For some decades the steamship meant as much in the south as in the north. Before the Bergen–Oslo railway was built, the only alternative to the summer post-road over the *vidde* was the sea route via Kristiansand, Stavanger and Haugesund. The daily service took about four days—much the same as that from Trondheim to the north-eastern outposts of Norway.

Another feature demonstrated by the coastal time-tables is the multiplication of local webs within the national network. All of these have helped to emphasise the regularity of contacts with an increasing number of places. The 1890 time-table, for example, listed 24 regular routes in Oslo fiord, 41 in Vestlandet, 7 in Sørlandet, 5 in Nordland, 2 in Finnmark and 1 in Troms. This regularity aided the tourist who was already "discovering" western Norway in the last quarter of the nineteenth century. The same time-table also enables one to assess the relative importance of rail and coast routes in 1890. Fifteen principal rail routes were balanced by twenty-three principal coastal routes. Coastal routes have multiplied, though not proportionately, with the passage of time.

Sometimes canal and coastal navigation have joined hands. Where routes along the coast are capable of shortening at reasonable outlay, canalisation has been carried out. Thus, there are twenty-two already improved stretches on the coastal route from Göteborg

[1] A. Fabritius, *Återblick på järnvägsväsendets första utvecklingsskede i Finland*, Helsingfors, 1887.
[2] *Innstilling fra Jernbanekommisjonen*, op. cit., pp. 384–6.

to Strömstad—the line of Sweden's principal west coast cabotage. There is also a general plan for the improvement of Sweden's harbours and fairways. Sweden, in particular, is interested in the improvement of its skerry fairways.

ACROSS THE SEAS

Among the most remarkable relics in the story of Scandinavian transport are the Viking ships at Bygdøy Museum, outside Oslo. They are symbolic of the fact that movement across the seas, as well as in home waters, has been a characteristic of Scandinavian shipping since early times. Few countries, indeed, have such a well-documented history of their sea-going vessels as these northern lands. From the Hjortspring boat (found in Hjortspringskobbel Moss in south Jutland in 1920 and dated 500 B.C.) to the Oseberg ship of Norway (found on a farm by that name near Tønsberg in 1904 and dated 800 A.D.),[1] there may be detected a sequence of evolution in boat type with few parallels in other regions. The saga of the Viking period would not be understandable in the absence of such perfection in boat-building. The tradition of ship construction remains. Ships, moreover, are a part of the daily thinking of a large percentage of the northern peoples. Samuel Laing, when he visited Norway in the 1830s, remarked that every Norwegian could afford his own boat. In twentieth-century Scandinavia, yachting is not the luxury sport of the few but the summer pleasure of the many.

Such a tradition lies behind a mercantile marine which, collectively, gives to the Northern Countries control of about 12% of the world's tonnage. Norway alone, with its 16 million tons of shipping (1966), owns more than 6% of the world's tonnage. On a *per capita* basis, the Northern Countries have a greater intensity of shipping than any other nation. Although the great bulk of the international trade of the Scandinavian countries moves by sea, such a volume of shipping is greater than that required for domestic needs, and the Scandinavian fleet is a supplier of international services.

The genesis of the mercantile marine of the Northern Countries belongs to the last century. Although an incipient Norwegian carrying trade may be detected two hundred years ago, the real stimulus was the liberation of West European trade after 1850. In this connection, the modification of the British Navigation Acts in 1849 played a leading role. A century ago, Norway was beginning to feel its way into the seven seas; within a generation its potential role as a world carrier was detectable.[2] This role was from the first closely bound to British trading. Historically, timber was the chief cargo; ice and coal followed. From south Norway to the Humber ports it was possible to make nearly a dozen voyages a season, and freight charges of nearly £150 on a 250–300 ton sail-boat could be economically contemplated. Norway provided shipping for transport services to the Black Sea during the Crimean War. Trans-Atlantic tentacles were also extended, and the volume of timber shipments during the period of open water on the St. Lawrence grew so vigorously that a Swedish–Norwegian consulate was opened in Quebec. Corn, grains and fruit constituted other Atlantic cargoes. Beyond the North Atlantic, tropical cargoes were sought from the equatorial lands and a South American market klippfish was established. The Horn was rounded in search of Pacific cargoes—where Chilean nitrates and guano spelt an initial Norwegian interest in fertilisers.

This omnivorous capacity for swallowing cargoes, coupled with the early rationalisation of ocean transport to keep in step with—if not ahead of—the times, have been behind the rise of Norway to a world shipping status. They have been behind Norway's politics as well as an integral part of its economics. The emergence of Norway as an independent state in 1905 cannot be viewed in detachment from its life on the sea. The issue of distinct consular representation from Sweden and the compelling need for a diplomatic policy independent of that of Sweden were both closely related to Norwegian maritime development. Although the other Northern Countries were

[1] T. Iversen, "Norske båttyper og fiskefartøyer", *Geografiska Annaler*, **21**, 1939, 132–63.
Cf. N. P Vigeland, *Norge på havet*, Oslo, 1954, Vol. II.

all to express themselves in an increasingly vigorous maritime life, none did so with the same singleness of purpose as Norway or on the same scale. As a world carrier, Norway is immediately different from the other Northern Countries. It has nearly 80% of its fleet engaged in foreign freighting, compared with 45% for Sweden and 70% for Denmark. Capital has been deliberately diverted from other uses into shipping. In some respects, of course, it is more fluid in this form than if invested in industry or agriculture.

In the management of the merchant fleets of the north there has been a sensitive response to the world need for specialisation. Thus tramping—already challenged between the wars—has been largely replaced by regular line freighting. It is difficult to make comparative assessments on a country basis. But even with the smaller fleets of Denmark and Sweden, line freighting occupies an increasingly dominant role. Probably more than 40% of Sweden's cargo fleet is engaged in this activity. Denmark estimates that 50% of its maritime income derives from line freighting. The larger the fleet, proportionately the greater the tonnage engaged in extra-territorial waters. Sixty per cent. of Norway's line traffic plies between other than Norwegian ports. Freighting demands increasingly differentiated facilities—in the handling of bulk cargo, piece goods, perishable commodities or passenger traffic. In order to maintain established routeways, the continuous modernisation of vessels is required. Finland apart, the Scandinavian merchant fleet is motor-powered to the extent of 70%. Side by side with modernisation has proceeded a steady increase in the size of vessels. Cargo ships of ten, twenty or even thirty thousand tons now become an established feature of line freighting. Vessels of more modest tonnage, however, persist in the cabotage trade.

In no field have these characteristics presented themselves more clearly than in the oil-tanker fleet. The Scandinavian countries collectively own a fifth of the world's tanker fleet. Half of Norway's merchant navy consists of tankers (531 vessels, totalling 8,769,000 tons in December 1965). In the other Northern Countries, the tanker proportion grows steadily. Perhaps the first time that a Norwegian vessel engaged in the carrying of oil was in 1866, when the barque *Bergljot* of Trondheim went to Bermuda with a cargo of petroleum and naphtha. The construction of small tankers was already the object of experiment by Robert Nobel in Sweden in the 1870s; though it was a Tönsberg company which in 1877-8 first had three ships built for the transport of oil. Of all the vessels in the Norwegian mercantile marine, the tankers are those most rarely seen in home waters. Norway's need for petroleum, though nationally vital is quantitatively modest. It is estimated that its entire annual needs could be met by sixteen 15,000-ton tankers making seven journeys each on the run from Kuwait or Abadan. In the search for shipping economies, tankers are now growing to well over 100,000 tons d.w.

More compelling than mere statistics in the appreciation of the Norwegian mercantile marine is the weekly supplement of *Norges handels- og sjøfartstidende*, which lists the location of active units of the commercial fleet. Figs. 66 and 67 represent the size and distribution of vessels for a representative issue of this ship's list at the end of March (which accounts for the location of the whaling fleet). The material does not lend itself easily to representation, because of the crowding of certain specialised shipping in particular areas. European territorial waters are naturally congested; while the localisation of the tanker fleet provides a second area of concentration. The map, however, emphasises a particular attribute of the Scandinavian economy. While the constituent units shown on such a map conform in their movements increasingly to fixed patterns, there is still a group of vessels operating general tramp services— and providing ship-adoption societies in Norway (offspring of their British parents) with elaborate tracings of their world journeyings.

The control of this web of routeways shows increasing tendencies towards concentration. First, there is centralisation in a diminishing number of controlling ports. Secondly, there is a steady concentration of ownership, which may be a reflection of federal tendencies in

Scandinavia at large. It is also a means of strengthening a group of countries faced with the common problem of a resurgence in cargo discrimination. Just a century ago, David Ricardo was inveighing against flag discrimination in the carrying trade. The new nationalism of the day threatens a widespread return to the restraints of the Navigation Acts. A succession of American commissions has indicated the uneconomic character of such national policies. Protection, however, is rooted in politics.

THE ESTABLISHMENT OF THE RAILROAD

The model for rail development was Great Britain. More than a century ago, Scandinavians came to Britain to investigate the possibilities of the steam railway for their individual countries. Some were pessimistic —like G. D. B. Johnson, author of *Haandbog for veiofficianter* (1839); some were a little fearful about the capacity of British rolling-stock to withstand the rigours of "so northerly a climate as Finland's" (Director Stjernvall in his report); some were even indignant—"The sea was the only proper road for all Danish traffic."[1] But arguments such as that put forward in *Morgenbladet* (Oslo, 68, 1822) were likely to prevail. It is easier, observed the editor, to travel from Oslo to London, Copenhagen or Amsterdam than to Bergen or Trondheim. Railway fever was as infectious as the plague and the possibilities seemed unlimited.

So British engineers crossed the North Sea —directly acquiring concessions (e.g. from Flensborg over Husum to Tønning in Jutland) or as planners and consultants (e.g. Robert Stephenson and the first Norwegian line, which was commemorated by engravings in the *Illustrated London News* of 1854), or as contractors and investors (e.g. Charles Fox, of Fox, Henderson and Co., builders of the Crystal Palace, who underwrote the Sjælland railway). Mechanics were also needed for the locomotives, which came from Manchester (to Denmark) or Birkenhead (to Finland). Two drivers came from Merseyside in February 1861 to teach the Finns how to operate the first stretch of track from Helsinki to Hämeenlinna. The first engineers on that track had to be preceded by horse-drawn snow-ploughs —almost confirming one of the worst suspicions of the railway antagonists. And the language of the early railroads was frequently English. Regulations on the south Slesvig railway were initially printed in English; in Oslo, the *Provisional Instructions to be observed* were printed jointly in English and Norwegian; likewise, in Sweden. The very word "rail" had no Scandinavian or Finnish counterpart. And, in the field of labour as well as of management, the railways brought a cosmopolitan touch; for foreign labour—such as Silesian to Denmark or Finnish to Norway— was to offset domestic deficiencies.

The pattern of development of the lines took different courses in each of the four countries.[2] Today, with low density per square kilometre, Scandinavia and Finland display a high length of rail per head of population (cf. Fig. 71, p. 226). In 1960, Norway had 4,358 km. of track; Sweden, 14,456; Denmark, 4,300; and Finland, 5,223. Iceland has no railways.

In Norway (Fig. 68, p.222), the major arterial lines developed largely in isolation and continue to operate to a large extent as separate entities. The Norwegian *Rutebok*, with its distinctly named routes, emphasises this individuality. Nor did the main lines necessarily link together the principal urban centres in the earlier stages of railway development. *Bergensbanen*, the Bergen line, is the best example of this. It was mooted as early as 1871 when trans-Alpine and trans-Rocky lines were giving plausibility to its construction. Indeed, the railway, in embryo, was called "The Scandinavian Pacific Railway". Oslo and Bergen, nevertheless, remained without railway contact until fifty years ago when the central fjell route was chosen and Gravhalsen tunnel (5,311 m. long) overcame the principal physical obstacles. The priorities in railway development have not always been to link together and serve population concentrations.

[1] Cf. A. Aagesen, *op. cit.*, p. 220.
[2] Standard works are G. Welin (ed.), *Statens-järnvägar, 1856–1906*, Stockholm, 1906; *Finska statsjärnvägarne, 1862–1912*, Helsingfors, 1912; *De Danske Statsbaner, 1847–1947*, København, 1947; Einar Østved, *De norske jernbaners historie*, Oslo, 1954.

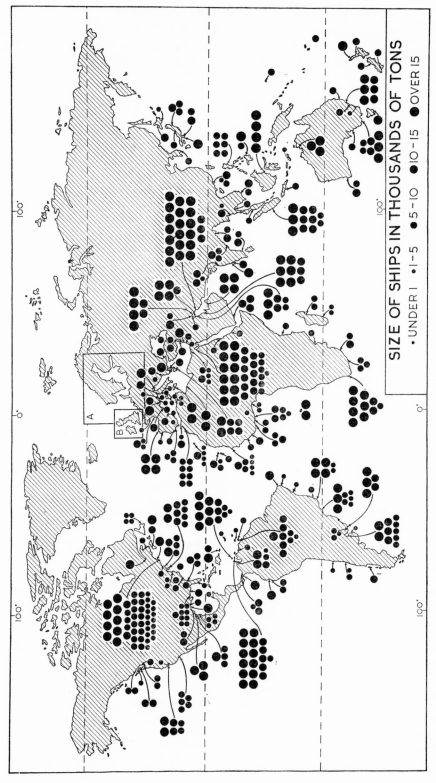

SIZE OF SHIPS IN THOUSANDS OF TONS

· UNDER 1   • 1-5   ● 5-10   ● 10-15   ● OVER 15

Fig. 66. A sample distribution of the Norwegian mercantile marine, compiled from the weekly shipping list in *Norges handels-og sjøfartstidende*, March 31st, 1955. Insets A and B refer to Fig. 67. A complementary map of the Swedish merchant fleet is given in the *Atlas of Sweden*.

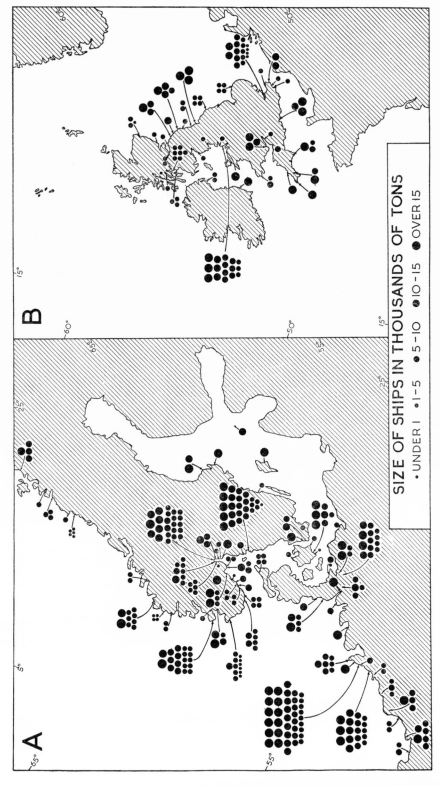

SIZE OF SHIPS IN THOUSANDS OF TONS

· UNDER 1   • 1-5   ● 5-10   ● 10-15   ● OVER 15

Fig. 67. The distribution of the Norwegian mercantile marine in European (A) and British (B) harbours on March 31st, 1955.

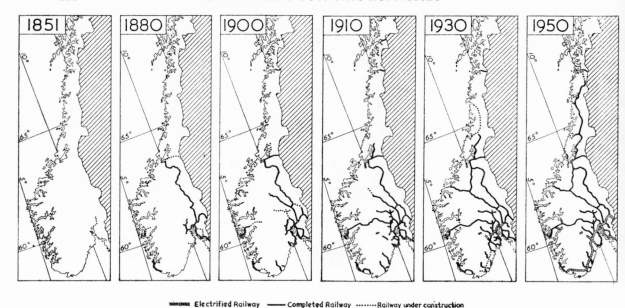

Electrified Railway ——— Completed Railway ·······Railway under construction

FIG. 68. The evolution of the Norwegian railroad system. (Source: E. Østved, *De norske jernbanershistorie* Oslo, 1954.)

Ofotbanen, the Ofoten railway, illustrates the effect of commodity pressure upon the railway plan. Fifty years before the Ofoten railway was built to Narvik, there had been a project for a railway from Gellivare to the Bothnian Gulf.[1] "The North of Europe Railway Company" came into existence in 1883 to give reality to a rail route from Narvik to Luleå. The Arctic line from Riksgrensen to Narvik is the most detached and distinctive portion of Norwegian state railways. Norway has elaborate plans for high-latitude development. They are not new, for in 1919 protagonists were urging a *Nordlandsbane* from Troms to east Finnmark.

Initial Danish plans for a railway system stirred in Slesvig-Holstein, where there were proposals to span the isthmus in order to promote the flow of Baltic–North Sea traffic. Commercial pressure in the isthmus was not, however, paralleled elsewhere in Denmark. There was an anti-railway school of thought which proclaimed that no part of Denmark really lay far enough from the sea to merit

railways—especially in virtue of the success of steamships. Strategic qualms also vexed some who were reluctant to add to the German exposure of Jutland.[2] Bishop Kierkegaard had fears that the railway would divide Denmark by uniting Jutland to Germany and Sjælland to Sweden. A composite picture of the compromise reached by rail, diligence and steamship in the early 1860s has been built up by A. Aagesen.[3] By then, railways were on the verge of challenging by their speed and capacity the competition of horse-drawn vehicles and steamships. Within a few decades, one of the densest networks of any country in Europe had been evolved.[4] Denmark thus had a railway system unrivalled in any other Scandinavian country. Two primary axes emerged—the east–west, extending from Copenhagen to the railway port of Esbjerg; the north–south, binding together the fiord cities and continuing south into Germany. As if in deference to sea transport, the railway was set back 5–15 km. from the coast. But it would be wrong to look

[1] Cf. E. Blix, "Engelskmennene og Ofot-Luleåbanen", *Historisk Tidsskrift* Oslo, 1952.
[2] F. C. Stiernholm, *Om Jernbaner betragtede fra et militaert standpunkt*, Copenhagen, 1854.
[3] *Op. cit.*, Fig. 9.
[4] *De Danske Statsbaner, op. cit.*, Fig. 1.

upon the maritime relationship of Denmark's railways as based wholly upon competition. Rather is it one of simultaneous co-operation and competition. The railway system can only function through a system of complementary ferries. On the score of commodity movement, rail transport still suffers disadvantages on many hauls. Road competition is, however, much more acute—a ubiquity of roads at once contrasting with so much of Scandinavia and existing side by side with a dense railway network. With the roads carrying much more on a ton per kilometre basis than the railways, it is not surprising that Denmark today witnesses the abandonment of many secondary lines. Even the railway port of Esbjerg receives more than a third of its agricultural exports from motor lorries.

Sweden was the third of the Scandinavian countries to set a railway system in motion. The usual contemptuousness of the antagonists balanced the fear that Sweden would be left in the rearguard by those who foresaw the drift of events. What would the railways carry? asked the former. "A little herring from Stockholm to Göteborg and a little coal back again." Build like our neighbours, urged the latter, or we shall be left as "isolated from Europe as Siberia". The head of the topographical corps was called in to make plans for central Swedish lines in 1852; the first railway was begun in 1854. Thereafter, it was a struggle between demand for and supply in the network—a state system and a private system of lines developing side by side.[1] Five primary *stambanor* or main lines were projected for the state system. A major axial line from Skåne to the Arctic was an early feature of the plan. The Norrland railway—its northern component—encountered much opposition from those who, like the governor of Norrbotten, regarded "The Baltic as Norrland's proper *stambana*". The speedy northern expansion of Finnish track, however, stirred the Swedes to counter with their Norrland railway lest Finnish settlement should flood over the northern valleys. The ore railway from Luleå to Narvik was part and parcel of the system. The Norrland line was paralleled in the early twentieth century by the *Inlandsban*—a line cutting through the interior of this colonial territory. This line, in part a pioneer line, has been one of a number of enterprises deliberately undertaken to open up the backwoods. It has also adhered to the principle of an earlier administrator that railways should, wherever possible, avoid watercourses and be constructed transverse to them. The density of railway lines is greatest in the southern third of the country. Here private enterprise has accompanied state development. Among private lines, none has been more significant in its impact upon economic development than *Bergslagsbanen*—the Bergslag railway. The railway, indeed, was one of the fundamental forces revitalising Swedish industry.[2]

Swedish and Russian experiences, having demonstrated that there were no physical obstacles to prevent the operation of railways, effectively silenced much would-be opposition in Finland. The main fear, that a rail link with Russia might swamp the Finnish market with cheap farm produce, was never realised. In fact, the route gave Finnish farmers new access to the St. Petersburg market. High construction and maintenance costs were unavoidable; but "Ilmarinen", the first engine, ran from Helsinki northwards in 1861.[3] The construction of the lines—projected as a unitary system by a central government authority—reached its greatest intensity at the turn of the century. "A railway between Helsinki and Åbo, three to six miles from the coast, would be so many wasted millions", commented an early observer. In principle, Finnish policy has been to strike inland from the coast and to create an interior network of lines as equidistantly from each other as is practicable. The first routes were tied to the south and linked the western cities with St. Petersburg. The evolution of the Finnish railway pattern is summarised in Fig. 69. As with the Norwegian system, it is still expanding, and 15% of the annual investment goes

[1] *Statens järnvägar*, Fig. 19, shows the expansion of the system.
[2] Cf. E. F. Heckscher, *Till belysning av järnvägarnas betydelse för Sveriges ekonomiska utveckling*, Stockholm, 1907.
[3] A. Fabritius, *Återblick på jernvägsväsendets första utvecklingsskede i Finland*, Helsingfors, 1887.

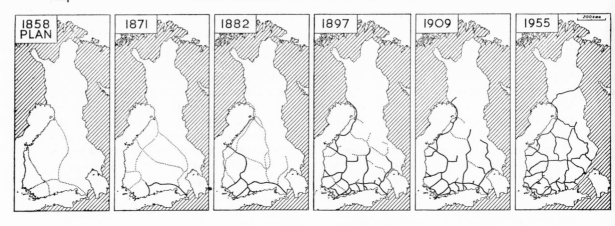

—— Constructed Railway   ·········Proposed Railway.

FIG. 69. The evolution of the Finnish railway system.   (Source: *Finska statsjärnvägarne*, Helsingfors, 1912.)

into new track.   In Finland, lines upon which work is in progress fall into three groups. First, there are the many minor adjustments occasioned by the adjustment of the south-eastern boundary in 1944. Secondly, there are the varied extensions directed towards the new industrial developments of the central lake district, e.g. Siilinjärvi–Juankoski, Jämsä–Jyväskylä. Thirdly, there are the new lines of the north-east. One of the stipulations by the settlement of 1940 was that a railway should be constructed between Rovaniemi and the Russian border at Kello-selkä. Subsequently, development has concentrated on the route between Hyrynsalmi and Kemijärvi—to which thousands of square kilometres of timbered land are tributary. Some measure of the lively interest in railway building is seen in the proceedings of *Eduskunta*, the Finnish parliament, which are liberally sprinkled with Acts for the construction of new tracks.[1] In the inter-war years there were plans for a Finnish Arctic railway, but no work was undertaken.

The railways of the four Northern Countries are both loosely linked with each other and slenderly tied to those of their non-Scandinavian neighbours. Norway has four independent links with Sweden—two in the south, one in the centre, one in the north. With the first lines across the Keel ridge reducing this barrier, the poet Andreas Munch claimed that

"east now lay by west". The urge for additional communications across the frontiers continues. The Swedish railway system strikes across the Torneå in a bridge to the Finnish town of Tornio; but the broad gauge (1,524 mm. instead of 1,435 mm.) effectively prohibits direct communication with Finland. Rail ferries tie Sweden and Denmark—Malmö–Copenhagen (1895) and Helsingborg–Elsinore (1891). Plans to institute a train ferry between Kristiansand and Fredrikshavn have never materialised. Finland also once entertained fanciful schemes for a rail ferry out into the Åland archipelago. More practically, it is currently investigating the possibilities of joint Norwegian routes to Porsanger or Skibotten, or of linking timber-processing centres like Kemi by a Central European gauge to the Haparanda–Narvik line. Inter-Nordic regional freight zones also simplify commodity movement in the north.

There has always been a small group of people who looked at Scandinavian railways in a continental perspective. Ole Tobias Olsen, a Nordland priest smitten with railway fever, advocated a line between his coast and St. Petersburg, "that a market could be opened for Lofoten and other Nordland fishery *vær*" (*Morgenbladet*, April 10th, 1872). The Russian railway hinterland was again quoted in connection with *Bergensbanen*, "the shortest route between St. Petersburg and the At-

[1] A summary of many plans is to be found in *Valtakunnan suunittelukomitean mietintö*, Helsinki, 1954, 104–10.

PLATE 17. RAW MATERIALS ON THE MOVE

Above. The ore train setting out for Ofoten from Kirunavaara.

Below. Timber rafts at Kröderen, Norway, waiting to be tugged across a lake.

PLATE 18. ASPECTS OF SHIPPING

Above. A part of the Burmeister and Wain shipyards in Copenhagen at Refshaløen, one of the largest in Scandinavia.

Below. An 80,000 ton Norwegian tanker in the roadstead of Stavanger.

lantic". In fact, continental association has been of limited effect, except in the extreme south-west. Denmark instituted a ferry service between Gjedser and Warnemünde in 1886; Sweden, between Trelleborg and Sassnitz in 1909. Swedish rail ferries now operate between Trelleborg and Travemünde and Odraport. In Jutland, Danish railways are linked with German at Tønder and Padborg. But the urge for speedier continental contacts has resulted in a new ferry service between Rødby and Putgarden (in West Germany). A new harbour has been constructed at Rødbyhamn. During the last quarter of the nineteenth century, Finland developed railways directly linked with those of Russia in the Karelian isthmus, and today Moscow coaches arrive in Helsinki by way of the Vainikkala frontier station. The new Kemijärvi line provides possible contact between the Murmansk railway and Tornio, but is currently known as "the line without a customs house".[1]

From the point of view of energy, one major change has occurred, albeit differentially, in the railway system of Northern Europe. In an effort to increase domestic economies independently of the desire to reduce dependence upon external sources of fuel, electrification has been adopted where practical. It is estimated that electrical traction can reduce fuel costs by two-thirds, that one electric locomotive can do the work of two steam locomotives, that the load can be correspondingly increased, and that—if required —the frequency of traffic can be multiplied. This latter consideration is important in an area where the single-track predominates.

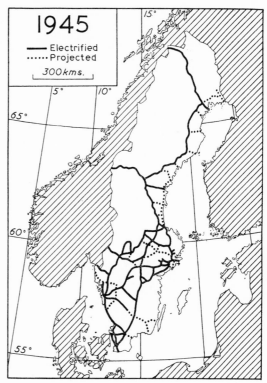

FIG. 70. The electrification of the Swedish railway system. (Source: T. Thelander, *op. cit.*)

Sweden holds a leading position in Europe in the electrification of its lines. Norway hopes to have 90% of its traffic moving over electrified track in a decade; in Denmark, only about 60 km. of suburban track are electrified. Finnish railways have no electrified track (although as long ago as 1908 there were plans to electrify the line between Helsinki and St. Petersburg). In 1960, about 6,800 km. of

TABLE 21

RAILWAYS (1965)

Country		km.	Electric	Per 1,000 sq. km.	Per 1,000 Inhabitants
Denmark	.	3,900	153	90·6	0·83
Finland .	.	5,544	—	16·4	1·22
Norway .	.	4,348	2,030	13·4	1·16
Sweden .	.	13,606	7,570	33·1	1·76

(Source: The comparative tables from the *Yearbook of Nordic Statistics*, Stockholm, 1967.)

[1] For this point of view, *vide* the interesting customs district map of Finland, No. 19, *Aluejakokomitean mietintö*, Helsinki, 1950.

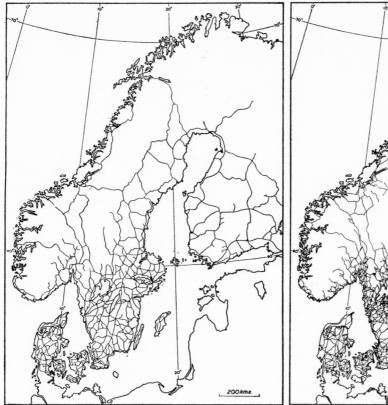

FIG. 71. The railway network of Scandinavia and Finland.

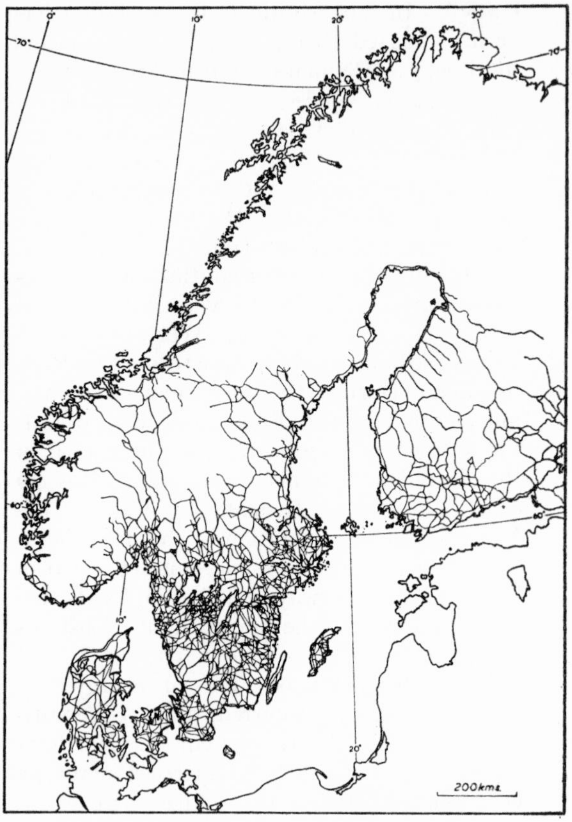

FIG. 72. The pattern of highways in Scandinavia and Finland at the beginning of the railway period. (Source: Principally C. F. Ström, *Karta öfver landswägarne uti Sverige och Norrige*, Stockholm, 1846.)

Sweden's track were electrified, i.e. about 40% of the total. About a third of Norway's track is electrified—principally in the south and including the 320-km. Oslo–Bergen line. Pioneering began in Sweden during the First World War; the greatest period of expansion occurred during the Second World War—when coal shortage was seriously felt. By 1944, it was possible to journey from Trelleborg in the south to Riksgrensen in the extreme north over a 2,000-km. route. Policy generally favours the electrification of main lines carrying the heaviest load.[1] Indeed, today 90% of Sweden's traffic is using the 40% of the lines which are at present electrified (Fig. 70). It is partly on the score of such a transformation that the journey from Stockholm to the Arctic has been reduced

from 47½ hours to 17½ hours since the beginning of the century. Diesel locomotives, used for both local and main line traffic, are also dependent upon imported sources of energy. In Finland, they stand in striking contrast to the woodburning locomotives, which still operate on most slower routes and which still account for half of the fuel costs of the state railways.

HIGHWAY AND BYWAY

A century ago, on the eve of the railway period, the Northern Countries supported a slender road network. Fig. 72, which is set beside Fig. 71, is compiled from post maps of

[1] T. Thelander, *The Electrification of Swedish State Railways*, Stockholm, 1951.

the several countries in the 1840s.[1] It emphasises the contrast between north and south. The post roads were rarely followed by any system of stage coaches, but were served by post chaises or diligences. These covered roughly ten Scandinavian "miles" between 7 a.m. and 10 p.m., and the general character of them can be appreciated by reading any of the *John Murray Blue Guides* for the time. Such roads made little impact on the European cartographers whose maps covered the north, and it is rare to find Scandinavian road systems marked by them until the early nineteenth century. Reconstruction of early highway patterns is an exacting task. Two examples—G. Hoppe's work on Norrbotten roads and M. V. Wallin's on the early highway pattern of Finland[2]—provide windows on to the varied type of source material available. Field work enables earlier trackways to be detected on the ground.[3]

surprising that most far-sighted men in the north pointed to the highway deficiencies as a major shortcoming. Gustavus III was an energetic reformer. "The old highways follow heaths and eskers, are commonly tied to hills and pursue an unnecessarily crooked course," observed H. G. Porthan[4] ". . . to go 8–10 miles, a curve of 30 must be followed." During the reign of Gustavus III, there was not merely road straightening and improvement but also the extension of highways into the interior of the kingdom. The new straight road, built from Närpiö to Vaasa—"straight as a die, without a bend"—can be traversed today. Highway straightening frequently ran side by side with the redistribution of land, and tended to lag where *storskiftet* was retarded. In Tuneld's *Geographie* (Stockholm, 1793, p. 520), it was noted of the interior lake district of Finland, "summer roads in this part of the country are a new development"—a

TABLE 22

VEHICLES IN NORTHERN EUROPE

Country	Passenger Cars	Vans and Lorries	Buses	Cars per 1,000 Inhabitants
Denmark . .	744,417	232,042	3,927	156
Finland . . .	376,254	86,101	7,704	82
Iceland . .	28,334	6,180	445	146
Norway . .	465,243	156,560	6,354	124
Sweden . .	1,792,671	131,554	10,295	231

(Source: The comparative tables from the *Yearbook of Nordic Statistics*, Stockholm, 1967.)

The construction and maintenance of these highways was largely a local responsibility. In Joseph Carenius's description of the Finnish parish of Hvittis (Huittinen), it may be learned that a main highway had to be maintained; while the principal bridges had to be reconstructed by the parish at seven-year intervals. In Norway, the highway law of July 28th, 1824, called peasantry thrice a year to maintain their local highways—after the disappearance of the snow, between seed-time and harvest, in the autumn for the clearance of the snow. When extension and improvement competed with maintenance, it is not

statement emphasising the role of waterway as the line of summer communication. From Chapter III the importance of the contrasting winter way will be appreciated. In length, it was commonly shorter than the corresponding summer route; in profile, simpler.

These roads were dirt roads and (Denmark apart) the unsurfaced highway remains absolutely dominant today. An abundance of road metal is available in most areas and its long-distance transport is unnecessary. Hitherto, construction has presumed abundant labour; but contemporarily, heavy machinery is increasingly available—for maintenance as

[1] The first significant guide to the highways of Sweden and Finland was published in Stockholm, with an accompanying map in 1742 (S. Biurman, *Vägvisare*).
[2] M. V. Wallin, *Fennia*, 8, 189, has maps showing the road network in 1556, 1639 and 1809.
[3] Cf. G. Hoppe, pp. 120–2. Plates IV and V in the same book show the evolution of parts of the coastal highway round the Bothnian littoral.
[4] "Beskrifning öfver vägarne i Finland", *Finska literatursällskapet*, Helsingfors, 1873.

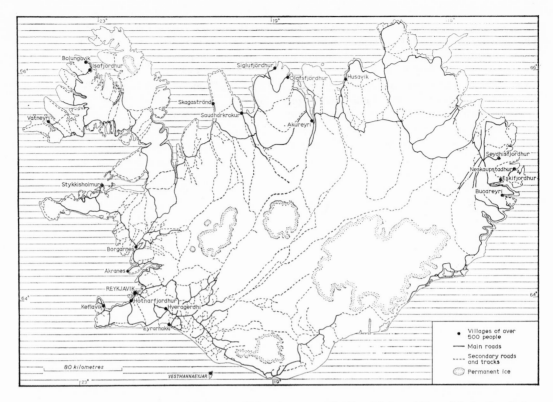

FIG. 73. The highway network of Iceland.   (After the map of the Tourist Association of Iceland, 1964.)

well as creation.   There is the same tug-of-war between the construction of byway and highway.   The multiplication of byways becomes extremely important for the forest economy.   Sweden, for example, is building approximately 2,000 km. of permanent woodland motor roads annually.   The extension of main roads becomes an equal necessity. The improvement of trunk roads in Finland, which bind together the main centres of population, is much the concern of the central highway authority.[1]   Sometimes special strategic highways have been constructed. Finland's inter-war Arctic highway to Petsamo (now severed by the Soviet boundary) and Norway's post-war Arctic highway are examples.   The strengthening of road links from Lake Saimaa shore to Kotka and Hamina on the Gulf of Finland may also be instanced.   Norway, Sweden and Finland

have today about three times the length of highway which they had a century ago.

The extension of the road network is a reflection of the increased means of transport. The "free agent" of the motor vehicle—not bound to fixed routes—shows a density of ownership in southern Scandinavia which equals that in most West European countries. Sweden, in fact, has the third or fourth highest density of motor vehicles per family in the world.   Denmark initiated international road research schemes and led European traffic flow investigations in the 1930s.   The motor vehicle is operated more easily in the metropolitan south of Scandinavia, where surfaced highways are most widespread.   But what the Swedes call *Bilism* fulfils an even more important personal and commercial function in the northern areas where railways are so sparse.[2] Here, of course, motor bus and lorry have

[1] Cf. Maps 5 and 6 accompanying *Tielaitoksen kehittäminen ja sen rahoitus*, Helsinki, 1954.
[2] C. W. Petri, *op. cit.*, Chapter 4.

come into their own—and they are vehicles of increasing size and weight. Norway has a bus route network of about 70,000 km.; Sweden, of over 100,000 km. While bus size is stable, lorry size continues to increase and the 5,000 kg. vehicle takes increasing precedence. Beyond the northern railheads, the state railways often operate their own system of post buses. Their routes, having already multiplied swiftly in the post-war years, are the subject of a regular succession of plans for expansion. Motor transport has been most revolutionary for Iceland. Fig. 73 gives the pattern of roads, upon which jeep and lorry dominate.

Viewed in the round, investment in highways sometimes seems inordinately high; but construction frequently absorbs labour which might otherwise be unemployed and costs may be partly offset against unemployment relief.[1]

ESCAPE TO THE AIR

Iceland, Norway, Sweden and Finland have much to gain from domestic airways which have established themselves in the post-war period. Not only are there long distances to be covered, but air transport is untrammelled by the complex topography which so hampers overland transport. In addition, it maintains uniform speeds over the entire area; while for other means of communication, speeds tend to slacken northwards. Of all the Northern Countries, perhaps Norway—commonly employing amphibious craft—has gained most. Before the air age, the time consumed in communications between the extremities of Norway was greater than that for Sweden and Finland. Domestic air routes can rival all but the cheapest class of rail travel for personal movement, and their role in freight transport grows rapidly. Indeed, for speed of increase, the number of passengers using airways grows as rapidly as the number using private cars. The intensity of domestic air routes

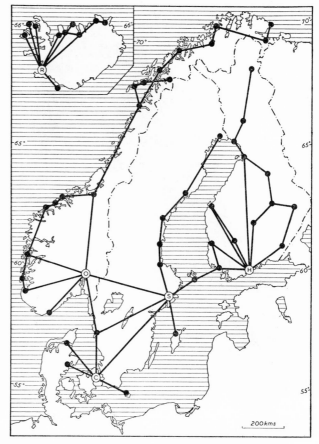

FIG. 74. Air routes in Scandinavia and Finland.

varies seasonally. In north Norway, for example, air communication lapses in the winter on the score of adverse flying conditions, and the country retreats fifty years to its steamboat communications. Air routes have, of course, become of especial importance in strengthening island links. The service from Stockholm to Gotland was the first domestic air route to be opened in 1933. Even rocky Åland has found enough level terrain on its main island for an airport, which is in daily communication with Stockholm and Helsinki. Airports are commonly under the control of the ministries of transport.

Iceland has, of course, found a new international status with the revaluation of aerial routeways. Its international communications today are more significant than its

[1] In Finland, 80% of the construction between 1945 and 1955 could be offset in this manner.

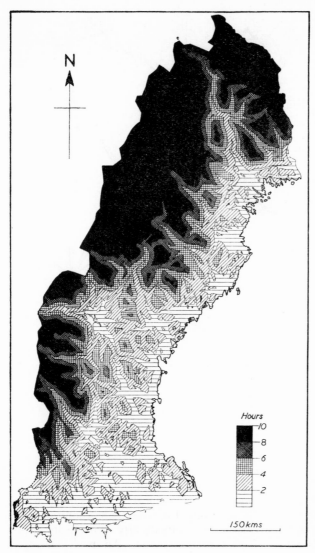

FIG. 75. Accessibility to market centres in Swedish Norrland. (After *Norrlands näringsliv*, Stockholm, 1943.)

has acquired a new significance as Scandinavian air services have developed their trans-polar routes to western North America. Spitsbergen might also become an air base on the Tokio route; though air communication with the Svalbard archipelago is commonly restricted to a summer mail service. In a region characterised by its co-operative endeavour, it is not surprising to find a federation of Swedish, Norwegian and Danish services.

THE DEGREE OF ACCESSIBILITY

Distance in Scandinavia is a feature underestimated by the rest of Europe. In the reassessment of it is rooted the revaluation of resource; in the appreciation of it is one of the keys to the understanding of Norway, Sweden and Finland. The significance of the transport patterns resulting from the tug-of-war of many interests has engaged the attention of a number of North European geographers. The concept of the transport system in motion as distinct from the transport system at rest began to take shape from the end of the last century onwards. The railway geography of Finland was represented in the first *Atlas of Finland* (1895), not merely by route maps but also by commodity flow diagrams. In more mature statements such as those of A. Aagesen and of W. William-Olsen in his commissioned monograph on the Nässjö railway, intensification of movement is analysed. The concept of the traffic area as derived from local transport services has engaged the attention of Lund geographers,[1] and the reorganisation of Sweden's essential administrative areas is planned along the lines of established transport routes. The sphere of urban influence is an expression of transport relations to which Northern Europe has paid willing regard. Transport geographers have been effectively imported to state (e.g. in Sweden) and city (e.g. Tampere) administration.

For transport touches immediately upon

domestic communications; although, as is evident from Fig. 74, these have multiplied rapidly in recent years. South Finland has simultaneously become an air corridor to the U.S.S.R., with Helsinki as a transfer point between east and west services. Revaluation of high latitudes has also given to Denmark's protectorate of Greenland a new importance in air routes. Thule, in north-west Greenland,

[1] S. Godlund, *Busstrafikens framväxt och funktion i de urbana influenssfälten*, Lund, 1954.

population distribution and migration, while it impinges ubiquitously upon industrial distribution and migration. Eli Heckscher gave early point to the effects of the railway on Sweden's economic development. His maps, on a parish basis, suggested a significant division into "railway parishes" and "non-railway parishes" from the point of view of population increase. Population naturally gravitates to lines of communication. The intensification of lines of communication is still a widespread need in Northern Europe, and it is argued contemporarily that by multiplying them the migration of population from rural areas can be arrested. In this connection, not merely have the requirements of one region to be balanced against those of other regions, but the effectiveness of various kinds of transport have to be balanced against each other. In general, the highway tends to take precedence over an intensification of other means of

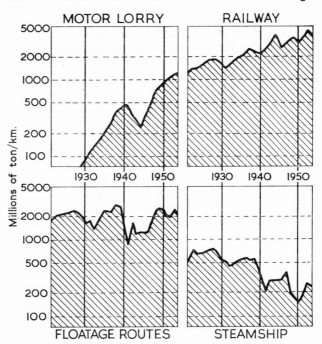

FIG. 76. Changes in commodity transport in Finland, 1922–52. (Source: A. Kiiskinen, *Maamme sisäisen kuljetuslaitoksen kehitys ja rakenne*, Helsinki, 1954.)

transport. It is not only of renewed consequence since the coming of the internal-combustion engine, it is increasingly easy to construct with modern equipment. The multiplication of large numbers of second- or third-class highways is generally of more consequence than the building of a small length of first-class highway.[1]

Besides intensifying local accessibility (cf. Fig. 75), improved communications have integrated the several parts of the individual countries. In 1927, *Tidens Tegn* (Pts. 18 and 19, I; 9, II) published material showing those parts of Norway which were not tied by direct road connections to the rest of the country. Including the extensive island forelands, this amounted to about half of the surface area of the country. Some parts of the country were tied to the communicational systems of Sweden and Finland without being directly linked to the rest of the realm. The situation has been largely remedied by highway—if not railway—construction during the last two

decades. But travelling time involved is still a problem. The accessibility of the capital to the constituent parts of the country is of growing consequence in this respect.

At any given time, the pattern of developing communications represents a compromise between a variety of rival interests and policies. The growth of the railway network, with its alternative plans in the past eventually crystallising in the contemporary pattern, enables the effects of some of these motives to be traced. With limited investment resources there is operating simultaneously a rivalry between different areas for the scarce funds and, within different areas, a rivalry between alternative means of communication. The ultimate principle of substitutability is limited in its application. The plan for Norwegian State Railways is an example of the eventual compromise reached between different areas over the network of lines (though it is still subject to change according to local pressures).[2]

[1] S.O.U. *Betänkande angående vissa åtgärder till förbättrande av transportförhållandena i Norrland*, Stockholm, 1946, 84, and *Riksdagens handlingar*, 1950, 32, give the Swedish and Finnish points of view on this issue.

[2] *Innstilling fra jernbanekommisjonen av 1949 om ny jernbaneplan*, Stavanger, 1953, much of which is a regional economic geography in itself and leant heavily upon professional geographical advice.

Plans for Swedish Norrland illustrate carto-graphically the eventual compromise reached within a particular area between different forms of land transport.[1] An example of the transport compromise in a national setting is given in the communicational summary of Finland.[2] For highway, byway and railway, the pulse of progress is detectable in the detailed annual reports of the ministries of transport in the Northern Countries. It is harder to discover, of course, the extent to which subsidisation supports the individual transport routes and the extent to which mere investment in new routeways calls for an extension of the system of subsidies.[3] The plans, however, which so neatly evaluate the potentialities of traffic for different areas find difficulty in balancing the imponderables in the picture—not merely the social but also the military facts.

The traffic services of the north are in process of lively adjustment (cf. Fig. 76). Both their contemporary form and power enable a more complete occupation and control of the land. The metropolitan areas of Scandinavia (in which the majority of the inhabitants dwell) assume services identical with those in any other developed country. Elsewhere, the automobile as a new personal means of transport has reduced the very real disparity hitherto existing between the railway and non-railway areas. The line of steel no longer limits the gathering ground of raw materials, the dispersal of impulses or the movement of men. Not merely is there a more equable distribution of amenity between urban and rural districts, but also a widespread inter-penetration of rural and urban areas. The retarding effects of isolation upon which Thomas Malthus dwelt in his Scandinavian journey of 1799 must, for certain purposes, continue to distinguish certain areas of the north. But only in a relative sense. Eli Heckscher observed that fifty years ago great stretches of countryside, unserved by the railway, continued to live much as in the sixteenth century. If this situation prevails anywhere today, it is increasingly a matter of choice rather than of necessity. What might be called "the battle of the gaps" is under way: new powers behind the wheel are overcoming the historical time-lag.

[1] *S.O.U. Norrlandskommitténs principbetänkande, Norrlands utvecklingslinje*, Stockholm, 1949.
[2] Reproduced in S. Jaatinen and W. R. Mead, *Economic Geography*, **33**, 1957, p. 39.
[3] There is a valuable Finnish study on the distribution of investment in and employment of the different means of transport, A. Kiiskinen, *Maamme sisäisen kuljetuslaitoksen kehitys ja rakenne*, Helsinki, 1954.

Chapter XI

THE SOFTWOOD INDUSTRIES [1]

"Widespread they stand, the Northlands dusky forests
Ancient, mysterious, brooding savage dreams".

Jean Sibelius, Prefix to the score of *Tapiola*

AN APPRAISAL OF THE SCANDINAVIAN SOFTWOODS

SOFTWOOD forests are found mostly in the northern hemisphere where 95% of them lie between latitudes 30° and 60° N. Sweden, Finland and Norway are found within the area where the softwood forest naturally predominates, and in this respect bear ready comparison with Canada. In the Scandinavian peninsula, the coniferous woodland blanket (commonly called *barrskog*) stretches farther north than anywhere else in the world. Børselvdalen (70° 20′ N.), in Finnmark, claims the most northerly portion of it. Although optimum growing conditions cannot be reduced to a formula, it would appear that from the standpoint of temperature, winter readings of 15°–32° F. and summer readings averaging 60° F. are most favourable. Softwood species require relatively moist conditions; though precipitation effectiveness is high in their latitudes of growth and absolute rainfall need not be great. The Scandinavian peninsula and Finland offer extensive areas which approach the ideal growing conditions for spruce and pine. The limited degree of woodland clearance in these areas compared with the rest of Europe is clear from the *World Forest Atlas*.

The Scandinavian softwood areas have a fine accessibility and, in this respect, they contrast appreciably with those of Canada (cf. Table 23). Their distribution coincides with the territory of glacial deposition, and they are set against an immature drainage pattern, rich in rivers, streams and lakes. Moreover,

TABLE 23
FOREST AREAS
(in 1,000 hectares)

Country	Accessible Productive	Others
Sweden .	22,250	1,285
Finland .	20,700	930
Norway .	6,470	439
Denmark .	380	0
Canada .	116,322	222,477

(Source: *F.A.O. Yearbook*.)

both maritime and lacustrine shorelines in this timbered land are remarkably indented. Such characteristics accord to the softwoods of an area of supply like Norrland, Värmland and Dalarna a network of 20,000 miles of natural floatage ways. The softwood stands are also accessible on the score of composition. In contrast to most timber stands, pine and spruce woods are largely void of undergrowth. The stands are, in addition, uniform with regard to species and display a homogeneity which contrasts with the heterogeneity of the tropical forest (where only one tree in one to ten acres may be felled for milling). The accessibility of the woodlands as a source of raw material is both hampered and eased by winter conditions. Snowfall favours felling operations, but the winter freeze closes waterways.

As a natural resource, softwood timber represents an extremely manœuvrable material. It is one of the most easily felled, sawn and worked. An extension of this quality is its

---

[1] Most of the publications mentioned in this chapter are available in the library of the Timber Trade Development Corporation, College Hill, E.C.1. The world distributional pattern of woodlands is being slowly built up in the *World Forest Atlas* (Hamburg, 1951), and figures are provided by the *Yearbook of Forest Products Statistics*, F.A.O., Rome, annually. Cf. also *A World Geography of Forest Resources*, New York, 1956, and K. Hare, "Boreal Forests of the Northern Hemisphere", *Geographical Studies*, I, London, 1954. I am indebted to Professor V. Holopainen for helpful criticism of this chapter.

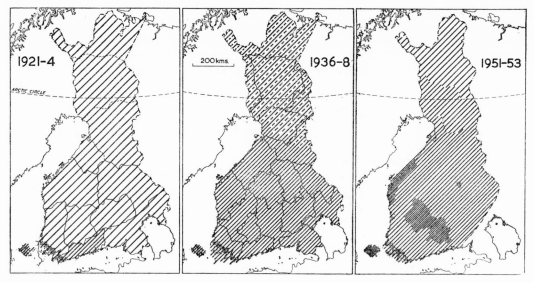

FIG. 77. The three line-surveys of the Finnish forests.

convertibility. Softwood timber has a wide range of alternative uses—a range which is also wide at different stages of the productive process. Countries like Finland, therefore, which may lack variety in their primary resources, are nevertheless able to offer a variety of end products from converted softwoods.

Softwood timber has another characteristic —it is a relatively speedily renewable resource. Properly managed, its raw material constitutes a flow which does not necessarily waste. Renewability depends upon both natural and human conditions. Climatic and edaphic conditions will speed or retard replacement of species on cut-over land. Thus, there may be a range of several decades between the period taken for timber to mature in central and north Sweden. The ease of replacement is also related to the abundance of seed— and seed years occur with differing frequency in different latitudes. The amount of soil water also modifies growing speed. In addition, softwood timber is subject to a variety of afflictions which affect replacement of stock. Fire hazards are appreciable—with the incidence of lightning being regionally related. Sweden, for example, records more than 1,000 fires annually. Both fungæ and insects are destructive agents which take their toll of growing stock. Human conditions modifying the maintenance of timber stands include both overcutting and open-range grazing. In Finland, for example, about half of the softwood timber stands are grazed. The foresters' associations have sought to create a forest *légende* which will encourage better softwood management. The foundation of smallholders' forest schools (there are seventeen in Sweden; three in Finland) to complement their farm schools is a means through which to preach the value and virtue of a timber cover and to demonstrate how management can reduce those "wanes, knots and shakes" which diminish the value of marketed lumber. Emphasis is less upon plantations than upon the improvement of existing stands through selective logging, trimming and ditching. Sweden, for example, digs 1,500 km. of forest ditches annually.

Appreciation of softwood resources implies measurement, and changing methods of survey have enabled increasingly accurate assessments. The woodlands have been measured by three methods. The oldest assessments have been the national censuses of land ownership and land use. The line survey method has succeeded to these for the national forest inventories of Sweden and Finland. Two line surveys have been made in Sweden—

during 1923–9 and 1938–53. Three have been made in Finland under the direction of the Forestry Institute in Helsinki (1922–4, 1936–8, 1951–3). The line survey is based on the principle of the "cruising belt" and the sampling plot. Within the sampling plot, trees are measured by calipers at breast height (c. 1½ m.). These surveys have revealed appreciable shortcomings in the national census. The growing intensity of line surveys in Finland is apparent from Fig. 77.

The third method, aerial survey[1] and sampling, has been used much more widely in Canada than Scandinavia; but the steady progress made in the large-scale air photography of Northern Europe enables softwood distributions to be stated more accurately. The experience of a Savo farmer illustrates the point. A discrepancy of 2 hectares was revealed on the topographic map of his 150 hectare farm when it was checked by an air survey.

Timber has to be expressed quantitatively when being prepared for the market and softwood products are measured by different units. Units of volume are preferred for the measurement of roundwood and sawnwood; weight is the least satisfactory unit because moisture content can introduce variations of up to 100% without any volume change. In the British market, lumber is measured in board feet; though the primary measurement is the standard—more specifically the St. Petersburg standard (165 cu. ft.). Firewood and pulpwood are measured in cords (one cord =128 cu. ft.); pit-props are measured in cubic feet and poles are quoted by number.[2] Metric measurement is used for international purposes. Stabilisation of terms of timber reference is a relatively modern matter. Great Britain is one of the few areas with a consistent run of timber trade figures for the last century. France, Germany and the Low Countries changed their terms of reference substantially during the nineteenth century. Timber must also be assessed qualitatively,

for it is far from a homogeneous commodity. Samuel Pepys wrote of Admiralty "leakages" owing to unsatisfactory systems of assessment. Grading is usually ascribed first to Sweden in the middle of the eighteenth century—when the terminology "best, good, common, cull" came into existence.[3] Today, Swedish, Finnish, Russian, Polish and Baltic timbers are graded into six qualities—the sixth being called "Utskott" or "Wrack". North American terminology is quite different. The growing need for precise terminology[4] has called forth at least two timber dictionaries— *Metsäsanakirja* (Helsinki, 1948) and the American Society of Foresters' *Forest Terminology* (Washington, 1950). Timber is also differently named once it reaches the marketing point—so that the familiar *Pinus* may appear as Archangel, Leningrad, Finnish or Swedish redwood or home-grown Scots pine. Its value will differ according to its origin, so that an appreciation of geographical background is fundamental to the dealer in commerical timbers. The finest redwoods derive from the Kara Sea, with Igarka on the Yenesei river as a primary export harbour. Thereafter, commercial assessments are regionally graded as follows—White Sea, Sweden (Gävle and northwards), Finland (north and east), Leningrad, Finland (south), Sweden (south of Gävle), the Baltic States and Poland.

The world value of primary forest products is estimated at twice that of crude steel or crude petroleum. World round-wood output, upon which this is based, is nearly equally divided between hardwood and softwood. The greater economic significance of softwoods derives partly from the fact that they are more fully processed than hardwoods. It is estimated that 80% of the softwood lumber is processed; while over 60% of the hardwood is consumed as fuel. Nearly 90% of the softwood lumber derives from Europe and North America. In the European output, the Northern Countries dominate so that they have a world status in the softwood scene.

[1] Cf. "Fotokartor för skogsbruket", *Svenska skogsvårdsföreningens tidskrift*, **36**, 6, 1938.
[2] Today terms are defined in the appendix to the *Yearbook of Forest Products Statistics*, which also includes conversion tables.
[3] R. F. A. Malleson and R. Grugeon, *Timber Trade Practice*, London, 1953, Chapter XIV and, for grading, Chapter XV.
[4] Consider the range in the terminology of imported softwoods alone—from familiar planks and deals through scantlings, slatings and flitches to shooks.

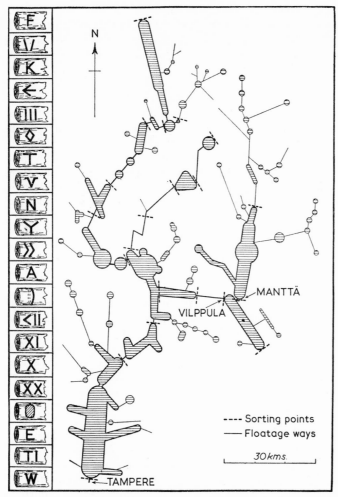

FIG. 78. The floatage system of the upper Kokemäki river.
(Source: *Kokemäenjoen uittoyhdistys vuosikirja*, Vammala,
1954.)

of softwood assembly, the forces involved in the localisation of processing plants and the technical changes behind these plants.

(a) The Detail of Softwood Assembly

Horse and waterway have been the traditional means of assembling softwood at the processing point. They have also been complementary—the horse for winter logging, the waterway for summer floatage. Both now experience a challenge in the softwood harvesting areas.

The organisation of waterways for timber movement has long attracted northern interest.[1] In both his Lapland and Dalarna journeys, Linnæus commented upon the value of streams and rivers for floatage. Organised floatage first took shape in conjunction with central Swedish mining operations. Improvement and interlinking of waterways through canals—both for floatage and navigation—encouraged widespread investment a century ago. In Finland, the successful completion of the Saimaa Canal in 1856 spurred the press to publicise additional schemes. Plans for the improvement of the Norrland rivers were formulated at the same time, e.g. Lule river, 1863; while softwood companies in Norway were commissioning private floatage maps, e.g. Glommen area.[2]

Today, Finland and Sweden produce a special series of floatage maps. The Finnish series (*Uittoväyläkartta*) define floatage districts, distinguish between public and private floatage ways, and identify flumes, dams and factories. The emergence of generalised maps has been accompanied by attempts to classify

THE TRANSFORMATION OF SOFTWOOD VALUES

Given this physical background, softwood exploitation has responded markedly to changed transport relations, differential exhaustion of timber and the discovery of new uses for an old resource. Some of these changes were dealt with in Chapter V. They are expanded here by reference to the detail

---

[1] The history of development in Finland is given in A. B. Helander, *Suomen metsätalouden historia*, Helsinki, 1949, Chapter XX. Floatage has also expressed itself in a wealth of local customs. In Norway, these have been collected in Kr. Østberg, *Av tømmerdriftens rets og sedvaneregler*, Oslo, 1926.

[2] Cf. manuscript maps in *Norges Geografiske Opmaaling*. Probably the first attention directed to this feature in geographical circles was the contribution of Gunnar Andersson, *Ymer*, 1907.

floatage ways—for example, in accordance with speed, volume and duration of flow. The volume and duration of flow may be closely linked. In Sweden, for example, hydrographers direct the attention of timber floaters to the contrast between the "winter low water" and "summer low water" areas. The progress of the spring thaw and the duration of the winter freeze will affect the value of (and frequently the amount of investment in) waterways. In the classification of floatage ways particular attention must be paid to the calm-water areas where wind speeds and directions can play havoc with timber movement.

Timber floatage, of course, embraces movement across stationary water (cf. Plate 17) as well as along running waterways. The timber raft, with its accompanying steam tug, is an all-important feature of the northern softwood scene. Six generations ago, John Atkinson wrote of "rafts of prodigious length which frequently have the appearance of villages".

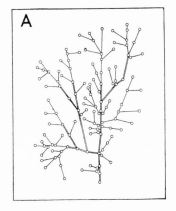

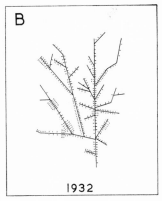
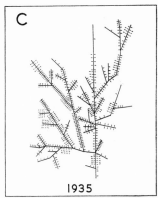

FIG. 79. Floatage and felling cartograms on the Kalix river. (After I. Winberg, *Flottning i Sverige fram till 1935*, Stockholm, 1938.)

Nor is rafting confined to the lakes: it belongs equally to the coastal fairways—particularly in Bothnia. The Swedish coastal areas, for example, are divided into timber floatage districts between the Torne estuary and Motala *ström*.

Timber floatage lends itself to cartographic expression. A portion of the Kokemäki river system is reproduced in Fig. 78; it shows, diagrammatically, the lakes and their intervening waterways with checking and sorting points (cf. also Plate 6). Fig. 79 provides a parallel picture from Sweden. Diagram A outlines the floating system with its control points. The two accompanying diagrams illustrate the quantity of felled timber moving out from the specifically controlled sections. Diagrams B and C illustrate years of relatively small output and of average output respectively. They show, at the same time, the annual changes which are likely to take place in a representative harvesting area of softwood timber.

Transport costs in the softwood industry begin as soon as the timber is felled. Transport labour, indeed, accounts for two-thirds of the cost of timber from stump to processing plant.[1] It is not surprising, therefore, that the employment of natural flow lines is questioned if, for any reason, they become costly to operate. Felled timber is inscribed with the owner's mark before being committed to the floatage way. Some floatage ways may be used by a score of mill operators. Ownership marks employed on a part of the Kokemäki system are illustrated in Fig. 78. Timber may also bear marks according to its intended use.

[1] "Synpunkter på Norrlands skogsbrukets biltransporter", *Svenska skogsvårdsföreningens tidskrift*, 2, 1950. Before the second world war, the figure was one third!

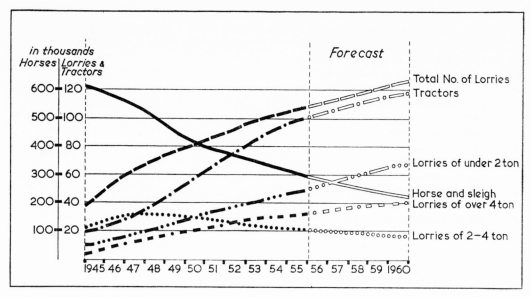

FIG. 80. Trends in Swedish timber transport. (Source: Materials from B. Ternstedt, *Skogsvårdsföreningens tidskrift*, 1956, 2.)

On the Skellefteå in Norrland, for example, there are approximately twenty ownership marks and thirty separate employment marks. Sorting points therefore become necessary in all tracts where floatage routes bifurcate or where processing plants intrude. These may be of a perplexity rivalling the Hampton Court maze. Log-sorting is a seasonal activity; it is a highly unionised activity, and its group of key workers has exerted a steady pressure for higher wages over a prolonged period. In Sweden in 1952–3, in fact, sorting costs were more than half the floatage costs. It is an interesting reflection that in Sweden, at the peak of the season 26,000 floaters balanced 5,600 loggers.

The well-nigh classical operation of timber floatage on Finnish lake and Bothnian river is therefore receiving a mid-twentieth century challenge. The waterway as a softwood timber route is experiencing local competition from the motorway and, less frequently, the railway.[1] The cost of floating plus sorter is balanced against the cost of motor lorry plus fuel and driver.[2] The challenge tends to increase as lorry sizes grow. In Finland, for

several additional reasons, the motorway has grown and grows in importance. The loss of the Saimaa canal encouraged the construction of an alternative motor road from the shores of Lake Saimaa to Kotka harbour. The opening up of forests which lie beyond the Baltic watershed calls for highway extension. In half of Kuusamo parish, for example, drainage flows into the Karelian A.S.R. In the north, Finland has no right of floatage on the Pasvik river—the international boundary between Norway and the U.S.S.R. Road movement of Finland's high-latitude softwoods to Norwegian ports of export or process is actively discussed. In some regions—for example, the Oulu valley—railways enter into competition with waterways. Indeed, unprocessed softwoods are, by bulk, the principal commodity carried on Finnish State Railways.

Yet it is important to keep the correct perspective in relative movements of timber. Spectacular summer logging scenes are repeated on literally tens of Scandinavian and Finnish rivers. An assembly of logs might be several miles in length. Again, on Lake Saimaa a boom of 25,000 logs may be drawn

[1] Cf. *Instilling fra Jernbanekommisjonen av 1949*, Stavanger 1953, pp. 60–2, 98–100, Diagram, p. 102.
[2] A representative Norwegian example is given in *Svenska flottningsförbundets årsbok*, 1948. Movement 33 km. by water cost 31·3 kr. per cu. m.; by lorry, 7·86 per cu. m.

from Kuopio to Lappeenranta in less than a fortnight. Clearly neither train nor lorry can compete seriously with movement on such a scale. Nevertheless, 2,000,000 tons of unprocessed wood are being moved annually on Swedish railways, and a quarter of Sweden's motor traffic is tied to forest operations.[1] Mid-twentieth century movement by water is again challenged in its familiar form by the building up of rivers for power purposes. The free floatage of timber is being regularly replaced by bundle-floating—and bundle movement by road. The motor lorry and railway have greatly broadened the field over which charcoal burning may be conducted.[2] The railway has also eased Swedish charcoal movement at large—in fact, 80% of this rather fragile commodity is borne by rail today.

Simultaneously, the motorised tractor challenges the traditional horse. A mechanical hauler for use on ice or snow has long fascinated engineers. The South Kensington Museum has a model of a locomotive approved in the late eighteenth century for use on the ice between St. Petersburg and Kronstadt. The first mechanical sleigh appeared in Scandinavia and Finland from North America just before the First World War.[3] The contemporary tractor is, silviculturally, a New World feature still modifying Old World practice. The horse remains dominant because it has greater mobility and adaptability than the tractor and because of the character of the rural areas in which it persists. Mobility is instanced in the continuing if reduced winter migration of lumbermen and their horses (complete with fodder supplies) from Ostrobothnia to Lapland. In extreme cases, this may amount to a trek by train of fully 300 km. The manœuvrability of the horse in the forest itself is also much greater than that of the tractor. The tractor, in fact, is likely to be at least as much complementary to, as competitive with, the horse. "Power logging" applies more to limited movement over open highways and lake surfaces than to general movement in the gathering area. Tractor and

cable therefore remain limited features in Scandinavia. It is not possible to reduce the relationship to a simpler equation and to balance horse and transported fodder *versus* tractor and transported fuel. Mechanisation in the woodlands is also seen in power appliances. There is no great economy in power felling, except where trees are larger in size;[4] the widespread distribution of power saws is as much related to prestige as to practical value. Transportable barking machines, however, represent a significantly labour-saving item.

(b) Localisation and Softwood Processing

There are at least five other forces in addition to its primary raw material which affect the location of the present softwood industries. Some of them are common to all industries; some are specific to the softwood group. Among the most significant is the availability of power.

The saw-milling industry first developed against a background of easily controlled water-power sites. In Harald Vik's study of changing distributions in the Norrland sawntimber industry, the migration to coastal sites occurring in the latter part of the nineteenth century is partly attributable to the revolution in maritime transport; partly to the way in which return cargoes of coal favoured coastal localisation of steam-driven saws. The third stage in his changing pattern of localisation is related in part to the coming of the railway, but simultaneously in many areas, to the establishment of hydro-electric power. Steady improvements in long-distance power transmission increase the range of alternative possibilities for processing locations. The first long-distance power-line of nine miles, from Hallsjön to Grängesberg completed in 1893, relaxed power control in localisation. Nils Menander has investigated the changing location of softwood industries in the Kemi and Oulu valleys of Finland—finding parallels with the pattern of evolution put forward by Harald Vik. In the softwood industry neither power supply nor power demand are simple

[1] B. Ternstedt, "Lastbilen i svenskt skogsbruk", *Svenska skogsvårdsföreningens tidskrift*, 1956, 2, 141–53.
[2] Cf. Gunnar Arpi, *op. cit.*, Fig. 4, which shows the wide dispersal of charring pits in relation to Uddeholms AB. for Hogfors iron-works.
[3] There is a picture in *Svenska flottningsförbundets årsbok*, 1939.
[4] F.A.O. Forests and Forest Product Studies, 6, 1953.

phenomena. Power is needed at least for driving machines, cooking the chips in the pulping process and paper drying. The supply sources are usually several—coal and diesel oil are common thermal adjuncts used in case of electrical shortage; while most mills burn considerable quantities of softwood waste.

Availability of water is a second requirement of the majority of processes. Chemical pulp dominates over mechanical in Northern Europe. It demands less water than mechanical pulp to reduce friction in the grinding process. Nevertheless, bleached sulphite pulp requires 150,000 gallons of water per ton and 30,000–50,000 gallons per ton are required beyond the pulp stage to complete the conversion into paper. Disposal of waste water at the end of the various processes may also affect considerations of siting.

Availability of labour is, regionally, a fact of controlling significance. Indeed, it is frequently averred that the supply of forest workers rather than availability of timber sets a ceiling to the progress of industry. Many modern mills are in thinly peopled tracts marginal to areas of agricultural production and settlement They are in pioneer areas of Scandinavia as they are in pioneer areas of Canada. The deliberate creation of a pool of labour is a feature common to many industrial sites in Northern Europe. Factory labour, having been attracted to a plant, must be retained at it. Mobility of labour is a feature of some softwood mills; stability of others. Nor is labour a simple concept. Labour in the mill and labour in the gathering area of the forest is not interchangeable. A fairly substantial mill complex may employ 1,200 men who call for the outside labour of 10,000 others for 200 days—given present technical conditions.[1]

The distribution of plants at any given time is a reflection of past availabilities as well as of present opportunities. The fixation of assets in a mill must be borne in mind. A self-contained pulp mill, for example, requires investment of at least £20,000 per ton of paper milled daily. Nor, in modern times, can

political and social controls be entirely ignored. The substantial post-war redistribution of softwood industries of Finland provides an illustration (cf. Chapter VI). For such reasons, a mere study of prevailing transport costs is not enough for the understanding of location and persistence in location. Nevertheless, an appreciation of total transport costs can indicate the incidence of freight rates upon particular plants. Olof Lindberg's *Studies in the Localisation of the Paper Industry* (Uppsala, 1951) examines the freight charges affecting fifty south and central Swedish paper plants. It employs the method of the isovecture[2] to bring out transport costs of the essential raw materials, and the isodapane[3] to show, suitably weighted, the transport costs of wood, coal, sulphur, lime and paper in *kronor* per ton of finished paper.

(c) Rationalisation in the Industry

Physical management in the woodland and economic investigation in the factory enable a steadily increasing rationalisation of the softwood industry. Forest and factory are regarded ideally as unitary—with one continuous process from softwood seedling to refined commodity. A tendency in many parts of the world to a vertical integration in the softwood industry underlines this. Partly as a result of land ownership conditions, the vertically integrated organisation is not common in Scandinavia. Woodland assets of a concern may expand, but unitary holdings tributary to a single plant are rare. Partly for this reason, horizontal integration of plants is more common in Scandinavia and Finland.

In his study *The Coming Age of Wood* (New York, 1949), Egon Glesinger impresses the unitary idea to the full and advances an ideal softwood complex. Given an optimum location in terms of transport relations, it envisages two primary features: first, a concentration of currently detached softwood processing units—saw-mill, pulp- and paper-mill, plywood factory, rayon plant, etc.; secondly, a compacting of their timber stands and a long-term, rotational harvesting operation (cf.

---

[1] Cf. E. Kinnunen, "The Wood-working Mill for Northern Finland", *Economic Review*, 3, Helsinki, 1956.
[2] A line joining points with equal transport costs for a certain commodity to a certain place.
[3] A line joining points with the same total transport costs for all the commodities entering the productive process.

PLATE 19. A SOFTWOOD PROCESSING COMPLEX

Central to this representative north Swedish coastal scene is the sulphite mill at Svartvik (cf. Chapter XI).

PLATE 20. CONTINUITY OF SETTLEMENT ON THE LIMFIORD

The chimneys of cement plants around Aalborg in Jutland are set beside an exposed pre-historic village with its burial ground.

Fig. 81). The difference between this ideal picture and an actual plant is measured below in relation to a specific Finnish plant.

Economies in detail independently of those in the large-scale organisation of mills are points of attack in most concerns. Waste is a marked feature of the softwood industry. It has been observed that the equivalent of only one out of four trees felled reaches the consumer in finished products. Several types of waste can be distinguished. In the woodlands themselves up to 12% damage may be inflicted upon residual stands by felling. There is loss in logging and peeling or barking waste. A sawdust loss of up to 12% may be incurred. A process loss is almost inevitable —in veneer, it may be as much as 65%, in cooperage, 70%. Indeed, Swedish timber economists aver that if all the saw-mill waste were employed in the sulphate mills it would provide raw material equal to one-third of the entire sulphate group production. The misuse of softwoods for fuel can account for a substantial loss; though it is difficult to provide alternative sources of heat in rural areas. In softwood countries, there is also considerable farm consumption for fencing. Waste arising during the pulp operation is now carefully processed for by-products. Crude alcohol is one of the principal of these.

While changes in transport were reducing restraints, changes in technique were multiplying opportunities. Basic to these was the pressing demand for paper in mid-nineteenth-century Europe and America. Réamur had already written an article on the possibility of using wood shavings as the basis for paper-making—employing wasps' nests experimentally for the purpose. Cylindrical paper drums had already been patented in the earlier nineteenth century by John Dickinson (1809, Hertfordshire) and Donkin (1804, Frogmore); while paper-making machinery began to invade Sweden from 1832 onwards. Mechanical pulp was produced in Germany in 1844, and a decade later *The Times* offered a £1,000 prize for recommendations leading to improved

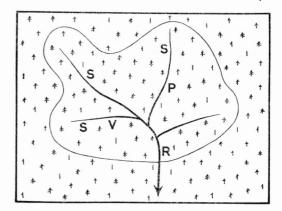

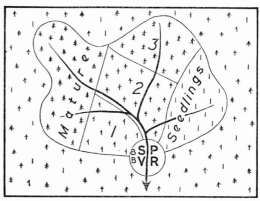

P = Pulp & paper **R** = Rayon **S** = Saw mill **V** = Veneer
B = By-products

FIG. 81. Simple rationalisation of softwood activities. (Based upon E. Glesinger, *The Coming Age of Wood*, New York, 1949.)

paper production. Esparto grass was first seriously imported into Western Europe for paper-making in the 1860s. In 1857, the first mechanical paper-mill in Scandinavia was built at Önan near Trollhättan;[1] the establishment of the first mechanical pulp-mill in Viborg parish in 1860 sounded the death-knell of all but two of the eleven small paper factories which lived on Finnish rag and straw. Paper-making was upon the eve of escaping from what Clapham called its "connection with the dustbin and the rag and bone man". In 1871, *Illustrerad Teknisk Tidning* was running a series of articles on the possibilities

[1] The Swedish story is told in Elis Bosaeus, *Utveckling av produktion och teknik i svensk massindustri, 1857–1939*, Uppsala, 1949, who lists the periodicals which are his principal sources (Ch. IV). Among these must be remembered the correspondence and memoirs in the archives of the Technical Museum in Stockholm. Swedes were clearly alert to pulping potentialities. In the archives of Uddeholm AB., for example, there is a manuscript dated 1869 proposing the establishment of a plant based on the experience of J. E. Cederblom following a study tour to Germany.

of the chemical process. Today, in contrast to Canada, the production of mechanical pulp is relatively less important in Norway, Sweden and Finland than the production of chemical pulp.

Two primary processes are used in the production of chemical pulp. The older of the two is the sulphate process, in which the softwood chips are reduced to pulp by about ten hours' cooking in a digester with a solution of sodium sulphate. This yields newsprints, bulk cardboards and coarse papers. It has given rise to large-scale plants, frequently standing in marked isolation. The sulphate process is capable of dealing with lumber waste and sawdust, and is more independent of the resin content. The commercially successful sulphite process, employing as its primary chemical calcium bisulphite, is attributed to a Swede—Carl Ekman at Bergvik, Hälsingland, in 1872. It yields more refined and improved papers; plants are usually smaller and less commonly occur in isolation.

Pulping is an essential preliminary to paper production. It has led both to a new elasticity in the siting of paper-mills and to a strengthening in the location of established plants. It has also created a more even demand for different kinds of timber; for example, spruce for the sulphite process; spruce and pine for the sulphate process (though pine is sometimes acclaimed the best). The marked distinction which prevails in the softwood countries between mechanical and chemical pulp production is repeated in their varying emphasis upon paper manufacture. The principal pulp producers are not the same as the principal paper producers. Indeed, some of the leading paper manufacturers do not produce pulp at all. Nor is a single word adequate to cover the broad range of specialities emerging from the paper plant. A leading speciality is newsprint; though there are plenty of plants which devote their entire output to wrapping papers (such as greaseproof) or packing materials (like cardboard). Newsprint represents a semi-finished commodity which is substantially modified in the importing country before final consumption.

In the idealised complex of Egon Glesinger,

a rayon plant is included. Artificial silks derived from cellulose pulps are, like paper production, not necessarily tied to softwood-producing regions. Indeed, rayon industries tend to be located less in softwood areas than in their market areas or in regions of established textile skills. The earliest output of rayon in Sweden dates from the close of the First World War; the most significant viscose textile factories in Finland have been constructed since the Second World War (at Oulu and Valkeakoski).

Plywoods and laminates also spring out of the softwood industry; though they are an extension of the saw-mill rather than of the pulp-mill. The first plywood factory in Sweden dates from 1912—sixteen years after the first plant had been erected at Reval. The most important tree for plywood in Europe is the birch. The familiar bonding together of a three-ply timber has yielded to more elaborate laminations—employing plastics as well as softwoods for raw materials. Plywood factories are of limited size, but neither the character nor the range of their products has yet stabilised. In the picture of world distribution, Finland assumes an important place because it is a country of surplus production. In fact, a quarter of the world trade in this commodity derives from Finland. Many countries have established plants during the past twenty years. Associated with the plywood industry is the production of veneer. The high percentage of waste in the industry would appear to favour its localisation close to the site of raw materials; but many countries have built up a plywood industry behind tariff walls. A significant production of wall-board has developed in Northern Europe during the last generation (though the U.S.A. still leads in its production). The first factory in Sweden, now the biggest exporter, dates from 1929. Finland is the second world exporter, and has done much to broaden the range of special insulating boards.[1]

The recovery of an increasing range of chemicals from softwood processing is tied to the research of some of the larger industrial combinations in Northern Europe. In Sweden, Stora Kopparbergs AB. (which owns

---

[1] A. D. Wood and T. G. Linn, *Plywoods*, London, 1951.

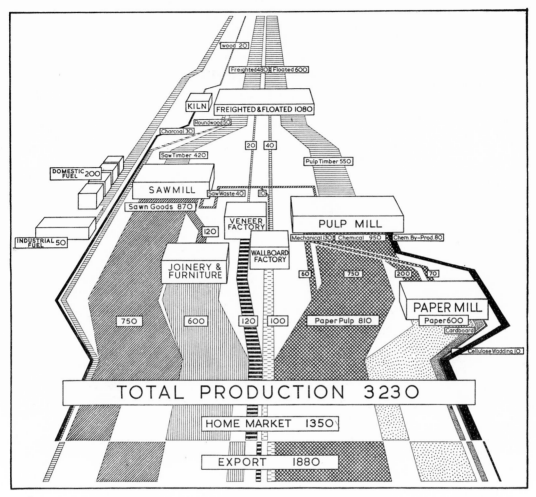

FIG. 82. Softwood processing in Sweden. (Based upon *Affärsbankernas planschserie, Bankföreningens statistiska byrå*, 1950.)

extensive softwood resources as well as mineral deposits) began softwood research as early as 1903. Industrial alcohol is the principal source of recoverable chemicals. Nor in the field of chemical by-products must the match industry be forgotten. The first Swedish match factory—for the production of "chemical tinder boxes"—was started in Stockholm 120 years ago.

The ultimate expression of all these changes is summarised in Table 24 (p. 245) and, for Sweden, in Fig. 82.

The softwood industries are still in process of lively change. To the production and ex-

port of unprocessed raw materials, Norway, Sweden and Finland have added the export of semi-refined products. Traditional products remain, but there is an increasing concentration on refined commodities. The growing range in the degree of finish of softwood exports is accompanied by a growing range in the variety of uses for the material. The distribution of softwood industrial concerns (cf. Fig. 83)[1] has not yet finalised, and plant construction remains a lively feature of the northern forests. In this connection, the birch has experienced considerable revaluation. The manufacture of bobbins gave to it an

[1] Cf. *Suomen Teollisuus*, Helsinki, 1949, 563.

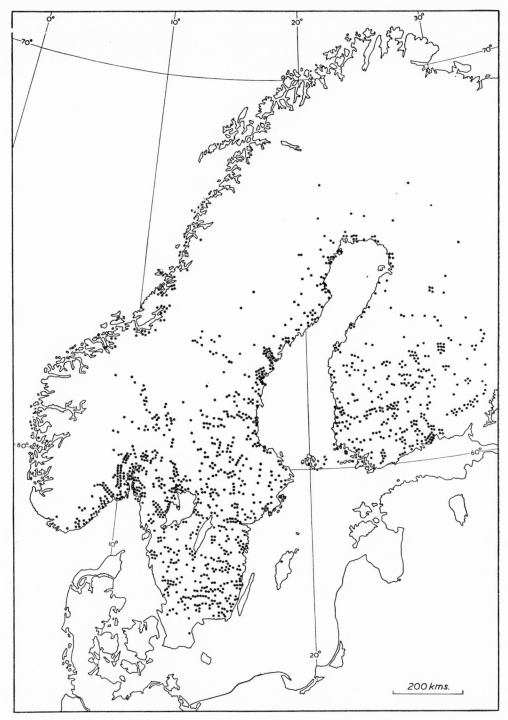

FIG. 83. A distribution map of softwood processing industries in Norway, Sweden and Finland. (Based on *AB. Svenska Trävaru-Tidning*.)

TABLE 24

OUTPUT, 1960

Product	Finland	Norway	Sweden	Canada
	(thousand cubic metres)			
Total fellings	48,090	7,713	44,900	96,429
Sawlogs and veneer logs . .	15,050	3,021	18,000	48,937
	(thousand metric tons)			
Wood pulp	3,699	1,523	4,949	10,397
Newsprint	781	226	582	6,068
Paper and paper board . .	1,978	807	2,151	7,934
Fibreboard . . .	192	125	608	191

(Source: *F.A.O. Yearbook of Forest Products Statistics*, 1962.)

initial significance in a circumscribed area. The plywood and veneer industry has broadened the demand for it. Hardwoods (birch and aspen) are now employed in the manufacture of chemical pulp; though problems of floatage restrict their employment. Their recurrent transformation indeed points the way to the comment of John Evelyn in *Sylva*, 1644: "A foot of wood may be of little value to one trade, but of great value to another."[1]

A SAMPLE SOFTWOOD COMPLEX— MÄNTTÄ[2]

(a) The Genesis of the Plant

The Mänttä concern in west central Finland provides a specific example of a softwood factory to set in the framework of the preceding observations. Mänttä is the parent plant in a combine of four industrial establishments which look to the coniferous woodlands as the source of their primary raw material. Its founder, G. A. Serlachius, an apothecary living in Tampere, might have chosen any one of a number of localities for the plant. In many respects in his youth, Mänttä was one of the least satisfactory localities in the northern part of Satakunta province. It was on the margins of established settlement in the extensive wastelands of Keuru parish. The decisive fact of siting was the fall of water between Koskela and Kuorovesi lakes. There were many superior water falls in the region, but they were either too expensive to acquire

with the available finance or too difficult to harness with the available equipment. The short, swift descent of water between the upper and lower lakes was split into three channels at the time the site was purchased in 1868. A good natural reservoir above the falls guaranteed a steady flow of water, but in order to regulate and maximise the 6-m. fall, the channels were reduced to one.

The location of Mänttä also ensured a generous supply of suitably sized timber. Here, again, there was no precise superiority of siting, though the location of the area peripheral to tar-producing tracts and its thin scatter of agricultural settlement probably guaranteed more abundant and untouched reserves than in many districts. Such a situation was hardly likely to produce a generous labour supply; but then the plant was modest in size in its early stages and factory labour was, from the beginning, brought in from outside rather than recuited from the surrounding unskilled sources. Local labour was, however, both suited to and adequate for the needs of lumbering; while its dispersed distribution was a definite advantage. A network of river and lakeways—rather than a sea of lakes such as characterised eastern Finland— provided routes for the raw material (cf. Fig. 84). The plant sat in the middle of its supply of raw materials and astride its source of energy.

For the receipt of essential equipment and for the marketing of finished products both

[1] The status of the European softwood industry is summarised in *The Timber Industry in Europe*, O.E.E.C., Paris, 1955.
[2] In the preparation of this section, I am very grateful for the ready help and generous hospitality extended by Bergsrådet Erik Serlachius of Mänttä.

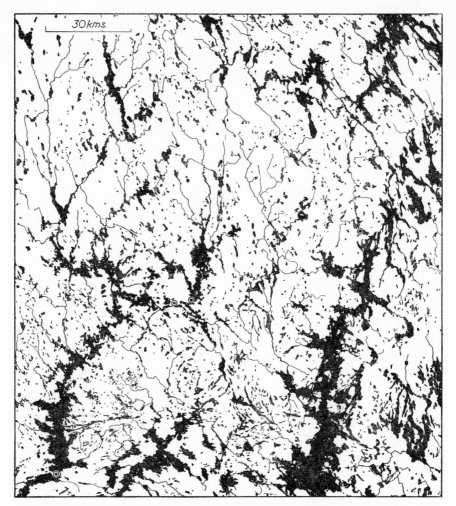

FIG. 84. The pattern of waterways around Mänttä pulp and paper plant.

site and location were initially disadvantageous. Mänttä, indeed, stood aside from established routeways; but slowly and deliberately it was brought into the web of communications. Today, it retains the initial advantages of site, and has shed many of the disadvantages associated with its original location. Consider the problem of marketing mechanical pulp. During the first two years of its existence, Mänttä had no highway communication with the outside world: everything had to move by water. Ten "church" boats were acquired to transport finished pulp over Kuorovesi lake to Maitovalkama, and it took two days for two men to take one boat on

its journey. Large boats could not negotiate the rapids. There followed a 6 km. journey by cart to Lankipohja (loading site of Längelmäki) and a 60 km. steamer journey over Lake Roine to Valkeakoski. Portage to Lake Päijänne, steamer to Hämeenlinna, rail to Lahti and finally (until the completion of the Lahti–St. Petersburg railway in 1870) horse and cart transport to the Neva brought the commodity to market. The miracle is that it ever withstood the physical ardours of the journey, let alone the transport costs piled on by such a plethora of transfer points. Beyond this, of course, such a journey could only be undertaken for a limited period. Autumn and

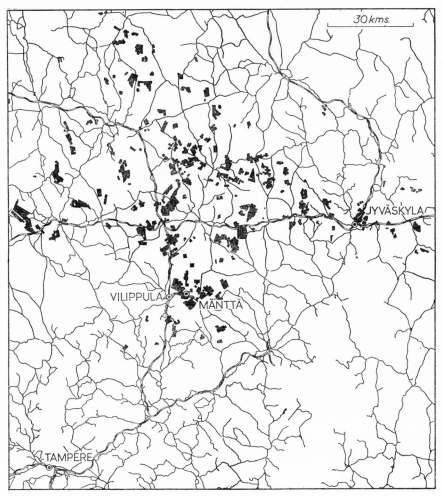

FIG. 85. Mänttä and its company-owned timber lands (marked in black) with its
supporting network of road and railway.

spring eliminated land movement; winter disturbed water movement, though it did offer
opportunity of sleigh transport. Generally
speaking, however, the output of the factory
was accumulated for seven months of the year
and dispatched during five months.

Release from transport restraints came
with surprising swiftness in the course of a
generation. In 1870, a highway link was
struck to Vilpula. In 1876, the railway line
between Turku, Hämeenlinna and Tampere
was to give a new emphasis to western markets already sought as alternatives to St.
Petersburg in 1869. A fundamental tug-of-
war with conflicting interests ended vic-

toriously in 1882 when the railway between
Tampere and Vaasa struck through the territory tributary to Mänttä and passed close by
the site of the parent plant. Two alternative
routes had been proposed for the line—one
running west of Lake Näsijärvi through
populous and developed farming country
which would guarantee a reasonable traffic,
the other running through the wastelands east
of Näsijärvi, which were part of the evolving
Mänttä domain. Numerically, the greatest
support was forthcoming for the former
route. Arguments favouring the latter were
based upon speculation rather than experience—new tracts would be made available for

settlement; new territories would be opened from which Vaasa might draw tar for export. And, of course, the interests of Mänttä were kept powerfully operative. The Vaasa line gave the wasteland location of Mänttä its link with the outer world. The precise site of Mänttä was eventually tied to the national rail system with the construction of a private line. The subsequent development of Finnish state railways gave outlets through Pori and Rauma as well as the established ports.

These lines led to the coastal gateways which gave Mänttä access to its markets. The domestic market was negligible, and from the first the factory looked to consumers beyond the frontiers of Finland. Here, again, the affliction of seasonal movement was felt —independently of the limited means of transport (or direct transport) with consuming centres. There is correspondence at Mänttä which refers to the "summer pleasure cruise" taken by certain machinery ordered in Great Britain for the plant; it visited Hamburg and Oslo before eventually turning up at Mänttä. Orders might take from three to five months to deliver even under most favourable circumstances. The descent of winter only exaggerated the difficulties. Mänttä agitated for improved steamship connections between Turku, Hanko, Helsinki and ports beyond the Baltic. It supported vigorously proposals for the establishment of an ice-breaker service to keep open longer the ports of south-western Finland.

The developing web of communications was significant not only for sales: it became increasingly important for purchases. The infant plant had drawn its original equipment, from Tampere, although its first technicians were German. Both Britain and Germany became sources of machine supply, and by the end of the century America was also supplying paper-making machinery. The location of present-day Mänttä and its daughter plants in relation to established patterns of communication is illustrated in Fig. 85. This relatively static system of routeways, though it does not represent a constant contribution to the operation of the plant is, nevertheless, basic to the main stream of production.

(b) The Flow of Raw Materials

In the factory complex there are several essential flow lines which blend in the main stream of production, which make their imprint on the land and which represent a co-operation of the closest kind between man and physical resource. There is, on the one hand, the flow of raw materials and power; on the other hand, the flow of finished products and waste materials. Raw materials may be divided into those which are available in the immediate vicinity of the plant and those which must be drawn from greater distances. The changing character of industrial processes at Mänttä has called forth a need for raw materials other than softwood timber.

(i) *The Supply of Timber.*— It is interesting to compare Mänttä and its sister plants in the light of the ideal softwood plant proposed by Egon Glesinger. The Mänttä concern owns 48,000 hectares of timbered lands in a relatively settled area. Since its foundation, the company has not ceased to acquire forest investments, but the elaborate pattern of property boundaries inscribed upon the countryside before the coming of the plant has restricted the acquisition of continuous blocks of woodland. Timberlands which have come into the market have rarely been close to each other, and there results as great a fragmentation in company woodlands as in private woodlands. Needless to say, the distribution of woodland owned by Mänttä departs widely from the ideal. It is held in 265 units which vary in size from a little over 1 hectare to considerably more than 1,000 hectares (cf. Fig. 85, p. 247). They are dispersed over hundreds of square kilometres, with some company stands a full 200 km. away from the parent factory. Such a situation might be less unusual in eastern Finland than in western Finland—and eastern Finland, more dominated by lakes, has easier access to timber. Company-owned woodland has been further fragmented as a result of the Karelian resettlement. Compulsory acquisition of cultivable farmland made its initial assault on the company-owned properties.

At the time of its establishment, Mänttä looked primarily to its own woodlands to meet the needs of the plant, while today only 10–15% of its annual timber needs are met by them. The figure varies annually, being higher in bad years, lower in good years. The orientation of the plant is, therefore, to privately-owned sources of supply. Here, of course, the situation departs even more substantially from Glesinger's idealised picture (Fig. 81, p. 241). The number of private purchases conducted annually (frequently through the big autumn timber auctions as well as private negotiations) may total up to 5,000. Quantities thus purchased on the stump may vary from several scores of trees to several square kilometres of woodland.

The expansion of the plant has made for an increasing demand upon the forest resources of the tributary area. Today, Mänttä requires 250–900 cubic metres per day to maintain its output. The rationale of Glesinger's diagram becomes obvious at this point. How is it possible to guarantee the production of a continuingly adequate supply of raw material from the same tributary area unless there is a carefully planned management of the woodlands? There was a short period in post-war years when Finland was eating into its timber supplies faster than their annual growth merited. It was an intrusion tied closely to the land-clearance programme for displaced people, to the demands of material reconstruction and to an economy artificially strained by a reparations programme. The area tributary to Mänttä, however, is assumed to have restored a proper balance between average annual growth and average annual cut. The maintenance of output can be guaranteed directly by rationalisation in silvicultural management; indirectly by all methods of timber treatment which reduce waste. It can also be ensured indirectly by any improvements in transport which spread the incidence of the annual cut more evenly over the available forest area.

Silviculturally, the management of company-owned woodlands is generally superior to that of most others. Commercial companies are better able to discount the present than many smaller private farmer-owners. They are, moreover, accustomed to planning. Silvicultural operations, therefore, simply be-

come another element in the long-term operation of the industrial complex. In this part of Finland, speed of timber replacement may be as brief as sixty years for softwoods, though eighty years is a nearer figure on average soils. Mänttä woodlands consist of 40% spruce, 46% pine and 14% deciduous species with the birch tree dominant. Natural regeneration is dominant, but when there is artificial regeneration the spruce is more commonly sown and the pine more commonly planted. The burn-beating of poor woodland has been reintroduced into the timber practice of the company, though the motives are different from those which prompted the forest firing which was a dominant feature of Finland's woodlands sixty years ago. Administratively, the scattered timber lots fall into twenty-two districts; roughly 100 foresters attend to them under the foremanship of ten advisers. Forestry operations, of course, show great seasonal variability. For the entire winter operation, in both company forests and purchased timber lots, a full 3,000 men may be required at the peak of the season. They may be attended by as many as 1,000 horses. A more average figure through the winter-felling season would be 1,600, with 700 to 800 employees at the low point of operations. In this part of Finland, most felling operations are done from the woodman's home. There is a widely scattered population of small farmers who form a pool of labour readily available for the operation. To a limited extent the caravan is employed, reducing greatly the time spent in travelling. Roughly twenty caravans, accommodating teams of six to ten men, introduce a new element of mobility into timber management.

Felling operations are rationalised increasingly on the cutting site. A hundred years ago in this area the axe was the traditional woodman's tool, and when the saw was introduced it was rejected by the foresters. Now, the motor saw, driven by a small petrol engine, introduces a new force to speed operations. The factory favours the purchase and sale of this equipment to operators. Stamping of logs on the cutting site is increasingly common; almost all timber is now half-barked on the spot by hand. There has been some experimenting with light barking machines.

Rationalisation in transport takes many forms. First, the introduction of the tractor speeds timber removal—especially in the creation of new woodland trackways. The tractor is also valuable for beating down firm sleighways at the onset of winter. Secondly, the motor lorry gains increasingly in prominence. There is some movement at all seasons, though least in autumn and spring. Of all timber converging on Mänttä, 25% travels by lorry, 65% by rail, 10% by waterway. Some twenty lorries are employed full-time; others are hired. Lorries will carry from 10 to 30 cubic metres—depending not only on their capacity but also on the type of timber transported.

(ii) *The Supply of Water.*—Water is needed in considerable quantities in almost all stages of the productive process. It is required as a means of transport in the logging, pulping and milling stages. It is needed for cleansing in the barking machine, for cooking in the digesters, for filtering (at the rate of 20,000 litres per minute) in the bleaching apparatus. Consumption in the pulp-mill at large approaches 80,000 litres per minute. Paper itself is literally born of water.

(iii) *The Supply of Other Raw Materials.*—Mänttä could not function without the micro-elements of its organism. Among them, 3 or 4 tons of pyrites are required daily for reduction to sulphur. They are drawn from Outukumpu, though occasionally and for short periods imported refined sulphur replaces them. Lime derives from Parainen, in south-west Finland, and the consumption is 17–18 tons per day. Some China clay is drawn from Kangas, though it is not an important constituent. Titanium dioxide and dyes for paper find a source in Great Britain and Germany. Chlorine, needed for bleaching, is drawn in equal parts from Great Britain, Germany and a Finnish plant at Aitsa. Rags are another raw material—especially for roofing felts (three parts pulp and one part rags). London, Paris and Antwerp are the traditional sources of this raw material, but exchange control may switch purchases to unexpected sources. Italy, Greece and Turkey have all replaced the West European countries

in the post-war years. It is a curious reflection in the commodity analysis of the continent that the beggar's rags of the Levant may end as Finnish roofing material to keep warm the homes of Muscovy.

(iv) *The Flow of Power.*—If timber decided the location of Mänttä, water-power decided the site. The factory has long since outgrown the 3½ million kWh. per annum which the falls generate. The entire power needed is 80 million kWh. per annum. Of the elements in the Mänttä power system, Kuhankoski is dominant. It dates from 1923, is located 100 km. from the plant and provides 10 million kWh. Additional water-power is purchased from *Imatran Voima*, the state power company; but of the total electricity production, some is also retailed to surrounding parishes. As with the rest of Finland, water-power sags in years of low rainfall so that steam-power is an essential supplement for Mänttä and 25 million kWh. are generated through steam turbines. Coal is the principal source of energy, and in post-war years it has derived from Poland at the rate of 1,000 tons monthly. The seasonal variation of supply is considerable, but stocks are laid in at Rauma, Pori and Helsinki, with Hanko as a winter port in case of emergency. Wood refuse is a third source of energy—two or three car-loads arriving daily from the adjacent saw-mill at Kolho. Southern Pohjanmaa is rich in peat, which was also burnt as an industrial fuel during the war years.

(v) *The Supply of Labour.*—Mänttä plant has 1,300 employees—nearly a quarter of them women. The greatest single demands for labour come from the paper-mill (440 employees) and the pulp-mill (210 employees). The former has a greater proportion of females (210) than the latter (20). A loosely strung settlement of some 6,000 persons is tributary to the mill, which draws some of its labour from distances up to 25 km. Tako mill has 800 employees, Kolho and Kanka average 400–500 each.

(vi) *The Character of Capital Equipment.*—The lay-out of the plant as seen in Fig. 86 gives some indication of the variety of function which has sprung out of the original saw-mill. The plant is stream-lined as much as

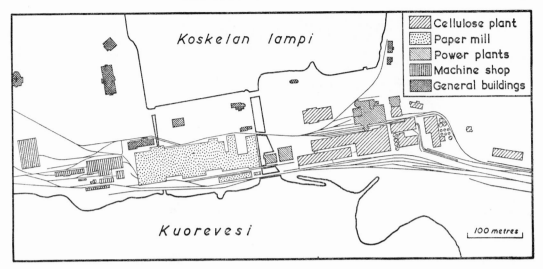

FIG. 86. Mänttä—the plant lay-out.

possible to maintain a continuous flow of material from pulp log to finished papers. In the process, the physical site of the original concern has been considerably altered. Economic operation demands that as complete a balance as possible be maintained between the major capital units required in the several processes. Thus, sulphur-burning ovens must be adjusted to acid tanks; acid tanks to pulp digesters (there are six at Mänttä); pulp digesters to paper-making machines (of which Mänttä has seven). The heaviest capital investment is in paper-making machinery. Such equipment demands uninterrupted operation, though an element of flexibility enters into the end product, since paper-making machinery is capable of producing a variety of different types of paper. The acquisition of ancillary plants—Tako (founded 1865, purchased 1917), Kanka (Swedish Kangas, founded 1871, purchased 1918), Kolho (established by Mänttä in 1910)—has had a twofold effect upon the central company. First it has put a brake upon the diversification of Mänttä. Secondly, the investment of capital in plants other than Mänttä disperses the interests of the company. The degree to which Mänttä and its related factories differ from the planned softwood complex of Egon Glesinger is a reflection of the natural process of industrial growth.

(c) The Output Picture

The production picture may be summed up in an output diagram (Fig. 87), but this cannot give a true impression of the flow of commodities from the plant. For the flow is constantly changing its character—and, in any case, it is a number of streams, not a single stream. Output from Mänttä embraces materials with varying degrees of finish which find their ways deviously as well as directly to the consumer. The degree of finish cannot fail to interest the economic geographer, for it implies an interruption in the process of conversion and the intermediacy of a transport organisation. The first main break in the flow of raw material occurs when it leaves the sulphite mill. The bulk is transferred directly to the paper-mill of Mänttä, but variable amounts are directed to other consumers. It is at this point that the first major integration of Mänttä with its related plants occurs. Tako and Kanka (producing fine papers) absorb the bulk of the pulp shipped, but a small percentage is exported. Of the paper product, two-thirds are shipped in a semi-finished state in the form of bleached and unbleached greaseproofs, semi-crêpes and cellulose wadding. The finished products, roofing felt apart, are dominated by tissues and tracing papers. Output is constantly changing

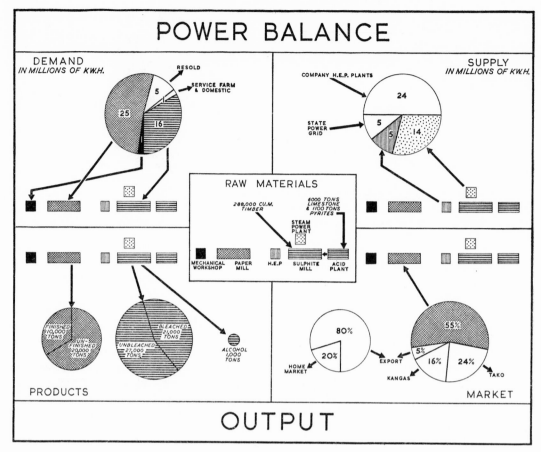

FIG. 87. Mänttä—the power balance.

its form in direct response to market modifications—most countries adjusting their tariff structures against finished papers. A thousand tons of sulphite alcohol are produced annually, and other liquid by-products are sold to highway authorities for binding road surfaces.

(d) *Marketing the Product*

The bulk of the end products of Mänttä are marketed overseas. Almost 100% of the exports travelling from Mänttä on the first stage of their journey go by rail. For the home-market, some 10–15% of the total sales go by road, and in this connection a road service to Helsinki has been initiated twice or thrice weekly. The arrangement of rail freight zones

is such that Mänttä is in a position to avail itself of a number of export harbours.[1] The nearest is Vaasa (231 km.); the most distant, Kotka (386 km.). The principal export harbour is Mantyluoto, outport of Pori (249 km.); though Helsinki (286 km.) is favoured, like Kotka, because of the variety and frequency of shipping services available. The mass of exports moves during the period of open water, but in so far as there is winter shipment, rates to Hanko (376 km.) are levelled to those paid on the normal summer export route.

From Mänttä exports move to markets in forty different countries. This wide dispersal of the finished products is another means of achieving market stability, though the relative significance of the various markets seems to

The relation of Mänttä to its various ports is illustrated in A. A. Säntti, *op. cit.*, Fig. 5, p. 53.

change continuously. It can, however, be said that Great Britain is the principal consumer of paper—taking half of the output of Mänttä. Denmark, Germany, France, Australia and Belgium are the other chief customers.

(e) A Saga in Foresight

Mänttä is the germ about which an industrial concern grew. Its progress has not merely to be measured by size, but by diversification—both characteristics of softwood industrialisation at large. Mänttä has aspired to a vertical integration—linking factory-owned coniferous woodlands with overseas marketing agencies. At the same time it has incorporated ancillary plants which it feeds in part but which in part operate independently. Simultaneously, too, its several constituents are linked horizontally in a loose cartel organisation with competing factories which manufacture similar products.

THE SOFTWOOD MARKET

In the archives of the Geographical Survey at Oslo, there is a manuscript chart by Mr. Holmboe, a custom house surveyor of Christiansand. It shows the distribution of Norway's softwood markets in the 1880s. The chart indicates the significance of softwood products even at a time when the management of this resource and the improvement of its material was in an under-developed state. Today, with softwood production increasingly rationalised, the market continues to expand. Sweden, Finland and Norway co-operate together in many of the markets to which they send their great surplus of softwood products. The volume of their output and the organisation of their marketing gives to them a world status in the softwood scene.[1]

It becomes gradually easier to put the softwood industries of Scandinavia and Finland in their world setting as a result of steady refinement in international statistical material. But by no means all countries make a return—or an adequate return—to

F.A.O. Thus, of the total world production, account is only claimed for 52% of the round-wood cut and 69% of the lumber. Ninety-three per cent. of the wood-pulp and 92% of the newsprint are, however, listed. Table 25 (p. 254) summarises the export picture of the Northern Countries and provides comparative figures for Canada.[2]

There are five primary facts about the softwood market which merit attention. First, softwoods account for the greatest amount of timber entering the annual statement of world trade. It was estimated by the International Timber Committee before the war that they accounted in one year for 92·5% by volume and 87% by value of all timber traded.[3] Neither the absolute quantity traded nor the proportion in relation to the total will have declined, though there are no precise means of assessment.

Next, the market is an expanding market. It is a market which has not yet fully manifested itself in the tropics. "There is no doubt," wrote J. W. Grønggryp, "that up to World War II, the tropics constituted a drain on the forest resources of the northern temperate zone."[4] For constructional, joinery, packing and plywood uses they offered the tropics a cheap material, and demand from these areas has barely begun to assert itself. It is forecast that the total demand in A.D. 2000 will be double that of the present time.

Thirdly, the market at the present time is essentially a hemisphere market. In general, North America and Europe are sufficient unto themselves. Output in each area tends to be almost identical; consumption roughly similar (if assessed by value of softwood imports). Among importers, the U.S.A. leads and the United Kingdom takes second place. In the "American hemisphere", Canada supplies the bulk of softwood exports; in Europe, the order of precedence is Sweden, Finland and Norway. The Northern Countries retain their traditional orientation to the British market, although the structure of their exports has changed. The British market, however, is not without

[1] The status of the European softwood industry is summarised in *The Timber Industry of Europe*, O.E.E.C., Paris, 1955.
[2] Sources of information for the investigator are the Swedish Wood Exporters' Association, the Finnish Sawmill Owners' Association. In Great Britain, the Timber Trade Federation (founded 1892) is the basic organisation.
[3] *Yearbook of the World Timber Trade*, Brussels, 1938, p. 4.
[4] "Outline of a General Forest Policy for the Tropics", *Unasylva*, 1948, II, 1.

TABLE 25

EXPORTS, 1960

(Thousands of Metric Tons)

	Finland	Sweden	Norway	Canada
Newsprint	691	394	177	5,616
Woodpulp:				
Mechanical	1,187	1,100	780	10,397
Chemical	1,101	1,454	581	2,113
Plywood (thou. cu. m.)	414	60	12	1,000
Pulpwood (thou. cu. m.) . . .	3,176	407	0	2,776
Pit-props (thou. cu. m.). . . .	934	18	28	18
Saw and veneer logs (thou. cu. m.) .	346	206	0	50
Total Value of Exports ($ mills.) (1962)	789	845	177	1,601

(Source: *F.A.O. Yearbook of Forest Products Statistics*, 1962.)

long-established links with the North American source of supply, so that the international softwood market is curiously poised about it.[1] North European products compete with Canadian in a market which both by volume and value was the largest in pre-war years, and which, in the post-war period, has again imported more than 95% of its softwood needs.[2]

Fourthly, the softwood market is an increasingly complex market; it is, in fact, many markets. The particular contributions to it vary from country to country. So-called "round wood" has been diminishing in relative importance in international movement. In the lumber picture Canada takes the world lead, with Sweden and Finland following. The same three countries dominate pit-prop production, though they have substantially reduced their exports in recent years. Pit-props apart, the amount of roundwood moving in Europe is very limited. Roundwood, however, is storable, so that the accumulation of stocks can have long-term effects upon world trade. Emphasis today is essentially upon processed timber—classified as sawn, planed and dressed or boxboards. Sweden and Finland, leading in these commodities,

find their main outlet in Great Britain. Here, London, Liverpool, Hull and Manchester are the chief softwood importing harbours; West Hartlepool, Cardiff and Hull specialise in pit-props; London, Hull and Liverpool in plywoods.[3] The centre of gravity of wood-pulp production is in the New World, with Canada and the U.S.A. producing nearly two-thirds. Sweden, Finland and Norway follow in that order. The world trade in wood-pulp presents a different picture from that of production. The U.S.A. and Canada consume together two-thirds of the wood-pulp production. The European countries account for a quarter of the remainder. Newsprint production in the Northern Countries is dwarfed by that of Canada, which accounts for half of the world's output. Within their more limited frames, however, newsprint represents a significant export.

Finally, Sweden, Finland and Norway are increasingly aware of the degree of control exerted by markets. In developing a great surplus of finished and semi-finished softwood products, they have tied themselves to outside markets. Changes in the intensity of world trading are transmitted to them

---

[1] Prices are given weekly in the *Timber Trades Journal*. In 1952, Canadian deals were £60 a standard, Scandinavian, £70, though the dollar shortage must be balanced against any qualitative consideration. (In the 1820s, Quebec deals were £14–£16 a unit, Swedish and Finnish, £17.)

[2] Cf. V. Holopainen, *Fluctuations in the United Kingdom Imports of Softwood and their Causes 1921–1950*, Helsinki, 1953, and also the *Report on the Supply of Imported Timber*, H.M.S.O., London, 1953.

[3] Cf. Malleson and Grugeon, *op. cit.*; also J. MacGregor, "Timber Statistics", *Journal of the Royal Statistical Society*, III, 1953, pp. 298–322.

principally through the softwood market. Similarly, changes in individual markets will be transmitted, for the timber markets are skirted around with a variety of customs duties. Great Britain, for example, imposed a general *ad valorum* duty equal to 10% of the value of the timber entering by the Import Duties Act, 1932. An immense range of variations about this figure, according to the precise nature of the imports (usually the precise degree of finish), makes it both difficult to interpret and to react to. Of all the supplying countries, none is more completely sensitive to softwood values than Finland. And ultimately, all of these changes are transmitted to affect the distributional pattern in the productive process which is the basic object of study in economic geography.

THE SOFTWOOD PROSPECT

After grass, the coniferous woodlands are probably the most important natural vegetative resource. They are not only demanded in their own right, but provide substitutes for many commodities while there are relatively few substitutes for them. Softwood is a multi-purpose resource, the keynote of which is its elasticity in the consumer field. The range of products derived from it continues to expand—there are nearly 5,000 different kinds of paper alone defined today. The range of locations for siting the industries based upon softwood resources is also infinitely elastic; though there is a marked tendency for the resource to give rise to a two-stage industrial structure—with semi-refinement at the source of raw material and final transformation near the point of consumption. This characteristic is largely attributable to tariff policy. Softwood plants are also stabilising elements in the rural communities where they usually take their rise, or in established industrial regions to which they are occasionally attracted.

The coniferous woodlands are a dominant landscape feature of Sweden, Finland and Norway, so that all of these attributes have an exaggerated importance for them. Nowhere in the world is there such keen appreciation of a resource which is not merely in regular but also increasing demand.[1]

The appreciation is the more keen because of the limits to which production is being pushed. Finland and Norway have entered a stage in softwood manufacturing which has called for the delivery of raw materials from the U.S.S.R. Some of Scandinavia's established softwood processing plants can now be supplied more cheaply from the U.S.S.R. than from domestic sources of supply.

[1] T. Streyffert, "World Timber Trends and Prospects", *Kungl. Skogshögskolans Skrifter*, **27**, Stockholm, 1957.

Chapter XII

MINING AND METALLURGY IN THE PATTERN OF INDUSTRIAL ACTIVITY

Der hvor vildsom Ort har været
Og sig grumme Dyr har næret
Nå et gude Skatkammer findes
Hvor den ædle Sølverts vindes.*

Kronene i Havet, Kongsberg silver-mine in Telemark, **Norway**

THE STATUS OF THE INDUSTRY

ONE of the most impressive works of the Finnish artist Axel Gallen-Kallela is called *The Forging of the Sampo*. Its Dark Age setting emphasises the antiquity of mining and metallurgy in the Northern Countries and the distinctive place accorded to them in daily life. Where metals have occurred, monarchs and chancellors have encouraged their development, so that minerals have been a powerful attraction to settlement of the wilderness. As the doggerel* runs at the entrance to Havet mine in Kongsberg—"where once was a wild place . . . now a bountiful source of national income is found".

It is in the nature of mineral occurrence that such "bountiful sources" should show an uneven distribution. There is a persistently uneven distribution of mining and metallurgy both between the five countries and within them; although, as has been observed in Chapter V, regional shifts in emphasis take place with changing techniques. In the Fenno-Scandinavian picture, Sweden leads in volume of raw material production, in the number of persons employed in mining and metallurgy and in the value of output. While mining and metallurgy contribute richly to the balance of Sweden's economy, they make a smaller contribution to the economies of Norway, Finland and Denmark.

It will be recalled that the Northern Countries have experienced a significant change in world status both as mineral and metallurgical producers. Although output has never been greater than today in most fields (Table 26), there has been a relative decline in international status. This decline is related to the supply of raw materials. The Scandinavian metallurgical industries are no longer independent of outside sources of supply. On the smelting side, for example, despite new methods and devices, coal and coke remain to a large extent indispensable. All Scandinavia suffers a deficiency of coal. Only Norway and Sweden produce a little—the former approximately 370,000 tons p.a. in Spitsbergen; the latter, about 200,000 in Skåne. Import is essential (cf. Table 18, Chapter IX). Import of metals also occurs, for they are not necessarily refined or mined

TABLE 26

MINERAL PRODUCTION IN 1964
(*1,000 tons*)

	Denmark	Finland	Norway	Sweden
Iron ore . .		3	1,369	16,220
Pig iron . .	75	644	894	2,336
Copper ore . .		35	15	16
Lead ore . .				68
Zinc ore . .		78	12	77
Aluminium . .		1	261	32

(Source: The comparative tables from the *Yearbook of Nordic Statistics*, Stockholm, 1967.)

within the processing country, as was historically the case. Even Sweden, which is rich in resources, imports iron and steel for specialist processing. The same facts which make such import possible favour an increase in the range of sites for metallurgical plants. Thus, although Denmark lacks primary resources, it has a labour force of 36,000 employed in "metallurgy" and 80,000 in the machine industry.

The relatively small size of the domestic markets of the Northern Countries also acts as a brake upon the scale of their operations compared with countries like the U.S.A., U.S.S.R., Great Britain or Germany. Population may have a relatively high *per capita* consumption, but demand is frequently not enough for significantly large economies to take effect. An international market in which Scandinavian metallurgical products have had considerable success is therefore called in to redress the shortcomings of the domestic market.

This success undoubtedly springs from the increasing diversity of manufactures and the related degree of specialisation. The range of production from the mineral base is being extended as with timber and fish. It is the broader because there is a significant non-ferrous as well as ferrous base. A world market in specialist products with quality taking precedence over quantity is the objective. It is this type of development which has encouraged metallurgy to multiply its growing points near to the final stages of production. Moreover, at this stage the volume of raw materials and transport costs are frequently not sufficiently great to have a restrictive effect upon location. Any one of a range of localities is suitable.

The wide dispersal of relatively small metallurgical and mechanical workshops within the main consuming area of Scandinavia and Finland is one of the continuing features. As a result, it becomes increasingly difficult to adopt any criterion for the satisfactory definition of a metallurgical manufacturing town. The definition of Sten de Geer—a settlement of 10,000 inhabitants with 1,000 engaged in manufacturing—is inadequate. Value added by manufacture or the volume of motive power employed are perhaps more satisfactory criteria in the smaller settlements.

It is natural for industry to breed industry, and mechanical and metallurgical workshops have sometimes grown up around primary processing plants. Sometimes they have emerged as complementary to other established plants. The original industrial development of Tampere in Finland, for example, was rooted in textiles. To this were added metal-working manufactories. It is not inconceivable that the balance of labour in the city also favoured the establishment of locomotive and automobile assembly, for good female employment opportunities in the textile industry have been accompanied by a pool of male labour. Sometimes, the location of metal-working plants has been encouraged by favourable transport, while the frequent association with timber industries[1] is an especially noticeable Bergslagen feature.

While workshop dispersal suggests that there is a growing tendency for some branches of the Fenno-Scandinavian metallurgical industries to be "market-oriented", the concentration of smelteries hints that this tendency does not operate in the earlier stages of processing. In Sweden, the number of centres engaged in the reduction of iron ore was halved between 1919 and 1955. A regional grouping of heavy industries seems to be balanced by a dispersal of lighter activities.

NATIONAL DISTRIBUTIONS

(a) Sweden

The raw material bases for Swedish industry are more varied and in general superior to those of the other Scandinavian lands. To generous timber, moderate agriculture and modest fisheries is added a substantial mineral contribution. The contribution is of long standing and was originally associated with the "iron-bearing lands" and copper mines of the Bergslagen area.[2] The distribu-

---

[1] W. William-Olsen, *Halmstad-Nässjö järnvägar*, Halmstad, 1950, p. 95 *et seq.* and Fig. 32.
[2] F. R. Tegengren tabulates over 300 years of copper and silver production in *Sveriges ädlare malmer och bergwerk*, Stockholm, 1924, Tables 1 and 2.

tion of Swedish ores, however, extends far beyond the confines of Bergslagen, and their range embraces precious and semi-precious, non-ferrous and ferrous metals.

Given means of exploitation and of transport, surveyors began to range the northlands. Their "iron-bearing lands" had been known for at least two centuries before the first loads were being shipped from (what a government commission called in 1736) the "most desolate and inhospitable wilderness" of north Sweden. The centre of gravity of ore output has now shifted to Lapland proper, with a secondary concentration on the coastal tract of Västerbotten. While the larger mines enjoy a European reputation and account for 8% of the world production, the smaller historical centres of production continue to make a distinctive contribution to the domestic economy. With a limited number of significant exceptions, such as Luleå iron-works and the Boliden complex, the centre of gravity of processing has not followed the shifting centre of raw material output.

Both the successful development of the Lapland ore region and the magnitude of its output have combined to focus international attention on it. The combined revolutions in technique and transport have been so profound as to lift Swedish ore production and export to a completely new plane within the span of a lifetime. The present daily production at Kiruna is approximately equal to the 20,000 tons, which represented the annual exports of ore in the 1880s. The Gilchrist-Thomas "basic process" was first applied to export products by the Grängesberg-Oxelösund Company in eastern Bergslagen, and in 1903 this company acquired the Lapland mines. The first ore had already been shipped from Luleå in 1888, and the Narvik railway was completed by 1902. The Lapland ores have a high iron content (60% or more); but even the richest lodes are interspersed with some lower-grade ores which must be sorted and graded. The high ore constituent is accompanied by a very low slag (gangue) content, so that the ores have a high blast-furnace yield. Apatite, occurring in association with the magnetite, is in itself valuable.

There are two principal centres of production in Lapland—Malmberget (Gällivara) and Kiruna (Fig. 88). Both produce the same types of ore and beyond their immediate vicinities there are many other deposits with less concentrated or continuous bodies of ore. Malmberget,[1] in the coniferous woodland zone at 500 m. above sea-level, is the smaller of the two and from it export was first initiated. Malmberget possesses a body of ore 6½ km. long and 100 m. wide. Both the earlier stage of development and the structure of the seam carried mining underground relatively quickly. Some of the product is exported directly after crushing; some goes to the concentrating plant at Vitåfors for magnetic separation. The annual capacity of the concentrating plant is 250,000 tons. There are about 3,400 inhabitants in the Malmberget community.

Kiruna, located in the birch region above and beyond Malmberget, lies about 160 km. from Narvik and 300 from Luleå. The planned settlement with its 12,000 inhabitants lies on the lower flank of Luossavaara ore mountain, commanding a prospect of Kirunavaara across Luossajärvi (cf. Plate 15). The principal Kiruna deposit is steeply pitched, is 5 km. long and as much as 200 m. broad; but there are other horizons and related adjacent deposits. It extends beneath Lake Luossajärvi to reappear as the Luossavaara deposit. Kiruna mines began life as a large-scale open-cast working, the ores from which moved naturally down inclines to the railway at its foot. A gorge over 3,000 m. long and up to 400 m. wide has now been opened up and the workings have struck down to lake level. The end of the open-cast operation is in sight, and underground mining is rapidly succeeding.

Already some underground operations have been under way, but they have hitherto been associated with the crushing of the ore. Improved equipment and mechanical methods of handling the ore at deeper levels offer a continuingly favourable prospect for output. The crushed ore moves off in trains of 40–60 trucks, carrying 1,500 tons (cf. Plate 17). Twenty such trains may leave for Narvik, 8 or 9 for Luleå when output

[1] P. Geijer, "Gällivare malmfält", *Svensk geologisk undersökning*, Series Ca 20, 22, Stockholm, 1930.

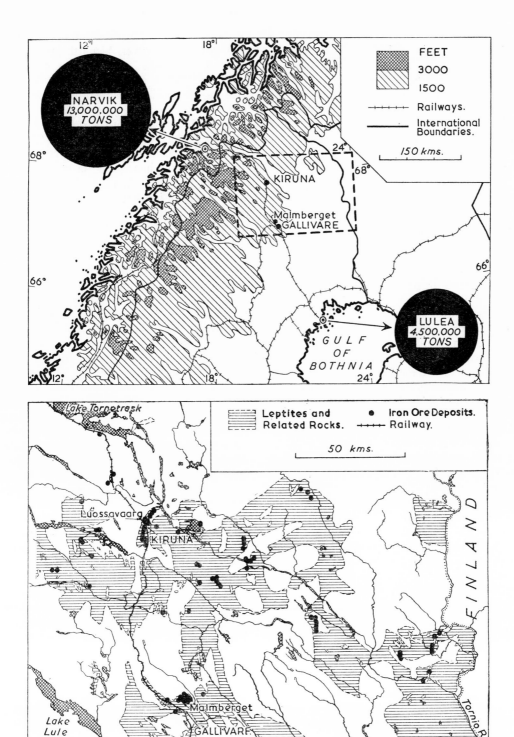

FIG. 88. Kiruna: (above) the setting, (below) with known iron-bearing ores in the vicinity.
(Source: *Swedish topographical survey*; 1:400,000.)

is at full pressure. Production at Luossavaara is modest: the ore body is only 1,200 × 50 m. From the small Rektor mine production has been intermittent.

Narvik, at the head of the Ofoten fiord, is the principal outlet for the ore. From a new settlement in 1899, it has grown to a town of over 13,000 (1960) inhabitants. Its largest quays can take vessels of up to 25,000 tons, which can be loaded by conveyor belt in as little as from 1 to 5 hours. Its facilities for shipment stand at 15 million tons annually. Additional crushing plants at Narvik carry forward the process begun at Kiruna. Stockpiling at the quayside, with 2 million tons in reserve, ensures an uninterrupted flow to waiting vessels; while sampling at the quays enables increasing adjustment to the purchasers' needs. The ore port at Luleå is on the island of Svartö, which can admit vessels of up to 12,000 tons during the 150 days of open water. It has a capacity to handle 13 million tons annually. There are also crushers and stockyards at Luleå. Today, ores are even being shipped from these two base ports by vessels of the Grängesberg group, the shipping interest of which dates from the absorption of the Lule-Ofoten Shipping Company in 1903. A score of ships, the largest of them 25,000 tons, now carry ore to overseas ports. The larger vessels are so designed that they can also carry substantial return cargoes of oil.

While Lapland production is more spectacular it must not be allowed to obscure the enterprise in the Skellefteå area of Vesterbotten— the *mina aurea* of Olaus Magnus. Here, new methods for treating sulphide ores have opened a source of wealth of a hitherto inaccessible character. In Bergslagen, the purification of sulphide ores and the simultaneous extraction of by-products has claimed attention at the Riddarhyttan and Bodås plants. But it is in Vesterbotten that the scale of operations is greatest. For approximately a generation and through a succession of improved processes, the Boliden company has transformed the value of ores in its province. The most noted constituents are the Rönnskär mills,

currently the chief producer of copper and lead, with gold,[1] silver, bismuth and arsenic by-products. Iron pyrites are a second product from the area, with somewhat more than 300,000 tons being shipped annually. The Rönnskär concentrators, having outstripped the resources of the original locating mine of Boliden, now look to the Renström mine as their source of raw materials. Kristineberg, started in 1941, is the second major extractor in the area, also exporting about 300,000 tons of iron pyrites annually by aerial tramway over Rönnskär. Tributary again to the Boliden complex, but more detached in location, is the galena refinery at Laisvall towards the Norwegian border. Its semi-refined lead is also directed to the Rönnskär smelteries. It is natural that in this enthusiastic exploitation of sulphide ores, there should be some failures to counterbalance the successes. Laver, with its copper pyritic plant dismantled and its ores exhausted, has become a virtual ghost site in the Norrbotten wilderness. It is the exception which proves the rule, for Sweden's sulphide enterprise has lifted its pyritic production to 4·7% of the world's total. At the same time contemporary processing yields an end product of considerably greater refinement, and Sweden enters the export market with a fine-grained commodity which stands in contrast to the coarse pyrites offered by many other producers.[2]

Having ores and lacking the most commonly employed fuel—coal and coke—Swedish ingenuity has been taxed to find alternative processes which either eliminate the need for these fuels or substantially reduce the role which they can play. Coke blast-furnaces still accounted for roughly two-thirds of the production in 1951. The persistent employment of charcoal storage sheds as striking components of the industrial "scene" indicates the continuing role of an historical source of fuel in the production of selected specialist steels. But charcoal is expensive. Much more important has been the improvement of processes, such as the Wiberg-Söderfors

---

[1] It is interesting that precious metals should now derive principally as a by-product in the processing of other ores. The northlands never became in precious metals the equivalent of "the King of Spain's West Indies", as Queen Kristina was promised.

[2] P. G. Kihlstedt, "Milling of Sulphide Ores in Sweden", *Anglo-Swedish Review*, 1952, 189–94.

method which dispense with the use of coke or charcoal as *direct* reducing agents. The elimination of solid fuel in the reduction process and its replacement by carbon monoxide and hydrogen in the furnace shaft have enabled substantial economies in the conversion cost. In principle, it is the substitution of hydro-electric power for at least a proportion of the solid fuels which characterises the methods. Thus, to produce 1 ton of so-called "sponge iron", about 260 lb. of coke (or a sixth of the commonly employed blast-furnace total), 140 lb. of oil, 950 kWh. of electrical power, 2 lb. of electrodes and 1 man-hour of work are consumed. To reduce imported fuel requirements means that coal can move increasingly to ore. As in all processes, of course, the economies become the more impressive relative to the scale of output. It is new methods which give to Sweden its continuing significance in the iron and steel industry. Sweden has a *per capita* consumption of iron even greater than that in Great Britain and second only (though only half in quantity) to that of the U.S.A. It has also become an exporter of steel-mills as well as steel products. At the same time, the electric furnace exacts a heavy toll of hydro-electrical energy, so that Sweden is already looking beyond its borders for additional power (cf. Chapter IX) and viewing atomic power as a supplement.

Upon the basis of processed ores, Sweden has erected an elaborate metallurgical activity. In the range of its output it has few rivals. Quality takes precedence over quantity and, although stability in certain fields of output is favoured, flexibility in design is also the objective. Some centres have guided their range of products along traditional lines. Eskiltuna, for example, is popularly known as the Swedish Sheffield, and specialises in knives, scissors, razors, planes, surgical and precision instruments and all kinds of blades. Other industries, such as *Svenska Kullager-fabriken* (S.K.F.), founded in Göteborg in 1907, have distributed their energies among a number of places and scattered their subsidiaries in dozens of overseas cities. It is natural that Sweden's metal-working industries should show an orientation towards electrical commodities—at capital goods and consumer level alike. The manufacture of generators by *Allmänna Svenska Elektriska AB.* (A.S.E.A.) from such cities as Västerås, is for an international market as well as for the domestic. Indeed, a full quarter of Sweden's heavy electrical output is exported and is represented by generators in over forty different countries. A whole variety of cable factories finds its outlet in the hundreds of miles of high-tension cables needed annually in the electrical and transport systems or in the low-tension wires called for by L. M. Ericsson's telecommunications (based on Stockholm). For home appliances, Elektrolux at Motala provides a representative plant; while the AGA company has created a name for itself in domestic stoves as well as in a range of signal appliances. It is natural that metallurgy should also be oriented to an agricultural market and such concerns as the De Laval (in Stockholm) epitomise inventiveness in this field. While the "edge of Swedish steel" has been largely beaten into ploughshares, there remains a persistent armament industry at Bofors (which includes a remarkable aircraft plant). Until more recent years, the traction industries have shown relatively limited development; but the rapid expansion of the domestic market has favoured the rise of electrical locomotive plants at Linköping and the *Volvo* automobile at Göteborg, *Scania-Vabis* at Södertälje and *Saab* at Trollhättan. The automobile assembly plants of Sweden today very closely resemble their Nuffield counterparts in Great Britain, and for their specialised components look to a range of producers (with which they are often integrated). Side by side with cars, aircraft also leave the assembly lines of *Saab*. Motorcycles (such as N.V. at Uppsala) and agricultural machinery extend the range of mechanically propelled vehicles.

Sweden also has a shipbuilding industry of international stature which, intermittently during the last decade has reached second place in volume of construction. There are as many as fifteen substantial shipbuilding concerns. The greatest concentration occurs on the Göta river, where leading enterprises are *AB. Götaverken, Eriksbergs Mekaniska Verkstads AB.* and *AB. Lindholmens Varv*. Malmö also

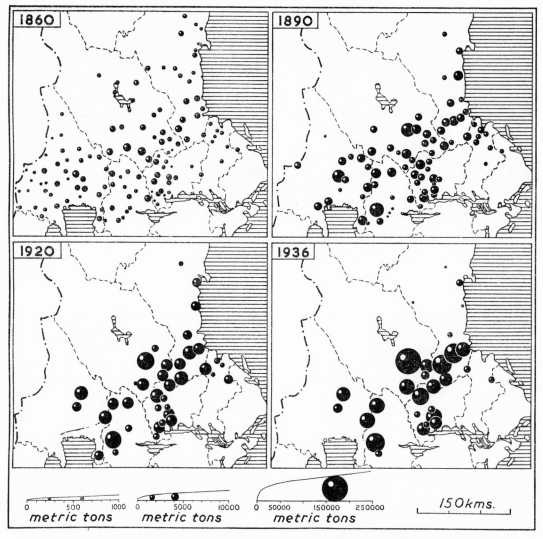

Fig. 89. The changing pattern of iron and steel output in Bergslagen. (After W. William-Olsson, *Ekonomisk geografisk karta över Sverige*, Stockholm, 1954.) See also G. A. Eriksson, "The decline of the small blast furnaces and forges in Bergslagen after 1850" *Geografiska Annaler*, **39**, 1957, 257–77.

has a shipbuilding yard of international scale —*Kockums Mekaniska Verkstad AB*.

Most of Sweden's metallurgical and mechanical workshops are aligned, along the axis between Stockholm and Göteborg—a localisation which continues in the historical tradition. Nevertheless, the present pattern of several thousand plants shows a relaxed distribution. If there are examples of concentration (cf. Fig. 89), there are equally manifold examples of dispersal.

(b) *Norway*

Norwegian mining and metallurgy, like the fisheries and softwood industries, have experienced a transformation. An enterprise, which was rooted in precious and non-ferrous metals, has shifted its mining energy to base metals and its industrial emphasis to ferro-alloys and aluminium. Norway has a range of base-metal reserves (to which a variety of geological surveys in commercial archives of the city of London would testify independently of Norwegian sources). Neither quantitatively nor qualitatively are they comparable with the major reserves of Sweden. For the most part, the reserves are located in high latitudes—a fact which has hitherto hampered, but currently aided their exploitation.

The most outstanding development is that of the Syd-Varanger mines at Bjørnevatn in the hinterland of Kirkenes. The field, with its open-cast workings, has been in operation for fifty years, but has been revivified following wartime destruction and post-war re-equipment. The ores, reserves of which total a minimum of 50 million tons, are of hard, magnetite character and have been compared with the taconites of Minnesota. Iron content is about 35%, while sulphur and phosphorus content is low. The hardness of the ore adds to the problem of crushing and separation, which precede export. The precise nature of the beneficiation (i.e. whether the ore is suitable for direct use in blast-furnaces or whether it must be sintered after import) automatically affects marketing. Briquettes, produced by the pre-war plant, have been succeeded by powdering into (what the Norwegians call) *slig*, while pelletisation will probably succeed this in the future. Power is a natural adjunct of the plant, with 45–50 kWh. consumed for each ton of concentrate. An electric ore railway and the conveyor belts consume additional modest quantities. A thermo-electric plant, employing imported coal, lies behind the activity and is supplemented by a series of smaller hydro-electric stations. Kirkenes exports about a million tons of ore annually and employs about a thousand persons in its industry. Exports, which represent about 80% of Norway's total, are to West Germany and the United Kingdom, with Mo i Rana absorbing growing quantities. In addition to several lesser iron-mines, there are seven companies producing pyrites, of which Orkla mine accounts for about half of the output. Pyrites, copper and zinc concentrates derive from the ores, but the scale of operations is not of the Syd-Varanger magnitude. Copper is also produced from pyrites in the Grong area of North Trøndelag. The products of these domestic mines, to-gether with a range of raw materials in varying stages of refinement from overseas, feed the ferro-alloy plants which account for the principal bulk of Norway's metal exports.[1] In turn, the ferro-alloys are closely related to hydro-electric power for smelting. Among producing plants are the ferro-chrome works at Indre Ålvik (on Hardangerfiord) and Meråker; ferro-silicon and/or ferro-manganese at Porsgrunn, Tinfoss (Notodden), Sauda and Trondheim; silicon carbide near Arendal; electrolytic zinc and cadmium are manufactured in Odda and special steels outside Stavanger. Most of the processing at the oldest significant Norwegian metallurgical establishment—*Christiania Spigerverk*—is now conducted in electric furnaces.

Electric power is similarly basic to the aluminium industry. In the initial stages of its development the production of aluminium was largely sponsored by foreign interests. Fifty years ago, the British Aluminium Company staked its claim, and of the six operating plants on the eve of the Second World War only one was partly Norwegian. The Norwegian Aluminium Company established its base at Høyanger on the Sogn fiord in 1915, linking this smeltery directly with its bauxite interests in Provence. The alumina plant proper, the only one in Norway producing directly from bauxite, dates from 1927. Output is about 8,500 tons p.a., with an additional 600 tons p.a. from scrap metal. Raw materials focusing on Høyanger have a diversity of origins—bauxite from Greece, cryolite from Greenland, petroleum coke from the U.S.A., coal from several European sources. An immediate shipping problem is the absence of return cargoes. Output (c. 6,000 tons p.a.) is directed principally to Holmestrand, on Oslo fiord, where it is converted into a multiplicity of consumer goods. Some is also received by the wire-rolling mills. Both Sweden and Denmark have affiliated plants at Avesta and Amager respectively. The product is increasingly sold to cable and canning enterprises. Although Høyanger is the oldest foundation, both the Tyssedal and Årdal plants have a larger production. The newest plants are at Sunndal and Mosjøen.

[1] H. Christensen (ed.), *The Metallurgical Industries of Norway*, Oslo, 1961.

Norway's shipping interests naturally encourage the development of marine engineering. For the most part, Norway's mercantile marine is constructed in foreign yards, but a significant contribution is derived from home wharves. The principal enterprises are in Oslo (*Akers Mekaniske Verksted*), Bergen, Stavanger and Trondheim. Ship-repairing, however, which is equally important in value and in the number employed to ship construction, is more widely dispersed. The varied skills for which it calls and the range of metal parts makes it of the essence of a metallurgical industry.

Mining, with its approximate score of detached centres of exploitation, stands in contrast to industry which shows a relative concentration. Norwegian industry has a marked southern emphasis, and a virtual industrial region can be detected about Oslofiord. About one half of the industrial establishments of Norway are concentrated there. The concentration includes many metallurgical plants and, on the score of value added by manufacture, Oslo fiord makes the major contribution to this branch of activity. The value of ores and metallurgical products in the export total of Norway now exceeds that of paper and pulp.

(c) *Mining and Metallurgy in Finland*

Mining has a limited development in Finland, but it would be dangerous to underestimate the Finnish potential. Mining has deep roots in the south-west of the country and the metal industry has been most persistent there. The country around Lohja, Tammisaari and Kisko bears relic evidence of the search for ores; while the outskirts of Helsinki have been pitted and tunnelled for them. Fiskars, founded in 1658, was one of the first significant steel-producing centres employing local ores. In its natural setting, Fiskars has many of the superficial characteristics of Dalarna, and eighteenth-century Sweden might well regard this as a little *Bergslag* across the water. "More sublime and interesting than Dannemora," appears the observation in the Fiskars visitors' book by

D. Pennefeather. The *Bergslag* geology is not repeated here in the same way; but it is clear that there is some continuity of contact between the Leptite area of east Sweden and the south-western corner of the Finnish peninsula. One of the characteristics of the old sea charts covering the route between Stockholm archipelago and the south coast of Finland is the warning—*Här kompass förvillas*. Magnetic ores disturb compass pointers in particular at the approach to Mariehamn and off the island of Jussarö. The tower of a new mine shaft at Nyhamn, in the Åland islands, now overtops any of the lighthouses and is the entrance to potential workings.

Iron ores occur in many places in Finland, but the mineral content of the parent rock is low and the volume of material offers no base for long-term production. Iron is, however, reduced from the copper-bearing rock of Outokumpu and the Vuoksenniska plant grew out of this waste material. In post-war years iron has been mined at Otanmäki (cf. p. 121), and its production at Kolari, in western Lapland, is debated.[1] The output is a modest 500,000 tons p.a. At no point in Finland is steel produced on the site of the ore. Such ore production as there is moves towards more powerful localising forces—labour, energy, established plant. A state-sponsored steel plant has been erected near Raahe, in Ostrobothnia.

Copper is much more important in the contemporary Finnish scene. Outokumpu, in eastern Finland, was established in 1925 and remains the controlling interest. The ores of the original mine have a $3\frac{1}{2}$–4% copper content (plus 27% iron): ancillary plants have now been opened at two other localities in eastern Finland—around Kisko and at Ylöjärvi. Copper undoubtedly occurs in other places. Zinc is the third ore of commercial consequence, and Finland accounts for 1% of the world's output with a somewhat larger production than Sweden. It is mined at Vihanti in Ostrobothnia. Finland's nickel deposit, probably the largest in Europe and developed from 1935 onwards by Canadian Nickel Mond, was sold to the U.S.S.R. with the loss of the Petsamo corridor in 1944. It is always diffi-

---

[1] *Bergwerkshandlungen* in the Finnish State Archives give past data; I. Hustich *Finlands råvarutillgångar*, Helsingfors **1953**, Chapter I, provides present data.

cult to forecast the direction of development, but government reports have at least cast an eye upon Tuusniemi, Kuortane, Nilsiä and Paltamo as possible centres of mineral extraction.[1] Summer prospecting and panning for gold—especially along Lemmenjoki in Lapland—give rise to much enthusiasm but a mere 30–50 kg. annually of refined ore.[2]

Metallurgical industry is based upon these domestic products and imported ores and fuels. Scrap is also an essential import, so that the plant at Karhula, in south-eastern Finland, employs a miscellany of European scrap for much of its smelted product. Metallurgical plants are located chiefly in the south and especially in the south-west. The Finnish industrial handbook, *Suomen teollisuus*, listed 165 major metallurgical plants in 1951. Among these, two types are perhaps outstanding. Historically, there are the machine shops which have been concerned essentially with transport. Shipbuilding, based initially on timber, was begun by Friherre Chapman in the wharves of Suomenlinna in the eighteenth century. It has its descendants in the yards of the South Harbour of Helsinki. Crichton Vulcan yards in Turku also build vessels of up to 7,000–8,000 tons. Related to transport are the locomotive, automobile and tractor assembly units. Copper is refined in a multitude of workshops; though, again, they are in detachment from the site of the mines. Outokumpu ores are manufactured in Pori; while Helsinki has the largest number of metallurgical workers using copper as an essential component. Copper is inseparable from the electrical industries—born, in some respects, in Varkaus, but contemporarily concentrated in the capital.

Finnish metallurgical industries occupy a peculiarly significant position in the economy, and in some ways their status is unnatural. The heavy reparations programme called for their rapid expansion, and at one time more than 80,000 employees were associated with them.[3] The completion of reparations in 1952 left the industry without a guaranteed market and, as a result of relatively high production costs, with little prospect of finding an outlet alternative to the U.S.S.R. The industry at large continues to look eastward for its market, though the labour force has fallen to about 60,000. Nevertheless, employees still number not far fewer than those engaged in the timber-processing industries, and value of output *per capita* is high.

(d) Denmark—Metallurgy Without Mining

The occupational census of Denmark lists almost half a million inhabitants as engaged in manufacturing, and within this group the diverse metallurgical activities have a labour force approached only by that in the textile and clothing industries. Until the war years, primary smelting was scarcely known in Denmark, but a rolling-mill, employing scrap-iron, was established at that time. A limited amount of pig-iron (*c.* 150,000 tons p.a.) is now also produced from imported ores; although the economics of this procedure become increasingly uncertain with movement towards an inter-Scandinavian customs union and the rise of the large-scale state projects of Luleå and Mo i Rana. Foundries (such as the 200-year-old De forenende Jernstøberier) and engineering works supply materials for a range of machine shops. They seem to conform to the general principle that economic activities tend increasingly to be located near to the markets and are less tied to the site of raw materials. Semi-processed materials (e.g. aluminium for the Copenhagen plant and copper for the Northern Cable and Wireworks of Copenhagen) are imported. Farm and dairy machinery, cement-making machinery (remembering the geological background which favours cement production in Denmark), marine and stationary internal-combustion engines (from the pioneering diesel plant of Burmeister and Wain in Copenhagen), swallow up much of the output. Shipbuilding yards, totalling fourteen in number and employing as many thousands, make steady demands for steel. The largest are located in the capital and at Elsinore The Scandinavian Iron and Steel Commission, reviewing future

[1] *Valtakunnansuunittelukomitean mietintö*, Helsinki, 1954.
[2] The continuing thread of interest in gold is evidenced from the appendix (pp. 208–22) of A. Laitakaari, *Geologische bibliographie Finnlands, 1555–1933*, Helsinki, 1934.
[3] Developments are outlined in *Finlands metallindustriförenings årsberättelse*, published yearly.

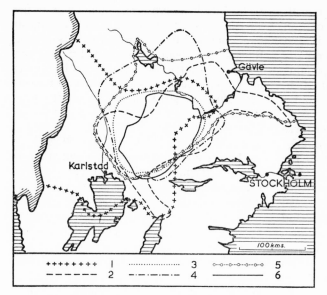

Fig. 90. A selection of boundaries defining the industrial region of Bergslagen: (1) S. de Geer, *Ymer*, 1918; (2) W. Credner, *Landschaft und Wirtschaft im Schweden*, Breslau, 1926; (3) N. Zenzen, *Nordisk familjebok*, Stockholm, 1925; (4) S. de Geer, *Ymer*, 1925; (5) H. Nelson, *Sveriges kulturgeografiska provinser*, *Ymer*, 1918; (6) S. de Geer, *Atlas*, Stockholm, 1917.

A personality of this kind is identifiable in Sweden's *Bergslagen*. *Bergslagen* has immediate meaning for a Swede; moreover, many of the elements which identify it can be pointed out on the ground. It would be possible to speak of *Bergslagen* as an economic region, for there is a similarity of human activity over a fairly continuous area; it could even be more narrowly defined as an industrial region. At one time *Bergslagen* had concordance with a group of physical features. For a number of reasons, however, the economic region has slipped the bounds of the earlier physical margins.

It is probably this particular quality which has defied the geographers who have attempted to pin down *Bergslagen* cartographically. A generation ago, the German geographer F. Seebass assembled more than a score of definitive statements about the area

developments in the north, must pay regard to the weaker position of Denmark. To compensate its mineral deficiencies by creating within it a coking plant to supply the needs of other northern consumers might well be a means of striking a balance.

BERGSLAGEN—AN ECONOMIC REGION IN A METALLURGICAL CONTEXT

The nineteenth century witnessed a rich proliferation of "geographical games" for children; among twentieth-century counterparts for the adult geographer, none has been more popular than "hunt the region". This game has been played with equal zest by British and continental geographers. At their most simple, regions may be defined as "areas homogeneous with respect to announced criteria"[1] and the criteria may be physical, human, economic, agricultural and so on. It is contended that as a result of their joint occurrence, associations of landscape features give to a particular place an especial personality.

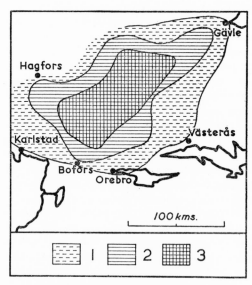

Fig. 91. The core of Bergslagen: (1) the ore-smelting area; (2) the zone of iron- and steel-works; (3) the zone of related mechanical workshops. (Source: E. Astmer, *Ymer*, 1937.)

[1] One of the most satisfying contemporary statements is by Preston E. James, "Towards a Fuller Understanding of the Regional Concept", *Annals of the Association of American Geographers*, 1953, XLII, 3, 195.

—a list which could be extended today.[1] In Fig. 90, the outlines of six of the principal definitions are superimposed upon a simple base map.[2] The broad transitional zone between the central core of coincidence and the outermost margin indicates the breadth of authoritative difference in the definition of *Bergslagen*. The degree of divergence of opinion is the more striking when the scale is recalled. The methods of delineation—whether they are field work or statistical analysis—will also affect the shape of the boundary (cf. Fig. 91). *Bergslagen* in its entirety is too big for satisfactory treatment by field work; while the character of its administrative framework sets limits to the accuracy of statistical plotting. *Bergslagen* has been approached in a number of different ways by Swedish geographers. Their work is used here to build up a descriptive picture of a significant constituent in what may be termed the hierarchy of economic units. Broadly speaking, it follows the approach of P. Fickeler in his appreciation of Siegerland, which presents a not dissimilar territory as an example of the harmonious association of economy and geography in historical evolution.[3]

Bergslagen is a loose name covering the mining district of Central Sweden. It is most extensive in the provinces of Värmland, Gästrikland and Dalarna, but extends beyond them into Västergötland. The area might with greater correctness be spoken of in the plural—*Bergslagerna*—since it consists rather more precisely of a group of ten mining districts. The suffix *lag* signifies a district or hundred and is found commonly in the Swedish administrative division *tingslag* or *skeppslag*—the framework of which is plotted on the Swedish topographical series 1:50,000. The word *bergslag* originally referred to a community of *bergsmänner* or miners who held legal rights to work co-operatively a specific mining district. The initial *bergslagerna* were, in fact, administrative areas in their own right, preceding the local government framework of

later years and leaving a legacy of placenames which, of course, refer no longer to their original geographical area (cf. Norbergsbergslag, Skinskattebergslag). The importance of the mining area for commercial and military purposes gave rise already to a central authority—*Bergs Kollegium* in Stockholm in the reign of Gustavus Adolphus. A rich storehouse of historical material appertaining to *Bergslagen* is found there, with minute accounts of the output of almost every mine, smeltery and forge. Records have been kept the more assiduously because the area has always made a substantial contribution to the national exchequer. One of these mining centres—Stora Kopparbergs AB. in Falun—was proclaimed by early monarchs to be the realm's primary source of taxes. The Central Statistical Bureau summarises mining and metallurical statistics in its annual publication *Bergshantering*, the figures of which place the region in its national setting.

Geographically, *Bergslagen* occupies an area of transition (Fig. 90, p. 266). It spans the territory between the midland plains and the northwestern mountains. *Bergslagen* has developed against the background of range and valley land—subdued in its southern reaches, monumental towards the Norwegian borders. Altitudes vary from less than 100 m. in the south to more than 1,000 m. in the north. Geological "atlases" accompanying descriptions of specific mining areas (for example, Dannemora, Nordmark) emphasise the varied and complicated bedrock. The most important geological feature for the development of *Bergslagen* has been the occurrence of a zone of leptite formations. It is within these that the mineralised lodes occur. The lodes are found in many different horizons which, coupled with the contorted and eroded topography, make for widely varying conditions of accessibility (Fig. 93, p. 269). One permissible definition of *Bergslagen* would be the mineralised area—the 15,000 sq. km. iron-bearing tract (*järnbäraland*) with its related copper, lead,

[1] "Versuch einer kulturgeographischen Beschreibung und Umgrenzung", *Nordische studien*, Braunschweig, 1928.
[2] The device of superimposition has been effectively employed ethnographically by H. R. Wilkinson, *Maps and Politics*, Liverpool, 1952, and politically by K. Sinnhuber in "Central Europe, an Analysis of a Geographical Term", *Transactions Institute of British Geographers*, 20, 1954.
[3] "Das Siegerland als Beispiel wirtschaftsgeschichtlicher und wirtschaftsgeographischer Harmonie" *Erdkunde*, VIII, 1954, 15–50.

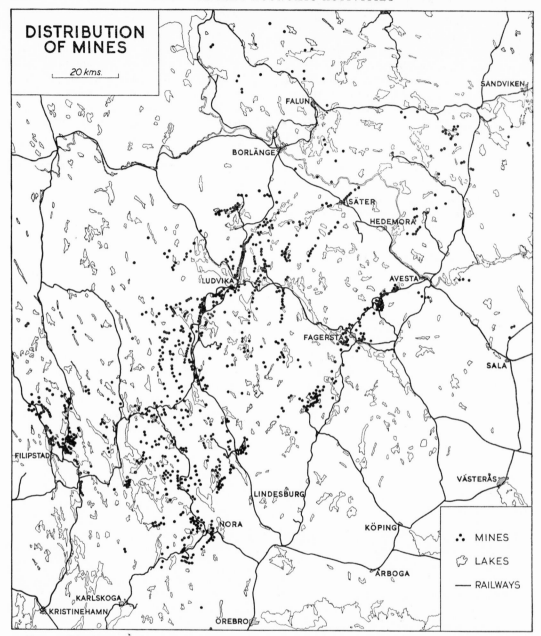

FIG. 92. Distribution of iron mines in the Central Bergslagen area. (After P. Geijer and N. H. Magnusson, *op. cit.*, Fig. 56.) F. R. Tegengren (*op. cit.*, Fig. 31) gives the complementary distribution
for precious and semi-precious ores.

zinc and sulphur—which the *bergmänner* operated. This definition satisfactorily includes Östergotlandsbergslag which lies south of Lake Mälaren and east of Lake Vättern.

Sample geological surveys, which give a good idea of the work of *Sveriges geologiska undersökning*, are those covering the Grängesberg[1] and Karlstad[2] sheets.

[1] N. H. Magnusson, *Svensk geologisk undersökning*, 177, 1934.
[2] N. H. Magnusson and G. Lundquist, *Svensk geologisk undersökning*, 174, 1933.

Bergslagen is also a countryside which has been much changed by ice action. The higher rock massifs have been substantially eroded; the valleys have experienced an immense volume of infill. As a consequence, the preglacial drainage pattern has been completely altered and the present network of waterways offers an extremely immature successor. Three observations of consequence for local development within the broader picture of *Bergslagerna* may be made. First, the volume of water flowing through the contemporary valleyways is less than that of the immediate post-glacial period. Secondly, the erosive power of the streams has been differentially modified by isostatic uplift. The changing form and contours of Lake Mälaren since Iron Age times

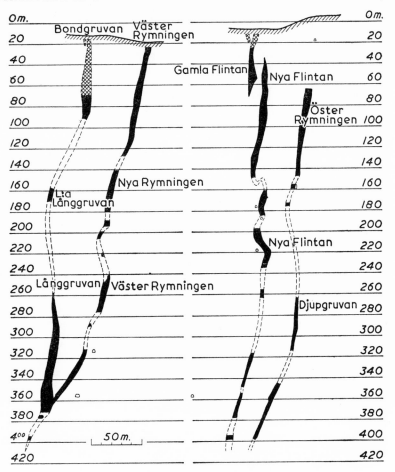

FIG. 93. Distribution of the ore body in a sample mine in Bergslagen. (Source: P. Geijer and N. H. Magnusson, *op. cit.*)

most clearly evidence this. Thirdly, the contemporary river systems in *Bergslagen* have highly irregular profiles. Their courses are beset with rapids and falls. Fig. 94 takes the single skein of a river—the Kolbäcksä— out of the warp and weft of *Bergslagen*. The Kolbäcksä emerges from the Dalarna border country and drains into Lake Mälaren. The course of the waterway and its related settlements are taken from *Topographic Map of Sweden*, 1:100,000. The single water-course which emerges between below Hallstahammar to cross the lacustrine plain has a bewildering array of head-waters. Such a capricious drainage pattern has encouraged men to play with water in a variety of ways. They have sought to master it as farmers, to harness it as

manufacturers, to modify it as navigators. Hydrographically, *Bergslagen* is divided between North Sea and Baltic Sea drainage. It shares the lakescape of central Sweden in its orientation of Lake Vänern and Mälaren and the southernmost of the major eastern rivers (Dalälven) which give such pronounced character to the Baltic slope. In the profiles of Dalälven to the east or Klarälven on the western margins are writ large the characteristics of lesser waterways like the Kolbäcksä.

The area is transitional in other respects. Climatically, it lies partly on the margins of the Swedish midlands (which admit the Atlantic cyclones) and partly in the lee of the Scandinavian keel (which largely excludes their influence). Climatic features of Sweden's

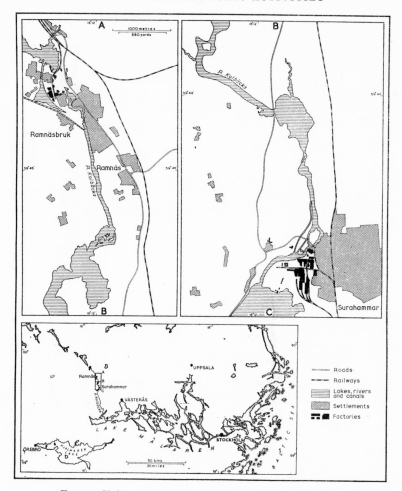

FIG. 94. Kolbäckså—the thread of a single Bergslag river.

northland penetrate deeply into certain of the *Bergslag* valleys where temperature inversions add to the hazards of cropping. Locally and by contrast, features of the south Swedish agricultural scene advance northwards. Thus, apart from the backdrop of furrowed uplands, the Stora Tuna plains recall the Scånian scene in the extent and continuity of their arable area.

Bergslagen spans the countryside between the agriculturally dominant midlands and the silviculturally dominant northlands. Many administrative districts within *Bergslagerna* return an 80% timber cover and as little as 5% cultivated area. Silviculturally, it is also transitional to the coniferous forest proper,

for the northern limit of the oak—running from north-west to south-east virtually bisects it. In few parts of Sweden have the coniferous woods been more valuable historically. Indeed, the softwood forest must be accounted the third definitive constituent of *Bergslagen*—for where the softwoods weakened or disappeared, there an essential element of *Bergslagerna* was withdrawn. Within *Bergslagen* there are extensive heaths, but even here the pine covers the sandy wastes. The weakening or disappearance of the softwood cover was attributable more to human action (clearing, charcoal burning, felling) than to innate physical restraints.

In brief, then, the physical characteristics

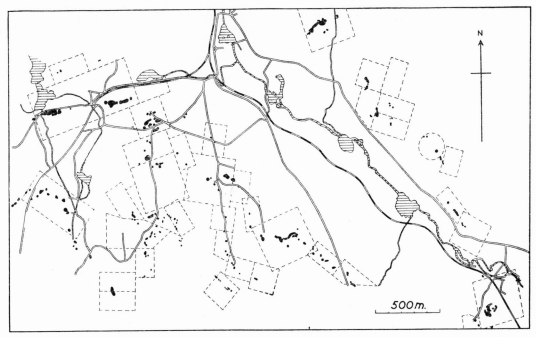

FIG. 95. Ore occurrence in relation to a sample distribution of property boundaries in Stribergs orefield in Bergslagen. (After P. Geijer and N. H. Magnusson, *op. cit.*)

of *Bergslagen* spring from the association of an easily recognisable mineralised zone with an area of topographic, climatic and vegetational transition. There is no readily defined central area where these features are strongly impressed and towards which topography naturally favours human gravitation.

Historically, the *bergmänner* practised a well-defined seasonal round—with summer in the fields, autumn charcoal-burning in the woods, winter in the pits or at the smeltery. Farming in *Bergslagen* shows almost the entire Swedish range—from restricted subsistence endeavour in the more isolated valleys, through the "yeoman" farming of the *Gösta Berling* country to the broad plains of Dalälven. The astute Hans Järta in his *Ämbetsberättelse över Stora Kopparbergslän* (written in December 1822) emphasised the organic unity of farming and mining—insisting upon their complementary demand for labour and pointing out that perhaps as a result of the metallurgical association, their "agriculture was more advanced than in most other provinces". The traditional link between farm and mine is now largely broken and the two operate in isolation

(so far as labour is concerned, in competition). There are, however, still some persistent associations, for most of the larger *bruk* or factory establishments embrace related estates. Uddeholm, for example, has sixteen farms—the one adjacent to the headquarters of the company is affectionately called "the home farm". Bearing all these facts in mind, it is small wonder that Dalarna, perhaps the most characteristic component province, should be called "Sweden in miniature".

In pursuing a regional theme, it is perhaps more helpful to seek it in the particular employment of the four resources of the area—timber, farmland, minerals and water. These constituents have naturally been of varying importance in the past, and the debris from their past use not merely gives some indication of changing values but in itself becomes a distinguishing feature of this Swedish tract. The peculiar employment of its resources and the widely varying conditions of their ownership (cf. Fig. 95) give to *Bergslagen* a landscape marked by curious, often violent juxtapositions. The smith and his smeltery have been at one with the farmer and his *fäbod* (or summer pasture). Antiquity and modernity sit side by side. New factories survey the overgrown ruins of old. The spent mines and spoil-heaps of one generation lie next to the new shafts which penetrate several thousands of feet into the ground to strike new horizons or new ores. Several stages of technical development may operate simultaneously in the same plant. A primitive tranquillity exists round the corner from heavy modern industry. The elk still roams within a kilometre of the electric furnace. "The native", in the Hardy sense, lives next door to cosmopolitan neighbours. In part it has been these aspects of *Bergslagen* which have appealed to travellers, for it has been a distinctive tourist area since the eighteenth century, and many fine topographical accounts have been written about it. Early visitors were especially impressed by Falun mine which, in its heydey, had few European rivals —and in its colour, if not its magnitude, remains a rival to the spectacles of northern Minnesota. Among visitors, the Cambridge mineralogist and topographer Edward Clark provided in his *Travels* (Vol. 3, London, 1823) one of the most graphic descriptions. Falun was "a cave of Cyclops rather than a city", smokedarkened so "that there is twilight at midday", blackened by soot, sterile of plant life, an industrial scab. Factory owners within the mining area were also frequently patrons of the arts and a substantial number of commissioned works give a clear impression of the *Bergslag* industrial scene from the last two centuries (cf. Plate 14). As a study in contrasts, the landscape of *Bergslag* was one likely to exert an especial appeal to artists. It remains, too, a countryside of Indian summer colouring—directly reflecting the minerals. As a by-product of smelting, sulphur and raw ochre are recovered. Raw ochre is basic to the red colouring which is ubiquitous in Sweden, but nowhere is it more a constituent of the landscape than in *Bergslagen*. One

may speak, indeed, of the red hamlets of Dalälven.[1]

Metals were won from ore in Sweden before *Bergslagen* existed as the centre of production. Bog ore and charcoal were the prehistoric foundations of an industry which continued to be dominated by these resources until the fifteenth century and which has employed modest quantities of them in the twentieth century. *Bergslagen* took precedence when the sources of reduced metal shifted from swamplands to ore-bearing rock. Rock-ore reduction began in the thirteenth century with silver smelting, to which copper smelting was added in the 1280s (from which decade Stora Kopparberg dates as a mining corporation). The first iron-mining charter was granted in 1340, and the *monte ferri* were calculated to become of increasing significance with growing Swedish military demands. The winning of ore disturbed land ownership. Olaus Magnus recorded the husbandman hastily covering ore veins with dung lest "some nobleman of the treasury shall put him out of possession". Increased output of ore and its refined products called for increased labour supplies. In the later sixteenth century, Finnish settlers were given the right of immigration, and they cleared parts of Värmland as well as engaging in metallurgical activities. Not many decades later, skilled Flemish, Walloon and German immigrants were encouraged to move in beside those of Savo and Häme.[2] The domestic policy of de Geer and the external policy of Gustavus Adolphus gave to *Bergslagen* a position of international stature. In the mid-eighteenth century, the cluster of mining and metallurgical centres exported half of their produce: copper went to forty different mints, and iron and steel became an essential basis for Britain's revolution in industry. As Selma Lagerlöf wrote in *Gösta Berlings Saga:* "Every stroke of the heavy hammers that forged the smelted iron into shape brought a ducat."[3]

---

[1] Red ochre has given rise to a book—A. L. Romdahl, *En bok om rödfärg*, Stockholm, 1950, and has prompted Eric de Maré (*Scandinavia*, London, 1952, p. 83) to write "a whole history could be written on the subject of the æsthetic influence of Falun red on Swedish landscape painting".

[2] The international character of *Bergslagen* population is persistent. In 1951, for example, nearly a tenth of Hallstahammar population were aliens, and they derived from a score of European countries.

[3] The scene is brought to life by the prolific topographer Abraham Hülphers (*Dagbok öfver en resa i Stora Kopparbergs Höfdingedöme*), and its processes were stimulated by men like Reinhold Angerstein, who went abroad on technical study tours (manuscript, *Dagbok öfver resan genom England, 1753–55*, Jernkontoret archive, Stockholm).

PLATE 21. THE HAGFORS PLANT IN BERGSLAGEN

This is one of the constituents of the Uddeholm concern and occupies a representative setting in the Swedish province of Värmland (cf. Chapter XII).

PLATE 22. A VIEW OF MO I RANA

The iron and steel plant of *Norsk Jernverk* is a state-sponsored industry which has been established in a rural area of Nordland in the post-war period.

The components of production employing *Bergslagen* metals have gradually assumed a recognisable form and established location. A number of these can be identified. Apart from the mine and the charring pit, there has been the *hytta* or blast-furnace. The suffix *hytta* is still a widespread place-name element in *Bergslagerna*, though it is no longer indicative of the contemporary occurrence of a furnace. The changing distribution of *hytta* is seen in a series of maps which illustrate the books of both Bergsten and Weinhagen.[1]

A second component which has left a legacy of place-names is the *hammar*. *Hammar* names indicate the sites of water-driven sledge-hammers. The original *hammar* sites were much more restricted in locality, and have been much more persistent in attachment to position than the *hytta* sites. This persistence is well illustrated at Morgårdhammar today, where a powerful millrace which once operated a hammer now generates hydro-electric power beneath the mechanical workshop. The *hytta* and *hammar* were, in effect, primary constituents in the economic hierarchy.

An example of a more evolved constituent in the *Bergslag* scene is the *bruk*—a distinctive concept in the vocabulary of the area.[2] *Bruk* is a Scandinavian collective noun, elastic in connotation, which can embrace the manufacturing plant together with its servicing institutions and related living accommodation. Some idea of the composition of a *bruk* (and, of course there are the *glasbruk*, *pappersbruk*, *sockerbruk* as well as the *järnbruk*) is obtained by turning to the telephone catalogue of a town such as Fagersta. Fagersta today consists of much more than its metallurgical plant, but Fagersta *bruk* existed as an administrative complex before the town existed as an administrative unit. The town adheres to the *bruk* rather than the *bruk* to the town. The *bruk* today has changed with the changing economy. The formerly independent institution has now been largely absorbed into a vertical or horizontal combine or has changed its function to become a specialist cog in the wheel of

Bergslagen industry. Yet at the local level, its influence and role have frequently altered little, and some independent organisations remain. The watchful eye which once surveyed the plant, with its associated domain, from the adjacent *herrgård* or patronal mansion, is now that of the company administrator. The community is subordinated to the *bruk* in the benevolently despotic manner which would have appealed to Robert Owen.

Bergslagen continues to be a territory of population transition. Its constituents span a steep population gradient which extends from the relatively densely peopled Swedish midlands to the thinly peopled spurs of the southern keel. Settlement density is reflected in the arrangement of church parishes and lesser civil divisions. The proliferation of local boundaries in the south and centre of *Bergslagerna* yields to the spacious northern parishes on its Jämtland flanks. *Bergslagerna* display population dispersal rather than concentration. One striking feature is that the area has no town which sums up its character and at the same time dominates it. This makes the undeniable industrial region even more nebulous and intangible. The shifts in technique, in resources and personal fortunes which have made for changing industrial distributions within *Bergslagerna* are continuingly active. Several scores of smaller towns, ranging from the compacted medieval to the loosely woven web of the newly-created *tätort* display the variety of urban form as well as of industrial character in *Bergslagen*.

The valley of Kollbäckså, with its continuity of settlement and relatively even dispersal of industrial plant, is very representative. Population concentrations occur at 10–20 km. intervals, usually have several thousand inhabitants and have a relatively restricted *umland*. The settlements are commonly well characterised, show a marked persistence of contemporary factories on the sites of old *hammar*, and are generous in relics of past activity. Ramnäs, for example, is a museum piece in itself—with an elaborate system of water-power controls, reflecting all ages and

---

[1] K. E. Bergsten, *Östergötlands bergslag*, Lund, 1946, and A. Weinhagen, *Norbergs bergslag*, Lund, 1947. The former treats a number of eighteenth-century *bruk* (p. 206 *et seq.*); the latter provides evidence of *hammar* localisation on waterways (pp. 160–1).
[2] Cf. E. Holmquist, *Bergslagens gruvspråk*, Uppsala, 1941.

stages of development, a charcoal storehouse, red-ochred dwelling complexes, a *bruk* church, a "patron's" house and factory buildings the walls of which glint with the glaucous green of slag bricks. Ramnäs has manufactured many things in the past. Today it seems that the production fittest to survive in this harbour of skills takes precedence—the manufacture of chains and chain cables—paradoxically, of course, just as far from the sea as possible. This specialist production claims a relatively stable market.

Settlements along Kolbäckså conform to the "textbook" concept of *Bergslagen* in a second way. Their employment structure agrees with that expected (cf. Table 27).

city size. Population concentration and redistribution have been closely related to the concentration of industrial plant. Concentration has taken two forms—one which makes a visual impact on the landscape and one which is only detectable through an appreciation of process. There is no way of concealing the development of Stora Kopparbergs Bergslags AB. in the iron and steel plant of Domnarvet (pop. 21,000) or of the Sandviken plant farther to the east. Similarly, the development of Uddeholm AB. at Hagfors on the western margins makes a visual impact. Another way of impressing the development visually is the diagrammatic method adopted by W. William-Olsen in Fig. 32. Yet neither the

TABLE 27

Settlement	Population	Percentage Engaged in Industry	Percentage in Metallurgy
Hallstahammar .	8,000	76	91
Surahammar .	5,000	83	95.9
Ramnäs . .	1,000	65	79
Smedjebacken .	3,500	64	86
Morgårdhammar .	800	71	89

(Source: *Befolkningsstatistik, Folkräkningen,* 1951.)

The proportion of the industrial population engaged in metallurgy might be a means of assessing the boundaries of *Bergslagen*. Such an assessment, however, might break down on two scores. First, within the isorhythms constructed around *Bergslagen*, there would be many urban centres which largely eschew the manufacturing function. Secondly, such a criterion is a relative not absolute expression. It tends to discount the absolute size of the population engaged in metallurgy. And, indeed, when this aspect is considered, it will be discovered that a number of substantial cities which display the industrial structure of *Bergslagen* most fully are peripherally rather than centrally located. Examples of such towns are Västerås, Falun, Sandviken and Örebro.

Twentieth-century developments have pointed the way to many relative changes in

landscape nor the distribution map can express company amalgamation—also a form of concentration.

A widespread integration of operating units in *Bergslagerna* has occurred at many different levels. In Kolbäck valley, for example, Bultafabrik AB. (founded in 1873 at Hallstahammar) has extended its control upstream to incorporate Ramnäs. The purchase of Ramnäs in 1943 gave to Bultafabrik control of the water-power stations of Wirsbo, Seglingsberg and Ramnäs, as well as extensive woodlands able to meet timber fuel requirements in an emergency.[1] It strengthened its position in Hallstahammar by the purchase, in 1938, of Kanthal steel rolling-mills, as well as stretching its tentacles outside the valley to daughter plants in Eskiltuna, Ralsta and Åshammar. An example on a larger scale is provided by Brukskoncernen.[2] In the late

[1] *Bultfabriks AB. Jubileumskrift,* 1948.
[2] Cf. H. Nelson, "Sveriges järnhantering och några drag i deras geografiska lokalisering", *Sydsvenska geografiska sällskapets årsbok*, Lund, 1936, **12**, 191-214; also "Steelworks in Sweden", *Baltic and Scandinavian Countries*, IV, i, 8, 1938, 47-52.

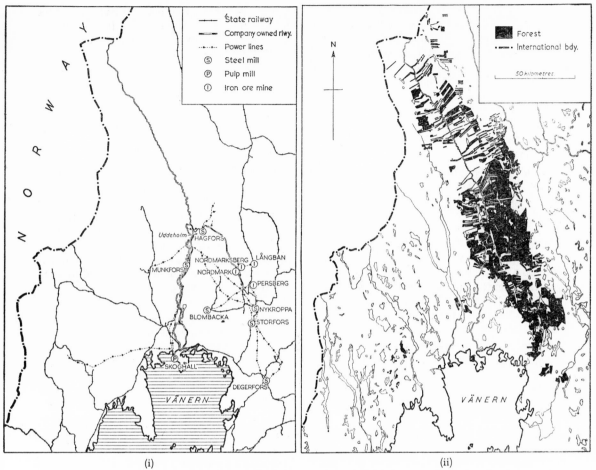

FIG. 96. The domain of Uddeholm: (i) the distribution of the processing plants; (ii) the pattern of company-owned land.

1920s, five companies were amalgamated under the leadership of Fagersta Bruks AB. The other four are located at Langshyttan, Horndal, Forsbacka and Dannemora. The continued association of these plants with their related communities is therefore attributable in part to the structure of management. The Uddeholm Company development (Fig. 96) in western *Bergslagen*, besides showing a concentration of plant of a visible and measurable character, also repeats the invisible integration of Brukskoncernen. It owns land as extensive in area as the island of Gotland (nearly 3,000 sq. km.), it is interested in three principal orefields (Persberg, Nord-

mark and Långban), it has concentrated smelting at four sites (Munkfors, Hagfors—Plate 21, Storfors and Nykroppa) and controls about thirty power plants. Its own railway links the main industrial points in the metallurgical complex with the pulp-, paper- and timber-mills at Skogshall on Lake Vänern. The Uddeholm Company has explored and employed in harmony the physical essentials of *Bergslagen* since it was first established nearly 300 years ago on the banks of the small River Uva.[1] The oldest of the concerns, Stora Kopparberg AB., presents an equally complete integration.[2]

Fig. 89 emphasises that today, as earlier,

[1] The volumes of *Uddeholmaren* for 1951 (Karlstad) summarise the components.
[2] G. Olssen and B. Anderson, *Stora Kopparberg*, Stockholm, 1951.

Bergslagerna show no tendency towards a focal point of commerce and industry. There are at least two reasons for this. First of all, topography denies to the area any natural route centre. The valley ways do not lead to any specific centre of concentration, rather are they the centres of concentration in themselves. Secondly, the main mass of *Bergslagerna* lies aside from the transverse "axis" of the Swedish midlands. *Bergslagen* never became a commercial area in its own right, its trading centres grew up peripherally and nearer to the main trading ways of Sweden.[1] Beyond these facts, the components of *Bergslagen* have been tied less closely to each other than they have been tied to cities outside their region. In the past, *Bergslagerna* have been competitive with each other and complementary to outside areas. Illustrative of this are the orientation of Filipstad and Karlskoga to Karlstad and Kristinehamn; of Ramsburgs-(lag) to Orebro; of Norbergs(lag) and Skinskattebergs(lag) to Västerås and of Falun itself still farther afield to Gävle. It might even be suggested that the elements of which *Bergslagen* is composed either tend to fly apart from each other or to follow in independence parallel lines of development; though the web of integration to which reference has been made cautions that this appearance may be deceptive.

Again, the transport network in the area is intended to meet local requirements rather than to cater for regional needs. Road communications have had precedence over water communications in the past and have gained a new significance with the coming of the automobile. *Bergslagen* has produced a surplus of metallurgical and forest products of varying degrees of transportability and movement to the market has always raised problems. Highways within the area have customarily followed riverways or, occasionally, the high and dry heathways (cf. the old copper way to Lake Mälar from Falun over Långheden and the highway over Strömsholmsås in Kolbäck valley have persisted through the centuries). An abundance of road metal has facilitated construction;

though in the days of horse transport, winter movement by sleigh was frequently as important as summer movement by road.

Water movement within the area has been restricted, because water-courses have been unnavigable. The very shallows, rapids and falls which made the water-courses so eminently manageable by early industrialists, prohibited their use by early navigators. In the case of the Kolbäck river there has been canalisation. Strömsholm Canal, named after its point of entry into Lake Mälar, was begun in 1774 and completed in 1792. It had 100 km. of navigable waterway, though only 14 km. were artificially constructed. Of the twenty-six locks, the major flight of six was sited at Hallstahammar. Its main function was to ease the shipment of ore and pig-iron, though it declined after the coming of the railroad to the area in the 1890s.

The railway has given only limited integration to the area, because both the wide dispersal of industrial sites and the infinite variations in relief make an adequate network impossible. The first significant route—called the Bergslag line—was constructed between 1875 and 1879. It linked Falun to Göteborg in the west and to Gävle in the east. There were a number of immediate industrial reactions to it—not merely in respect of direct changes in raw material values, but also in respect of industrial location. The relocation of Stora Kopparbergs iron and steel plant at Domnarvet between 1872 and 1877 at the point where the railway crossed the rapids of the Dalälv, was initially a compromise move to maximise power and transport potentialities. At the same time it signalled concentration of nearly a score of smaller enterprises in Dalarna. The line retains a backwoods character dominated by raw material shipment, and although it strikes through the area it has never become its backbone. The railway network is not dense. The routes which it followed were watched with some anxiety by industrialists in the crucial last quarter of the nineteenth century. Kolbäck valley first sensed the significance of the railroad in 1875 with the construction of the track between Köping,

---

[1] Relevant points are also to be found in G. Enequist, "Yrkesgruppernas fördelning i Svergies kommuner år 1940", *Geographica*, Uppsala, 1946.

Kolbäck, Västerås and Tillberga. In 1889, a branch line struck out from Kolbäck to Ramnäs.

In some ways, the most important communicational integration has come through power plants. Bergslagen Joint Power Administration (with Stora Kopparbergs AB., Asea AB. and Grängesberg AB. as the principal shareholders) largely unifies the present-day sources of energy of *Bergslagen*. Perhaps in no single field has *Bergslagen* seen so many changes as in the field of power supply for the forges and wheels of its characteristic industry. Concentration of industrial development is in part a response to changing sources of energy. Local water-power and local charcoal have been superseded by coal and coke from overseas, and hydro-electricity from outside the region. *Bergslagen*, which was characteristically self-sufficing as an industrial region, has correspondingly lost a measure of its independence. Coal and coke comes in by rail from continental sources over Gävle and Göteborg (giving continuing significance to *Bergslagen* railway). Hydro-electric power demand has forced an intensive utilisation of the steeply graded courses of such rivers as Dalälven—when it has promoted the succession of power-stations of which Kvarnsveden, Bullerforsen and Forshuvudet (tied in with Stora Kopparbergs AB.) are representative. Klarälven in Värmland has been similarly transformed, with schemes now pressing back beyond its watersheds and beyond the Swedish boundary into Norway. It has also called forth an import of power by long-distance transmission line.

Historical *Bergslagen*, with its independent sources of supply, operated as a complex of separate units and was but loosely integrated. The present-day area, dependent upon so many and such varied external sources of supply for its raw materials, is often more united as a result. It has not always outgrown its supply base. Thus, Stora Kopparberg AB. anticipated technical changes in the smelting process with the advent of the Gilchrist-Thomas method by the acquisition first of the Grängesberg ore concessions and subsequently of Idkeberget. So specialised

has the demand for ores become that today the ore from Idkeberget is not wholly consumed in *Bergslagen*, but is even exported through Gävle to Sunderland, while Stora Kopparberg plants import coke converted from coal in Gävle and ores from other parts of the world. Hallstahammar iron-works provide a second example and draw their raw material principally from Oxelösund (at one time Sweden's biggest ore harbour) and Norrbotten. The result of this is another change in the identity of *Bergslagerna*. Once the area claimed a world market which was based on a local supply base. Today the market has expanded commensurately with world economic development, though *Bergslagen* has declined in relative international importance. The supply base today, however, has broadened out and rests upon many distant places.

It is as revealing to reflect upon the evolution of the study of a region as it is to attempt to identify it. An early and almost classical statement on *Bergslagen* is that of Helge Nelson.[1] Nelson, like Sten de Geer, has claimed that the region is the summit of geographical consideration. The study, written in the field by its young author, attempted to recognise the essentials of *Bergslagen* in a limited area, and it married historical appreciation with field observation. Yet its impact upon the geographer of forty years after— especially if the manuscript be subjected to the acid test of being read aloud on the spot— is much the same as the impact of Mendelssohn upon the ears of a contemporary musicologist.

There are several reasons why the contemporary geographer is restrained from attempting a re-appraisal of this admitted economic region. First, he is aware that the varying interpretations of the economic region—an area homogeneous with respect to certain visible criteria, an area supported by certain specific activities, an area with certain common needs (as announced in its flow of imports and exports)—represent a groping towards rather than a grasping of its essentials. Secondly, he is aware of the formidable task of satisfactorily undertaking a survey with all the paraphernalia of current statistics, cartographic devices and observational team-

---

[1] "En Bergslagsbygd", *Ymer*, 1913.

work. If prepared for the large-scale assault, he may have doubts about the techniques. Studies of the area have therefore continued in the Nelson tradition. *Bergslagen* is, after all, *Bergslagerna*, and contemporary interpretations have tended to restrict their field to one of the constituent areas. Studies in depth of areas limited in space, like those of Bergsten and Weinhagen, have therefore resulted. Though they also encounter problems of a different character in source material,[1] such studies give a rounded appreciation of the scene.

Then, too, there is the whole dynamic concept of the region. *Bergslagen* means different things structurally and areally to different generations. There was a time when it might be said that *Bergslagerna* ended where the discipline of the mine and its related activities weakened. Today, it would be more accurate to say "where the discipline of metallurgy and its related activities relaxed". But, as has been indicated, the source of supply of ores and fuel is frequently outside the historic region. Increasing strength, indeed, may be given to locations marginal to the historic region(s) for the pursuit of activities at one time associated with its core area(s). *Bergslagen* must also be looked at in its Swedish setting. It has lost much of its uniqueness, and it has contributed its skills and experience to other areas. A generation ago, Seebass declared that

"in character, *Bergslagen* belongs to the northland: by development, to the south. It lies between and unites the three most important economic regions of Sweden—the mining, lumbering and agricultural" (*op. cit.*, p. 232).

In more recent years, many of the characteristics of south Sweden have spread to the north—and in particular the centre of gravity of mining has changed. Mining, a *raison d'être* of *Bergslagen*, is today much more important in Norrbotten than in central Sweden. *Bergslagen* must be seen, too, in its European setting. It is a minor industrial region by comparison, though in area it occupies a territory as extensive as that occupied by more significant industrial concentrations. By comparison with other parts of Sweden, the degree of concentration and specialisation in economic activity is high in *Bergslagen*; by comparison with other regions of similar production in other parts of the world, the degree of concentration is slighter.

Bergslagen has changed much, but were an eighteenth-century topographer like Abraham Hülphurs to return to it, he would be less likely to lose his way than if his counterparts returned to other comparable industrial regions of Western Europe. There are still flashes of the baroque copper-plates of Eric Dahlberg to be recognised in the area.[2] The intensity and scale of operations has not been enough to obliterate the green of the valleys. Perhaps by happy accident rather than conscious policy the area which nurses the apex of Swedish opportunity has been controlled by just the right degree of natural and national restraint.

THE PROSPECT AHEAD

Two centuries ago, field observers like Daniel Tilas in Sweden were scientifically recording their sketches of *malmtrakter*, ore-bearing regions, and calling for petrographical and mineralogical maps.[3] Side by side with them, mining apprentices were taught a virtual catechism from the great lexicons, which occupied a place next to the Bible at the *bruk*.[4] Such traditions lie behind the meticulous reports of the Swedish Geological Survey, the careful husbanding of ores and the diversity of labouring skills. Sweden in particular—and therefore Scandinavia in general if we bear in mind its present integration—can face an assured future from the point of view of most base metals. Its iron reserves especially are estimated at more than 2,500 million tons—an amount which at the current rate of consumption (17 million tons, of which 15 million tons are exported) would last for

---

[1] Olof Nordström, "Källkritiska problem beträffande bergskollegii och bergmästardömens arkiv", *Svensk geografisk årsbok*, 1953.
[2] *Suecia antiqua et hodierna*, Stockholm, 1660–1716.
[3] *Kunlige vetenskaps academiens handlingar*, 1760, XXI, 14–29.
[4] These probably originated in Germany. There is a good selection of them in the museum at Kongsberg. An example from Sweden is S. Rinman, *Bergwerk lexikon*, Stockholm, 1788–9, 2 vols.

nearly two centuries. Nor is the entire reserve known or easy of economic assessment. Thus prospecting, with its increased range of detectors, may well reveal new deposits; while the extent and difficulty of the terrain no longer obstruct investigation, for aero-magnetic survey replaces ground operations. Mining to greater depths is also made practicable and economic by new methods.

New vistas are also opened in other directions. Thus, known reserves are inclined to show an appreciable increase in value simply through the great speed of exhaustion of deposits in other countries. Poorer ores are also revalued in the same way. New methods of treatment of the constituents of known reserves also steadily change mineral values. These become especially important for separating ores existing in combination in the parent lode. A mid-century survey of Langban field in the Uddeholm domain, for example, lists the occurrence of more than 110 distinct metals.[1] From reference to the Boliden area (p. 260), it will be clear that the introduction of the flotation process has revolutionised the recovery of metals existing in combination. Problems of separation are being increasingly resolved.

Of this technical revolution are born both distributional and structural changes in the industry. The centralisation of concentrating plants has already been emphasised—and, by and large, the more heterogeneous the parent rock the greater the necessity for the concentration of the smelteries. For, while it is possible for relatively small plants to engage in the flotation process both technically and economically, economy and scale of operations are undoubtedly linked in a very real way. The small plant cannot extract to the full the varied products of a richly blended parent ore. The contemporary extractor is therefore planned for long-period operations, becomes relatively static in location and is designed to serve a large area. Its transport facilities are important, but their costs are interestingly subordinated when arguments for location are matched against those for other plants. And beyond these developments, there is the steady discovery of completely new minerals—with Fennoscandia as a fertile bedrock in which they may be anticipated. Such discovery becomes tantamount to the discovery of new resources. Today, strategic minerals or micro-constituents can be appraised above old familiar ores, and a small power—or even a small country—may stand revealed as a quasi-monopolist of an essential resource, e.g. titanium from Egersund; niobium, prized for its heat-resisting qualities in jet aircraft, mined only at Søve in Telemark. Many new sources of economic illumination cast political shadows before them.[2]

Though blessed with mineral resources, many countries nevertheless remain pessimistic about future prospects. Thus, some Swedes are afraid that world requirements of iron and steel may eventually reach the point of saturation and that the circulation of scrap will be such that new additions to the pool will be checked. It is a point about which to argue, but a tendency which has yet to show itself even within the frame of the greatest producing and consuming country. If such a long-period challenge were to emerge, it is essentially in its diversity of output and its micro-constituents that the Fenno-Scandinavian group would be likely to redress the balance.

A review of the Scandinavian and Finnish metallurgical industries—and particularly the Swedish—shows that the wheel has come full circle. The manufacture of relatively few products is restricted by scale of production today. The historical concentration upon consumers' goods has been complemented by the production of capital goods. The diffusion of the "legion of machines" now takes place from a North European hearth of invention.

[1] *Uddeholmaren*, Karlstad, 1951, **1**, 6–7.
[2] "Pray God, we do not find uranium in Finland", commented a Finnish business man!

PART 5

THE LAPP WORLD[1]

"Gukken davven Dawgai vuolde
sabma suolgai Same-aednam:
Duoddar laebba duoddar duokken,
jawre saebba jawre lakka."

Isak Saba (1906) (Translation on p. 289.)

THE Lapps and their economy have made an impression upon the British out of all proportion to their numbers and significance. The impression goes back to at least A.D. 880 when King Alfred was informed by the West Troms chieftain Ottar of the existence of a reindeer-keeping people in Helgeland, North Norway. At the dawn of the thirteenth century, their land was christened "Lappia" for the Western world by Saxo Grammaticus. "Lapland" was upon Elizabethan lips, and in the Jacobean age a translation of the Alsatian Johannes Schefferus's *Lapponia* (Frankfurt, 1673; Oxford, 1674) gave to it wider and more influential circulation. Herman Moll's *Atlas* (1701 *et seq.*) devoted a double-page spread of pictures illustrating the activities of this "most remarkable people in Europe" (Plate 23).[2] James Thomson's poem *The Seasons* opened a new vista of Lapland to a romantic age in which a number of observant travellers elected to go north rather than to the Mediterranean south on their Grand Tours. The impact of Lapps continues to be disproportionate to their significance in the North European scene. At the same time there is a persistent confusion of Finns with Lapps —to the amusement and occasional resentment of the former.

ETHNOGRAPHY AND ECONOMY

The distinctiveness of the Lapps from the rest of the inhabitants of Norway, Sweden and Finland prompted early speculation upon their origins. First theories gave to them an eastern origin; others suggested that their arrival coincided with the Fimbuhl winters of the Iron Age. Horizons expanded with the discovery and investigations into the Stone Age Komsa culture of north Norway during the 1920s. Some (e.g. K. B. Wiklund) even suggested that the Lapps were an "interglacial" people who over-wintered in coastal refuge, while the ice-sheet expanded and contracted behind their littoral settlements. Anthropologists discern at least two main groups of Lapps—a northern group, substantially modified by Scandinavian-Norwegian elements, and a southern group, of East European but not Mongoloid origin, which has the same primitive Norwegian elements.[3] A sub-division of the southern group is also proposed in Swedish circles, with a boundary-line running through the Arjeplog area.

Lapp ethnography, like Lapp origins, lies beyond the scope of this book; but in the Lapp realm it is difficult to separate ethnographic and economic matters. The student of Lapp antecedents may well conclude that the origins of the Lapps are several not solitary; contemporarily, too, it is difficult to be definitive about the classification of Lapp people. Attempts have been made, for example, in the Norwegian census returns (cf. E. Arosenius, *Lappar och finnar i Sveriges tre nordligaste län*, *Statistisk tidskrift*, 1913, 264–73) and in the Finnish State Commission's *Report on Lapp Affairs, 1949–51* (Helsinki, 1953). Language is the usual criterion adopted in "racial" grouping; but this is unsatisfactory because

[1] I am grateful to Dr. E. J. Lindgren-Utsi and to Mr. Utsi for helpful criticism of this section.
[2] Rivalled pictorially only by K. Leem, *Beskrivelse över Finnmarkens Lappar*, Copenhagen, 1767.
[3] Cf. *The Race Biology of the Swedish Lapps*, Uppsala, 1932 and 1941; B. Lundman, "On the Origin of the Lapps", *Ethnos*, Stockholm, 1946–7 –88; Ø. Vorren and E. Manker *Lapp Life and Customs*, London, 1962.

many who have the physical appearance of Lapps have given up the Lapp tongue. Contrastingly, there are others who speak Lappish, but who do not always have the physical characteristics commonly associated with Lapps. It must be remembered, too, that the word "Lapp" is decreasingly employed in the Northern Countries. The Lapps call themselves *samik* (sing. *sambi*). To Norwegians and Swedes, they are *samer* (sing. *same*); though formerly they were called Lapps. The Finns now use *saamelaiset* (sing. *saamelainen*); the Russians *saami* (sing. *saam*). There is an extremely rich bibliography of "Lappology", as it was first called by K. B. Wiklund; but most of it is in the Scandinavian languages.[1] The culture of the Lapps—one of residual herding groups most closely juxtaposed with modern life and one of those which superficially have been least altered—must be judged by a different set of values from that of the other Scandinavians; their economy shows a different set of rhythms. Nevertheless, their daily life touches that of the Scandinavians and Finns at many points, and must be carefully integrated with it—if ethnographically and economically it is not to be fused with and submerged beneath it. In the space of three generations, the Lapp has exchanged the status of an officially perplexing constituent for that of a carefully protected minority. A whole body of knowledge, the result of diligent field work, has been assembled about him.

The territory used by Lapps covers a full third of Scandinavia and Finland; it has its extreme points in the Swedish province of Dalarna and in Cape Ponoi on the Kola peninsula. This area exceeds that of Great Britain in size. The precise definition of "Lapland" has been the subject of much differing opinion. For Sweden, Lapland is mentally associated with Norrbotten and Västerbotten. The interior of these provinces has been traditionally referred to as Lappmarken—the subdivisions of which have been named after the river valleys along which Lapps migrate; for example, Lule Lappmark, Pite Lappmark. Today, there are fifty nomad districts in Sweden. The Finns gave administrative shape to their Lapp world when they created the northernmost province of Lappi in 1938; though its capital Rovaniemi (pop. 15,000), which has risen impressively from wartime ashes, is far removed from the outsider's mental image of Lapland.

It must be appreciated that reindeer husbandry is an extensive activity and that animal stocks are spread thinly over the range land. They are only in occupation of a very limited area at any given time. As will be more fully appreciated below, the grazing stock is in any case highly selective of pasturage. Lapps are spread even more thinly than their livestock, so that Lapland has one of the lowest population densities of the inhabited world. Sweden has absolutely the greatest area devoted to Lapp enterprise.

The total Lapp population is about 33,000, and it is divided roughly as follows: Norway 20,000; Sweden, 10,000; Finland, 1,500; U.S.S.R., 1,500. This small and widely scattered community is well differentiated ethnographically. Three main groups are recognised—the eastern (Russian Lapps and Inari fisher Lapps), the central (Finnish mountain Lapps and Scandinavian Lapps south to the district of Arjeplog) and the southern. The dialect differences are so appreciable that northern and southern Norwegian Lapps do not understand each other. Economically, too, there are marked differences. Reindeer management, universally associated with the Lapps,[2] is in fact only practised by a minority of them. Reindeer management is believed to belong to the last 1,500 years; but is probably not of equal antiquity among all Lapp groups, and to some may only be three or four hundred years old. Today, roughly 5,000 Lapps engage in one or another type of transhumance, and no less than 3,000 of these are found in Sweden. About a third of the Swedish Lapps and a

[1] Two up-to-date reviews of research with bibliographies are ound in G. Gjessing, Norwegian contributions to Lapp ethnography, *Journal of the Royal Anthropological Institute*, LXXVII, 1, 1947, and E. Manker, Swedish contributions to Lapp ethnography, *ibid.*, LXXXII, I, 1952. Probably the best recent works in English are B. Collinder, *The Lapps*, Princeton, 1949, and G. Gjessing, *Changing Lapps: A Study in Culture Relations in Northernmost Norway*, London, 1954.
[2] Conversely, reindeer farming occurs in the U.S.S.R., where collective reindeer farms are an integral part of plans for the Soviet North of the reindeer industry of the Soviet Arctic, *Polar Record*, 6, 41, 1941, pp. 107-10.

tenth of Norway's Lapps therefore migrate seasonally.

The actual occupations and precise names given to the settled Lapps vary from one to another of the three countries. In Sweden, the Lapps who occupy holdings in the wood-land zones are commonly known as "forest Lapps" (*skogslappar*). Among them, there is some residual reindeer management; but it is subordinated to subsistence agriculture on a settled holding. In Finland, a distinction is made between the "Mountain Lapps" (*tunturisaamelaiset*), who practise reindeer management, and the "Fisher Lapps" (*kalastaja-saamelaiset*), who are chiefly concerned with fishing (on the Inari water system). Their precise distribution is shown on the map accompanying the Finnish *Report on Lapp Affairs*. There is a threefold division in Norway into "Sea Lapps", "River or Inland Lapps" and "Reindeer or Mountain Lapps".[1] The Sea Lapps are historically a distinctive people and formerly followed a well-defined seasonal rhythm of life—hunting wild reindeer inland in winter; migrating to the skerries in summer for fishing, whaling and sealing; boat-building and trading at other seasons.[2] The Mountain Lapps are the reindeer herders, and in historical time their expansive economy has forced them to seek pastures farther and farther afield. It was natural that their tame herds should trespass upon the hunting-grounds where the Fisher Lapps sought their wild deer—leading virtually to an extermination campaign against the wild beasts. It was natural, too, that expansion should carry herding southwards—to Trøndelag and even to the Røros area. The Inland or River Lapps of Norway are a rather more hybrid group—much intermarried with immigrant Finns. They are subsistence farmers for the most part—with some ancillary fishing and hunting.

The replacement by a commercial of a self-sufficient economy has had different effects upon each of these groups—generally favouring the established settler, and if not actually reducing the nomad certainly introducing new elements into his routine. The effect has been largely negative upon the Sea Lapps, and has eliminated them as a distinct economico-ethnographic group. On the other hand, contact with the new order has strengthened rather than weakened the Lapp population numerically. The Lapp population of Norway is stated to be increasing—though differentially, with the migrating group most stationary.

THE BOUNDARIES OF LAPLAND

It will be evident already that the area subject to Lapp use has been variable in historic time; showing regional expansion and contraction. Some texts have defined the Lapps as a people in retreat. In certain areas there has been retreat, though elsewhere compensating expansion. In Finland, the long-period Lapp retreat has been demonstrated by T. I. Itkonen in a study based on less reliable place-name evidence and more reliable church tax and tithe books.[3] More extensive grazing grounds undoubtedly supported more beasts in former times; though ill-defined international boundaries meant that many Lapps were subject to a triple tax by Denmark, Sweden and Russia. The Lapp retreat to high latitudes has not been simultaneous in time or parallel in form from country to country. Thus, while the eighteenth century witnessed a retreat to the fells of Finland, in Sweden the Lapps penetrated to their most southerly point of advance at Idre in Dalarna. As settled agriculturists expanded and developed, their relations with the Lapps were forced into a legal mould. "Lapland boundaries" were outlined—considerably to the south of the Arctic watershed.

The succession of legal adjustments now favoured the Lapp, now the immigrant farmer. In 1695, a practical step was taken in Sweden and Finland to restrict the practice of burn-beating the land for cultivation, and thereby to protect the lichen of the reindeer pasture. Invasion of Lappish grazing lands from the south—primarily a river-valley invasion—reached its maximum during the latter half of the nineteenth century. In Finland the 1908

---

[1] G. Gjessing, *Changing Lapps*, typifies the three in chapters on Laksefiord, Karasjok and Kautokeino.
[2] A. Nessheim, "Traits from Life in a Sea Lappish District", *Nord-norske samlinger*, Oslo, 1949, VI, 2, 3.
[3] "Lapparnas förekomst i Finland", *Ymer*, Stockholm, 1947. T. I. Itkonen, of the National Museum of Finland, has also written the classical work on Finnish Lapps—*Suomen Lappalaiset*, Helsinki, 1948.

State Commission favoured cultivation over reindeer holding for Lapland. Invasion was undertaken partly by farmer colonists misguidedly seeking escape from lower-lying, frost-afflicted lands to the south; partly by mining engineers and their succeeding communities (e.g. in Finland, gold discoveries in the Ivalo valley in the 1860s and in the Lemmenjoki valley today; in Sweden, the ores of Kiruna and Gällivare).[1] In Sweden, the advance was stemmed by an unusual protective measure initiated in 1867—when the *odlingsgräns* or limit of cultivation was officially defined.[2] *Odlingsgräns* created a westward boundary to Swedish agricultural settlement in Norrbotten and Västerbotten, and attempted to define an area where Lapp migrants would no longer conflict with the steady incursion of settled people. The boundary runs from north-east to south-east, passing near Muonio, Vittangi, Gällivare, Jokkmokk, Laisvall, Umnås and Alanås. Land west of the boundary may, in fact, be leased by Swedish farmers; but the tenant has to bear any damage which may result from reindeer. Mineral- and water-power resources within the boundary line may be detached from Lapp use by royal authority where it is in the interests of the community, provided suitable compensation is paid into the State Lapp Fund (e.g. 50,000 kroner p.a. are paid by Porjus power-plant). *Odlingsgräns* is defined as an established feature of many Swedish maps. In Norway, Lapps have the right of movement with their herds all over land that is not privately owned. The onus for protecting his cropland is upon the farmer; no compensation for reindeer damage can be claimed if fences are not stockproof.[3] The Finnish State Commission's *Report on Lapp Affairs* outlines a new southern boundary of the *saamelaisalue* or Lapp area.

Encroachment of sedentary people upon Lapland was complemented by a new form of disturbance within the transhumance territory. In their train followed the political boundary maker, whose lines imposed a new type of restraint upon established routes of movement. A shadow was cast in 1751 when a joint Swedish and Dano/Norwegian commission began to define a more precise boundary.[4]

THE IMPACT OF POLITICAL DEFINITION IN LAPLAND

The boundary took more real form on the ground in the 1820s, by which time the advance of Imperial Russia to the frontiers of Sweden called forth a new boundary commission to demarcate a definitive eastern boundary for the dual monarchy Sweden-Norway. The general indifference to international movement in high latitudes was first jolted when the Finnish-Norwegian boundary was closed in 1852.[5] A group of 300 Lapps with 20,000 reindeer who occupied the upper Reisin river valley of Norway were obstructed in their traditional path of migration. The attempt to impose a contemporary system of controls upon a prehistoric economy is witnessed in the struggle between national and activist interests, including that of Norwegian and Swedish Lapps during the last century. Friction over migration eventually gave rise to a common law in 1883, the most important conclusion of which was to define the periods of frontier migration: for the Swedes into Norway, from May to September inclusive; for the Norwegian Lapps into Sweden, from October to April inclusively. The problem of restraint during periods of unusual weather represented a nice example of animal instinct being forced to curb itself to the man-made calendar.

Following the dissolution of the Swedish-Norwegian Union in 1905, the whole issue was reviewed and a joint commission published its report—*Renbeteskommissionen af år 1907*. Continuing disagreement, especially over the crucial period of migration between May 1st and June 15th called for a court of arbitration

---

[1] I. Hustich, "Några drag i kolonisationen av Lapland", *Nordenskiöldsamfundets tidskrift*, Åbo, 1942, and the very relevant German study, A. Wolfe, *Kolonisation de Finnen an der Nordgrenze ihres Lebensraumes*, Kiel, 1939.

[2] S. de Geer, *op. cit.*, pp. 97–9.

[3] E. Solem, *Lappiske rettsstudier*, Oslo, 1933.

[4] And, incidentally, to contribute a most valuable series of large-scale maps to Riksarkivet in Oslo.

[5] K. Nissen, "Lapper og Ren i Norge", *Norsk geografisk sellskaps årbok*, Kristiania, 1915, has much relevant detail. The administration of mountain Lapps in Sweden is dealt with in E. Manker, *The Nomadism of the Swedish Mountain Lapps*, Stockholm, 1953.

in Copenhagen in 1909 at which a Reindeer Pasture Commission was appointed. During 1910–11, the Commission engaged in widespread field work and enquiry. Information was collected under seven principal headings: the natural conditions of importance to herding; the influence of snow on pasture availability; the number of reindeer which could be grazed in given areas during this time; herding and calving conditions; grazing resources under normal conditions from May 1st to June 15th; the effects of grazing during this period; and the likely effect of changes in pasture accessibility over the same six weeks.[1]

Among more important consequences of the ensuing convention were the definition of reindeer pasture districts in the disputed areas, their precise allocation to Lapp settlements, the definition of migration routes, the arrangement of compensation for damage and the control of reindeer numbers in migration.[2] The convention, scheduled to last until 1952, was slightly modified in favour of grazing areas in Norway in December 1949. Increasing settlement in north Norway, together with intensification of communications and farming, have called for the closing of thirteen reindeer pasture districts to Swedish Lapps.

The revision of Petsamo boundaries has also disturbed certain migration routes; though in the case of the Lapps concerned, the *raison d'être* of their movement was largely eliminated by the German army. In any case, a fence now checks reindeer movement across the Russian boundary, and a similar feature has been discussed for the Finnish-Norwegian boundary.

Although recent years have witnessed conferences of Lappologists, there is still remarkably little uniformity in the information concerning Lapp communities which emanates from the three countries. Co-ordination of information is proceeding apace; but a readily available map collating basic data for all three countries is still lacking. Indi-vidual items are shown for individual countries in a number of publications, but the dates of material and the methods of presentation differ substantially. In Norway, one of the more interesting cartographic exercises is that of Ørnulf Vorren; it is an attempt to show quantitatively the herd held in different administrative districts and their principal seasonal pastures.[3] The framework of the Swedish districts and essential items of regional movement are outlined by Ernest Manker (*Svenska Lapparna*, Stockholm, 1947).[4] The two maps do not fit readily together. On the other hand, it must be admitted that the behaviour and responses of Lapps on the different flanks of the Scandinavian peninsula do not lend themselves to easy comparative treatment and cartographic expression. It is their very complexity which complicates Lapp adjustments to outside interference.

REINDEER MIGRATION

In Norway, the greatest areas of herding are in Finnmark and Troms. A second main concentration occurs in central Nordland, with subsidiary groups in the hinterlands of Bodö and Trondheim. In Norway, winter grazing is in the fell country—usually inland; the migration to the grazings of *Havlandet*, the sealand, which occurs in spring is characterised by widespread local variations. In Finnmark and Troms, for example, summer pastures are less extensive than the winter pastures. This necessitates the subdivision of the larger herds for the season and, in certain instances, their migration even to offshore islands. Per Höst's remarkable film *Same Jakke* records this. Some parts of Norway lack the normal summer migration. Thus, at least five grazing districts north of Trondheim have identical winter and summer grazing grounds; the same applies to the grazings of the more limited herds of Vesterålen and Lofoten. More than 170,000 reindeer are found in Norway, three-quarters of them being

---

The results of the field survey—*Renbeteskommissionens af 1913 handlingar* Stockholm, 1917—are available at the Scott Polar Research Institute, Cambridge. They have been summarised by J. G. Elbo, "Lapp Reindeer Movements across the Frontiers of North Scandinavia", *Polar Record*, 6 (1952), 348–58.
[2] Detailed maps were drawn to illustrate the more important features in the accompanying *Kartatlas* (available at the Royal Geographical Society).
[3] "Reindriften i Norge", *Norsk geografisk tidsskrift*, 11, 199–220. This map is a more up-to-date version of Reindrift-inspektør K. Nissen's pioneer map (1:2,000,000) accompanying his 1915 paper.
[4] Also relevant is C. A. Calleberg, "Nomader och nomadskolor", *Ymer*, 62, 367–402.

owned by Lapps and the remainder by farmers and commercial organisations (e.g. in Trøndelag or around Jotunheim). Five main districts in Norway are commonly grazed in summer by Swedish reindeer herds. They include an extensive territory north of Narvik and south of Skibotn; tracts north of Junkerdal, south of Bjellanes, east of Rosvassbukt and south-east of Grane. Altogether 10,000 square miles of Norway are ranged by Swedish Lapps; though, as has been inferred above, both the number of herders and their herds are controlled. About 39,000 reindeer use the Tromsø area and 29,000 the Nordland grounds—i.e. roughly 30% of the registered Swedish stocks.

The physical background to the Lapp economy is markedly different on the Swedish-Finnish flank, where a threefold morphological division is present. The lowest third is the westernmost part of the Fennoscandian shield—granite country overlain with marine sediments coastwards and elsewhere differentially burdened by reassorted glacial deposits. Broad, shallow valleys at regular intervals open up lines of movement across it—the natural meadows of their flood-plains contrasting with the coniferous blanket of their interfluves. Reindeer lichen is common to the drier lands of the area right down to the sea coast. The middle third, altitudinally between 600 and 1,000 m., is sub-alpine country commonly recognised as a birch-scrub zone. Emblematic of it are great lakes like Torneträsk, which leap spectacularly over falls like Harsprånget into entrenched valleys. It is generally agreed that this intermediary zone is the more crucial for the future of reindeer breeding, owing to the limited capacity of its lichen grazings and their vulnerability to overgrazing and trampling. The upland third is the classical *regio alpina*—a country lying about the 1,000 m. contour, of limestones and shales smoothly eroded and dominated by resistant peaks and blocks.[1]

Sweden's winter pastures, equinoctial pastures and summer pastures belong to the lowland, sub-alpine and alpine zones respectively,

and therefore contrast with the Norwegian situation. Swedish herds total about 250,000. The areas of greatest concentration are in the northernmost district of Könkämä, Lainiovuoma, Saarivuoma (c. 30,000); the district around Ran, Umbyn, Vapsten and Vilhelmina (c. 30,000) and in the Sirkas district of central Norrbotten (c. 11,500).

The scale of Finnish herding has been much more variable. Stocks have multiplied six or sevenfold since the immediate post-war years, and estimates suggest that there are probably over 180,000 adults today. In Finnish Lapland, Lapps have merged most fully with Finns—socially and economically as well as personally. Utsjoki is the only remaining Finnish parish with a Lapp majority. Finns are competing with Lapps as reindeer herders —indeed, in some *paliskunta*, or local associations of herders, reindeer per Finnish owner exceed reindeer per Lapp owner. In Finnish Lapland there is not only juxtaposition of two systems with a natural conflict between them, but the appropriation by the Finns of what is generally regarded as a Lapp function. Similarly, in the post-war period there has been a widespread extension of the area of reindeer-keeping in Finnish Lapland. Salla, for example, has reindeer herds today. Recent accounting investigations by the Central Reindeer Breeders' Association (*Paliskuntain yhdistys*) emphasise other contrasts between Lapp and Finn management. Finnish herds have higher labour costs, largely as a result of the close watch kept upon them; Lapp herds pay more by way of compensation for damage to farm crops.[2]

The geographical extent of ranging is tied closely to fodder resources—not merely to their absolute extent but to their composition and renewability. Animal and husbandry texts now pay due regard to the palatability of species grown in temperate latitudes; but few domestic animals in the familiar farm scene have a more refined palate than the reindeer. During the dominant winter season, a restricted range of lichens is sought, and principal among these is *Cladonia rangiferina* (popularly called

---

[1] This is a countryside familiar to Swedish mountain lovers through the series of Swedish fell maps (*Svenska fjällkartor*, 1:100,000, 1:200,000).
[2] K. Nikul, "The Finnish Lapps in Wartime and After", *Man*, May 1950. Swedish law, incidentally, restricts the ownership of reindeer (with certain very limited exceptions) to persons of Lappish descent.

reindeer moss). If an ice-banded snow cover (*flen*) prevents access to this fodder, the bearded tree moss and *Usnea* species of the softwood forests may be consumed. In spring—especially if light rain or moist snow encourage it—stonemoss (*Gyrophora*) or birch moss (*Parmelia olivacea*) may be eaten. Neither beard nor crust lichens, however, are very nutritious. As supplementary spring fodder, willow, birch and mountain-ash twigs are sought. Summer pastures supply green grazing, and there is a fastidious selection of species. Among the plants consumed are *Oxyria digyna*, *Rumex acetosa* and *Angelica archangelica* (sometimes known as Lapland rhubarb); among the grasses, *Festuca orina* and *Deschampsia alpina* are favoured; semi-grasses like the cotton grass as well as *Eriophorum vaginatum*, several *Carex* species and two *Equisetums* are also among the selected few. The *Festuca* and *Deschampsia* have a certain frost resistance which enables them to keep green (even under snow) well into the autumn and to prolong the green grazing period in certain areas. There is a special collective Lapp noun—*sitno*—for this type of fodder. Not only must the Lapp herder have an eye and memory for the locality which supplies these favoured foods, he must take care also that they are not overgrazed.

The seasonal search for the most agreeable climatic milieu is related partly to fodder supplies.[1] Snow is a fundamental control here, but snow is not a simple factor. To the Lapp and his herd it spells a whole range of different considerations. They are concerned with the character of its layering, with the nature and behaviour of its crust and with the form of the thaw. This affects the time and direction of the spring movement—sometimes, for example, favouring night movement when there is a frost crust. The depth of the snow in the winter woodlands controls the precise areas grazed—frequently encouraging a strong coastward movement in Norrland because of the lighter snowfall in the east. Disappearance of the snow cover, followed by drying and hardening of the lichens, also spurs the search for alternative and more palatable pastures or

fodders. Nor is snow cover unimportant in the height of the summer, July, for the migration to the high fells is partly an attempt to escape the insect plague of the lower lands. Insect life in higher altitudes will be partly a response to summer heat; in extremely hot spells, reindeer will seek the protection of perennial snow patches.

Reindeer migration is an extremely individual phenomenon—individual to place and peculiar to the migratory group. It is possible to do no more than make broad generalisations. First, migrational routes show considerable fixity. Secondly, the range of movement varies widely; it is most restricted in the south, broadest where the three countries meet. Fodder yields, however, are not necessarily commensurate with area. Today, for example, the southern reaches of the rangelands, where lichen grows ankle high, are qualitatively the richest. Next, migration is tied to no dates in the calendar. There is a distinguishable annual rhythm, but detail within it is modified substantially from year to year. Again, the tempo of migration is variable. In general, it is swiftest in spring, when a suitable calving place is the objective. The number of halting-places on the migration route is commonly identical for each reindeer year.[2]

Migration routes in Sweden (and, to a large extent, in Finland) show a south-east to north-west trend. Their pattern is a response to the great parallel system of drainage which furrows the Baltic flank of Sweden and to the related boundaries of Lapp settlement. The migratory routes between lowland winter grazing and upland summer grazing show precise definition and organisation during the autumn and spring when they are gathered together. At either end of the journey, the routes branch out adventitiously into a number of end points—which are the individual grazing-grounds of the separate family herds. In the high fells, the established routeways follow the lines of depression; in the sub-alpine area they avoid the valley-ways (and must also avoid the bogland); in the woodland zone, they follow the frozen rivers and established

[1] R. Helle, "An investigation into reindeer husbandry", *Acta Lapponica Fenniae*, Rovaniemi, 1966, 5.
[2] The details for Sweden's *siidas* are given by E. Manker, *The Nomadism of the Swedish Mountain Lapps*, pp. 59–242.

lines of communication. The amplitude and length of migration depend largely upon seasonal conditions: in Norrbotten varying from 10 to 40 Swedish miles; in Jämtland from 5 to 23. Today, herders accompany the migrating animals, but the family man usually moves from one settlement to another by bus or car. For three-quarters of the year movement is on ski, with accompanying sleigh. Migration demands a variety of shelters over the head— indeed, Ernest Manker gives a new Lapp interpretation of the Biblical phrase "in my father's house are many mansions". The Lapp home is traditionally called the *kåta*— the *vaga domus* as first described by Saxo Grammaticus. The word refers to a variety of constructional forms—branch and brushwood shelter, tent type or boat type—the latter, for example in the Gällivare area, recalling a primitive version of Mr. Peggotty's Yarmouth home. A permanent timber house is increasingly customary for the family; likewise the shelter for the spring and autumn herding.

Reindeer management looks to three types of beast—the breeding reindeer, the reindeer for meat and the special-purpose reindeer (for example, draught animal). Management has been steadily changing its form—with full "nomadism", the historical practice, yielding to partial "nomadism". Full "nomadism"— transhumance is a more accurate word—is associated with an intensive system of ranging, together with virtually complete dependence upon the reindeer. The central position of reindeer in the intensive economy was graphically expressed by Pehr Högström two centuries ago. "They are the equivalents to the Lapp of ploughland and meadow, horses and cattle." More than this, the true Reindeer Lapp derives from his beasts meat (worth five times the value of the skin), milk, cheese, butter, clothes, implements (from bone) and means of transport. He exchanges their products only for grain (cooked traditionally into an unleaven bread), salt, sugar and, in more recent generations, coffee. The reindeer economy is based upon the fundamental fact that a female will produce calves annually over twelve to fifteen years, and that the average herd will increase annually at a rate of 20–30%.[1] Full "nomadism" embraces the Lapp family as well as the male herders, and has, as an accompaniment, division of labour between men and women. Milking is a female task. It is tied primarily to the summer months and, when calves are controlled, a beast may yield up to a quarter of a litre daily. Goats are also kept for milking. Peaks of activity in the annual cycle of work are the calving period in mid-May, the assembly (*renskillning*) for earmarking (of which an elaborate register is kept), castration and the autumn and winter mustering for slaughter (the animals then being at their fattest and the storage of meat— in conditions of natural refrigeration—at its easiest). The *renskillning*, when animals are herded for these latter purposes into palisaded or bush-fenced corrals, is a spectacular feature of at least Dark Age origin, as Egil Skallagrimson's saga attests. This intensive system still prevails in restricted areas around Jokkmokk, for example, but usually it has been replaced by a period of partial "nomadism."[2] The principal feature of this more extensive type of management is joint herding in the summer months. Joint herding reduces demands on man-power; it is also eliminating the practice of summer milking. At autumn round-ups, giant herds of 7,000–8,000 beasts are becoming an increasingly common feature. Meat production for sale introduces another commercial characteristic to the traditional economy.

A precise example of the phases in the annual round may be found in the Könkämä Lapp community of Karesuando parish, Torne Lappmark. There are 215 reindeer keepers in the community, and a herd of roughly 11,000 deer registered under 55 reindeer marks. The regional migrations of one group of eleven families are summarised in Fig. 97 (p. 288). The absolute distance of migration from winter feeding-grounds to summer pastures is 140–

[1] Practical details in reindeer management are provided by M. Utsi, "The Reindeer-breeding Methods of the Northern Lapps", *Man*, 114, 1948.
[2] Three works in English describe the daily and annual rounds of Lapp communities: Johan Turi (1854–1936), *Turis Book of Lapland*, London, 1931, edited by E. D. Hatt; Anta Pirak (ed. H. Grundström), *En nomad och hans liv*, Uppsala, 1933; Yrjö Kokko, *The Way of Four Winds*, London, 1954. The seasonal round has also been presented in drawings and paintings from the eight seasons of the reindeer year by Nils Nilsson Skum (1872–1951), a Lapp from the Kebnekaise area *Same sita—Lapp byn*, *Acta Lapponica*, II, Stockholm, 1938.

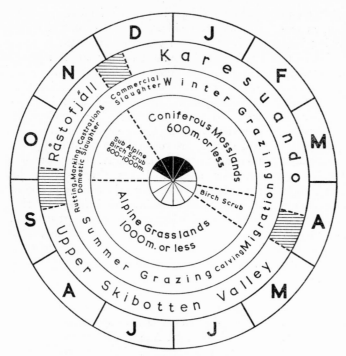

FIG. 97. Könkämä—the annual round of activity and movement of a Swedish Lapp community. (Based on material of E. Manker.)

bandry of a primitive people whose seasonal rhythm of life has been recurrently disturbed by changes in the political geography of Lapland. This Greek Orthodox community, direct descendants of converts from St. Trifon's monastery, suffered severance of a part of its homeland by the creation of the Petsamo corridor in 1920; its established way of life was next threatened by the State Committee's plan for the economic development of Lapland put forward in 1938; its herds were decimated and its territory laid waste by German forces in 1944; Suenjel, as a part of Petsamo, was finally detached from Finland and incorporated in the U.S.S.R. with the cessation of hostilities. The Skolt Lapps were evacuated as a displaced people.

In Fig. 98 (p. 289), three details are extracted from the cartographic summary which Karl Nickul appends to his work. They show the controlling pattern of lakes and rivers in Suenjel, its slender footpath communications, the organisation of the family areas of summer migration and the migration routes of individual families. On the eve of its dissolution, the Suenjel community differed appreciably from that of Könkämä. The biogeography behind the migration was at least as much concerned with lake and river fishing as with reindeer husbandry. The Suenjel Lapps had relatively small herds: families customarily owning several dozen with only five possessing herds in excess of 200. They were traditionally migratory according to the fishing season (April/May—November/December), leaving the semi-permanent winter village (*talvsijd*) between late March and early May for summer camps in the recognised family areas. The community lived on fish and reindeer meat

150 miles. The timber dwelling is customary for the herders throughout the year; the migratory route has several established reindeer corrals. Family migration to summer pastures is normally by bus or car on the Finnish side of the Könkämä river. The intensive system was given up in the early 1920s.

Variety in the Lapp round of life can best be appreciated by juxtaposing the detail of published regional studies. Such investigations, restricted in number but substantial in size, cover Gällivare,[1] Jukkasjärvi,[2] Kautokeino,[3] Suorva[4] and the Petsamo area.[5] The finely produced series *Acta Lapponica* (Nordiska museum, Stockholm) includes in English translation a regional study of a Skolt Lapp community at Suenjel.[6] The book summarises an abundance of detailed field work marginal to anthropology and human geography, and places on record the delicately adjusted hus-

[1] F. Hultblad, *Geographica*, **1.** Uppsala, 1936.   [2] I. Ruong, *Geographica*, **3,** Uppsala, 1937.
[3] P. L. Smith, *Instituttet for sammenlignende kulturforskning*, Series B, XXXIV, Oslo.
[4] E. Manker, *Lapsk kultur vid Stora Lule älvs kjällsjöar*, Stockholm, 1944.
[5] V. Tanner, *Fennia*, **49,** 4, 1944.
[6] K. Nickul, *The Skolt Lapp community Suenjelsijd during the year 1938*, Stockholm, 1938.

PLATE 23. MANNERS OF LIVING

"The manner of the Laplanders living in summer and winter" according to the wood-cut from
Herman Moll's *Atlas* of 1701.

PLATE 24. "A BRIEF SUMME OF GEOGRAPHIE"

Roger Barlow's title can be fittingly employed to describe the totality of the northern world as depicted by Olaus Magnus. This part of his *Carta Marina* is centred upon Swedish and Finnish Bothnia.

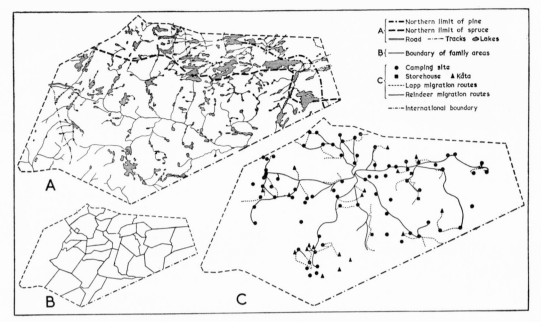

FIG. 98. Suenjel—a summary of the background to a Skolt Lapp community.
(Source: K. Nickul, *op. cit.*)

(two to eight beasts being slaughtered for the family annually); exchange was provided by the annual slaughter of some 5–10% of the total herd. A few sheep and cattle were kept, some potatoes were grown; but all of these items tended to restrict mobility. Hunting (sometimes for protective purposes, sometimes for commercial), berry picking and mushroom gathering supplemented pantry and purse.

Two hundred years ago Johannes Tornaeus, in his *Manuale lapponicum*, declared: "To the Lapps the reindeer is more valuable and useful than any other animal is to any other people on the earth." His remarks still hold for a minority of this minority people. The changing Lapp economy, born of indigenous as well as external forces—must reduce the relative importance of this picturesque husbandry, so that the average Lapp life more closely approaches that of other Scandinavian subsistence farmers than measuring up to the life so widely publicised. Yet the migratory Lapps maintain a numerical stability, and the illusion must not be created that the Lapps are a dying race with a migrant minority in danger of immediate disappearance.

ITER LAPPONICUM

"Far away in the North, under Charles's wain, is Lapland to be seen faintly in the distance. Mountains lie stretched behind mountains"—runs the Lapp national anthem (the Lappish of which is given at the head of Part 5). Over two centuries ago, Linnæus was drawn on his youthful journey to them; today, Lapland horizons attract a mounting tourist traffic. A new and sophisticated element therefore enters the Lapp scene —in winter as well as summer, for winter sports on the fells are an established tourist attraction. In general, the nomad Lapp practises the principle of social avoidance as far as tourists are concerned. Nor must his attitude be regarded as conditioned by fear; he is, as an eighteenth-century Finnish historian expressed it, as proud as a Bedouin. He even looks at his settled kith and kin "much as an old tar looks at a land-lubber," remarks Collinder (*op. cit.*, p. 46); how much the more is he removed from the southern intruders! The intrusion has its good sides. It displays to visitors the problems of the northland; it

E.G.—20

encourages the construction of highways and the reduction of famine conditions which still prevailed in parts of Lapland well into the twentieth century. Contrastingly, new communications have increased the threat to lichen pastures through a higher fire risk, and have introduced a new commercial emphasis to the Lapp economy. As Lord Baltimore said in relation to Lapland in his *Gaudia poetica* (London, 1770): "When there was no gold, then was the golden age."

Curiously enough, it is the indirect effect of the commercial emphasis rather than the direct effect of the intruders which represents the most serious threat. In so far as the reindeer herders react in a normal commercial manner to rising prices by increasing their herds, they run a serious risk of exhausting their natural grazing. Lichen pastures are vulnerable to overstocking, and when domesticated herds can no longer be controlled for want of natural pasture and perforce trespass on improved lands. Past fluctuations in reindeer numbers are probably a reflection of a cyclical overgrazing and recovery of the pastures. The mechanism of the Lapp economy therefore tends to have biogeographical controls, but it would be wrong to conclude that because it is a primitive economy, it is to be either simply explained or easily understood.[1] For all these reasons, it is with reserve that one anticipates the emergence of the herding type of man once defined by Lord Dufferin as "the Lapp Crœsus". Indeed, one of the biggest tasks in dealing with Lapp issues is the intensely local sense of situation of the people who range this broad land. The tragedy is that as this acute local and community sense is weakened it is not replaced by any comparable force from within the contrasting culture.

[1] Side by side with legislation applying to higher economic policy, it is refreshing to come across a law (Helsinki, 1955/83) which restricts the number of reindeer to be kept in a particular district and defines the maximum number per family.

PART 6

UNITY AND DISUNITY IN SCANDINAVIA AND FINLAND

THE COSMOS OF OLAUS MAGNUS

SAXO GRAMMATICUS spoke of "the presumptuous Jutlander", but few Scandinavians —let alone Jutlanders—have been so presumptuous as to attempt a survey of Scandinavia. One northerner was so bold, though he published his account in exile. More than this, and because of his dissatisfaction with the representation of the north in Pliny's *Geographia*, he compiled a map. He was Olaus Magnus (1490–1557), a Goth from Linköping and last Roman Catholic archbishop of Uppsala. The book, entitled *Historia de Gentibus septentrionalibus*, was published in 1555 and appeared in an abridged English translation in 1658. The text is divided into twenty-two sections and is illustrated by more than 400 woodcuts.[1] The "Marine map and description of the northern lands and their marvels," popularly known as the *Carta Marina*, was printed in Venice in 1539.[2] All copies of the original appear to have been lost for 300 years prior to 1886, though an Italian, Lafreri, had the map redrawn and reproduced in 1572. Map and illustrated text represent together a northern equivalent to Flavius Bondus's *Italia illustrata*, a work much admired by Olaus Magnus.

The works of Olaus Magnus have a direct relevance for this final chapter. They are a convenient yardstick by which progress in the geographical appreciation of the north may be measured. They are at the same time the product of a man who was aware of the physical forces which stimulated or compelled the northern peoples and the political and economic forces which moved them. The map and the book are mirrors held up to political

aspirations and commercial enterprise, and the peculiarly animated scene which they reflect stands in curious contrast to the general oblivion surrounding the north in the world of the Renaissance. The works of Olaus Magnus have a further relevance, for they are the product of a man who grasped the unity of *de Gentibus septentrionalibus* over 400 years ago.

From what sources did Olaus Magnus derive his encyclopædic information? First of all, from personal observation and from "the faithful assertions" of priest and soldier, farmer and forester, hunter and fisher. At the age of fifteen he made his first journey—to Oslo. Between 1518 and 1519, he travelled widely in the northern half of Scandinavia on a Church mission. He was in Jämtland (then Norwegian), Medelpad and Ångermanland in the summer, and spent the latter part of the year in the Trondheim area. Here, it is assumed that he met Eric Wallendorf, Archbishop of Nidaros. From the archbishop he might well have gleaned much concerning the topography of north Norway, about Iceland and Greenland, for Wallendorf was the acknowledged authority of the day.[3] In the spring-winter, he returned to Jämtland— depicting himself in the *Carta Marina* on his ski-shod journey. Midsummer 1519 found him in Torneå, probably having made the journey by a Bothnian trading vessel after the break-up of the ice. He continued up Tornedal to Lapland and eventually back to his midland home. Four years later the Scandinavian chapter of his life ended.

His sources of information about the north then changed. Papal business carried him for a number of years to the Hanseatic coast of

---

[1] The history ran through a number of continental editions, the most striking of which is that of J. B. Fickler (Basel, 1567). The 1658 translation, dedicated to Sir Bulstrode Whitlock, "late Lord Ambassador to the Crown of Sweden", is a collector's piece. The modern standard edition is *Historia om de nordiska folken*, Michaelsgillet, Stockholm, 1909–51, 5 vols. See also H. Lidell, "Om Olaus Magnus och hans källor", *Lychnos*, Uppsala, 1936.

[2] It is reproduced by E. Lynam, *The Carta Marina of Olaus Magnus, Venice, 1539 and Rome, 1572*, Jenkintown, 1949. The original map, 1·70 × 1·25 m., was accompanied by keys in German and Italian published in the same year.

[3] Cf. "Finmarkens beskrivelse af Erkebiskop Erik Wallendorf", *Norsk geografisk selskabs aarbog*, 12, Kristiania, 1902.

Germany and the Netherlands. In Lübeck, Bremen and Danzig he had the opportunity of continuous contact with a stream of official travellers from Scandinavia, independently of the pilots and merchant skippers who carried on such a lively trade with the north-land. The greater part of what he regularly called his "gothic map" was, in fact, completed during his Danzig sojourn.

It goes without saying that personal observation and word of mouth were accompanied by voracious reading and absorption of existing cartographic information. Olaus Magnus was nursed in a classical world, and retained a fine respect for the Mediterranean geographers throughout his written work. They are quoted everywhere. Printed sources from farther north include Saxo Grammaticus, Jordanes and Vincent of Beauvais. Olaus Magnus had an obvious delight in the "beasteries" of the day; nor, should the need arise, was he averse to borrowing woodcuts from a source as irrelevant as Hans Holbein's illustrations for the Bible. Cartographically, elements from at least three earlier maps are incorporated in the *Carta Marina*. They are from Ptolemy's *Geographia*, Claudius Clavus's *Tabula moderna Norvegia et Gottie* and Jacob Ziegler's map of the north (1521). It is conceivable that, while in the Netherlands, Olaus Magnus may also have seen the preparations for Mercator's globe or world map.

The quality and reliability of his information were naturally variable. It is not surprising, therefore, that fiction sometimes consorts with fact. On the map, for example, barnacle geese are seen to sprout from a tree-top in Karelia, an otter near Korsholm is so domesticated that it will catch fish for its master and carry it to the cooking-pot, the whirlpool in Lofoten is swallowing a ship—*hic est horrenda caribdis*—and there is such a fine assembly of sea monsters that they were gathered together on one page by the editor of Munster's *Cosmographia* (much the same as the identification page for fish in the annual report of the Norwegian fisheries). Yet the remarkable fact is that in the midst of so much information the shades of Sir John Mandeville should be so few. An essential honesty, coupled with a knowledge of the land which he

described, kept Olaus Magnus fairly safely anchored to reality; although even when departing into the unknown he was rather more repeating the accepted fancies of his day than fabularising.

Edward Lynam has called Olaus Magnus "the interpreter and geographical liberator" of the Scandinavian peoples. Certainly he was the first to give recognisable shape to their lands—and many subsequent cartographers retreated significantly from his position. His map was a maritime map and gave predominance to the role of the sea in the life of the north. If fragmentation of the land by the sea is the first feature which derives from the map, the second is the related water penetration by river artery and broad lake. Though the lakes may be disproportionate in size to one another and their company erroneously shared by Lacus Albus (the White Sea), Olaus Magnus identified for the first time many of the essential water bodies. The amphibious emphasis on his map is understandable, for in his day people moved by water or along waterways or across frozen water. Water gave access to a countryside so frequently boxed in by mountains or enclosed by woodlands. Shipping is a feature of any area which reacts so much like an island—or, perhaps, an archipelago. The outlands also encouraged continuous overseas movement. There is "great necessity for shipping by reason of the multitude of waters", Olaus Magnus wrote. The map reflects this. Merchantmen are identified according to their country and their city-state of origin. Off the coast of Iceland—littered on its north-east with a debris of pack-ice—are vessels from Hamburg and Scotland, Bremen and Lübeck. Moored unknowingly to a whale, which its sailors believe to be an island, is a British trading vessel; in the toils of an ocean monster a vessel from Gothia. Ships from Holland and Danzig are plying to the *emporia maxima* of the north—Bergen, Visby, even Torneå—and to the many minor trading-posts. Fire-towers and lighthouses flame along the inhabited coasts, though mariners commonly negotiate the waters with "a more presumptuous than skilful art of sailing". Kayaks coast in Greenland waters side by side with driftwood brought on a polar current. Off the Lofotens is a multiple-oared galley and in the White Sea a trio of row-boats. Sealers are scattered among the ice-floes in the Bothnian Gulf, and there are conventional ships shown in the midst of most of the lakes. Inland from Oulu, there is boat building. The many small vessels are made of the cleft boards of pine and fir trees, bound together with the "pliable green roots of trees" or "the nerves of beasts . . . especially ranged deer"—"as spiders do their webs". Major fastenings are with "wooden pins". The vessels are "diligently smeared with pine-tree pitch", anchored with "crooked roots of strong wood" and hoist with "sails of woollen cloth". Their short and broad hulls yield "to the reflection of the waters". Ice closure of the inner Baltic gulfs reduces shipping for much of the year, though ice-bridges, as at the narrows of Quarken, open alternative routes. The depths of the Outer Ocean contrast with the shallows of the inner sea, and a plumb-line is symbolically suspended in the Sognefiord.

Ways upon the waters are in many respects a reflection of wealth within the waters. Many thousands of fishermen dwell in villages in the uttermost borders of Norway, the text observes. In January, February and March they "go in strong ships into the deep", and bring forth from the "dangerous water" fish to pickle, salt and dry. Stacked up "like great piles of wood", stockfish is awaiting shipment from the coasts of Iceland, North Norway and North Bothnia. Much is re-exported from Bergen, and therefore called "Bergen fish". The map shows klippfish awaiting export from Hålogaland. For fish from Icelandic waters, Olaus Magnus observes, "there are fought great battles at sea among the merchants of divers nations". Besides special fishing for mackerel, there is also specialised hunting for many varieties of whales. A whale is being cut up in Olaus Magnus's representation of the Færoe islands. Thirty or forty "Roman bariles" of fat derive from an average whale (barrels are shown around the Icelandic coast); it is used for lamp-oil and fuel. The hide yields belts, bags, ropes—or sufficient material "to cloathe forty men". Carters' and shippers' grease is a by-product from blubber boilers; while whale-bones may be used for the framework of buildings. There are other rich fishing-grounds than those of the outer ocean. The coastal waters of "threefold Bothnia" have a variety of resources. Salmon seasonally choke the "huge, deep river" of Torne. They are "like soldiers in bright armour" and break the nets of fishermen. "Siick", herring, mullet, eel and lamprey, "dried in the wind or wafted in smoke", are even carried from here "in Flanders bottoms into Spanish ports". Five-hundred-pound bundles are seen ready for shipment on the pictorial map. So, too, are the pelts and train oil of the "vast company of sea-calves". Fishermen, counterfeiting their prey in black sealskins, are shown hunting on the Bothnian ice-floes. Leather and fur also result, as well as flitches of meat, "cured like bacon", which are a "perplexity to those that eat it in Lent". The herring fisheries of Skåne are a third phenomenon— "suffice among salt fish to feed the greatest part of Europe". From August to October there are "lightnings" and "glitterings over the sea" where the herring "swims by heaps", while the camp-fires of tented merchants flicker around the shores. For two months they are encamped by the banks, paying the king's tribute and purchasing cargoes which have been cured by sun, salt and wind.

The sea encounters land either in crowded mountains or in congested woodlands; lake and river merge on shore and bank with forest. A deciduous tree symbol is employed almost everywhere, although distinctly coniferous symbols occur in north-east Finland. The oak—"most fit for the ribs of ships"—is not separately identified. Sometimes woodlands occur in conjunction with uplands, as in "The Forest of the Land Ridge" in north Finland, or in Dalecarlia and Värmland. Sometimes the woodlands are arranged in an orderly linear manner to denote boundaries. Woodland and mountain are barriers. The Scandinavian Keel—here and there defined as "Alps" and in one place complete with trolls—is scant of *via montanorus*. Wolves also add to the hazard of the mountain passage. In winter, hooves and feet are furnished with "hurdles or bows made with . . . the light bark of trees", and the assault of the uplands is undertaken by moonlight.

The woodlands are a fourfold source of wealth. First, they are complementary to the sea. Trees, "as high as steeples", are used "for masts and foreyards of great ships"; the lesser timbers for planks and pitch. Next, they provide constructional work—"fir-tree rafters are highly esteemed . . . being strong to last and light". Fir-tree boughs serve as fences for fields, hoops about vessels and for cross-bows. Thirdly, the woodlands are a source of fuel—specifically charcoal for the metallurgical industries. The dedication of the English translation of Olaus Magnus makes great play with "the ripping up of the Bowels and Interels of Nature in [Sweden's] various and admirable minerals". Silver, copper and iron veins in the wooded mountains are "very many, great, divers and very rich". Gold, too, is presented symbolically on the map. Mining, in Pluto's domain, is a task for giants and heroes, Olaus Magnus asserts. "Drawing engines", operated by horses and captive bears, lower men into pits and raise ore and spoil. The miners make timber arches to hold up the mountains above them and seek lodes "that run east and south" which are "better ripe". In the mining tracts of Dalecarlia and Helsing, the art and ingenuity of smith and refiner reaches its peak, while the husbandman looks apprehensively at veins exposed on mountains flanks "as men shining in armour".

The woodlands are a fourth source of wealth through their wild life. Ermine, marten, sable, squirrel and beaver skins are prey to the trapper and sold in bundles of forty to "far distant countries". Bear, wolf, fox, lynx and elk are the objective of the hunter. The woodlands are also the home of game birds. In Olaus Magnus's time, the reindeer was a much more widespread inhabitant of the woodland than today, and is depicted several times in this habitat.

From the woodlands have been won the farmlands. Although the map concerns itself but little with these, the woodcuts heading the chapters of the Thirteenth Book of the early text are a source of much detailed knowledge concerning techniques and implements. The account is divided between "Tame and Domestique Creatures" and "Husbandry and Men's Food"—"The Swedes have a world of wheat and more rye". This, they dry on cloths like ships' sails and finally store in oak containers. Such grain, which is sown late and ripens speedily, is used mostly on the farm, though some is shipped to the north country. Animal products, however, are widely exported—principal among them, butter. Värmland, Dalecarlia and Västergötland "by reason of their gallant pastures, breed most stately oxen—for ploughs, summer and winter carts; but not draught cows because of calves". Open-range pasturing is described—and smoke fires against harmful summer insects. "A wonderful abundance of butter" is also attributed to Iceland. For this (and for fish curing) there is little or no salt boiling—imported Bay salt being cheap save in time of war. Cheese making—from cow, goat and sheep milk—is also widespread. "There is greater store of he and she goats in the northern parts than in any other parts of Europe." Small, strong horses are bred, while "ranged deer" in herds of up to 500 are found on the flanks of the fells. Square houses and barns, fastened with huge pieces of timber at the corners, with narrow windows, low doors and turfed roofs, house man and beast. Fruit trees are sometimes planted about them, but their produce is enough "to dull the sword's edge with its juice". Honey and honey drinks counteract the sharpness. On the farmstead, a domestic division of labour is defined. The tasks of women are "spinning, weaving, baking of bread, boiling beer, to deck themselves . . . to provide for lambs, calves and other small creatures"; of men, "to till the ground, thresh the corn, break the horses, sharpen weapons, make fences, order ploughs and dress fields". For the lean years, there is assembled advice concerning famine practice.

Farm, fishery, forest and mine provide the essential goods for trading. Domestic trading is usually a winter undertaking when, at full moon, there are "Marts upon the plain and wide ice . . . that are observed by a rich confluence of merchants". In higher latitudes, caravanseries of deer "yoked like oxen" may be encountered carrying "salt, hard iron, linen and woollen cloth, silver, copper and precious skins". Torneå, where there is "no more frequent mart in all the country near the Pole", is a great centre of barter. Money transactions are scarcely known between the Laplanders who come by sleigh or boat, the sea-going merchantmen from France, Germany, Spain, Portugal, Flanders and Britain, and the Muscovites, who portage overland at the summer solstice. Peaceful exchange with the fur-hatted, skin-tented Russians is less evident from map and text than military hostility. An eastern zone of conflict bounds the "Gothic" world—from where Orthodox monks proselytise among the Lapps to where Swedish cavalry tilt lances and loose cannon shot eastwards over the Gulf of Finland.

Reviewing map and text in their entirety, one abiding contrast remains—the contrast between the developed south and the under-developed north. The map recalls the historical occupation of the south by the dispersal of runic stones and rings, and the greater density of settlement by the number of place-names tied to church, castle or cabin. The northern half of the "Gothic" world was more primitive, rough-hewn, dangerous country, with its economy focused on raw materials and wild life and its political fate still undecided. It was both a reservoir from which supplies drained southwards and an arena into which the south spilled some of its surplus energies. More than this, as Dr. Granlund has pointed out, Olaus Magnus's "great revelation was that when he travelled northwards he simultaneously travelled back into the past". Having seen its spaciousness and sensed its emptiness, Olaus Magnus undoubtedly had motives other than merely artistic for imparting an impression of fullness and vigour to Scandinavia's high latitudes. The motives were, in fact, the same as those which prompted him to undertake his joint pictorial and written exercise. In his autobiographical notes, Olaus Magnus confessed that his map was intended to show the Catholic world how great an area it had lost in this *terra incognita*. His work was, in some ways, a memorial to a personal loss. Olaus Magnus was, in fact, the spiritual heir to the greater part of the territory which he described. for it was centred

upon a see to which he was appointed but at which he never sat. He once wrote of his brother, the historian and archbishop, Johannes Magnus, that he was drawn towards him as "iron to a magnet". He was, without doubt, drawn by an equally compelling force to the country of his birth and the lands which seized his youthful imagination.

DEPENDENCE AND INDEPENDENCE

For Olaus Magnus, born in an age of monarchical unity, the Northern Countries had a natural coherence. They were, moreover, a convenient unit for consideration. Yet during his lifetime the apparent unity of the north was destroyed and the Scandinavian world became a territory riven with national jealousies and void of a corporate personality. This disunity of the north is something which impresses itself intermittently upon human considerations. The theme of unity and disunity runs through all Nordic history.

Disunity persists in the mechanical age. It is easy to attribute it to physical circumstances—even Georg Brandes pronounced geography to be the chief stumbling-block to unity. Physical barriers to common association are, however, no longer a serious consideration. Indeed, the physical challenge to unity may be great in the Scandinavian world, but it is far less than the challenge of particularism existing in such a component country as Norway. The natural background becomes more tractable, but national institutions are persistently intractable. The very concept of a national unit, built upon a community of experience not shared by others outside it, is inimical to complete amity. Nationhood dies if it does not regularly invoke this exclusive sense of the past. Disunity, it may be said, is the choice of the human variable; after all, there is the option of unity.

Contemporarily, unity is strengthened by the web of integration which is spun with increasing fineness and firmness by a multitude of corporate organisations. No considerations of Scandinavian economy or society can ignore these integrating forces. Administrative, agricultural, industrial, trading, transport, banking, educational and professional groups all have their Fenno-Scandinavian organisations. The judiciaries of the north have recognised and acted upon a widening basis of common law since 1872. The very professors of geography are commonly elected only after the considered opinion of experts in the universities of sister countries. At the summit of this integrating structure is the inter-parliamentary council of the Northern Countries—and now the Nordic Council which Finland has ultimately entered. The only parallel degree of unity is that existing within the framework of the British Commonwealth; but here, in the Scandinavian world, independent sovereign nations have integrated themselves more closely, in contrast to a politically unified group which has gradually relaxed its degree of centralisation. Benelux has a similar unity at the higher level, but it lacks the multiplicity of lowlier organisations. This is no place to search for the causes of functional unity in the Northern Countries, though the experience contributed by co-operative institutions in each of them must not be underestimated. Perhaps it is the literal day-to-day working together which is important, the search for common denominators being left as an academic exercise.

Unity and disunity are not chosen independently of external issues. For Scandinavia and Finland are not exclusive to the European scene, but very much inclusive. While the form of the countries offers peninsular—even insular—detachment, their location has denied to them many opportunities commonly available to other countries. It will be evident that they possess a limited number of raw materials rather than a rich variety, though the diversity of these has been successfully multiplied by human ingenuity. Within their restricted area, there is frequently a sufficient abundance to lift the Scandinavian supply base to a position of international eminence. Each Scandinavian component is, however, characterised by a number of major as well as a whole variety of lesser deficiencies. The revaluation of resources has provided increasing opportunity for overcoming these deficiencies through exchange. It is only, indeed, through exchange that the Scandinavian countries have contrived to build up the developed economy which is a feature of their

life today. They have the means to specialise, and the choice of specialisation has frequently meant the relinquishment or subordination of alternative activities in their particular economies. Before the period of specialisation and of exchange, deficiencies—especially of foodstuffs—resulted in intermittent famine. There was a dependence on the physical evironment, but there was a general independence of outside areas. Dependence on the physical environment has been relaxed, but, to a large extent, relaxation has been accompanied by a growing dependence upon the economic environment. This external dependence has been inherent in the Northern Countries, and there has been a measure of it in the past. The trade in salt, for example, elaborate in route and mart, has left a legacy of idiom which still bears testimony to its role.

It is, however, not merely dependence but the changing character and degree of dependence which is of growing consequence. As a phenomenon it was clear to the Arendal merchant who wrote in 1811 that Norway would be as little without England "as a suckling would be without its mother". The specialised development of the Norwegian mercantile marine, providing escape from the restraints of the country, made it immediately sensitive to freedom of the seas. To a large extent, the several Scandinavian countries are commonly dependent upon much the same outside markets. Their principal trading partners tend to be much the same—with Britain their chief export market and source of supply. An element of community therefore arises in their common dependence on what might be called the North Sea market. There is simultaneously an element of political dependence upon what might be called the Baltic arena. Finland's relationship to Russia is the extreme expression of this. It is a relationship which necessarily divides the attitudes of the five countries to the European Common Market. All belong to E.F.T.A., Finland having been accorded a special relationship.

While the Scandinavian countries are commonly dependent upon external economic relationships, they are not bound to each other by any substantial compensatory mechanism of exchange. Indeed, they often stand in nominal competition. Yet, side by side with this competition there exists co-operation, some testimony of which is given in the number of buyers' and sellers' cartels (from the wholesale purchases of the inter-Scandinavian co-operative associations to the selling activities of the Uniscan organisation).

Growing administrative and social organisation, however, has enabled the Scandinavian countries and Finland to overcome some of the inherent weaknesses of dependence upon outside economic forces and to make increasing proposals for community of action within the political frame of their five units. The first step was the creation of a common labour market, initiated in 1954 and to which reference has already been made (Chapter IV). The second step is the promotion of a common customs union. As a result of the very nature of their competitive domestic conditions, the variable stages of evolution in the several countries and the varying range of customs duties and excises, there are essential disparities which must make the transition to a common producing and marketing area slow and complex.[1] Investigations show that about 30% of the present inter-Scandinavian commerce is in duty-free commodities. Practical estimates suggest that it might take more than a decade to make the necessary adjustments to double this figure to 60%.

Yet, in an economic community between this northern group, there exist theoretical possibilities beyond the range of choice of a single country. "Nature is no spendthrift in any part of the Scandinavian peninsula; small economies are the alphabet of her teaching," wrote an American observer before the First World War. It is just this issue which makes common activity so vital. Scale in economic activity, which favours technical units of growing size, forces on a variety of new approaches. Increasing specialisation resulting from increasing refinement of processing is already widely practised in the Scandinavian economies. Adjustments are eased by broadening the territorial frame to create a common market within which such refinement operates. Specific examples from the field of traditional

activities in the Northern Countries illustrate this. The pre-war tanker was a vessel of up to 10,000 tons; today, the figure is rising to 100,000 or more (an investment exceeding £50,000 per member of crew). The pre-war aluminium plant (e.g. Høyanger) operated satisfactorily with an output of less than 10,000 tons; the most economic operations now call for a capacity several times this amount. Adjustments within established industries must also be balanced against potential new plants. If the Scandinavian countries and Finland are able to contemplate inter-Nordic enterprises, operations at a new level become a practical possibility. It will be remembered that the inter-Scandinavian market was fully taken into account in planning the new high-latitude, state-owned iron and steel plants. A tractor-producing plant, with a minimum output of 10,000 p.a., is an economic proposition for Sweden if it looks to an inter-Nordic market[2] (even to the extent of exporting components for assembly elsewhere). The minimum output for a tin-plate plant is about 300,000 tons p.a., and the Fenno-Scandinavian market consumes approximately this quantity. The Swedish car and tractor manufacturing organisation Volvo seeks to import car and tractor parts from Raufoss and Kongsberg in Norway in exchange for car exports to Norway.

Another aspect of inter-Scandinavian co-operation lies in the field of large-scale conversion of raw materials into semi-refined consumer goods. In a number of industrial fields, semi-refined raw materials are commonly imported. To replace these raw materials and to undertake the preliminary stages of conversion in Scandinavia and Finland calls for heavy capital investment and a guaranteed demand. Coke-producing plants are considered in this light, so are the new large-scale oil refineries. At Skjebergskilen on Oslo fiord a refinery, importing 2 million tons of crude oil p.a., is intended to replace expensive refined imports by cheaper crude-oil imports. The number of industrial possibilities is considerably multiplied within the compass of the larger consuming area, though all such planning assumes that a satisfactory compromise can be reached about the location

[1] *Nordisk økonomisk samarbeid, et felles marked,* Trondheim, 1954.   [2] *European Tractor Industry,* Geneva, 1952.

of plants. The problem of scale, then, is operating at a number of levels. In the collective approach to it, the Northern Countries display a new economy in planning. Though they can never dispose of all of them, they can, through this collective approach, at least overcome some of the lesser disadvantages of dependence upon external supply.

Viewed in its international setting, this "Nordic" integration suggests a significant regional unit in the hierarchy of world organisations. It is a feature of undeniable interest to the economic geographer, both because of its origins and because of its effects upon the productive process and distributional scene. Yet the drive towards simplicity in mutual relations within the political framework of the area is often frustrated by the impact of outside forces and the ultimate impossibility of separating economic and political considerations. Even if the final step towards federation is never taken, the degree of regional consciousness remains a remarkable feature. For the first great geographer of the north, Scandinavia was a world apart. This distinction, which is a persistent feature, is evident in human organisation as well as in physical setting. And, as a territory of experiment in human organisation, the "Nordic" community achieves a functional integration which does more than serve its own regional ends. The result is a body of experiences capable of practical application to problems and territories far beyond those of the five countries of Norden.

Not surprisingly, the countries of Norden have become models for many of the younger nations of the modern world. They have given generously of their expertise and resources to emerging lands. They have received into their midst hundreds of students and trainees through their programmes of multilateral assistance. The designs for living that the Scandinavians have conceived in their high latitudes may not always be relevant to the developing lands; but, regardless of habitat, the solutions that have been employed for the problems of society and economy merit attention. These facts are recognised in the generous recruitment from the countries of Norden to the cadre of international civil servants. In such ways, the Scandinavian lands make their own particular contribution to changes in world economic geography.

INDEX

The Scandinavian practice is adopted in the alphabetical arrangement of the modified vowels (å ä ö ø).